THE EIGHTEEN-NINETIES

Aubrey Beardsley
Illustration to THE THREE MUSICIANS

THE EIGHTEEN-NINETIES

*A Period Anthology in Prose
and Verse chosen by*
MARTIN SECKER
with an Introduction by
JOHN BETJEMAN

LONDON: THE RICHARDS PRESS
NO. 8 CHARLES STREET, ST. JAMES'S SQUARE

The frontispiece, Beardsley's illustration to his own poem, appeared in No. 1 of The Savoy, *published by Leonard Smithers in January* 1896.

First published 1948

LONDON : THE RICHARDS PRESS LTD.
MARTIN SECKER: DIRECTOR

To
SIR MAX BEERBOHM
SOLE SURVIVING
CONTRIBUTOR TO THESE
ENSUING PAGES THIS
BOOK IS RESPECTFULLY
DEDICATED

CONTENTS

CONTENTS

CONTENTS

ix

CONTENTS

INTRODUCTION

Most of us can remember those spacious books with their broad margins, well-proportioned typography, plainly elegant bindings and an unassuming individuality about them which said "Martin Secker" without one's having to look at the imprint on the title-page to obtain confirmation. The books published at Number Five John Street were as good to read as they were to handle. More than any publisher in the tens and twenties Martin Secker took on the tradition of John Lane. He had Lane's gift of picking out promising writers. He had his own gift of reviving those on whom the more commercial-minded publishers were unwilling to take a risk. Of all publishers he was the most willing to back his judgement of someone completely unknown. The Martin Secker of whom I write is the publisher of this book as well as its compiler, and I feel it is justice to this anthology that his previous good judgement should be recorded for the benefit of those who may have let it slip from their memories.

For many years Mr. Secker has read the work of nineties' writers, and this collection is the fruit of his reading. Many a slim volume bound in vellum, printed on antique paper with, perhaps, some decoration by Charles Ricketts to give it éclat, or a title-page by Patten Wilson; many a rare essay printed at the expense of the author, talked of in some mood of reminiscence, forgotten like its author who may, even as I write, be but freshly buried in the white marble forest of a suburban cemetery without so much as three lines in The Times; *every work in the Keynotes Series, the Mayfair Set, Pierrot's Library; many a Yellow Book, Dome, Pageant and Savoy; many a choice work published by Leonard Smithers; many a bold venture into literature by some less adventurous publisher—all these has Mr. Secker collected and read, compared and selected and re-selected. It is not until a man starts reading the literature of the nineties that he realises how much there is, even if he confines himself, as in this case, strictly to the years of the period. Only one remarkable anthology of this time has appeared, to my knowledge, in the past, and that was* An Anthology of Nineties Verse, *edited by the late A. J. A. Symons. The verse itself was not, I venture to think, so remarkable as that in this volume, but Mr. Symons' introduction was, perhaps, the most stimulating and perceptive piece of writing of that distinguished wanderer among the ghosts of the old Café Royal.*

Readers will notice that this selection is confined to pieces which are complete in themselves. The temptation must have been great to include extracts. There are purple passages from Walter Pater, amusing extracts from Robert Hichens' two delightful nineties novels, The Green Carnation *and* The Londoners. *But the essence of 'nineties' writing is that it is complete, polished, rounded-off, something which has to be swallowed whole or its full flavour is untasted. Mr. Secker has gone so far as to give Arthur Machen's* The Three Imposters, *which is the length of a short book, in its entirety; only by so doing can the effect of mounting horror be obtained. There are writers of the time who outlived the age in reputation as well as in years—Kenneth Grahame, A. E. Housman, George Moore, W. B. Yeats—all the more honour then to their beginnings.*

Draw the curtains, kindle a joss-stick in a dark corner, settle down on a sofa by the fire, light an Egyptian cigarette and sip a brandy and soda, as you think yourself back to the world which ended in prison and disgrace for Wilde, suicide for Crackenthorpe and John Davidson, premature death for Beardsley, Dowson, Lionel Johnson, religion for some, drink and drugs for others, temporary or permanent oblivion for many more. Of all that brilliant company only Sir Max Beerbohm survives today, his complete eighteen-ninety self. What, for instance, happened to Theo Marzials, so famous once for his drawing-room songs, for his poems and his company? He it was who, Sir Max told me, was a clerk in the British Museum Reading-Room with Edmund Gosse in the time of the great Librarian Panizzi. One still day, when learned heads were bent over books in that great circular room Marzials was in the gallery when Panizzi came in. Marzials leant on the rail and addressed the room thus: "Am I, or am I not, the darling of the Reading-Room?" We see him at a Private View in the Grosvenor Gallery on p. 17 of Max's essay in this book. We have a glimpse of him looking into a cage of stuffed birds in the South Kensington Museum, and with chocolate creams loose in his pocket "he had eaten five large chocolates in the space of two minutes; in his young days the handsomest, the wittiest, the most brilliant and the most charming of poets, he had a career tragic in the extreme." Thus Ford Madox Hueffer in Ancient Lights. *And only lately I read in a book of reminiscences by H. de Vere Stacpoole that*

Marzials led an exotic life in Paris. What really happened to him? Mr. Secker learnt from a friend of Marzials that he died, cheerful to the last, but poor and forgotten, as a paying-guest in a farmhouse in Colyton, Devon. Are his remains in Colyton churchyard? What, if any, was his tragedy?

What furnished rooms, what rest-homes for the aged, what bungalows, what little inns and smelly public-houses, what pensions in the south of France, have roofed over the last hours of other nineties writers whose fame died with the twentieth century? Some I have known myself, who, with the stimulus of hospitality and a sympathetic ear, have flashed their old fire. In little flats I have seen them, surrounded by the relics of former fame and riches, leather luggage and silver-framed photographs. Some, connected with art, not letters, I have found in real poverty. To very few was justice ever done except in those happy last ten years of the old Queen's reign.

Another sip of brandy and another Egyptian cigarette; a whiff of opium perhaps and we can see the mood of the time. Carriages from Mayfair to Belgravia, sun-blinds on verandahs in Park Lane, stable-smells in the mews behind, and stretching in front of us the plane-trees, the grass, the pedestrians and the riders in the Park. The scene will serve, for I quote now from The Londoners:

" 'Really! There is no art except in Paris, no possibility of dining out of Paris, no good dressmakers beyond the limits of Paris, no perfect language except the perfect language of Paris, no gaiety, no verve, no dancing, no love-making worthy of the name, but in Paris.' 'Then, Mr. Ingerstall, why on earth do you always live in London?' said the Duchess heavily."

And although Mr. Ingerstall replied with a bon mot, *his answer would have been "Because I like to shock and to rebel. Because I read Baudelaire, because I hate the conventionalism of English life and like the supposed looseness of the French."*

Ah, the wheels of the well-sprung carriages of those British conventions knew their place, bowling along on the ground under the weight of the élite *who sat in the cushioned seats.*

> *The rich man in his castle,*
> *The poor man at his gate,*
> *He made them high and lowly*
> *And ordered their estate.*

*That verse of the hymn was not omitted (as it often is now) in fashionable
London churches. The tenantry bobbed in the villages, only money could
buy a position equal to that of good birth. An economist—and they were
as rare in those days as were their invitations to smart parties—an
economist might say the world was cracking. But most of those who sat
back in the carriages saw nothing wrong with the horses. For was not
the pair which pulled them along sound? Was it not Money and Birth?
And did not the road stretch on in the everlasting sunshine of those days
when most people thought everything was getting better and better, with
the Queen on the throne and the millenium in the offing?*

*What the Duchess believed in Park Lane, the knight's wife believed
in South Kensington, and Mr. and Mrs. Pooter believed near the
Holloway Road. In the villages it was easier still to trust in a settled
order of things—squire, parson, tenant, labourer. "Oi knows moi place,'
said the last, as he took off his rustic hat, and "I know mine," said the
squire's lady as she came round with the jellies to his sick wife.*

*Of course there were shades of opinion. There were Liberals and
Radicals as well as Conservatives, but the majority even of the first
two did not think that anything was so seriously wrong that it could not
be cured by model cottages, the advance of science, baths, sanitation,
votes for women, and raising the school-leaving age.*

*In this materialist world which had forgotten Original Sin, in this
unwieldy industrialism grafted on to the dying roots of agricultural
feudal life, where was the place for the artist? The true artist is always
a rebel and in advance of his time. So he delighted to shock. And because
the conventions of the time now seem so remote, the shock of his revolution
seems so feeble.*

> *"Tell me not of Philosophies,*
> *Of morals, ethics, laws of life;"*

*sang Lord Alfred Douglas in a poem he afterwards regretted. In 1892
such thoughts must have seemed startling indeed, from one in his position.
You might think and do outrageous things, but you should never write them.*

*So the nineties' writers delighted to outrage the Duchess, the knight's
wife and Mr. and Mrs. Pooter. And the measure of these people's
delight at being outraged is the fame at the time of the nineties' authors.
The Wilde scandal was a blow from which the writers who delighted
to tell of Sin, to create an atmosphere of Evil and to deny their Maker,
never fully recovered. For these writers were in advance of their time,*

in that most of them were beginning to believe again that there really were such things as Sin and Evil, and that there might be a Maker to deny.

In this anthology the note of rebellion is not the loudest. Our ears, deafened by "socially conscious" writers, by realism, reportage and propaganda will hardly be able to hear it at all. The rebellion was largely formulated by the Paterian dictum that Art should not be "socially conscious", and should have nothing to do with philosophies, morals, ethics, laws of life. It was, as it were, the equivalent in prose and verse, of the abstract painting of more recent years.

If we do not recognise the note of rebellion, we will hear, those of us who can hear rhythm and rhyme, the accompaniment of sound craftman-ship. Never was English more carefully written than in the nineties. Infinite pains were taken to use balanced sentences in prose, to create atmosphere, to write mellifluously, to delight in language. The story by Henry Harland in this anthology is a forgotten piece of light romance, so delicately and beautifully written and constructed, that it hangs like intricate lace over solid truth, and by its very lightness and intricacy enhances the quality of that which it overlies. The writers seem not to have minded so much what they wrote about, as that they wrote well. Such fastidiousness proclaims Housman a nineties poet. He published so little in his lifetime, and what appeared posthumously was a long way short of it. The poem by John Davidson here, about a sort of nineties Lady of Shalott, seems melodramatic if read to oneself, but if read aloud, the sound of the words gives the poem another life. By the same standards of sound, Yeats writing merely sonorously and decoratively in these his early poems is but half the poet he became when he emerged from the sunflowers and Morris patterns of Bedford Park, untwisted his Celtic knots, and became the great poet of his later years.

The time has come to open the windows, quench the joss-stick and Egyptian cigarette, and substitute cocoa for brandy and soda. We are in the present. Once more, what happened to most of these writers? As Mr. A. J. A. Symons has said: "Some doubtless found salvation in the Fabian Society, others in the Catholic Church; but a minority remained that, despairing of truth outside itself, looked inward to the only verities that had not seemed to crumble while it watched, the cultivation of the self, the consolations of art."

To-day Trollope, that most un-ninetyish Victorian, is a popular novelist.

The peace of mind of his world is a relief after our own. Therefore we can at present have little sympathy with the rebellion of the ninetyish authors against Trollopian standards of life. But the Art with which they expressed their Art for Art's sake is shown in all its beauty and ingenuity in these pages. They should help to bring back to English the melody and rhythm which the haste of popular writing has killed. These precious jewels may look incongruous on our utility clothes, but they are none the less precious and none the less jewels.

JOHN BETJEMAN

THE EIGHTEEN-NINETIES

AUBREY BEARDSLEY

The Three Musicians

ALONG the path that skirts the wood,
    The three musicians wend their way,
Pleased with their thoughts, each other's mood,
    Franz Himmel's latest roundelay,
The morning's work, a new-found theme, their breakfast
    and the summer day.

One's a soprano, lightly frocked
    In cool, white muslin that just shows
Her brown silk stockings gaily clocked,
    Plump arms and elbows tipped with rose,
And frills of petticoats and things, and outlines as the warm
    wind blows.

Beside her a slim, gracious boy
    Hastens to mend her tresses' fall,
And dies her favour to enjoy,
    And dies for *réclame* and recall
At Paris and St. Petersburg, Vienna and St. James's Hall.

The third's a Polish Pianist
    With big engagements everywhere,
A light heart and an iron wrist,
    And shocks and shoals of yellow hair,
And fingers that can trill on sixths and fill beginners with
    despair.

The three musicians stroll along
    And pluck the ears of ripened corn,
Break into odds and ends of song,
    And mock the woods with Siegfried's horn,
And fill the air with Gluck, and fill the tweeded tourist's
    soul with scorn.

B

The Polish genius lags behind,
    And, with some poppies in his hand,
Picks out the strings and wood and wind
    Of an imaginary band,
Enchanted that for once his men obey his beat and under-
        stand.

The charming cantatrice reclines
    And rests a moment where she sees
Her château's roof that hotly shines
    Amid the dusky summer trees,
And fans herself, half shuts her eyes, and smoothes the frock
        about her knees.

. The gracious boy is at her feet,
    And weighs his courage with his chance;
His fears soon melt in noonday heat.
    The tourist gives a furious glance,
Red as his guide-book grows, moves on, and offers up a
        prayer for France.

Under the Hill[1]

CHAPTER I

THE ABBE FANFRELUCHE, having lighted off his horse, stood doubtfully
for a moment beneath the ombre gateway of the mysterious Hill,
troubled with an exquisite fear lest a day's travel should have too cruelly
undone the laboured niceness of his dress. His hand, slim and gracious as
La Marquise du Deffand's in the drawing by Carmontelle, played nervously about the gold hair that fell upon his shoulders like a finely-
curled peruke, and from point to point of a precise toilet the fingers
wandered, quelling the little mutinies of cravat and ruffle.

It was taper-time; when the tired earth puts on its cloak of mists and
shadows, when the enchanted woods are stirred with light footfalls and
slender voices of the fairies, when all the air is full of delicate influences,
and even the beaux, seated at their dressing-tables, dream a little.

[1] A fragment—Beardsley did not live to complete his only prose work.

A delicious moment, thought Fanfreluche, to slip into exile.

The place where he stood waved drowsily with strange flowers, heavy with perfume, dripping with odours. Gloomy and nameless weeds not to be found in Mentzelius. Huge moths, so richly winged they must have banqueted upon tapestries and royal stuffs, slept on the pillars that flanked either side of the gateway, and the eyes of all the moths remained open and were burning and bursting with a mesh of veins. The pillars were fashioned in some pale stone and rose up like hymns in the praise of pleasure, for from cap to base, each one was carved with loving sculptures, showing such a cunning invention and such a curious knowledge that Fanfreluche lingered not a little in reviewing them. They surpassed all that Japan has ever pictured from her maisons vertes, all that was ever painted in the cool bath-rooms of Cardinal La Motte, and even outdid the astonishing illustrations to Jones's "Nursery Numbers."

"A pretty portal," murmured the Abbé, correcting his sash.

As he spoke, a faint sound of singing was breathed out from the mountain, faint music as strange and distant as sea-legends that are heard in shells.

"The Vespers of Helen, I take it," said Fanfreluche, and struck a few chords of accompaniment, ever so lightly, upon his little lute. Softly across the spell-bound threshold the song floated and wreathed itself about the subtle columns, till the moths were touched with passion and moved quaintly in their sleep. One of them was awakened by the intenser notes of the Abbé's lute-strings, and fluttered into the cave. Fanfreluche felt it was his cue for entry.

"Adieu," he exclaimed with an inclusive gesture, and "good-bye, Madonna," as the cold circle of the moon began to show, beautiful and full of enchantments. There was a shadow of sentiment in his voice as he spoke the words.

"Would to heaven," he sighed, "I might receive the assurance of a looking-glass before I make my début! However, as she is a Goddess, I doubt not her eyes are a little sated with perfection, and may not be displeased to see it crowned with a tiny fault."

A wild rose had caught upon the trimmings of his ruff, and in the first flush of displeasure he would have struck it brusquely away, and most severely punished the offending flower. But the ruffled mood lasted only a moment, for there was something so deliciously incongruous in the hardy petal's invasion of so delicate a thing, that Fanfreluche with-

held the finger of resentment and vowed that the wild rose should stay
where it had clung—a passport, as it were, from the upper to the under
world.

"The very excess and violence of the fault," he said, "will be its excuse;" and, undoing a tangle in the tassel of his stick, stepped into the
shadowy corridor that ran into the bosom of the wan hill—stepped with
the admirable aplomb and unwrinkled suavity of Don John.

CHAPTER II

BEFORE a toilet that shone like the altar of Nôtre Dame des Victoires,
Helen was seated in a little dressing-gown of black and heliotrope. The
coiffeur Cosmé was caring for her scented chevelure, and with tiny
silver tongs, warm from the caresses of the flame, made delicious intelligent curls that fell as lightly as a breath about her forehead and over her
eyebrows, and clustered like tendrils round her neck. Her three
favourite girls, Papperlarde, Blanchemains and Loreyne, waited immediately upon her with perfume and powder in delicate flaçons and
frail cassolettes, and held in porcelain jars the ravishing paints prepared
by Châteline for those cheeks and lips that had grown a little pale with
anguish of exile. Her three favourite boys, Claud, Clair and Sarrasine,
stood amorously about with salver, fan and napkin. Millamant held a
slight tray of slippers, Minette some tender gloves, La Popelinière—
mistress of the robes—was ready with a frock of yellow and white, La
Zambinella bore the jewels, Florizel some flowers, Amadour a box
of various pins, and Vadius a box of sweets. Her doves, ever in attendance, walked about the room that was panelled with the gallant paintings
of Jean Baptiste Dorat, and some dwarfs and doubtful creatures sat here
and there lolling out their tongues, pinching each other, and behaving
oddly enough. Sometimes Helen gave them little smiles.

As the toilet was in progress, Mrs. Marsuple, the fat manicure and
fardeuse, strode in and seated herself by the side of the dressing-table,
greeting Helen with an intimate nod. She wore a gown of white watered
silk with gold lace trimmings, and a velvet necklet of false vermilion.
Her hair hung in bandeaux over her ears, passing into a huge chignon at
the back of her head, and the hat, wide-brimmed and hung with a
vallance of pink muslin, was floral with red roses.

Mrs. Marsuple's voice was full of salacious unction; she had terrible little gestures with the hands, strange movements with the shoulders, a short respiration that made surprising wrinkles in her bodice, a corrupt skin, large horny eyes, a parrot's nose, a small loose mouth, great flaccid cheeks, and chin after chin. She was a wise person, and Helen loved her more than any other of her servants, and had a hundred pet names for her, such as Dear Toad, Pretty Poll, Cock Robin, Dearest Lip, Touchstone, Little Cough Drop, Bijou, Buttons, Dear Heart, Dick-dock, Mrs. Manly, Little Nipper, Cochon-de-lait, Naughty-naughty, Blessèd Thing, and Trump. The talk that passed between Mrs. Marsuple and her mistress was of that excellent kind that passes between old friends, a perfect understanding giving to scraps of phrases their full meaning, and to the merest reference a point. Naturally Fanfreluche the newcomer was discussed a little. Helen had not seen him yet, and asked a score of questions on his account that were delightfully to the point.

The report and the coiffing were completed at the same moment.

"Cosmé," said Helen, "you have been quite sweet and quite brilliant, you have surpassed yourself to-night."

"Madam flatters me," replied the antique old thing, with a girlish giggle under his black satin mask. "Gad, Madam; sometimes I believe I have no talent in the world, but to-night I must confess to a touch of the vain mood."

It would pain me horribly to tell you about the painting of her face; suffice it that the sorrowful work was accomplished; frankly, magnificently, and without a shadow of deception.

Helen slipped away the dressing-gown, and rose before the mirror in a flutter of frilled things. She was adorably tall and slender. Her neck and shoulders were wonderfully drawn, and the little malicious breasts were full of the irritation of loveliness that can never be entirely comprehended, or ever enjoyed to the utmost. Her arms and hands were loosely, but delicately, articulated, and her legs were divinely long. From the hip to the knee, twenty-two inches; from the knee to the heel, twenty-two inches, as befitted a Goddess. Those who have seen Helen only in the Vatican, in the Louvre, in the Uffizi, or in the British Museum, can have no idea how very beautiful and sweet she looked. Not at all like the lady in "Lemprière."

Mrs. Marsuple grew quite lyric over the dear little person, and pecked at her arms with kisses.

"Dear Tongue, you must really behave yourself," said Helen, and called Millamant to bring her the slippers.

The tray was freighted with the most exquisite and shapely pantoufles, sufficient to make Cluny a place of naught. There were shoes of grey and black and brown suède, of white silk and rose satin, and velvet and sarcenet; there were some of sea-green sewn with cherry blossoms, some of red with willow branches, and some of grey with bright-winged birds. There were heels of silver, of ivory, and of gilt; there were buckles of very precious stones set in most strange and esoteric devices; there were ribbons tied and twisted into cunning forms; there were buttons so beautiful that the button-holes might have no pleasure till they closed upon them; there were soles of delicate leathers scented with maréchale, and linings of soft stuffs scented with the juice of July flowers. But Helen, finding none of them to her mind, called for a discarded pair of blood-red maroquin, diapered with pearls. These looked very distinguished over her white silk stockings.

Meantime, La Popelinière stepped forward with the frock.

"I shan't wear one to-night," said Helen. Then she slipped on her gloves.

When the toilet was at an end all her doves clustered round her feet loving to frôler her ankles with their plumes, and the dwarfs clapped their hands, and put their fingers between their lips and whistled. Never before had Helen been so radiant and compelling. Spiridion, in the corner, looked up from his game of Spellicans and trembled.

Just then, Pranzmungel announced that supper was ready upon the fifth terrace. "Ah!" cried Helen, "I'm famished!"

CHAPTER III

SHE was quite delighted with Fanfreluche, and, of course, he sat next her at supper.

The terrace, made beautiful with a thousand vain and fantastical things, and set with a hundred tables and four hundred couches, presented a truly splendid appearance. In the middle was a huge bronze fountain with three basins. From the first rose a many-breasted dragon and four little loves mounted upon swans, and each love was furnished with a bow and arrow. Two of them that faced the monster seemed to recoil in fear, two that were behind made bold enough to aim their shafts at him. From the verge of the second sprang a circle of slim golden columns that supported silver doves with tails and wings spread out. The third, held by a group of grotesquely attenuated satyrs, was centred with a thin pipe hung with masks and roses and capped with children's heads.

From the mouths of the dragon and the loves, from the swans' eyes, from the breasts of the doves, from the satyrs' horns and lips, from the masks at many points, and from the children's curls, the water played profusely, cutting strange arabesques and subtle figures.

The terrace was lit entirely by candles. There were four thousand of them, not numbering those upon the tables. The candlesticks were of a countless variety, and smiled with moulded cochonneries. Some were twenty feet high, and bore single candles that flared like fragrant torches over the feast, and guttered till the wax stood round the tops in tall lances. Some, hung with dainty petticoats of shining lustres, had a whole bevy of tapers upon them devised in circles, in pyramids, in squares, in cuneiforms, in single lines regimentally and in crescents.

Then on quaint pedestals and terminal gods and gracious pilasters of every sort, were shell-like vases of excessive fruits and flowers that hung about and burst over the edges and could never be restrained. The orange-trees and myrtles, looped with vermilion sashes, stood in frail porcelain pots, and the rose-trees were wound and twisted with superb invention over trellis and standard. Upon one side of the terrace a long gilded stage for the comedians was curtained off with Pagonian tapestries, and in front of it the music-stands were placed.

The tables arranged between the fountain and the flight of steps to the sixth terrace were all circular, covered with white damask, and strewn with irises, roses, kingcups, colombines, daffodils, carnations and lilies; and the couches, high with soft cushions and spread with more stuffs than could be named, had fans thrown upon them.

Beyond the escalier stretched the gardens, which were designed so elaborately and with so much splendour that the architect of the Fêtes d'Armailhacq could have found in them no matter for cavil, and the still lakes strewn with profuse barges full of gay flowers and wax marionettes, the alleys of tall trees, the arcades and cascades, the pavilions, the grottoes and the garden-gods—all took a strange tinge of revelry from the glare of the light that fell upon them from the feast.

The frockless Helen and Fanfreluche, with Mrs. Marsuple and

Claude and Clair, and Farcy, the chief comedian, sat at the same table. Fanfreluche, who had doffed his travelling suit, wore long black silk stockings, a pair of pretty garters, a very elegant ruffled shirt, slippers and a wonderful dressing-gown; and Farcy was in ordinary evening clothes. As for the rest of the company, it boasted some very noticeable dresses, and whole tables of quite delightful coiffures. There were spotted veils that seemed to stain the skin, fans with eye-slits in them, through which the bearers peeped and peered; fans painted with figures and covered with the sonnets of Sporion and the short stories of Scaramouch; and fans of big, living moths stuck upon mounts of silver sticks. There were masks of green velvet that make the face look trebly powdered; masks of the heads of birds, of apes, of serpents, of dolphins, of men and women, of little embryons and of cats; masks like the faces of gods; masks of coloured glass, and masks of thin talc and of indiarubber. There were wigs of black and scarlet wools, of peacocks' feathers, of gold and silver threads, of swansdown, of the tendrils of the vine, and of human hair; huge collars of stiff muslin rising high above the head; whole dresses of ostrich feathers curling inwards; tunics of panthers' skins that looked beautiful over pink tights; capotes of crimson satin trimmed with the wings of owls; sleeves cut into the shapes of apocryphal animals; drawers flounced down to the ankles, and flecked with tiny, red roses; stockings clocked with fêtes galantes, and curious designs; and petticoats cut like artificial flowers. Some of the women had put on delightful little moustaches dyed in purples and bright greens, twisted and waxed with absolute skill; and some wore great white beards, after the manner of Saint Wilgeforte. Then Dorat had painted extraordinary grotesques and vignettes over their bodies, here and there. Upon a cheek, an old man scratching his horned head; upon a forehead, an old woman teased by an impudent amor; upon a shoulder, an amorous singerie; round a breast, a circlet of satyrs; about a wrist, a wreath of pale, unconscious babes; upon an elbow, a bouquet of spring flowers; across a back, some surprising scenes of adventure; at the corners of a mouth, tiny red spots; and upon a neck, a flight of birds, a caged parrot, a branch of fruit, a butterfly, a spider, a drunken dwarf, or, simply, some initials.

The supper provided by the ingenious Rambouillet was quite beyond parallel. Never had he created a more exquisite menu. The *consommé impromptu* alone would have been sufficient to establish the immortal reputation of any chef. What, then, can I say of the *Dorade bouillie sauce maréchale*, the *ragout aux langues de carpes*, the *ramereaux à la charnière*, the *ciboulette de gibier à l'espagnole*, the *paté de cuisses d'oie aux pois de Monsalvie*, the *queues d'agneau au clair de lune*, the *artichauts à la grecque*, the *charlotte de pommes à la Lucy Waters*, the *bombes à la marée*, and the *glaces aux rayons d'or?* A veritable tour de cuisine that surpassed even the famous little suppers given by the Marquis de Réchale at Passy, and which the Abbé Mirliton pronounced "impeccable, and too good to be eaten."

Ah! Pierre Antoine Berquin de Rambouillet; you are worthy of your divine mistress!

Mere hunger quickly gave place to those finer instincts of the pure gourmet, and the strange wines, cooled in buckets of snow, unloosed all the décolleté spirits of astonishing conversation and atrocious laughter.

As the courses advanced, the conversation grew bustling and more personal. Pulex and Cyril, and Marisca and Cathelin, opened a fire of raillery, and a thousand amatory follies of the day were discussed.

From harsh and shrill and clamant, the voices grew blurred and inarticulate. Bad sentences were helped out by worse gestures, and at one table Scabius expressed himself like the famous old knight in the first part of the "Soldier's Fortune" of Otway. Bassalissa and Lysistrata tried to pronounce each other's names, and became very affectionate in the attempt; and Tala, the tragedian, robed in roomy purple, and wearing plume and buskin, rose to his feet, and, with swaying gestures, began to recite one of his favourite parts. He got no further than the first line, but repeated it again and again, with fresh accents and intonations each time, and was only silenced by the approach of the asparagus that was being served by satyrs dressed in white.

CHAPTER IV

It is always delightful to wake up in a new bedroom. The fresh wallpaper, the strange pictures, the positions of doors and windows, imperfectly grasped the night before, are revealed with all the charm of surprise when we open our eyes the next morning.

It was about eight o'clock when Fanfreluche awoke, stretched himself deliciously in his great plumed four-post bed, murmured "What a pretty room!" and freshened the frilled silk pillows behind him. Through the slim parting of the long flowered window curtains, he caught a peep of the sun-lit lawns outside, the silver fountains, the bright flowers, the gardeners at work, and beneath the shady trees some early breakfasters, dressed for a day's hunting in the distant wooded valleys.

"How sweet it all is," exclaimed the Abbé, yawning with infinite content. Then he lay back in his bed, stared at the curious patterned canopy above him and nursed his waking thoughts.

He thought of the "Romaunt de la Rose," beautiful, but all too brief. Of the Claude in Lady Delaware's collection.

Of a wonderful pair of blonde trousers he would get Madame Belleville to make for him.

Of a mysterious park full of faint echoes and romantic sounds.

Of a great stagnant lake that must have held the subtlest frogs that ever were, and was surrounded with dark unreflected trees, and sleeping fleurs de luce.

Of Saint Rose, the well-known Peruvian virgin; how she vowed herself to perpetual virginity when she was four years old; how she was beloved by Mary, who from the pale fresco in the Church of Saint Dominic, would stretch out her arms to embrace her; how she built a little oratory at the end of the garden and prayed and sang hymns in it till all the beetles, spiders, snails and creeping things came round to listen; how she promised to marry Ferdinand de Flores, and on the bridal morning perfumed herself and painted her lips, and put on her wedding frock, and decked her hair with roses, and went up to a little hill not far without the walls of Lima; how she knelt there some moments calling tenderly upon Our Lady's name, and how Saint Mary descended and kissed Rose upon the forehead and carried her up swiftly into heaven.

He thought of the splendid opening of Racine's "Britannicus."

Of a strange pamphlet he had found in Helen's library, called "A Plea for the Domestication of the Unicorn."

Of the "Bacchanals of Sporion."

Of Morales' Madonnas with their high egg-shaped creamy foreheads and well-crimped silken hair.

Of Rossini's "Stabat Mater" (that delightful *démodé* piece of decadence, with a quality in its music like the bloom upon wax fruit).

Of love, and of a hundred other things.

Then his half-closed eyes wandered among the prints that hung upon the rose-striped walls. Within the delicate curved frames lived the corrupt and gracious creatures of Dorat and his school, slender children in masque and domino smiling horribly, exquisite lechers leaning over the shoulders of smooth doll-like girls and doing nothing in particular, terrible little Pierrots posing as lady lovers and pointing at something outside the picture, and unearthly fops and huge bird-like women mingling in some rococo room, lighted mysteriously by the flicker of a dying fire that throws great shadows upon wall and ceiling.

Fanfreluche had taken some books to bed with him. One was the witty, extravagant, *Tuesday and Josephine*, another was the score of *The Rheingold*. Making a pulpit of his knees he propped up the opera before him and turned over the pages with a loving hand, and found it deliciou to attack Wagner's brilliant comedy with the cool head of the morning. Once more he was ravished with the beauty and wit of the opening scene; the mystery of its prelude that seems to come up from the very mud of the Rhine, and to be as ancient; the abominable primitive wantonness of the music that follows the talk and movements of the Rhine-maidens; the black, hateful sounds of Alberic's love-making, and the flowing melody of the river of legends.

But it was the third tableau that he applauded most that morning, the scene where Loge, like some flamboyant primeval Scapin, practises his cunning upon Alberic. The feverish insistent ringing of the hammers at the forge, the dry staccato restlessness of Mime, the ceaseless coming and going of the troup of Niblungs, drawn hither and thither like a flock of terror-stricken and infernal sheep. Alberic's savage activity and metamorphoses, and Loge's rapid, flaming tongue-like movements, make the tableau the least reposeful, most troubled and confusing thing in the whole range of opera. How the Abbé rejoiced in the extravagant monstrous poetry, the heated melodrama, and splendid agitation of it all!

At eleven o'clock Fanfreluche got up and slipped off his dainty night-dress.

His bathroom was the largest and perhaps the most beautiful apartment in his splendid suite. The well-known engraving by Lorette that forms the frontispiece to Millevoye's "Architecture du XVIIIme

Siècle" will give you a better idea than any words of mine of the construction and decoration of the room. Only in Lorette's engraving the bath sunk into the middle of the floor is a little too small.

Fanfreluche stood for a moment like Narcissus gazing at his reflection in the still scented water, and then just ruffling its smooth surface with one foot, stepped elegantly into the cool basin and swam round it twice very gracefully. However, it is not so much at the very bath itself as in the drying and delicious frictions that a bather finds his chiefest joys, and Helen had appointed her most tried attendants to wait upon Fanfreluche. He was more than satisfied with their attention, that aroused feelings within him almost amounting to gratitude, and when the rites were ended any touch of home-sickness he might have felt was utterly dispelled. After he had rested a little, and sipped his chocolate, he wandered into the dressing-room, where, under the direction of the superb Dancourt, his toilet was completed.

As pleased as Lord Foppington with his appearance, the Abbé tripped off to bid good-morning to Helen. He found her in a sweet white muslin frock, wandering upon the lawn, and plucking flowers to deck her breakfast table. He kissed her lightly upon the neck.

"I'm just going to feed Adolphe," she said, pointing to a little reticule of buns that hung from her arm. Adolphe was her pet unicorn. "He is such a dear," she continued; "milk white all over, excepting his nose, mouth, and nostrils. *This* way." The unicorn had a very pretty palace of its own made of green foliage and golden bars, a fitting home for such a delicate and dainty beast. Ah, it was a splendid thing to watch the white creature roaming in its artful cage, proud and beautiful, knowing no mate, and coming to no hand except the queen's itself. As Fanfreluche and Helen approached, Adolphe began prancing, and curvetting, pawing the soft turf with his ivory hoofs and flaunting his tail like a gonfalon. Helen raised the latch and entered.

"You mustn't come in with me, Adolphe is so jealous," she said, turning to the Abbé, who was following her, "but you can stand outside and look on; Adolphe likes an audience." Then in her delicious fingers she broke the spicy buns and with affectionate niceness breakfasted her snowy pet. When the last crumbs had been scattered, Helen brushed her hands together and pretended to leave the cage without taking any further notice of Adolphe. Adolphe snorted.

Catullus: Carmen CI

By ways remote and distant waters sped,
Brother, to thy sad grave-side am I come,
That I may give the last gifts to the dead,
And vainly parley with thine ashes dumb:
Since she who now bestows and now denies
Hath ta'en thee, hapless brother, from mine eyes.

But lo! these gifts, the heirlooms of past years,
Are made sad things to grace thy coffin shell,
Take them, all drenchèd with a brother's tears,
And, brother, for all time, hail and farewell!

MAX BEERBOHM

Eighteen-Eighty

*Say, shall these things be forgotten
In the Row that men call Rotten,
  Beauty Clare?* Hamilton Aidé.

"History," it has been said, "does not repeat itself. The historians repeat one another." Now, there are still some periods with which no historian has grappled and, strangely enough, the period that most greatly fascinates me is one of them. The labour I set myself is therefore rather Herculean. But it is also, for me, so far a labour of love that I can quite forget or even revel in its great difficulty. I would love to have lived in those bygone days, when first society was inducted into the mysteries of art and, not losing yet its old and elegant *tenue*, babbled of blue china and white lilies, of the painter Rossetti and the poet Swinburne. It would be a splendid thing to have seen the *tableaux* at Cromwell House[1] or to have made my way through the Fancy Fair and bartered all for a cigarette from a shepherdess; to have walked in the Park, straining my eyes for a glimpse of the Jersey Lily; danced the live-long afternoon to the strains of the Manola Valse; clapped holes in my gloves for Connie Gilchrist.

It is a pity that the historians have held back so long. For this period is now so remote from us that much in it is nearly impossible to understand, more than a little must be left in the mists of antiquity that involve it. The memoirs of the day are, indeed, many, but not exactly illuminative. From such writers as *Frith*, *Montague Williams* or the *Bancrofts*, you may gain but little peculiar knowledge. That quaint old chronicler, *Lucy*, dilates amusingly enough upon the frown of Sir Richard (afterwards Lord) Cross or the tea-rose in the Prime Minister's button-hole. But what can he tell us of the negotiations that led Gladstone back to public life or of the secret councils of the Fourth Party, whereby Sir Stafford was gradually eclipsed? Good memoirs must ever be the cumulation of gossip. Gossip (alas!) has been killed by the Press. In the tavern or the barber's-shop, all secrets passed into every ear. From newspapers how little can be culled! Manifestations are there made manifest to us and we are taught, with tedious iteration, the things we knew, and need not have known, before. In my research I have had only such poor guides as *Punch, or the London Charivari* and *The Queen, the Lady's Newspaper*. Excavation, which in the East has been productive of rich material for the archeologist, was indeed suggested to

---

[1] "Cromwell House." *The residence of Lady Freake, a famous hostess of the day and founder of a brilliant* salon, *where even Royalty was sure of a welcome. The writer of a recent monograph declares that "many a modern hostess would do well to emulate Lady Freake, not only in her taste for the Beautiful in Art but also for the Intellectual in Conversation."*

"Fancy Fair." *For a full account of this function, see pp.* 102 124 *of the* "Annals of the Albert Hall."

"Jersey Lily." *A fanciful title bestowed, at this time, upon the beautiful Mrs. Langtry, who was a native of Jersey Island. See also p.* 43.

"Manola Valse." *Supposed to have been introduced by Albert Edward, Prince of Wales, who, having heard it in Vienna, was pleased, for a while, by its novelty, but soon reverted to the more sprightly* deux-temps.

me. I was told that, just before Cleopatra's Needle was set upon the Embankment an iron box containing a photograph of Mrs. Langtry, some current coins and other trifles of the time was dropped into the foundation. I am sure much might be done with a spade, here and there, in the neighbourhood of old Cromwell House. Accursed be the obduracy of vestries! Be not I, but they, blamed for any error, obscurity or omission in my brief excursus.

The period of 1880 and of the two successive years should ever be memorable, for it marks a great change in the constitution of English society. It would seem that, under the quiet *régime* of the Tory Cabinet, the upper ten thousand (as they were quaintly called in those days) had taken a somewhat more frigid tone. The Prince of Wales had inclined to be restful after the revels of his youth. The prolonged seclusion of Queen Victoria, who was then engaged upon that superb work of introspection and self-analysis, *More Leaves from the Highlands*, had begun to tell upon the social system. Balls and other festivities, both at Court and in the houses of the nobles, were notably fewer. The vogue of the Opera was passing. Even in the top of the season, Rotten Row, I read, was not impenetrably crowded. But in 1880 came the tragic fall of Disraeli and the triumph of the Whigs. How great a change came then upon Westminster must be known to any one who has studied the annals of Gladstone's incomparable Parliament. Gladstone himself, with a monstrous majority behind him, revelling in the old splendour of speech that not seventy summers nor six years' sulking had made less; Parnell, deadly, mysterious with his crew of wordy peasants that were to set all Saxon things at naught—the activity of these two men alone would have made this Parliament supremely stimulating throughout the land. What of young Randolph Churchill who, despite his halting speech, foppish mien and rather coarse fibre of mind, was yet the greatest Parliamentarian of his day? What of Justin Huntly McCarthy, under his puerile mask a most dark, most dangerous conspirator, who, lightly swinging the sacred lamp of burlesque, irradiated with fearful clarity the wrath and sorrow of Ireland? What of Blocker Warton? What of the eloquent atheist, Charles Bradlaugh, pleading at the Bar, striding past the furious Tories to the very Mace, hustled down the stone steps with the broadcloth torn in ribands from his back? Surely such scenes will never more be witnessed at St. Stephen's. Imagine the existence of God being made a party question! No wonder that at a time of such turbulence fine society also should have shown the primordia of a great change. It was felt that the aristocracy could not live by good-breeding alone. The old delights seemed vapid, waxen. Something vivid was desired. And so the sphere of fashion converged with the sphere of art, and revolution was the result.

Be it remembered that long before this time there had been in the heart of Chelsea a kind of cult for Beauty. Certain artists had settled there, deliberately refusing to work in the ordinary official way, and "wrought," as they were wont to asseverate, "for the pleasure and sake of all that is fair." Little commerce had they with the brazen world. Nothing but the light of the sun would they share with men. Quietly and unbeknown, callous of all but their craft, they wrought their poems or their pictures, gave them one to another, and wrought on. Meredith, Rossetti, Swinburne, Morris, Holman Hunt were in this band of shy artificers. In fact, Beauty had existed long before 1880. It was Mr. Oscar Wilde who managed her *début*. To study the period is to admit that to him was due no small part of the social vogue that Beauty began to enjoy. Fired by his fervid words, men and women hurled their mahogany into the streets and ransacked the curio-shops for the furniture of Annish days. Dados arose upon every wall, sunflowers and the feathers of peacocks curved in every corner, tea grew quite cold while the guests were praising the Willow Pattern of its cup. A few fashionable women even dressed themselves in sinuous draperies and unheard-of greens. Into whatsoever ballroom you went, you would surely find, among the women in tiaras and the fops and the distinguished foreigners, half a score of comely ragamuffins in velveteen, murmuring sonnets, posturing, waving their hands. Beauty was sought in the most unlikely places. Young painters found her mobled in the fogs and bank-clerks, versed in the writings of Mr. Hamerton, were heard to declare as they sped home from the City that the Underground Railway was beautiful from London Bridge to Westminster, but not from Sloane Square to Notting Hill Gate.

Æstheticism (for so they named the movement) did indeed permeate, in a manner, all classes. But it was to the *haut monde* that its primary appeal was made. The sacred emblems of Chelsea were sold in the fashionable toy-shops, its reverently chanted creeds became the patter of the *boudoirs*. The old Grosvenor Gallery, that stronghold of the few, was verily invaded. Never was such a fusion of delightful folk as at its Private Views.[1] There was Robert Browning, the philosopher, doffing his hat with a courtly sweep to more than one Duchess. There too was Theo Marzials, poet and eccentric, and Charles Colnaghi, the hero of a hundred tea-fights, and young Brookfield, the comedian, and many another good fellow. My Lord of Dudley, the *virtuoso*, came there, leaning for support upon the arm of his fair young wife. Disraeli, with his lustreless eyes and face like some seamed Hebraic parchment, came also, and whispered behind his hand to the faithful Corry. And Walter Sickert spread the latest *mot* of "the Master,"[2] who, with monocle, cane and tilted hat, flashed through the gay mob anon.

Autrement, there was Coombe Wood, in whose shade the Lady Archibald Campbell suffered more than one of Shakespeare's plays to be enacted. Hither, from the garish, indelicate theatre that held her languishing, Thalia was bidden, if haply, under the open sky, she might resume her old charm. All Fashion came to marvel and so did all the Æsthetes, in the heart of one of whose leaders, Godwin, that superb architect, the idea was first conceived. Real Pastoral Plays! Lest the invited guests should get any noxious scent of the footlights across the grass, only amateurs were accorded parts. They roved through a real wood, these jerkined amateurs, with the poet's music upon their lips. Never under such dark and griddled elms had the outlaws feasted upon their venison. Never had any Rosalind traced with such shy wonder the writing of her lover upon the bark, nor any Orlando won such laughter

---

[1] "Private Views." *This passage, which I found in a contemporary chronicle, is so quaint and so instinct with the spirit of its time that I am fain to quote it:*

"There were quaint, beautiful, extraordinary costumes walking about—ultra-æsthetics, artistic-æsthetics, æsthetics that made up their minds to be daring, and suddenly gave way in some important point—put a frivolous bonnet on the top of a grave and flowing garment that Albert Durer might have designed for a mantle. There were fashionable costumes that Mrs. Mason or Madame Elise might have turned out that morning. The motley crowd mingled, forming into groups, sometimes dazzling you by the array of colours that you never thought to see in full daylight. . . . Canary-coloured garments flitted cheerily by garments of the saddest green. A hat in an agony of pokes and angles was seen in company with a bonnet that was a gay garland of flowers. A vast cape that might have enshrouded the form of a Mater Dolorosa hung by the side of a jauntily-striped Langtry-hood."

[2] *The "Master." By this title his disciples used to address James Whistler, the author-artist. Without echoing the obloquy that was lavished at first nor the praise that was lavished later upon his pictures, we must admit that he was, at least, a great master of English prose and a controversialist of no mean power.*

C

for his not really sportive dalliance. Fairer than the mummers, it may be, were the ladies who sat and watched them from the lawn. All of them wore jerseys and tied-back skirts. Zulu hats shaded their eyes from the sun. Bangles shimmered upon their wrists. And the gentlemen wore light frock-coats and light top-hats with black bands. And the Æsthetes were in velveteen, carrying lilies.

Not that Art and Fashion shunned the theatre. They began in 1880 to affect it as never before. The one invaded Irving's *premières* at the Lyceum. The other sang pæans in praise of the Bancrofts. The French plays, too, were the feigned delight of all the modish world. Not to have seen Chaumont in *Totot chez Tata* was held a solecism. The homely mesdames and messieurs from the Parisian boards were "lionized" (how strangely that phrase rings to modern ears!) in ducal drawing-rooms. In fact, all the old prejudice of rank was being swept away. Even more significant than the reception of players was a certain effort made at this time, to raise the average of aristocratic loveliness—an effort that, but a few years before, would have been surely scouted as quite undignified and outrageous. What the term "Professional Beauty" signified, how any lady gained a right to it, we do not and may never know. It is certain, however, that there were many ladies of tone, upon whom it was bestowed. They received special attention from the Prince of Wales, and hostesses would move heaven and earth to have them in their rooms. Their photographs were on sale in the window of every shop. Crowds assembled every morning to see them start from Rotten Row. Preëminent among Professional Beauties were Lady Lonsdale (afterwards Lady de Grey), Mrs. Wheeler, who always "appeared in black," and Mrs. Cornwallis West, who was Amy Robsart in the *tableaux* at Cromwell House, when Mrs. Langtry, *cette Cléopatre de son siècle*, appeared also, stepping across an artificial brook, in the pink kirtle of Effie Deans. We may doubt whether the movement, represented by these ladies, was quite in accord with the dignity and elegance that always should mark the best society. Any effort to make Beauty compulsory robs Beauty of its chief charm. But, at the same time, I do believe that this movement, so far as it was informed by a real wish to raise a practical standard of feminine charm for all classes, does not deserve the strictures that have been passed upon it by posterity. One of its immediate sequels was the incursion of American ladies into London. Then it was that these pretty creatures, "clad in

Worth's most elegant confections," drawled their way through our greater portals. Fanned, as they were, by the feathers of the Prince of Wales, they had a great success, and they were so strange that their voices and their dresses were mimicked *partout*. The English beauties were rather angry, especially with the Prince, whom alone they blamed for the vogue of their rivals. History credits His Royal Highness with many notable achievements. Not the least of these is that he discovered the inhabitants of America.

It will be seen that in this renaissance the keenest students of the exquisite were women. Nevertheless, men were not idle, neither. Since the day of Mr. Brummell and King George, the noble art of self-adornment had fallen partially desuete. Great fops like Bulwer and *le jeune Cupidon* had come upon the town, but never had they formed a school. Dress, therefore, had become simpler, wardrobes smaller, fasnions apt to linger. In 1880 arose the sect that was soon to win for itself the title of "The Mashers."[1] What this title exactly signified I suppose no two etymologists will ever agree. But we can learn clearly enough, from the fashion-plates of the day, what the Mashers were in outward semblance; from the lampoons, their mode of life. Unlike the dandies of the Georgian era, they pretended to no classic taste and, wholly contemptuous of the Æsthetes, recognized no art save the art of dress. Much might be written about the Mashers. The restaurant— destined to be, in after years, so salient a delight of London—was not known to them, but they were often admirable upon the steps of clubs. The Lyceum held them never, but nightly they gathered at the Gaiety Theatre. Nightly the stalls were agog with small, sleek heads surmounting collars of interminable height. Nightly, in the *foyer*, were lisped the praises of Kate Vaughan, her graceful dancing, or of Nellie Farren, her matchless fooling. Never a night passed but the dreary stage-door was cinct with circlet of fools bearing bright bouquets, of flaxen-headed fools who had feet like black needles, and graceful fools incumbent upon canes. A strange cult! I once knew a lady whose

---

[1] "Masher." *One authority derives the title, rather ingeniously, from "Ma Chère," the mode of address used by the gilded youth to the barmaids of the period —whence the corruption "Masher." Another traces it to the chorus of a song, which, at that time, had a great vogue in the music-halls:*

"I'm the slashing, dashing, mashing Montmorency of the day."
This, in my opinion, is the safer suggestion, and may be adopted.

father was actually present at the first night of "The Forty Thieves," and fell enamouied of one of the *coryphées*. By such links is one age joined to another.

There is always something rather absurd about the past. For us, who have fared on, the silhouette of Error is sharp upon the past horizon. As we look back upon any period, its fashions seem grotesque, its ideals shallow, for we know how soon those ideals and those fashions were to perish; and how rightly; nor can we feel a little of the fervour they did inspire. It is easy to laugh at these Mashers, with their fantastic raiment and languid lives, or at the strife of the Professional Beauties. It is easy to laugh at all that ensued when first the mummers and the stainers of canvas strayed into Mayfair. Yet shall I laugh? For me the most romantic moment of a pantomime is always when the winged and wired fairies begin to fade away and, as they fade, clown and pantaloon tumble on joppling and grimacing, seen very faintly in that indecisive twilight. The social condition of 1880 fascinates me in the same way. Its contrasts fascinate me.

Perhaps, in my study of the period, I may have fallen so deeply beneath its spell that I have tended, now and again, to overrate its real import. I lay no claim to the true historical spirit. I fancy it was a chalk drawing of a girl in a mob-cap, signed "Frank Miles, 1880," that first impelled me to research. To give an accurate and exhaustive account of that period would need a far less brilliant pen than mine. But I hope that, by dealing, even so briefly as I have dealt, with its more strictly sentimental aspects, I may have lightened the task of the scientific historian. And I look to Professor Gardiner and to the Bishop of Oxford.

Diminuendo

IN THE year of grace 1890, and in the beautiful autumn of that year, I was a freshman at Oxford. I remember how my tutor asked me what lectures I wished to attend, and how he laughed when I said that I wished to attend the lectures of Mr. Walter Pater. Also I remember how, one morning soon after, I went into Ryman's to order some foolish engraving for my room, and there saw, peering into a portfolio, a small, thick, rock-faced man, whose top-hat and gloves of *bright* dog-skin struck one of the many discords in that little city of learning or laughter. The serried bristles of his moustachio made for him a false-military air. I think I nearly went down when they told me that this was Pater.

Not that even in those more decadent days of my childhood did I admire the man as a stylist. Even then I was angry that he should treat English as a dead language, bored by that sedulous ritual wherewith he laid out every sentence as in a shroud—hanging, like a widower, long over its marmoreal beauty or ever he could lay it at length in his book, its sepulchre. From that laden air, the so cadaverous murmur of that sanctuary, I would hook it at the beck of any jade. The writing of Pater had never, inded, appealed to me, ἀλλ' αἰεί having regard to the couth solemnity of his mind, to his philosophy, his rare erudition, τινα φῶτα μέγαν χαὶ χαλὸυ ἔδέγμζυ. And I suppose it was when at length I saw him that I first knew him to be fallible.

At school I had read *Marius the Epicurean* in bed and with a dark lantern. Indeed, I regarded it mainly as a tale of adventure, quite as fascinating as *Midshipman Easy*, and far less hard to understand, because there were no nautical terms in it. Marryat, moreover, never made me wish to run away to sea, whilst certainly Pater did make me wish for more "colour" in the curriculum, for a renaissance of the Farrar period, when there was always "a sullen spirit of revolt against the authorities"; when lockers were always being broken into and marks falsified, and small boys prevented from saying their prayers, insomuch that they vowed they would no longer buy brandy for their seniors. In some schools, I am told, the pretty old custom of roasting a fourth-form boy whole upon Founder's Day still survives. But in my school there was less sentiment. I ended by acquiescing in the slow revolution of its wheel of work and play. I felt that at Oxford, when I should be of age to matriculate, a "variegated dramatic life" was waiting for me. I was not a little too sanguine, alas!

How sad was my coming to the university! Where were those sweet conditions I had pictured in my boyhood? Those antique contrasts? Did I ride, one sunset, through fens on a palfrey, watching the gold reflections on Magdalen Tower? Did I ride over Magdalen Bridge and hear the consonance of evening-bells and cries from the river below? Did I rein in to wonder at the raised gates of Queen's, the twisted pillars of St. Mary's, the little shops lighted with tapers? Did bull-pups snarl at me, or dons, with bent backs, acknowledge my salute? Anyone who knows the place as it is, must see that such questions are purely rhetorical. To him I need not explain the disappointment that beset me when, after being whirled in a cab from the station to a big hotel, I wandered out into the streets. *On aurait dit* a bit of Manchester through which Apollo had once passed; for here, among the hideous trams and the brand-new bricks—here, glared at by the electric-lights that hung fiom poles, screamed at by boys with the *Echo* and the *Star*—here, in a riot of vulgarity, were remnants of beauty as I discerned. There were only remnants.

Soon also I found that the life of the place, like the place, had lost its charm and its tradition. Gone were the contrasts that made it wonderful. That feud between undergraduates and dons—latent, in the old days, only at times when it behoved the two academic grades to unite against the townspeople—was one of the absurdities of the past. The townspeople now looked just like undergraduates and the dons just like townspeople. So splendid was the train-service between Oxford and London that, with hundreds of passengers daily, the one had become little better than a suburb of the other. What more could extensionists demand? As for me, I was disheartened. Bitter were the comparisons I drew between my coming to Oxford and the coming of Marius to Rome. Could it be that there was at length no beautiful environment wherein a man might sound the harmonies of his soul? Had civilization made beauty, besides adventure, so rare? I wondered what counsel Pater, insistent always upon contact with comely things, would offer to one who could nowhere find them. I had been wondering that very day when I went into Ryman's and saw him there.

When the tumult of my disillusioning was past, my mind grew clearer. I discerned that the scope of my quest for emotion must be narrowed. That abandonment of one's self to life, that merging of one's soul in bright waters, so often suggested in Pater's writing, were a counsel impossible for to-day. The quest of emotions must be no less keen, certainly, but the manner of it must be changed forthwith. To unswitch myself from my surroundings, to guard my soul from contact with the unlovely things that compassed it about, therein lay my hope. I must approach the Benign Mother with great caution. And so, while most of the freshmen were doing her honour with wine and song and wreaths of smoke, I stood aside, pondered. In such seclusion I passed my first term—ah, how often did I wonder whether I was not wasting my days, and, wondering, abandon my meditations upon the right ordering of the

future! Thanks be to Athene, who threw her shadow over me in those
moments of weak folly!

At the end of term I came to London. Around me seethed swirls,
eddies, torrents, violent crosscurrents of human activity. What uproar!
Surely I could have no part in modern life. Yet, yet for a while it was
fascinating to watch the ways of its children. The prodigious life of the
Prince of Wales fascinated me above all; indeed, it still fascinates me.
What experience has been withheld from His Royal Highness? Was
ever so supernal a type, as he, of mere Pleasure? How often he has
watched, at Newmarket, the scud-a-run of quivering homuncules over
the vert on horses, or, from some nightboat, the holocaust of great
wharves by the side of the Thames; raced through the blue Solent;
threaded *les coulisses*! He has danced in every palace of every capital,
played in every club. He has hunted elephants through the jungles of
India, boar through the forests of Austria, pigs over the plains of
Massachusetts. From the Castle of Abergeldie he has led his Princess
into the frosty night, Highlanders lighting with torches the path to the
deer-larder, where lay the wild things that had fallen to him on the
crags. He has marched the Grenadiers to chapel through the white
streets of Windsor. He has ridden through Moscow, in strange apparel,
to kiss the catafalque of more than one Tzar. For him the Rajahs of
India have spoiled their temples, and Blondin has crossed Niagara along
the tight-rope, and the Giant Guard done drill beneath the chandeliers
of the Neue Schloss. Incline he to scandal, lawyers are proud to whisper
their secrets in his ear. Be he gallant, the ladies are at his feet. *Ennuyé*,
all the wits from Bernal Osborne to Arthur Roberts have jested for him.
He has been "present always at the focus where the greatest number of
forces unite in their purest energy," for it is his presence that makes
those forces unite.

"*Ennuyé?*" I asked. Indeed he never is. How could he be when
Pleasure hangs constantly upon his arm! It is those others, overtaking
her only after arduous chase, breathless and footsore, who quickly
sicken of her company, and fall fainting at her feet. And for me, shod
neither with rank nor riches, what folly to join the chase! I began to
see how small a thing it were to sacrifice those external "experiences,"
so dear to the heart of Pater, by a rigid, complex civilization made so
hard to gain. They gave nothing but lassitude to those who had gained
them through suffering. Even to the kings and princes, who so easily

gained them, what did they yield besides themselves? I do not suppose that, if we were invited to give authenticated instances of intelligence on the part of our royal pets, we could fill half a column of the *Spectator*. In fact, their lives are so full they have no time for thought, the highest energy of man. Now, it was to thought that *my* life should be dedicated. Action, apart from its absorption of time, would war otherwise against the pleasures of intellect, which, for me, meant mainly the pleasures of imagination. It is only (this is a platitude) the things one has not done, the faces or places one has not seen, or seen but darkly, that have charm. It is only mystery—such mystery as besets the eyes of children—that makes things superb. I thought of the voluptuaries I had known—they seemed so sad, so ascetic almost, like poor pilgrims, raising their eyes never or ever gazing at the moon of tarnished endeavour. I thought of the round, insouciant faces of the monks at whose monastery I once broke bread, and how their eyes sparkled when they asked me of the France that lay around their walls. I thought, *pardie*, of the lurid verses written by young men who, in real life, know no haunt more lurid than a literary public-house. It was, for me, merely a problem how I could best avoid "sensations," "pulsations," and "exquisite moments" that were not purely intellectual. I would not attempt to combine both kinds, as Pater seemed to fancy a man might. I would make myself master of some small area of physical life, a life of quiet, monotonous simplicity, exempt from all outer disturbance. I would shield my body from the world that my mind might range over it, not hurt nor fettered. As yet, however, I was in my first year at Oxford. There were many reasons that I should stay there and take my degree, reasons that I did not combat. Indeed, I was content to wait for my life.

And now that I have made my adieux to the Benign Mother, I need wait no longer. I have been casting my eye over the suburbs of London. I have taken a most pleasant little villa in ——ham, and here I shall make my home. Here there is no traffic, no harvest. Those of the inhabitants who do anything go away each morning and do it elsewhere. Here no vital forces unite. Nothing happens here. The days and the months will pass by me, bringing their sure recurrence of quiet events. In the spring-time I shall look out from my window and see the laburnum flowering in the little front garden. In summer cool syrups will come for me from the grocer's shop. Autumn will make the boughs of my mountain-ash scarlet and, later, the asbestos in my grate will put forth its blossoms of flame. The infrequent cart of Buszard or Mudie will pass my window at all seasons. Nor will this be all. I shall have friends. Next door, there is a retired military man who has offered, in a most neighbourly way, to lend me his copy of *The Times*. On the other side of my house lives a charming family, who perhaps will call on me, now and again. I have seen them sally forth, at sundown, to catch the theatre-train; among them walked a young lady, the charm of whose figure was ill concealed by the neat waterproof that overspread her evening-dress. Some day it may be . . . but I anticipate. These things will be but the cosy accompaniment of my days. For I shall contemplate the world.

I shall look forth from my window, the laburnum and the mountain-ash becoming mere silhouettes in the foreground of my vision. I shall look forth and, in my remoteness, appreciate the distant pageant of the world. Humanity will range itself in the columns of my morning paper. No pulse of life will escape me. The strife of politics, the intriguing of courts, the wreck of great vessels, wars, dramas, earthquakes, national griefs or joys; the strange sequels to divorces, even, and the mysterious suicides of land-agents at Ipswich—in all such phenomena I shall steep my exhaurient mind. *Delicias quoque bibliothecae experiar.* Tragedy, comedy, chivalry, philosophy will be mine. I shall listen to their music perpetually and their colours will dance before my eyes. I shall soar from terraces of stone upon dragons with shining wings and make war upon Olympus. From the peaks of hills I shall swoop into recondite valleys and drive the pigmies, shrieking little curses, to their caverns. It may be my whim to wander through infinite parks where the deer lie under the clustering shadow of their antlers and flee lightly over the grass; to whisper with white prophets under the elms or bind a child with a daisy-chain or, with a lady, thread my way through the acacias. I shall swim down rivers into the sea and outstrip all ships. Unhindered I shall penetrate all sanctuaries and snatch the secrets of every dim confessional.

Yes, among books that charm, and give wings to the mind, will my days be spent. I shall be ever absorbing the things great men have written; with such experience I will charge my mind to the full. Nor will I try to give anything in return. Once, in the delusion that Art, loving the recluse, would make his life happy, I wrote a little for a yellow quarterly and had that *succès de fiasco* which is always given to a young writer of talent. But the stress of creation soon overwhelmed me. Only Art with a capital H gives any consolations to her henchmen. And I, who crave no knighthood, shall write no more. I shall write no more. Already I feel myself to be a trifle outmoded. I belong to the Beardsley period. Younger men, with months of activity before them, with fresher schemes and notions, with newer enthusiasm, have pressed forward since then. *Cedo junioribus.* Indeed, I stand aside with no regret. For to be outmoded is to be a classic, if one has written well. I have acceded to the hierarchy of good scribes and rather like my niche.

F. W. BOURDILLON[1]

Aucassin and Nicolette

WHAT magic halo rings thy head,
Dream maiden of a minstrel dead?
What charm of faerie round thee hovers,
That all who listen are thy lovers?

What power yet makes our pulses thrill
To see thee at thy window-sill,
And by that dangerous cord down-sliding,
And through the moonlit garden gliding?

True maiden art thou in thy dread;
True maiden in thy hardihead;
True maiden when, thy fears half-over,
Thou lingerest to try thy lover.

And ah! what heart of stone or steel
But doth some stir unwonted feel,
When, to the day new brightness bringing,
Thou standest at the stair-foot singing!

---

[1] His best known and most quoted piece is "The Night has a Thousand Eyes," once popular as a drawing-room song, in a variety of musical settings.

Thy slender limbs in boyish dress,
Thy tones half glee, half tenderness,
Thou singest, 'neath the light tale's cover,
Of thy true love to thy true lover.

O happy lover, happy maid,
Together in sweet story laid;
Forgive the hand that here is baring
Your old loves for new lovers' staring!

Yet, Nicolette, why fear'st thou fame?
No slander now can touch thy name,
Nor Scandal's self a fault discovers,
Though each new year thou hast new lovers.

Nor, Aucassin, need'st thou to fear
These lovers of too late a year,
Nor dread one jealous pang's revival;
No lover now can be thy rival.

What flower considers if its blooms
Light haunts of men, or forest glooms?
What care ye though the world discovers
Your flowers of love, O flower of lovers?

BARON CORVO[1]

About Beata Beatrice and the Mamma of San Pietro

"Ah, sir, don't be angry with me, because I really do love her so! What else can I do when she is as pretty as that, and always good and cheerful and patient? And when I met her last evening by the boat-house I took her into my arms asking her to kiss me, and, sir, she did. And then I told her that I loved her dearly, and she said she loved me too. And I

[1] Otherwise Frederick Rolfe. This is one of the six tales which comprise "Stories Toto Told Me."

said that when I grew up I would marry her, and when I looked into her eyes they were full of tears so I know she loves me; but she is ashamed because she is so poor and her mamma such a hag. But do I mind her being poor—the little pigeon? Ma che! for when I feel her soft arms round me and her breath in my hair, then I kiss her on the lips and neck and bosom, and I know it is Beatrice, her body and her soul, that I want and that I care for, not her ragged clothes."

Toto jumped off the tree-trunk and stood before me, with all his lithe young figure tense and strung up as he went on with his declamatory notices.

"Has not your Excellency said that I am strong like an ox, and will it not be my joy to work hard to make my girl happy and rich and grand as the sun? Do you think that I spend what you give me at the wine-shop or the tombola? You know that I don't. Yes, I have always saved, and now I shall save more, and in a year or two I shall ask your per-mission to marry her. No, I don't want to go away, or to leave you. May the devil fly away with me to the pit of hell and burn me for ever with his hottest fire if I do! Nor will Beatrice make any difference to your Excellency; you need never see her, you need never even know that there is such a flower of Paradise, such an angel, living near you if you don't wish to know it. And I can assure you that Beatrice has the greatest respect for you, and if you will only be so good and so kind as to let us make each other happy she will be quite proud and glad to serve you as well as I do, and to help me to serve you too. And, sir, you know how fond you are of a fritto? Ah well, Beatrice can make a *rigaglie* so beautiful that you will say it must have come straight from Heaven; and this I know because I have tried it myself."

He flung himself down on the ground and kissed my hands, and kissed my feet, and wept, and made me an awful scene.

I told him to get up and not be a young fool. I said that I didn't care what he did, and asked if I had ever been a brute to him, or denied him anything that was reasonable.

He swore that I was a saint, a saint from Heaven, that I always had been and always should be, because I could not help myself; and was going down on his knees again, when I stopped that, and said he had better bring me the girl and not make me hotter than I was with his noise.

"To tell you the truth, sir," he replied, "I was always quite sure that you would have pity upon us when you knew how very much we loved each other. And when you caught us last night I told Beatrice that now I must let you know everything, because I was certain that as long as I did not deceive you (and you know that I have never done so) there was nothing to be afraid of; and I told her you would without doubt like to see her to give her good counsel, because she was my friend; and she said she would call that too much honour. Then I felt her trembling against my heart, so I kissed her for a long time and said she must be brave like I am; and, sir, as you are so gracious as to want to see her, I have taken the liberty of bringing her and she is here."

I had always admired the cleverness of this lad, and was not much surprised at his last announcement.

"Where?" I said.

"I put her behind that tree, sir," and he pointed to a big oak about twenty yards away. I could not help laughing at his deepness; and he took courage, I suppose, from my auspicious aspect. All sorts of clouds of hesitation, uncertainty and doubt moved out of his clear brown eyes, while his face set in a smile absurd and complacently expectant. "Shall I fetch her, sir?"

I nodded. I had had some experience of his amours before; but this was a new phase, and I thought I might as well be prepared for *anything*. He went a few paces away, and disappeared behind the oak tree. There was a little rustle of the underwood, and some kissing for a minute or two. Then he came out again, leading his companion by the hand. I said I was prepared for anything, but I confess to a little gasp at what I saw. It was not a boy and girl who approached me, but a couple of boys —apparently, at least. They came and stood beside the hammock in which I was lying. Toto, you know, was sixteen years old, a splendid, wild (*discolo*) creature, from the Abruzzi, a figure like Cellini's Perseus; skin brown, with real red blood under it; smooth as a peach, and noble as a god. He had a weakness for sticking a dead-white rose in the black waves of hair over his left ear, and the colour of that rose against his cheeks, flushed as they were now, was something to be truly thankful for. I used to make him wear white clothes on these hot summer days down by the lake—a silk shirt with all the buttons undone and the sleeves rolled up, showing his broad brown chest and supple arms, and short breeches of the same, convenient for rowing. (He had half-a-dozen creatures like himself under his command, and their business was to carry my photographic and insect-hunting apparatus, and to wait upon me while I loafed the summers away in the Alban hills or along the eastern coast.) The seeming boy, whom he had called Beatrice, looked about fourteen years old, and far more delicately dainty even than he was. The bold magnificent independence of his carriage was replaced in her by one of tenderness and softness, quite as striking in its way as the other. She wore her hair in a short silky mop like Toto, and her shirt was buttoned up to the spring of her pretty throat. She was about as high as her boy's shoulder, and stood waiting before me with her poor little knees trembling, and a rosy blush coming and going over her face. They were so exquisitely lovely, in that sun-flecked shade with the blue lake for a background, that I could not help keeping them waiting a few minutes. Such pictures as this are not to be seen every day. Presently he put his arm round her neck, and she put hers round his waist, and leaned against him a little. But he never took his eyes off mine.

"Go on, Toto," I said, "what were you going to say?"

"Ah, well, sir, you see I thought if Beatrice came to live with us—with me, I mean—it would be more convenient for you if she looked like the rest of us, because then she would be able to do things for you as well as we can, and people will not talk."

It struck me immediately that Toto was right again as usual; for upon my word, this girl of his would pass anywhere for a very pretty boy, with just the plump roundness of the Florentine Apollino, and no more.

"So I got some clean clothes of Guido's, and brought them here early this morning, and then I fetched Beatrice and put them on her, and hid her behind the tree, because I knew you would scold me about her when you came down to read your newspapers; and I determined to tell you everything, and to let you know that the happiness of both of us was in your hands. And I only wanted you to see her like this, in order that you might know that you will not be put to any discomfort or inconvenience if you are so kind as to allow us to love each other."

This looked right enough; but, whether or not, there was no good in being nasty-tempered just then, so I told them to be as happy as they liked, and that I would not interfere with them as long as they did not interfere with me. They both kissed my hands, and I kissed Beatrice on the forehead, and cheeks and lips, Toto looking on as proud as a peacock. And then I told him to take her away and send her home properly dressed, and return to me in half an hour.

I could see very well that all these happenings were natural enough, and that it was not a part I cared to play to be harsh or ridiculous, or to spoil an idyll so full of charm and newness. Besides, I have reason to know jolly well the futility of interfering between the male animal and his mate.

So when Toto came back I said nothing discouraging or *ennuyant* beyond reminding him that he ought to make quite sure of possessing an enduring love for this girl, a love which would make him proud to spend his life with and for her, and her only. I told him he was very young, which was no fault of his, and that if he would take my advice he would not be in a hurry about anything. He said that my words were the words of wisdom, and that he would obey me just as he would the Madonna del Portone in her crown of glory if she came down and told him things then and there; that he had known Beatrice since they had been babies together, and had always loved her far better than his sisters, and in a different way too, if I could only understand. Last night when he had held her in his arms he told her that he knew she wished him well, and felt himself so strong and she so weak, looking so tender and so tempting, that all of a minute he desired her for his own, and to give somebody a *bastonata* of the finest for her, and to take her out of the clutches of that dirty mean old witch-cat of a mamma of hers who never gave her any pleasure, kept her shut up whenever there was a festa, and, Saints of Heaven! sometimes beat her simply because she envied her for being beautiful and delicate, and bright as a young primrose. "What a hag of a mamma it was to be cursed with, and what could the Madonna be thinking about to give such a *donnicciuola* of a mamma to his own *bellacuccia!* Not but what the Madonnina was sometimes inattentive, but then, of course, she had so many people to look after or she could not have given such a mamma to San Pietro as she did."

Here I saw a chance of changing the subject, and remarked that it would be nice to know what sort of a mamma the Madonna had given to San Pietro.

"Ah, well, sir, you must know that the mamma of San Pietro was the meanest woman that ever lived—scraping and saving all the days of her life, and keeping San Pietro and his two sisters (the nun and the other one, of whom I will tell you another time) for days together with nothing to eat except perhaps a few potato peelings and a cheese rind. As for acts of kindness and charity to her neighbours, I don't believe she knew what they were, though of course I am not certain; and whatever good San Pietro had in him he must have picked up somewhere else. As soon as he was old enough to work he became a fisherman, as you know, because when the Santissimo Salvatore wanted a Pope to govern the Church, He went down to the seaside and chose San Pietro, because He knew that as San Pietro was a fisherman he would be just the man to bear all kinds of hardships, and to catch people's souls and take them to Paradise, just as he had been used to catch fish and take them to the market. And so San Pietro went to Rome, and reigned there for many years. And at last the Pagans settled that all the Catholics had to be killed. And the Catholics thought that though they had no objection to being killed themselves it would be a pity to waste a good Pope like San Pietro, who had been chosen and given to them by the Lord God Himself. Therefore they persuaded San Pietro to run away on a night of the darkest, and to hide himself for a time in a lonely place outside the gates of the city. After he had gone a little way along the Via Appia—and the night was very dark—he saw a grey light on the road in front of him, and in the light there was the Santissimo Himself; and San Pietro was astonished, for His Majesty was walking towards Rome. And San Pietro said: 'O Master, where do you go?' And the Face of the Santissimo became very sad, and He said: 'I am going to Rome to be crucified again.' And then San Pietro knew it was not a noble thing that he was doing to run away on the sly like this, because a shepherd doesn't leave his sheep when wolves come—at least, no shepherd worth a *baiocco*.

"Then San Pietro turned round and went back himself to Rome, and was crucified with much joy between two posts in the Circus of Nero; but he would not be crucified like the Santissimo, because he wished to make amends for his weakness in trying to run away, and he begged and prayed to be crucified with his head where his feet ought to be. The Pagans said most certainly if he liked it that way, it was all the same to them. And so San Pietro made no more ado but simply went straight to Heaven. And, of course, when he got there his angel gave him a new cope and a tiara and his keys, and the Padre Eterno put him to look after the gate, which is a very great honour, but only his due, because he had been of such high rank when he lived in the world. Now after he had been there a little while his mamma also left the world, and was not allowed to come into Paradise, but because of her meanness she was sent to hell. San Pietro did not like this at all, and when some of the other saints chaffed him about it he used to grow angry. At last he went to the Padre Eterno, saying that it was by no means suitable that a man of his quality should be disgraced in this way; and the Padre Eterno, Who is so good, so full of pity, and of mercy that He would do anything to oblige you if it is for the health of your soul, said He was sorry for San Pietro and He quite understood his position. He suggested that perhaps the case of San Pietro's mamma had been decided hurriedly, and He ordered her Angel Guardian to bring the book in which had been written down all the deeds of her life, good or bad.

" 'Now,' said the Padre Eterno, 'We will go carefully through this book and if We can find only one good deed that she has done We will add to that the merits of Our Son and of hers so that she may be delivered from eternal torments.'

"Then the Angel read out of the book, and it was found that in the whole of her life she had only done one good deed; for a poor starving beggar-woman had once asked her, for the love of God, to give her some food, and she had thrown her the top of an onion which she was peeling for her own supper.

"And the Padre Eterno instructed the Angel Guardian of San Pietro's mamma to take that onion-top and to go and hold it over the pit of hell, so that if by chance she should boil up with the other damned souls to the top of that stew, she might grasp the onion-top and by it be dragged up to Heaven.

"The Angel did as he was commanded and hovered in the air over the pit of hell holding out the onion-top in his hand, and the furnace flamed, and the burning souls boiled and writhed like *pasta* in a copper pot, and presently San Pietro's mamma came up thrusting out her hands in anguish, and when she saw the onion-top she gripped it, for she was a very covetous woman, and the Angel began to rise into the air carrying her up towards Heaven.

"Now when the other damned souls saw that San Pietro's mamma was leaving them, they also desired to escape and they hung on to the skirts of her gown hoping to be delivered from their pain, and still the Angel rose, and San Pietro's mamma held the onion-top, and many tortured souls hung on to her skirts, and others to the feet of those, and again others on to them, and you would surely have thought that hell was going to be emptied straight away. And still the Angel rose higher and the long stream of people all hanging to the onion-top rose too, nor

D

was the onion-top too weak to bear the strain. But when San Pietro's mamma became aware of what was going on and of the numbers who were escaping from hell along with her, she didn't like it: and, because she was a nasty selfish and cantankerous woman, she kicked and struggled, and took the onion-top in her teeth so that she might use her hands to beat off those who were hanging to her skirts. And she fought so violently that she bit through the onion-top, and tumbled back for always into hell flame.

"So you see, sir, that it is sure to be to your own advantage if you are kind to other people and let them have their own way so long as they don't interfere with you."

I chuckled at Toto's moral reflections.

HUBERT CRACKENTHORPE

When Greek Meets Greek

I

"Why don't you say at once that you hate me? Of course you do. What have you to do with a poor, broken-down devil like me?" and the concentrated exasperation of his sneer was ugly.

He stood planted on the hearth-rug, his face flushed, and a swollen vein standing out across his forehead. He had finished speaking, and there was silence in the room now; yet the figure of the girl opposite remained motionless. Seated in the far corner of the room, she was but an indistinct mass of shadow, for the feeble light of the shaded lamp did not reach her.

There was no freshness on the man's face—the battered skin, wrinkling at every corner, was stretched as loosely as an old man's, and hung in folds under the chin; the hair, scanty on the temples, was here and there strongly streaked with grey; but the moustache, with its slender waxed points, was coal-black, and the frame, despite the stoop in the shoulders, had all the spontaneous elasticity of youth. Fifty or thirty? Which was nearer the mark?

Duncan Ralston had lived a long time in India. Those in England who had known him before he had gone out as a young subaltern, freshly commissioned, talked vaguely of his brilliant bravery in the Afghan War, though no one could say exactly the manner in which he had distinguished himself. Then, about three years ago, selling out under apparently disadvantageous conditions, he had come home for the first time. When he appeared in London, some said that the climate had aged him strangely; but others, who knew him better, hinted that hard living had done as much as unhealthy heat. Now and then there were ugly rumours of a scandal with the wife of a Government officer up at Simla; but since no one spoke with certainty on the subject, they never attained any definite form.

After a minute or two, the girl came and stood by his side before the fire, stretching out one foot towards the grate. The flickering light which played about her face revealed that the violence of his words had not affected her self-possession; there was only a tired, weary look, as if she had played the same scene many times before, and it palled upon her.

Her hair was drawn into a single coil on the top of her head, and her black evening dress revealed her warm-tinted throat and breast and her delicately modelled arms: she wore no ornament of any kind, and this enhanced the purity of her charm. Though she stood almost as high as he did, she was little more than a child.

The contrast between the two was a violent one; the man, with infinite possibilities of one kind in the past, the girl with infinite possibilities of another kind in the future.

And to Duncan the sight of her seemed to bring the bankruptcy of his own life very near at hand. Gradually the hardness went out of his face, all his anger fading as it had come, quickly. A glance of almost abject self-abasement and he laid one hand on her bare shoulder, while with the other he lifted her fingers to his lips, slowly, almost reverently.

"I'm sorry, Pearl," and he kissed her fingers again; "I couldn't help it."

But on her part there was no movement in response to his, passive with the same dreary look she let her arm fall limp to her side again; and he, all occupied with his own emotion, noticed nothing.

Duncan Ralston was a ruined man. Eighteen months ago he had fancied himself within a few days of the crash; yet, week after week, month after month, he had managed to stave off the disaster, till he accepted his difficulties as a natural part of his life, and, a victim to the almost incredible blindness of self-deception, imagined that, sooner or later, by some means or other, he would emerge from them all. Perhaps, but for his passion for Pearl, despair would have taken the place of this reckless hopefulness; perhaps it was her presence alone that encouraged him to go on living. Yet it was only occasionally that he resented, as he had done just now, that she made no pretence of returning his love, and it was very rarely that the whole extent of his degradation betrayed itself in her presence. The scattered remnants of a craving for religion or its equivalent, which years of loose living had not been able to eradicate, had centred themselves in his worship of her, so that there were moments when he could have knelt down before her, and prayed to her as a child prays to God. Once, nay twice, when he was absolutely penniless, she had given him money to go on gambling with, and on each occasion her money had brought him remarkable runs of luck. Hence there grew up in his mind a superstition that when the worst came, she would be there to save him, and this superstition was a source of considerable comfort to him in his worst moments of dread.

In the beginning, when his passion for her was purely selfish, he had determined to become her lover, cost what it might; but as, with each fresh batch of losses, he sank deeper and deeper into the mire, the reality of this resolve dwindled, and now the idea, had it been put before him, would have seemed little short of sacrilege. The fierceness with which the passion for gambling—become of late an almost nightly struggle for existence—has fastened upon him, had chastened his love for Pearl, making of it a haven wherein all the better part of his nature took refuge; and he had enough moral sense left to recognize his own enslavement.

"Pearl," he said in a low voice, "can you let me have another hundred? I must have it," he went on, speaking more rapidly. "I haven't five pounds left, and I must play to-night. Your husband's banking, and it's my last chance."

"Simon's banking?" she murmured after him. She spoke with a foreign accent that made the words very musical. "Simon's banking?" and a change came over her face, whether of anger, or of dread, or of pain, it would be difficult to say.

She crossed the room, and unlocking a drawer, handed him some notes.

He took them, counted them, and gave her in return a long look of hungry gratitude.

Pearl went back to her old position before the fire, gazing vacantly into the flames.

"I shall come to-morrow," said Duncan, briskly, moving towards the door.

"Yes, come to-morrow," she answered absently.

The door shut. She was alone. And, as the twilight creeps over the earth, steadily, stealthily, a feeling of loneliness crept over Pearl. Everything grew greyer and greyer, blacker and blacker. She was ignorant of the reason for her gloom, and indeed it would have been vain for her to attempt to arrive at its subtle and complex causes. There was, too, at the back of it all, a sense of uneasiness, the dread of some nameless disaster. "Simon's banking to-night," she repeated to herself, and at once the dread doubled in intensity. Then the reaction. How often had she not felt like this before, and there had been nothing? Besides, after all, what did she know? Perhaps it was all right. Yes, it must be all right. But, as if by command, a crowd of incidents leapt up in her memory to remind her of the truth of her suspicion. To speak to him about it never occurred to her; to implore him to give up playing was more than she would have dared. Once or twice indeed she had thought of it, but almost immediately, appalled at her own audacity, she had rejected the idea. For how could they live? He could not work, that was out of the question. Besides, had he not saved her? Did she now owe everything to him? And for the fiftieth time the conflict between right and wrong distracted her, till from sheer weariness she gave it up, as she had done many times before. Already eight o'clock, why was he not yet back?

*　　*　　*　　*　　*　　*

Three years, and several months of the fourth year had come and gone, since that early morning when Simon Alvary, on his way home, after a heavy night at the Cercle du Mont d'Or, Nice, was attracted down a narrow side-street by a sound of muffled moaning. The figure of a man was stooping over a black mass lying in the roadway. It was a girl crouching all huddled in a heap on the cobbles, her elbows raised across her face to protect her eyes. The man was hitting at her with a piece of rope. As Simon came up, he paused before swinging the rope above his head and bringing it down heavily on the girl's neck. In an instant Simon's gloved fist was in his mouth, the fellow reeled and dropped with an incoherent oath. The girl lay on a moment; but presently, surprised that the blows had ceased, she cautiously lowered her arms. Next she crawled up to the groaning body of her assailant, and when she saw the blood trickling from his mouth she whispered hoarsely to Simon:

"*Merci, monsieur. Il allait me tuer si vous n'étiez pas venu. Merci*," then turned over in a faint, face downwards.

Simon ran for a cab, took her home in it to his lodgings, sent for a nurse from the hospital, and the best doctor in the town, gave her his own bed, and slept that night on a sofa in the dining-room. It was three weeks before she was able to get up again, and during that time he did everything that could be done for her, waiting on her himself, as anxiously and as tenderly as if she were his own child. Two nights even when her fever was running dangerously high, he was absent from the card-room of the Cercle, though the luck was with him, and he had been winning largely.

He made cautious inquiries and discovered that the man from whom he had rescued her was her father, an *ancien professeur de lycée*, whom absinthe was fast driving into the gutter. This and the fact that he led his daughter a dog's life was all that Simon could learn, for the man was not a native of the town, and the day after the encounter he disappeared—either afraid that he would be arrested for ill-treating his daughter, or anxious to take the opportunity of ridding himself of her.

Meanwhile Simon was exercising the faculty for secretiveness, which in him amounted almost to genius, inducing the doctor, the nurse and the *concierge*, all by different means, to keep their tongues from wagging, so that the incident was kept absolutely quiet. And since for certain reasons it was necessary, that his life, when he was not at the Cercle or locked up by himself as was his wont for a certain number of hours each day, should be as retired as possible, afternoon upon afternoon he would relieve the nurse by her bedside, smooth her pillows, mix her medicine, shift her poultices, and often, when she grew stronger, read aloud to her in his hard, English voice, chapters from a dog's-eared copy of the *Le Capitaine Fracasse*, which he found lying in the room.

At first this playing the nurse amused him, varying as it did the forced monotony of his life; after a while, as the fascination for her blanched, childlike face and of the big, brown-ringed eyes, wide open in wondering gratitude, grew, he came to regard her as belonging to him absolutely. This sense of proprietorship was especially pleasant— he liked to think of that straight, clean blow—he had never delivered a better—by which she had come into his possession; and of her hundred and one charming little ways of showing her gratitude, not one jarred upon him. From the moment when she had first realized what he had done for her, she had started to worship him, with a sort of wondering superstition, telling herself that he had been sent by Providence to save her. This idea when she told it to him charmed him and strengthened the bond between them. The first morning that she was well enough to leave the house, it occurred to him that he should like to keep her, so with the promptitude of action that was habitual with him, he took her back with him to London. It was not till a full year later that he had consented, with a smile of good-humoured indulgence, to go through the marriage ceremony with her. For months before this they had been living as man and wife, and any ratification had seemed to him quite superfluous.

This was the story of their marriage—a strange enough binding together by chance of two individualities.

Pearl—for so Simon always called her, though her real name was Marie—was now nineteen, ripening every day from a quaint, winsome child into a finely built, beautiful woman. The cowed look had gone from her face—or rather it had developed into an air of delicious gravity, the mysterious thoughtfulness of one for whom the task of living had some hidden meaning.

The many months of their life in common had dulled but little the vividness of her gratitude to Simon. She had felt that the least she could do in return for what he had done for her was to give herself up to him, body and soul, studying all his tastes and habits that she might the more easily merge in them all her own desires and aspirations. And this she had accomplished with no ordinary single-mindedness, till her submission was so complete that he was never aware of it. Yet, in spite of it all, there was not that close sympathy between them which would have made of this sense of duty a source of joy.

Simon was kind to her—more than kind to her—just as he had

always been. Ah, that was it, it was the perpetual monotony of his kindness that at times maddened her, stirring up within her a fierce desire to break out into bitter reproaches against him. She was conscious of a distantness in his indulgence towards her, that he was constantly "thinking apart" from her, as if he were never quite off his guard in her presence. It was not of a sudden that this impression had flashed upon her, it had grown up, built bit by bit from the observation of subtle changes of manner, look, tone. And yet, strong as the temptation to pour out her heart to him was, an indefinable dread had up till now prevented her from yielding to it.

Once she had imagined that it was the memory of some other woman over which he was brooding; but something—what she had forgotten —banished this idea from her mind.

Then appeared the suspicion, which at certain moments crystallized itself into a certainty—it was the card-playing. Wherever they went, London, Paris, or the various fashionable resorts on the Continent— and they were constantly moving from one place to another—Simon played. Even this she did not learn all at once; for when he started out late at night, he never volunteered where he was going. At first in the full flush of her gratitude she had given but little thought to this, the idea that he was playing for large sums never entered her head. But once, when he came back in the middle of the night, she watched him, as she lay in bed, take from the pocket of his ulster a leather bag, and lock it away in a drawer of the writing-table. And as he carried it across the room she heard the muffled chink of money. When the morning came, and he was still sleeping heavily, she slipped out of bed and, unlocking the drawer, loosened the string round the mouth of the bag. Inside lay gold and silver, and a bundle of papers—notes? —yes, notes. The sight of all this money—thousands of francs, as it seemed to her—scared her. Hastily she tied up the bag again and, locking the drawer, crept back into bed.

After this, though she had never dared say a word to him about it, she began to spy upon him. She had always taken for granted that he possessed *rentes*—the word to her meant something at once vague and reassuring. How much she had never stopped to calculate; but that it must be a good deal she felt sure, for they always lived at the best hotels, and he gave her more money than she knew how to spend.

Now, frequent spyings on the writing-table drawer made her

understand that all the money he gave her came from the card-playing, and that he had nothing but what he brought home at nights.

At the beginning of the third year after their marriage they went back to London, to the set of rooms in a little hotel near King's Cross, where he had first taken her. This was a great change from the lavish living to which he had accustomed her on the Continent; but meekly she accepted as final his curt explanation—they must reduce their expenditure.

For a whole fortnight he never once went out at night-time; but after eleven o'clock, when she had gone to her bed-room, he would remain by himself in the sitting-room till past midnight.

Now, since the solitude of her life caused every trivial incident to assume the proportions of an important event, this change in his habits inflamed her curiosity to fever heat. Seated on the bed, or standing in the doorway of the bedroom she would wait listening. Presently a scraping as of the gentle turning of a key. Then for a long while, sometimes an hour, sometimes two hours—nothing—only the movements of the other inmates of the house as they retired for the night. At last the scraping sound again and his tread in the passage.

One night she had worked herself up into such a state of nervous excitement concerning this mystery that she stole out in her stockinged feet to listen at his door. All was still. What could he be doing? She put her eye to the key-hole.   Yes, there he was sitting at the table. There was no one else in the room. He was muttering to himself then. What was he doing with his hands? Cards? Yes, cards! He was lifting them from a heap in the middle of the table and was scattering them over the table. For a long while she remained watching breathlessly, till the draught against her eye became very painful: stealthily she slunk back again.

From that moment the great suspicion lived with her, at times attaining the definite proportions of a certainty, at times fading to the indistinctness of a blurred shadow.

Not long after this the little hotel saw them no more. They had moved to a house in Maida Vale. And here, excepting a month spent in Paris towards the end of the last year, they had been ever since. In reality her life remained as retired as before, though outwardly it was much less so. There came to the house a certain number of men —yet with not one of them did she feel she had anything in common.

It was certainly not their low standard of taste before which she re-coiled, for many of the chance acquaintances with whom she had been thrown on the Continent could boast of but little refinement, but rather as if a portion of her husband's secretiveness had communicated itself to her, teaching her to retreat more and more within herself. To Duncan Ralston alone was she at all accessible; but even with him it was little more than a passive tolerance of his presence, partly on account of his dog-like devotion to her, partly because the pathos of his wrecked life touched her sentimentality.

And so he was with her constantly. And Simon, reticent as usual, made no comment: only when he remembered the soundness of her fidelity, he smiled inwardly, and the smile was entirely pleasant.

Women friends she had none. Barely half a dozen acquaintances— the wife of an actor in whose house (next door) she had met all the others—mostly mere names.

*   *   *   *   *   *

"Well, Pearl, how are you?"

A rotund figure, insignificant in height, but sturdily built, curly, black hair, no moustache or beard, a healthy pink and white com-plexion, the eyes small and metallic, the mouth thin-lipped, the chin full and heavy. But for his voice, a hard, mechanical voice, with no modulation of tone, the last word sounding the same level note as the first, he would have seemed a mere boy. And when he spoke every feature of his face remained impassive, as if he had no consciousness of what he was saying. Thus the first impression that Simon Alvary conveyed was one of well-fed, crass stupidity. But to Pearl he was the all-important centre of her tiny world; and the hardness of his voice— of course she had never heeded it, for it had always been the same.

As he came in she ran towards him, saying impulsively:

"Oh! I thought you were never coming."

"Poor little Pearl!" and he patted her on the cheek. "Has it been very dull all the afternoon? Well, little woman, you shall have a treat this evening, and we'll go to the theatre."

"*Chéri*," she answered, nestling her head on his shoulder.

Presently he moved away from her, arranging his white tie, which she had crumpled, in the mirror.

"By the way," he said (his back was still turned towards her), "just give me back those notes I gave you yesterday. I shall want them to-night. You shall have them again in the morning."

"Give you them back!" she repeated.

He said nothing, only went on straightening his tie.

"I—I haven't got them."

"Haven't got them? Haven't got them? What have you done with them?" His voice was a tone louder, and every syllable sounded with ruthless distinctness.

"Where are they?" he repeated, facing her.

"I—I gave them away—to Ralston," she faltered.

His face was unmoved, but he snapped his fingers once or twice, and this movement, which she knew, made her still more frightened.

"What did he want them for?" he went on.

"For to-night—he said it was his last chance—I am so sorry—forgive me—*je ne savais pas*."

"*Sotte*," was all his reply.

She burst into tears.

"*Je ne savais pas*," she cried.

"It's no good making a fuss. But this is the last time."

"*Je te jure*," she interrupted.

"All right. Now let's come to dinner. Stop! How often have you done this before?"

"Twice. Once a long time ago, and once after we came back from Paris." She answered him eagerly, hoping by the fulness of her confession to atone for her fault.

"How much?"

"Twenty the first time, and fifty the second."

"Was that the fifty I gave you on your birthday?"

"Yes."

He laughed a short, contemptuous laugh, and then they went in to dinner.

2

It was half-past twelve before Simon entered the card-room of the Athenian Club. Still and silent stood the shapeless mass of figures which crowded the far end of it. So still, so silent, that the ticking of the clock was distinctly audible. Then, suddenly, the brutal outburst of a fierce gabbling of voices, incoherent and indescribable, and the crowd started to sway to and fro, feverishly.

Simon handed his overcoat and crush-hat to an attendant, leisurely bit the end from a cigar and sauntered up to the table, that quick glance of his scanning the crowd; it flashed across his face and was gone. But so high ran the game that no one heeded his arrival. It was indeed a full night—not only was every seat round the oval table occupied, but on both sides they stood huddled together, two or three deep, some grey-headed, some bald; some stout and horsey-looking; some boyish, beardless and flashily dressed; some with dark skins, coarse lips and hooked noses; some insignificant like the people one meets every day in the street, a few in evening dress, several with their hats on; most smoking cigars or cigarettes; each and all craning over the table and the disorder of counters, white, gilt, and silvered, which lay strewn up and down it.

Simon stepped on to the daïs which skirted the room, and stood there, a little apart, stolid and expressionless, revealing nothing of the quickening glow that was stealing over him—the deliciously exhilarating glow of fine expectation, coupled with a sense of entire satisfaction with himself.

"Gentlemen, please make your stakes."

(The chink of counters, accompanied by a shower of the disjointed remarks which form the gambler's ritual.)

"*Rien ne va plus,*" called a voice.

"Cards?"

"Cards?"

"Six," and a fresh outburst of hubbub drowned the voice of the banker.

Simon was not a constant visitor at the Athenian—the scene of his operations was usually laid elsewhere—most of the faces were unknown to him; yet he was at once conscious from the demeanour of the crowd that something unusual was taking place. But the gap in the wall of bodies surrounding the table was now closed, and, from where he was, he could see nothing of what was going on.

"Hullo, good evening." It was Duncan.

Simon nodded shortly, and after a pause:

"The bank's low."

"A devil of a run," the other answered excitedly. "The German started at three hundred and was broke in half an hour. This chap took one at five hundred and he's only been on about ten minutes."

At that moment the voice of the croupier was heard.

"Gentlemen, there are only twenty-three pounds in the bank."

A sullen murmur of grumbling, a reckless laugh or two, not a few astonished oaths, an expansion of the crowd, and a noise of the shifting of chairs as the punters rose from their seats. The buzz of conversation swelled till it filled the room, there was a popping of corks, and waiters, armed with glasses, glided in and out of the various groups. The croupier was sweeping away the mess of cards by his side; gazing at him absently, bald and flabby-faced, sat the banker. Presently, however, he swept the little pile of counters before him into the palm of his hand, rose and was lost in the crowd. It was the merchant Stendermann.

The buzz of conversation flagged and rose, flagged and rose again. The croupier had cleared the table, and now was idly examining a crack in his rake.

So the minutes slipped by. But the chairs remained untenanted. No one would risk another bank. A few anxious-looking punters, excited by their gains, were wandering restlessly about, others were moving towards the door, a group was forming round a couple of *écarté* players, who had just seated themselves at the other end of the room.

Simon was biding his time; he loved to toy with the temper of the crowd. At last he stepped forward and, without a word, seated himself in the banker's chair. Instantly there was a rush for seats at the table; those who were on the point of going divested themselves of their overcoats; the two *écarté* players were left almost alone.

"A thousand," he said, throwing a bundle of notes on the table. The croupier ran his fingers through them with the precision of a bank clerk, and the light from the chandelier glinted on the counters which he poured on the table in return.

Then he began dexterously to church together the six packs of cards. Simon, calling for a match, relit his cigar, disguising with admirable skill his keen scrutiny of the punters. On his right sat Duncan, the swollen vein standing out across his forehead as it always did when he was excited—meddling fool!—he at least should go to bed that night with empty pockets; next to him, a hollow-cheeked, filmy-eyed fellow, whose straggling black beard he remembered having seen before in other gaming rooms; beyond, three young "bloods" in evening dress, all chattering in noisy excitement over their winnings off the last two banks. (Simon's eye lingered almost lovingly on this little group, and he observed that two more of the same party stood behind.) Of the punters seated on the other side of the table, three at least, by the quiet determination of their demeanour, were players of calibre, and, next the croupier, a seedy-looking individual, whose fingers were tremulously sorting his small pile of counters—a broken-down specimen, tottering on the brink, without one of which at least no gaming-room is complete. Ah! there in the crowd behind, the fat Stendermann (he had come back then)—a noble loser he, for, during Simon's last visit to Paris, had the merchant not written him out a cheque for seventeen hundred without a murmur after an hour's piquet!

A few minutes later the game was in full swing. Simon had not yet begun to work; as yet he was only playing. For fine as was the pleasure of controlling chance, he was epicure enough to render it quite exquisite by a period of preliminary deliberation. Playing was to him what the *hors-d'œuvre* is to the glutton—and what are the joys of the gambler compared with the joys of the Greek? Besides, in spite of, or rather on account of, the previous runs against the bank, all were staking in small sums, except the three young "bloods" in the corner, and Stendermann, who threw down a heap of ten-pound counters before each deal. Nothing makes the veteran gambler so cautious as heavy winnings.

As yet there were no signs of a run. The hesitation of the cards, declaring first in favour of the punters, then in favour of the bank, had been up till now almost complete, as if, conscious that the struggle had not begun in real earnest, they feared to commit themselves to one side or the other. It was nearly five weeks since Simon had had the chance of a serious game at the Athenian—one of the few clubs open to him where the banker was allowed to handle the cards. Hence the ridiculous proportion of the stakes to the amount of his bank irritated him, or rather provoked that almost imperceptible ruffling which was all he ever allowed himself to indulge in. He determined to raise them by a method all his own, which, though dangerous, was rarely unsuccessful. Waiting till the cards were almost exhausted, he called for three fresh packs. Directly they were placed on the table, he exchanged them, all but the last dozen or so, for a "poultice" which he carried concealed in his waistcoat pocket. In this "poultice" every figure-card, every eight, every nine, and a quantity of combinations making up these two numbers were delicately cogged, so that by passing his fingers along the edges of the pack, he could at once detect their whereabouts. Next, he proceeded to "slip" in favour of the punters five "naturals", three to one side and two to the other. The manœuvre cost him over a hundred pounds, but it accomplished his object. At the beginning of the tenth deal there was more money on the table than there had ever been before, and henceforward with each deal the stakes rose higher and higher. The blood of the players was warmed. He could now begin to work. Yet for a while he continued to dally with the game; that was the weak spot in his strength. How he loved to refine upon the thrill that the consciousness of his power sent through him. So, if he still led the punters on, first to the right, next to the left, it was only to render the joy of plundering them in the following deal all the more acute. The preliminary operation of deposing the "poultice" successfully accomplished—and in truth, for him, this was no difficult feat—all was secure; for the indentations on the cogged cards were so delicate as to be invisible to the naked eye, and imperceptible to any but his exquisite touch. So absolute was his control over the cards, that any moment he could have dealt fifteen "naturals", or fifteen baccarat hands running, had he been so minded. His whole being was concentrated on the game, and he made no attempt to disguise it. The assumption of carelessness, or of nervousness, of high spirits, of loquacity, of bluster, or of extreme civility— the hackneyed devices of the modern Greek—he scorned them all. For to-night at least, he was on a higher plane; he could afford to dispense with them; no salad-shuffle, no churning together of the cards, however conscientious, could impair his omnipotence.

Meanwhile Duncan, whirled along by the savage tide of the vice, won and lost, lost and won again in blind senselessness, only alive to the fluctuation of the pile of counters before him. Off the first two banks he had taken eighty pounds, and his madness wrought in his mind out of this sum the annihilation of all his difficulties. Tradesmen's debts, overdue promissory notes, miscellaneous debts of honours, all vanished, lost to sight amid the magnificent vista of possibilities now stretching before him.

Before now, in a single night, men had won fortunes—fortunes, ay, fortunes large enough to enrich them for life. And he? Why not he? The luck was with him. And did not Pearl's money always bring him luck? The sight of the masses of counters strewn up and down the table fed the fierceness of his lust, intoxicating him, causing him to plunge more and more desperately. He was losing now, but a couple of "naturals", at the rate at which he was staking, would right him again; then in real earnest he would start to break the bank. Alvary— little sleek-faced devil!—he had always hated him—he would break him yet, down to his last farthing. And when he had broken his bank to-night, he would dog him from gaming-room to gaming-room till he had stripped the very clothes from off his back. He sent a glance of hatred at the stolid, round face. Pearl, when he was rich, he would take her from him, and Alvary, he would kick him into the gutter. And, when all these things were done, he would never touch a card again. He would settle down to enjoy life. Ha, there were two winning cards, and as the croupier pushed half a dozen counters towards him, the glow of self-sufficiency that accompanied the vision of a new life of unbroken enjoyment was as vivid as if it had been real. Yet he was losing again. Two "baccarat" hands shattered his castles in the air. His eyes ran rapidly over the counters—thirteen gilt ones, £130; eleven silvered ones, £55; about a dozen white ones. Barely two hundred. Damn these cursed cards! Why, he had only won twenty pounds on this bank.

Six and a figure card.

"Seven," sounded Alvary's clear voice.

While the croupier swept away five of his gilt pieces, Duncan gave vent to a smothered exclamation of fury, and the vein across his forehead swelled as if it would burst. He was a bad loser.

The next deal saw five more disappear. He swore a foul oath between his teeth.

"*Il faut savoir perdre, mon ami,*" said Simon, his teeth gleaming.

The blear-eyed owner of the straggling beard laughed nervously; but Duncan heard nothing.

The following hand was a winning one, but the next two, four and five against Alvary's seven and six brought him back to where he was before. And for a while he plunged on, neither winning nor losing. Once he possessed at least half a dozen gilt counters, then a run of four losing hands in succession, and they were gone every one. A couple of five pound counters and a small heap of whites ones were all that remained. With the caution of despair he refrained from staking them all, pushing only the silvered ones over the line. Knave—six—thank god!

"Stand," he gasped.

"Seven," called Alvary.

And the last of the silvered pieces went to swell the mass in front of the banker. Unconscious of all around him, as if stunned by a heavy blow, he forgot to stake. In the agony of his despair, he was trying to recollect whether, when he had left her, Pearl was wearing the coral necklace he had given her. Then gradually his thoughts came back to the game, and mechanically he pushed forward three white counters. They followed the others, and he sank to staking in sovereigns. One by one they were swept away, and, as they disappeared, the lust of his greed waxed imperious within him, at the sight of the enormous mass heaped within a few feet of him in front of Alvary. Once more he staked again and, as he lifted his cards, the players, the table, everything seemed blurred and distant. Nine! God, and he only had a sovereign on. Swiftly, like a wild beast from its lair, sprung up the impulse—passionate, ungovernable—the *pousette*. There was no time to lose, now, at once. Instantly all his self-possession returned. Coolly he looked round the table, and dropped four counters by the side of the ones he had already staked.

Then Alvary turned up his cards—seven!—and immediately a loathsome terror swept through Duncan. Someone must have seen him—he would be exposed—and he fell to wondering whether they would let him get his hat, or whether they would hound him bareheaded into the street. He dared not look up. He felt the gaze of the whole room upon him. But at last he mustered courage. Strange, no one seemed to be paying any attention to him. Alvary, surely he? But no—and look, the croupier unmoved was pushing a gilt piece towards him. Then he was not discovered. He was free! ha! ha! and a wild spasm of joy swept through him. When it was gone his head swam, and tossing off a brandy and soda, let three deals pass, while he struggled to calm himself.

He was better now. Good god, what an escape! Never again as long as he lived. It fell to him to hold the cards. Eight!—"natural". In an instant he had pushed a second gilt counter over the line. This

E

time a cold sweat came out over his body, and his mouth grew suddenly quite dry. He made a supreme effort to conceal his agitation by beckoning the waiter to bring him another brandy and soda. Twenty pounds he had won. He had three shining gilt pieces.

After this he was wild to win. In the recklessness of his intoxication he had lost all self-control. It was with a clumsiness that was quite pathetic that he was cheating.

He noticed nothing. Alvary whispered to the croupier, the croupier to a man standing behind him; there was a hushing of the hubbub; the game suddenly flagged. But still he noticed nothing. He was staking three gilt counters on each deal now, increasing them to five if the cards were favourable. All fear of detection had vanished. He only knew that he was winning. It was as if some strange force within him were driving him on—as if he were performing some task, imposed upon him by some unknown authority. Half the room was watching him. But he was aware of nothing.

Yet for a while no one made any comment. Each shrank from being the first to speak. At last a nervous laugh burst from one of the young bloods in the corner.

"I say, this is a bit too thick!"

The spell was broken. The storm burst.

"Good god!"

"Who is he?"

"What?"

"He must have been at it all night."

"I know him. Ralston—army man."

"No—retired."

"Kick him out."

"Yes, out with the skunk."

"The window!" yelled the young "bloods", leaping to their feet.

Then above the uproar, quelling it with its harsh imperious note, rang Alvary's voice:

"Gentlemen, gentlemen!"

By degrees there was silence. He was the banker. He had a right to be heard. They waited for him to speak.

"Let the poor devil go," was all he said.

"No, no."

"Out with him."

"Open that window," yelled a sallow-faced youth.

But from the other side of the room arose a murmur of dissent. Some of the older men made themselves heard.

"No violence."

"Shut the window."

"Don't shout."

And again everyone began to speak at once, till the uproar grew quite incoherent. The sallow-faced youth was disputing violently with a man who was trying to shut the window.

"Now's your chance," said Alvary to Duncan. "Out you get."

But the wretched man sat limp, helpless, amid the storm that was raging around him.

"Come, man." And Alvary, gripping him by the shoulder, shook him. "They'll chuck you if you don't run for it."

"Here, get him out of the way or those fellows over there will kill him, if they once get at him," called the fat Stendermann.

Duncan rose and two attendants, at a sign from Alvary, half pushed, half dragged him out of the room.

When those who were for summary measures learnt that he was gone—so great was the uproar that it was fully a minute before they did so—they shouted the louder.

"Who let the blackguard go?" howled the sallow-faced youth.

"I did, young man," thundered back Stendermann, shouldering his way through the crowd. The threatening attitude of the merchant's bulky frame had its effect on the other. Changing his tone considerably, he stammered:

"Why did you let him go?"

"Because we're not going to have an infernal shindy because some of you fellows can't play without getting drunk," interrupted Alvary. The contrast between the heat of his words and the coolness of his demeanour was very striking. The crowd was impressed, for, as he finished speaking, a chorus of approval went round the room.

"Drunk? What the ——? Who are you?" burst out the other.

"Look here, stop it," thundered the merchant, seizing him roughly by the arm, while two or three bystanders instantly put themselves menacingly between Alvary and his antagonist.

"There's been enough for one night," remarked one.

"Yes, the young idiot. What does he want?"

"Something to settle the drink inside him," facetiously answered a third.

Alvary stood, his face absolutely unmoved, waiting while the croupier counted his bank.

"Come, let's get out of it," said someone.

And there was a general move towards the door.

3

Pearl had not gone to bed. Outside the rain pattered against the window-pane; inside the fire was dying, slowly but surely. She wrapped the shawl closer about her shoulders; the book that lay on her lap glided on to the ground. And the rain beat against the window-pane a little louder than before.

After Simon had brought her back from the theatre, and, going out again into the night, had left her to herself, the old sinking sense of uneasiness had come upon her. Vain were all her attempts to beat it back. "It is only because I am unwell," she kept on insisting to herself. But against the advance of the growing dread she was helpless. Waiting, waiting, waiting, listening for the sound of his key in the door, she sat on.

Her father, what had become of him? Dead—a round, green, nameless grave, or perhaps still alive, sitting in a dingy café, with the yellow-green drink before him. Simon! Oh, why did he not come?

Duncan! Was he winning to-night. Those notes! How angry Simon had been when he had snapped his fingers. What was he doing? Perhaps at this moment, now at this very moment, he was taking their money. Oh, why did he not come?

Ah! Stop! What was that? A noise—a knocking—muffled, as if something soft against the door. Ah, there it was again. What could it be? Simon! It had come then. She rushed into the hall and struggled to unfasten the door.

Outside the figure of a man. Not Simon—he was too tall. No hat, wet through, his clothes were clinging to his body.

"Who are you? What do you want?" she gasped, hoarse with terror.

"It's me."

"Ralston. *Oh! comme vous m'avez fait peur! Que faîtes vous la? Qu'est-il arrivé?* Speak, for god's sake! Come in out of the wet."

She seized his dripping sleeve and pulled him inside the door.

"Here, in here; there's a light here," as he stumbled in the dark.

She still held him by the sleeve. He dropped heavily into a chair. His matted hair clung close to his forehead: the water dripped from his finger-tips on to the carpet.

"Simon—where is he? *Dîtes, je vous supplie!* Where is he? What has happened?"

He sent her back a dull stare: he had not understood.

"Speak! For the love of god, speak!" she cried. "Where is he?"

"He's—he's at the club," he answered, grasping her meaning with a visible effort.

"There's no danger? Nothing's happened to him?"

"Nothing's happened," he repeated mechanically. "No, I suppose nothing's happened to him."

"But why are you so wet? Where's your hat? And your coat? See, your trousers are covered with mud."

"Are they?" he asked listlessly.

For an instant neither of them spoke. She, lost in wonder at his woeful appearance; he, stupidly examining the mud on his boots.

"Pearl, I'm done for at last!"

"Done for? How much have you lost? Are they all gone?"

"Lost, worse than lost! They all went. I had only five left, white ones. I tried to win, but—the cards were awful, I was mad—*poussette*. I couldn't help it; it was stronger than myself. At first I won, five times I think. Then they saw. I had to go out—into the street—pouring rain," and he shivered as he spoke the last words.

She tried to stir the dying fire to a flame.

"Come near," she said. "It's not a grand fire. You must take off those wet things. You'll catch cold."

"No," he answered, "leave it."

"And Simon? What did he do?"

"Simon? He won a great pile, I don't know how much."

"But when you were discovered?"

"He told me to go out. He and a big, fat man. Don't know his name. German, I think."

"But you mustn't sit in those wet things. You will kill yourself."

"I'm going home."

"Let me get you a coat."

"No, good-bye."

"Why good-bye? *Au revoir, n'est-ce pas?*'

"It's good-bye."

"What are you going to do? You're not going to———"

"No, I've thought of that; I'm going away abroad. I shall start to-morrow. Good-bye."

"*Adieu.*"

An instant later, he came back and said, "Give me a couple of shillings to get home with."

She handed him her purse.

"Have you got any brandy open?"

She pointed to a decanter and glasses by the door.

He drank a wineglassful, greedily, as if it were water, then went out again, quickly, without looking behind him.

An instant later the hall door slammed, shaking the whole house.

And Pearl, burying her face in her hands, burst into tears.

In the distance a rattle of wheels, louder and louder—before the house it stopped. She ran to the window and, pushing aside the blind, peeped out. Through the murky atmosphere she perceived that it was a hansom cab. Bang! bang! the doors flew open. A man stepped out on to the footboard, and stood there, paying the driver. Simon, at last! Now he was opening the door! Now he was in the hall! She did not go to meet him.

There he was! To her surprise, he was unchanged. There was nothing unusual about him—his hair was unruffled, and his shirt-front was spotless and uncrumpled.

"Hullo, little woman, not gone to bed!" The hard, toneless voice was the same as ever.

She made no answer.

"Has my little Pearl been sitting up all alone for me? But she mustn't do such silly things. Why, it's nearly three o'clock." He put his arms on her shoulders, drawing her towards him.

A slight shudder ran through her; she wrenched herself away.

"*Ne me touche pas.*"

He stepped back, surveying her critically, puzzling for the reason of her anger.

"What's up?" he asked, not interrogatively, but rather to gain time.

Still she made no answer.

"Come," he said, taking both her hands in his and softening the hardness of his voice. "Come, you may as well tell me."

"*Je sais tout.*"

"Ah!" The exclamation was deep-drawn, but the slightly theatrical form of her reply had not escaped him. "That fellow has been here," he added rapidly.

She nodded, and something in that nod betrayed to him her weakness. There would be no battle, after all, he saw.

Instinctively, he divined what to do. Picking up the novel that lay on the floor, and holding it to the lamp, he turned over its pages. Presently his eye travelled to the mud on the carpet. His eyes blinked briskly, as he sought the interpretation of this sign; as its meaning came there was an almost invisible twitching of his nostrils.

He turned and faced her. Their eyes met. He had calculated the strength of his influence. She made one step towards him, and threw both arms round his neck.

"*Simon, je suis si malheureuse!*" she sobbed.

"There, there," he said soothingly, stroking her on the back. "Don't take it so to heart. Don't cry. There, *ma petite* Pearl. Why, you'll make your eyes all red. Now sit down here on my knee and tell me all about it."

He dropped into an armchair and drew her on to his lap.

"*Je t'aime,*" she murmured, burying her face in his shoulder.

He sat quite still, waiting, till she should grow calmer. At last she lifted her head. He wiped away her tears and kissed her on both eyes. Then with parted lips, he looked her full in the face. She smiled.

But immediately her face clouded again; the vision of Ralston's bedraggled figure had come back; but it had lost much of its vividness.

"Now tell me all about it," said Simon. "What did he want?"

"Nothing; he was wet through, and he had no hat—he said good-bye. He said he was going abroad. *Que deviendra-t-il? Dis!*"

"He'll find something to do. They always do."

"*Mais c'est affreux!*"

"Well, but if people will do these things."

"*Mais toi. C'est la même chose, n'est-ce pas?*"

"What do you mean?"

"*Oh! Je l'ai soupçonné depuis—oh! il y a bien des mois—dis, je t'en supplie. C'est vrai, n'est ce pas? J'aimerais mieux savoir. Est-ce la même chose?"*

"You're hurting me—sit a little higher, more to one side. That's it. No, by Jove, it's not quite the same thing—not by a long chalk," and he laughed mirthlessly.

"Mais tu gagnes toujours!"

"And where would the little Pearl be if I didn't?"

This indirect reminder of all she owed him touched her; she drew a little closer to him.

"Mais si tu gagnes toujours?"

"Yes, I always take good care of that."

"Le danger. Ce doit être terrible?"

"No."

"Mais lui?"

"That's different. He lost his head."

"Il n'y a pas de danger, alors?"

"No, not for me."

"Mais si tu étais découvert?"

"I never shall be." At the absolute decision in his voice, her face brightened. The movement was not lost upon him.

"Now, little woman, are you reassured?"

She did not answer, yet he could see the conflict within her was practically at an end.

"Combien as-tu gagné ce soir?"

"Six hundred and thirty-four."

"Pounds?"

"Of course."

She caught her breath in astonishment.

"Mon Dieu!" she exclaimed.

Then she looked up at him, and there was admiration in her eyes.

"You won't hide things from me now. Promise, when you are away, you will tell me what has happened—everything. Won't you? You can trust me. I swear you can trust me."

"Yes, *ma petite* Pearl. In the future you shall know everything. You shall be the banker and keep all the money for me. Would you like that?"

"Oui." The word shot out quickly between her teeth.

"Six hundred and thirty-four pounds!" she repeated, half to herself.
"How much is that in francs?"

"Nearly sixteen thousand."

"And my Pearl isn't angry any more?"

"*Je t'aime*," she murmured in reply.

Their lips met.

OLIVE CUSTANCE[1]

Peacocks

IN GORGEOUS plumage, azure, gold and green,
They trample the pale flowers, and their shrill cry
Troubles the garden's bright tranquillity!
Proud birds of Beauty, splendid and serene,

Spreading their brilliant fans, screen after screen
Of burnished sapphire, gemmed with mimic suns—
Strange magic eyes that, so the legend runs,
Will bring misfortune to this fair demesne.

And my gay youth, that, vain and debonair,
Sits in the sunshine—tired at last of play
(A child, that finds the morning all too long),
Tempts with its beauty that disastrous day
When in the gathering darkness of despair
Death shall strike dumb the laughing mouth of song.

Pierrot

PIERROT, Pierrot, at first they said you slept,
And then they told me you would never wake.
I dared not think . . . I watched the white day break,
The yellow lamps go out . . . I have not wept.

[1] Afterwards Lady Alfred Douglas.

But now I kiss your dear cold hands and weep;
　　Shaken with sobs I cower beside the bed.
　　At last I realize that you are dead,
Drawn suddenly into the arms of sleep.

Love! You will never look at me again
　　With those rain-coloured heavy-lidded eyes,
　　Closed now for ever . . . Pierrot, was it wise
To love so madly since we loved in vain?

In vain, in vain! But, Pierrot, it was sweet
　　To stem the stealthy hours with wine and song!
　　Though death stood up between us stern and strong,
And fate twined nets to trip our dancing feet.

Too soon, alas, too soon our summer swooned
　　To bitter winter . . . and against the lace
　　Of tossed white pillows lay a reckless face,
With feverish parched mouth like a red wound.

Yet still was our brave love not overthrown,
　　And I would nestle at your side and see
　　Your large sad eyes grow passionate for me. . . .
Love, wake and speak. . . . I cannot live alone.

Blue as blue flame is the great sky above,
　　The earth is wonderful and glad and green;
　　But shut the sunlight out, for I have seen
Forgetfulness upon the face of love.

ELLA D'ARCY

The Pleasure-Pilgrim

I

CAMPBELL was on his way to Schloss Altenau, for a second quiet season with his work. He had spent three profitable months there a year ago, and he was hoping now for a repetition of that good fortune. His thoughts outran the train; and long before his arrival at the Hamelin railway station, he was enjoying his welcome by the Ritterhausens, was revelling in the ease and comfort of the old Castle, and was contrasting the pleasures of his home-coming—for he looked upon Schloss Altenau as a sort of temporary home—with his recent cheerless experience of lodging-houses in London, hotels in Berlin, and strange indifferent faces everywhere. He thought with especial satisfaction of the Maynes, and of the good talks Mayne and he would have together, late at night, before the great fire in the hall, after the rest of the household had gone to bed. He blessed the adverse circumstances which had turned Schloss Altenau into a boarding-house, and had reduced the Freiherr Ritterhausen to eke out his shrunken revenue by the reception, as paying guests, of English and American pleasure-pilgrims.

He rubbed the blurred window-pane with the fringed end of the strap hanging from it and, in the snow-covered landscape reeling towards him, began to recognize objects that were familiar. Hamelin could not be far off. . . . In another ten minutes the train came to a standstill.

He stepped down with a sense of relief from the overheated atmosphere of his compartment into the cold, bright February afternoon, and saw through the open station doors one of the Ritterhausen carriages awaiting him, with Gottlieb in his second-best livery on the box. Gottlieb showed every reasonable consideration for the Baron's boarders, but had various methods of marking his sense of the immense abyss separating them from the family. The use of his second-best livery was one of these methods. Nevertheless, he turned a friendly German eye up to Campbell, and in response to his cordial "Guten Tag, Gottlieb. Wie geht's? Und die Herrschaften?" expressed his pleasure at seeing the young man back again.

While Campbell stood at the top of the steps that led down to the carriage and the Platz, looking after the collection of his luggage and its bestowal by Gottlieb's side, he became aware of two persons, ladies, advancing towards him from the direction of the Wartsaal. It was surprising to see anyone at any time in Hamelin Station. It was still more surprising when one of these ladies addressed him by name.

"You are Mr. Campbell, are you not?" she said. "We have been waiting for you to go back in the carriage together. When we found this morning that there was only half-an-hour between your train and ours, I told the Baroness it would be perfectly absurd to send to the station twice. I hope you won't mind our company?"

The first impression Campbell received was of the magnificent apparel of the lady before him; it would have been noticeable in Paris or Vienna—it was extravagant here. Next, he perceived that the face beneath the upstanding feathers and the curving hat-brim was that of so very young a girl, as to make the furs and velvets seem more incongruous still. But the sense of incongruity vanished with the intonation of her first phrase, which told him she was an American. He had no standards for American conduct. It was clear that the speaker and her companion were inmates of the Schloss.

He bowed, and murmured the pleasure he did not feel. A true Briton, he was intolerably shy; and his heart sank at the prospect of a three-mile drive with two strangers who evidently had the advantage of knowing all about him, while he was in ignorance of their very names. As he took his place opposite to them in the carriage, he unconsciously assumed a cold, blank stare, pulling nervously at his moustache, as was his habit in moments of discomposure. Had his companions been British also, the ordeal of the drive must have been a terrible one; but these young American ladies showed no sense of embarrassment whatever.

"We've just come back from Hanover," said the girl who had already spoken to him. "I go over once a week for a singing lesson, and my little sister comes along to take care of me."

She turned a narrow, smiling glance from Campbell to her little sister, and then back to Campbell again. She had red hair; freckles on her nose, and the most singular eyes he had ever seen; slit-like eyes, set obliquely in her head, Chinese fashion.

"Yes, Lulie requires a great deal of taking care of," assented the little sister sedately, though the way in which she said this seemed to imply something less simple than the words themselves. The speaker bore no resemblance to Lulie. She was smaller, thinner, paler. Her features were straight, a trifle peaked; her skin sallow; her hair of a nondescript brown. She was much less gorgeously dressed. There was even a suggestion of shabbiness in her attire, though sundry isolated details of it were handsome too. She was also much less young; or so, at any rate, Campbell began by pronouncing her. Yet presently he wavered. She had a face that defied you to, fix her age. Campbell never fixed it to his own satisfaction, but veered in the course of that drive (as he was destined to do during the next few weeks) from point to point up and down the scale from eighteen to thirty-five. She wore a spotted veil, and beneath it a pince-nez, the lenses of which did something to temper the immense amount of humorous meaning which lurked in her gaze. When her pale prominent eyes met Campbell's, it seemed to the young man that they were full of eagerness to add something at his expense to the stores of information they had already garnered up. They chilled him with misgivings; there was more comfort to be found in her sister's shifting, red-brown glances.

"Hanover is a long way to go for lessons," he observed, forcing himself to be conversational. "I used to go there myself about once a week, when I first came to Schloss Altenau, for tobacco, or note-paper, or to get my hair cut. But later on I did without, or contented myself with what Hamelin, or even the village, could offer me."

"Nannie and I," said the young girl, "meant to stay only a week at Altenau, on our way to Hanover, where we were going to pass the winter; but the Castle is just too lovely for anything." She raised her eyelids the least little bit as she looked at him, and such a warm and friendly gaze shot out, that Campbell was suddenly thrilled. Was she pretty, after all? He glanced at Nannie; she, at least, was indubitably plain. "It's the very first time we've ever stayed in a castle," Lulie went on; "and we're going to remain right along now, until we go home in the spring. Just imagine living in a house with a real moat, and a drawbridge, and a Rittersaal, and suits of armour that have been actually worn in battle! And oh, that delightful iron collar and chain! You remember it, Mr. Campbell? It hangs right close to the gateway on the courtyard side. And you know, in old days the Ritterhausens used it for the punishment of their serfs. There are horrible stories connected with it. Mr. Mayne can tell you them. But just think of being chained up there like a dog! So wonderfully picturesque."

"For the spectator perhaps," said Campbell, smiling. "I doubt if the victim appreciated the picturesque aspect of the case."

With this Lulie disagreed. "Oh, I think he must have been interested," she said. "It must have made him feel so absolutely part and parcel of the Middle Ages. I persuaded Mr. Mayne to fix the collar round my neck the other day; and though it was very uncomfortable, and I had to stand on tiptoe, it seemed to me that all at once the courtyard was filled with knights in armour, and crusaders, and palmers, and things; and there were flags flying and trumpets sounding; and all the dead and gone Ritterhausens had come down from their picture-frames, and were walking about in brocaded gowns and lace ruffles."

"It seemed to require a good deal of persuasion to get Mr. Mayne to unfix the collar again," said the little sister. "How at last did you manage it?"

But Lulie replied irrelevantly: "And the Ritterhausens are such perfectly lovely people, aren't they, Mr. Campbell? The old Baron is a perfect dear. He has such a grand manner. When he kisses my hand I feel nothing less than a princess. And the Baroness is such a funny, busy, delicious little round ball of a thing. And she's always playing bagatelle, isn't she? Or else cutting up skeins of wool for carpet-making." She meditated a moment. "Some people always *are* cutting things up in order to join them together again," she announced, in her fresh drawling young voice.

"And some people cut things up, and leave other people to do the reparation," commented the little sister enigmatically.

And meantime the carriage had been rattling over the cobble-paved streets of the quaint mediæval town, where the houses stand so near together that you may shake hands with your opposite neighbour; where allegorical figures, strange birds and beasts, are carved and painted over the windows and doors; and where to every distant sound you lean your ear to catch the fairy music of the Pied Piper, and at every street corner you look to see his tatterdemalion form with the frolicking children at his heels.

Then the Weser bridge was crossed, beneath which the ice-floes jostled and ground themselves together, as they forced their way down the river; and the carriage was rolling smoothly along country roads, between vacant snow-decked fields.

Campbell's embarrassment began to wear off. Now that he was getting accustomed to the girls, he found neither of them awe-inspiring. The red-haired one had a simple child-like manner that was charming. Her strange little face, with its piquant irregularity of line, its warmth of colour, began to please him. What though her hair was red, the uncurled wisp which strayed across her white forehead was soft and alluring; he could see soft masses of it tucked up beneath her hat-brim as she turned her head. When she suddenly lifted her red-brown lashes, those queer eyes of hers had a velvety softness too. Decidedly, she struck him as being pretty—in a peculiar way. He felt an immense accession of interest in her. It seemed to him that he was the discoverer of her possibilities. He did not doubt that the rest of the world called her plain; or at least odd-looking. He, at first, had only seen the freckles on her nose, her oblique-set eyes. He wondered now what she thought of herself, how she appeared to Nannie. Probably as a very ordinary little girl; sisters stand too close to see each other's qualities. She was too young to have had much opportunity of hearing flattering truths from strangers; and besides, the average stranger would see nothing in her to call for flattering truths. Her charm was something subtle, out-of-the-common, in defiance of all known rules of beauty. Campbell saw superiority in himself for recognizing it, for formulating it; and he was not displeased to be aware that it would always remain caviare to the multitude.

The carriage had driven through the squalid village of Dürrendorf, had passed the great Ritterhausen barns and farm-buildings, on the tie-beams of which are carved Bible texts in old German; had turned in at the wide open gates of Schloss Altenau, where Gottlieb always whipped up his horses to a fast trot. Full of feeling both for the pocket and the dignity of the Ritterhausens, he would not use up his beasts in unnecessary fast driving. But it was to the credit of the family that he should reach the Castle in fine style. And so he thundered across the drawbridge, and through the great archway pierced in the north wing, and over the stones of the cobbled courtyard, to pull up before the door of the hall, with much clattering of hoofs and a final elaborate whip-flourish.

2

"I'm JOLLY glad to have you back," Mayne said, that same evening, when, the rest of the boarders having retired to their rooms, he and Campbell were lingering over the hall-fire for a talk and smoke. "I've missed you awfully, old chap, and the good times we used to have here. I've often meant to write to you, but you know how one shoves off letter-writing day after day, till at last one is too ashamed of one's indolence to write at all. But tell me—you had a pleasant drive from Hamelin? What do you think of our young ladies?"

"Those American girls? But they're charming," said Campbell, with enthusiasm. "The red-haired one is particularly charming."

At this Mayne laughed so strangely, that Campbell questioned him in surprise. "Isn't she charming?"

"My dear chap," Mayne told him, "the red-haired one, as you call her, is the most remarkably charming young person I've ever met or read of. We've had a good many American girls here before now— you remember the good old Choate family, of course—they were here in your time, I think?—but we've never had anything like this Miss Lulie Thayer. She is something altogether unique."

Campbell was struck with the name. "Lulie—Lulie Thayer," he repeated. "How pretty it is!" And, full of his great discovery, he felt he must confide it to Mayne, at least. "Do you know," he went on, "*she* is really very pretty too? I didn't think so at first, but after a bit I discovered that she is positively quite pretty—in an odd sort of way."

Mayne laughed again. "Pretty, pretty!" he echoed in derision. "Why, *lieber Gott im Himmel*, where are your eyes? Pretty! The girl is beautiful, gorgeously beautiful; every trait, every tint, is in complete, in absolute harmony with the whole. But the truth is, of course, we've all grown accustomed to the obvious, the commonplace; to violent contrasts; blue eyes, black eyebrows, yellow hair; the things that shout for recognition. You speak of Miss Thayer's hair as red. What other colour would you have, with that warm, creamy skin? And then, what a red it is! It looks as though it had been steeped in red wine."

"Ah, what a good description," said Campbell, appreciatively. "That's just it—steeped in red wine."

"Though it's not so much her beauty," Mayne continued. "After all, one has met beautiful women before now. It's her wonderful generosity, her complaisance. She doesn't keep her good things to herself. She doesn't condemn you to admire from a distance."

"How do you mean?" Campbell asked, surprised again.

"Why, she's the most egregious little flirt I've ever met. And yet, she's not exactly a flirt, either. I mean she doesn't flirt in the ordinary way. She doesn't talk much, or laugh, or apparently make the least claims on masculine attention. And so all the women like her. I don't believe there's one, except my wife, who has an inkling as to her true character. The Baroness, as you know, never observes anything. *Seigneur Dieu!* if she knew the things I could tell her about Miss Lulie! For I've had opportunities of studying her. You see, I'm a married man, and not in my first youth, and the looker-on generally gets the best view of the game. But you, who are young and charming and already famous—we've had your book here, by-the-bye, and there's good stuff in it—you're going to have no end of pleasant experiences. I can see she means to add you to her ninety-and-nine other spoils; I saw it from the way she looked at you at dinner. She always begins with those velvety red-brown glances. She began that way with March and Prendergast and Willie Anson, and all the men we've had here since her arrival. The next thing she'll do will be to press your hand under the table-cloth."

"Oh come, Mayne, you're joking," cried Campbell a little brusquely. He thought such jokes in bad taste. He had a high ideal of Woman, an immense respect for her; he could not endure to hear her belittled, even in jest. "Miss Thayer is refined and charming. No girl of he class would do such things."

"But what is her class? Who knows anything about her? All w know is that she and her uncanny little friend—her little sister, as she calls her, though they're no more sisters than you and I are—they're not even related—all we know is, that she and Miss Dodge (that's th little sister's name) arrived here one memorable day last October from the Kronprinz Hotel at Waldeck-Pyrmont. By-the-bye, it was the Choates, I believe, who told her of the Castle—hotel acquaintances— you know how travelling Americans always cotton to each other. And we've picked up a few little auto- and biographical notes from her and Miss Dodge since. *Zum Beispiel,* she's got a rich father somewhere away back in Michigan, who supplies her with all the money she wants. And she's been travelling about since last May: Paris, Vienna, the Rhine, Düsseldorf, and so on here. She must have had some rich experiences, by Jove, for she's done everything. Cycled in Paris; you should see her in her cycling costume, she wears it when the Baron takes her out shooting—she's an admirable shot, by the way, an accomplishment learned, I suppose, from some American cow-boy—then in Berlin she did a month's hospital nursing; and now she's studying the higher branches of the Terpsichorean art. You know she was in Hanover to-day. Did she tell you what she went for?"

F

"To take a singing lesson," said Campbell, remembering the reason she had given.

"A singing lesson! Do you sing with your legs? A dancing lesson, *mein lieber*. A dancing lesson from the ballet-master of the Hof Theatre. She could deposit a kiss on your forehead with her foot, I don't doubt. I must ask her if she can do the *grand écart* yet." And when Campbell, in astonishment, wondered why on earth she should wish to learn such things, "Oh, to extend her opportunities," Mayne explained, "and to acquire fresh sensations. She's an adventuress. Yes, an adventuress, but an end-of-the-century one. She doesn't travel for profit, but for pleasure. She has no desire to swindle her neighbour, but to amuse herself. And she's clever; she's read a good deal; she knows how to apply her reading to practical life. Thus, she's learned from Herrick not to be coy; and from Shakespeare that sweet-and-twenty is the time for kissing and being kissed. She honours her masters in the observance. She was not in the least abashed when, one day, I suddenly came upon her teaching that damned idiot, young Anson, two new ways of kissing."

Campbell's impressions of the girl were readjusting themselves completely, but for the moment he was unconscious of the change. He only knew that he was partly angry, partly incredulous, and inclined to believe that Mayne was chaffing him.

"But, Miss Dodge," he objected, "the little sister, she is older; old enough to look after her friend. Surely she could not allow a young girl placed in her charge to behave in such a way——"

"Oh, that little Dodge girl," said Mayne contemptuously; "Miss Thayer pays the whole shot, I understand, and Miss Dodge plays gooseberry, sheep-dog, jackall, what you will. She finds her reward in the other's cast-off finery. The silk blouse she was wearing to-night, I've good reason for remembering, belonged to Miss Lulie. For, during a brief season, I must tell you, my young lady had the caprice to show attentions to your humble servant. I suppose my being a married man lent me a factitious fascination. But I didn't see it. That kind of girl doesn't appeal to me. So she employed Miss Dodge to do a little active canvassing. It was really too funny; I was coming in one day after a walk in the woods; my wife was trimming bonnets, or had neuralgia, or something. Anyhow, I was alone, and Miss Dodge contrived to waylay me in the middle of the courtyard. "Don't you find it vurry dull walking all by yourself?" she asked me; and then blinking up in her strange little short-sighted way—she's really the weirdest little creature—"Why don't you make love to Lulie?" she said; "you'd find her vurry charming." It took me a minute or two to recover presence of mind enough to ask her whether Miss Thayer had commissioned her to tell me so. She looked at me with that cryptic smile of hers; "She'd like you to do so, I'm sure," she finally remarked, and pirouetted away. Though it didn't come off, owing to my bashfulness, it was then that Miss Dodge appropriated the silk "waist"; and Providence, taking pity on Miss Thayer's forced inactivity, sent along March, a young fellow reading for the army, with whom she had great doings. She fooled him to the top of his bent; sat on his knee; gave him a lock of her hair, which, having no scissors handy, she burned off with a cigarette taken from his mouth; and got him to offer her marriage. Then she turned round and laughed in his face, and took up with a Dr. Weber, a cousin of the Baron's, under the other man's very eyes. You never saw anything like the unblushing coolness with which she would permit March to catch her in Weber's arms."

"Come," Campbell protested again, "aren't you drawing it rather strong?"

"On the contrary, I'm drawing it mild, as you'll discover presently for yourself; and then you'll thank me for forewarning you. For she makes love—desperate love, mind you—to every man she meets. And goodness knows how many she hasn't met in the course of her career, which began presumably at the age of ten, in some 'Amur'can' hotel or watering-place. Look at this." Mayne fetched an alpenstock from a corner of the hall; it was decorated with a long succession of names, which, ribbon-like, were twisted round and round it, carved in the wood. "Read them," insisted Mayne, putting the stick in Campbell's hands. "You'll see they're not the names of the peaks she has climbed, or the towns she has passed through; they're the names of the men she has fooled. And there's room for more; there's still a good deal of space, as you see. There's room for yours."

Campbell glanced down the alpenstock—reading here a name, there an initial, or just a date—and jerked it impatiently from him on to a couch. He wished with all his heart that Mayne would stop, would talk of something else, would let him get away. The young girl had interested him so much; he had felt himself so drawn towards her; he had thought her so fresh, so innocent. But Mayne, on the contrary, was warming to his subject, was enchanted to have someone to listen to his stories, to discuss his theories, to share his cynical amusement.

"I don't think, mind you," he said, "that she is a bit interested herself in the men she flirts with. I don't think she gets any of the usual sensations from it, you know. My theory is, she does it for mere devilry, for a laugh. Or, and this is another theory, she is actuated by some idea of retribution. Perhaps some woman she was fond of—her mother even—who knows?—was badly treated at the hands of a man. Perhaps this girl has constituted herself the Nemesis for her sex, and goes about seeing how many masculine hearts she can break, by way of revenge. Or can it be that she is simply the newest development of the New Woman—she who in England preaches and bores you, and in America practises and pleases? Yes, I believe she's the American edition, and so new that she hasn't yet found her way into fiction. She's the pioneer of the army coming out of the West, that's going to destroy the existing scheme of things, and rebuild it nearer to the heart's desire."

"Oh, damn it all, Mayne," cried Campbell, rising abruptly, "Why not say at once that she's a wanton, and have done with it? Who wants to hear your rotten theories?" And he lighted his candle without another word, and went off to bed.

3

IT WAS four o'clock, and the Baron's boarders were drinking their afternoon coffee, drawn up in a semi-circle round the hall fire. All but Campbell, who had carried his cup away to a side-table, and, with a book open beside him, appeared to be reading assiduously. In reality he could not follow a line of what he read; he could not keep his thoughts from Miss Thayer. What Mayne had told him was germinating in his mind. Knowing his friend as he did, he could not on reflection doubt his word. In spite of much superficial cynicism, Mayne was incapable of speaking lightly of any young girl without good cause. It now seemed to Campbell that, instead of exaggerating the case, Mayne had probably understated it. He asked himself with horror, what had this girl not already known, seen, permitted? When now and again his eyes travelled over, perforce, to where she sat, her red head leaning against Miss Dodge's knee, and seeming to attract to, and concentrate upon itself all the glow of the fire, his forehead set itself in frowns, and he returned to his book with an increased sense of irritation.

"I'm just sizzling up, Nannie," Miss Thayer presently complained, in her child-like, drawling little way; "this fire is too hot for anything." She rose and shook straight her loose tea-gown, a marvellous plush and lace garment created in Paris, which would have accused a duchess of wilful extravagance. She stood smiling round a moment, pulling on and off with her right hand a big diamond ring which decorated the left. At the sound of her voice Campbell had looked up, and his cold, unfriendly eyes encountered hers. He glanced rapidly past her, then back to his book. But she, undeterred, with a charming sinuous movement and a frou-frou of trailing silks, crossed over towards him. She slipped into an empty chair next his.

"I'm going to do you the honour of sitting beside you, Mr. Campbell," she said sweetly.

"It's an honour I've done nothing whatever to merit," he answered, without looking at her, and turned a page.

"The right retort," she approved; "but you might have said it a little more cordially."

"I don't feel cordial."

"But why not? What has happened? Yesterday you were so nice."

"Ah, a good deal of water has run under the bridge since yesterday."

"But still the river remains as full," she told him, smiling, "and still the sky is as blue. The thermometer has even risen six degrees."

"What did you go into Hanover for yesterday?" Campbell suddenly asked her.

She flashed him a comprehending glance from half-shut eyes. "I think men gossip a great deal more than women," she observed, "and they don't understand things either. They try to make all life suit their own pre-conceived theories. And why, after all, should I not wish to learn dancing thoroughly? There's no harm in that."

"Only, why call it singing?" Campbell enquired.

Miss Thayer smiled. "Truth is so uninteresting!" she said, and paused. "Except in books. One likes it there. And I wanted to tell you, I think your books perfectly lovely. I know them, most all. I've read them away home. They're very much thought of in America.

Only last night I was saying to Nannie how glad I am to have met you, for I think we're going to be great friends, aren't we, Mr. Campbell? At least, I hope so, for you can do me so much good, if you will. Your books always make me feel real good; but you yourself can help me much more."

She looked up at him with one of her warm, narrow, red-brown glances, which yesterday would have thrilled his blood, and to-day merely stirred it to anger.

"You over-estimate my abilities," he said coldly; "and, on the whole, I fear you will find writers a very disappointing race. You see, they put their best into their books. So not to disillusion you too rapidly"—he rose—"will you excuse me? I have some work to do." And he left her sitting there alone.

But he did no work when he got to his room. Whether Lulie Thayer was actually present or not, it seemed that her influence was equally disturbing to him. His mind was full of her: of her singular eyes, her quaint intonation, her sweet, seductive praise. Twenty-four hours ago such praise would have been delightful to him: what young author is proof against appreciation of his books? Now, Campbell simply told himself that she laid the butter on too thick; that it was in some analogous manner she had flattered up March, Anson, and all the rest of the men that Mayne had spoken of. He supposed it was the first step in the process by which he was to be fooled, twisted round her finger, added to the list of victims who strewed her conquering path. He had a special fear of being fooled. For beneath a somewhat supercilious exterior, the dominant note of his character was timidity, distrust of his own merits; and he knew he was single-minded—one-idea'd almost—if he were to let himself go, to get to care very much for a woman, for such a girl as this girl, for instance, he would lose himself completely, be at her mercy absolutely. Fortunately, Mayne had let him know her character. He could feel nothing but dislike for her— disgust, even; and yet he was conscious how pleasant it would be to believe in her innocence, in her candour. For she was so adorably pretty; her flower-like beauty grew upon him; her head, drooping a little on one side when she looked up, was so like a flower bent by its own weight. The texture of her cheeks, her lips, was delicious as the petals of a flower. He found he could recall with perfect accuracy every detail of her appearance: the manner in which the red hair grew round her temples; the way in which it was loosely and gracefully fastened up behind with just a single tortoise-shell pin. He recollected the suspicion of a dimple that shadowed itself in her cheek when she spoke, and deepened into a delicious reality every time she smiled. He remembered her throat; her hands, of a beautiful whiteness, with pink palms and pointed fingers. It was impossible to write. He speculated long on the ring she wore on her engaged finger. He mentioned this ring to Mayne the next time he saw him.

"Engaged? Very much so, I should say. Has got a *fiancé* in every capital of Europe probably. But the ring-man is the *fiancé en titre*. He writes to her by every mail, and is tremendously in love with her. She shows me his letters. When she's had her fling, I suppose she'll go back and marry him. That's what these little American girls do, I'm told; sow their wild oats here with us, and settle down into *bonnes ménagères* over yonder. Meanwhile, are you having any fun with her? Aha, she presses your hand? The 'gesegnete Mahlzeit' business after dinner is an excellent institution, isn't it? She'll tell you how much she loves you soon; that's the next move in the game."

But so far she had done neither of these things, for Campbell gave her no opportunities. He was guarded in the extreme, ungenial; avoiding her even at the cost of civility. Sometimes he was downright rude. That especially occurred when he felt himself inclined to yield to her advances. For she made him all sorts of silent advances, speaking with her eyes, her sad little mouth, her beseeching attitude. And then one evening she went further still. It occurred after dinner in the little green drawing-room. The rest of the company were gathered together in the big drawing-room beyond. The small room has deep embrasures to the windows Each embrasure holds two old faded green velvet sofas in black oaken frames, and an oaken oblong table stands between them. Campbell had flung himself down on one of these sofas in the corner nearest the window. Miss Thayer, passing through the room, saw him, and sat down opposite. She leaned her elbows on the table, the laces of her sleeves falling away from her round white arms, and clasped her hands.

"Mr. Campbell, tell me, what have I done? How have I vexed you? You have hardly spoken two words to me all day. You always try to avoid me." And when he began to utter evasive banalities, she stopped him with an imploring "Ah, don't! I love you. You know I love you. I love you so much I can't bear you to put me off with mere phrases."

Campbell admired the well-simulated passion in her voice, remembered Mayne's prediction, and laughed aloud.

"Oh, you may laugh," she said, "but I'm serious. I love you, I love you with my whole soul." She slipped round the end of the table, and came close beside him. His first impulse was to rise; then he resigned himself to stay. But it was not so much resignation that was required, as self-mastery, cool-headedness. Her close proximity, her fragrance, those wonderful eyes raised so beseechingly to his, made his heart beat.

"Why are you so cold?" she said. "I love you so, can't you love me a little too?"

"My dear young lady," said Campbell, gently repelling her, "what do you take me for? A foolish boy like your friends Anson and March? What you are saying is monstrous, preposterous. Ten days ago you'd never even seen me."

"What has length of time to do with it?" she said. "I loved you at first sight."

"I wonder," he observed judicially, and again gently removed her hand from his, "to how many men you have not already said the same thing?"

"I've never meant it before," she said quite earnestly, and nestled closer to him, and kissed the breast of his coat, and held her mouth up towards his. But he kept his chin resolutely high, and looked over her head.

"How many men have you not already kissed, even since you've been here?"

"But there've not been many here to kiss!" she exclaimed naïvely.

"Well, there was March; you kissed him?"

"No, I'm quite sure I didn't."

"And young Anson; what about him? Ah, you don't answer! And then the other fellow—what's his name—Prendergast—you've kissed him?"

"But, after all, what is there in a kiss?" she cried ingenuously. "It means nothing, absolutely nothing. Why, one has to kiss all sorts of people one doesn't care about."

Campbell remembered how Mayne had said she had probably

known strange kisses since the age of ten; and a wave of anger with her, of righteous indignation, rose within him.

"To me," said he, "to all right-thinking people, a young girl's kisses are something pure, something sacred, not to be offered indiscriminately to every fellow she meets. Ah, you don't know what you have lost! You have seen a fruit that has been handled, that has lost its bloom? You have seen primroses, spring flowers gathered and thrown away in the dust? And who enjoys the one, or picks up the others? And this is what you remind me of—only you have deliberately, of your own perverse will, tarnished your beauty, and thrown away all the modesty, the reticence, the delicacy, which make a young girl so infinitely dear. You revolt me, you disgust me. I want nothing from you but to be let alone. Kindly take your hands away, and let me go."

He shook her roughly off and got up, then felt a moment's curiosity to see how she would take the repulse.

Miss Thayer never blushed: had never, he imagined, in her life done so. No faintest trace of colour now stained the warm pallor of her rose-leaf skin; but her eyes filled up with tears, two drops gathered on the under-lashes, grew large, trembled an instant, and then rolled unchecked down her cheeks. Those tears somehow put him in the wrong, and he felt he had behaved brutally to her, for the rest of the night.

He began to seek excuses for her: after all, she meant no harm: it was her upbringing, her *genre*: it was a *genre* he loathed; but perhaps he need not have spoken so harshly. He thought he would find a more friendly word for her next morning; and he loitered about the Mahlsaal, where the boarders come in to breakfast as in an hotel just when it suits them, till past eleven; but she did not come. Then, when he was almost tired of waiting, Miss Dodge put in an appearance, in a flannel wrapper, and her front hair twisted up in steel pins.

Campbell judged Miss Dodge with even more severity than he did Miss Thayer; there was nothing in this weird little creature's appearance to temper justice with mercy. It was with difficulty that he brought himself to inquire after her friend.

"Lulie is sick this morning," she told him. "I've come down to order her some broth. She couldn't sleep any last night, because of your unkindness to her. She's vurry, vurry unhappy about it."

"Yes, I'm sorry for what I said. I had no right to speak so strongly,

I suppose. But I spoke strongly because I feel strongly. However, there's no reason why my bad manners should make her unhappy."

"Oh, yes, there's vurry good reason," said Miss Dodge. "She's vurry much in love with you."

Campbell looked at the speaker long and earnestly to try and read her mind; but the prominent blinking eyes, the cryptic physiognomy, told him nothing.

"Look here," he said brusquely, "what's your object in trying to fool me like this? I know all about your friend. Mayne has told me. She has cried 'Wolf' too often before to expect to be believed now."

"But, after all," argued Miss Dodge, blinking more than ever behind her glasses, "the wolf really did come at last you know; didn't she? Lulie is really in love this time. We've all made mistakes in our lives, haven't we? But that's no reason for not being right at last. And Lulie has cried herself sick."

Campbell was a little shaken. He went and repeated the conversation to Mayne, who laughed derisively.

"Capital, capital!" he cried; "excellently contrived. It quite supports my latest theory about our young friend. She's an actress, a born comédienne. She acts always, and to everyone: to you, to me, to the Ritterhausens, to the Dodge girl—even to herself when she is quite alone. And she has a great respect for her art; she'll carry out her rôle, *coûte que coûte*, to the bitter end. She chooses to pose as in love with you; you don't respond; the part now requires that she should sicken and pine. Consequently, she takes to her bed, and sends her confidante to tell you so. Oh, it's colossal, it's *famos!*"

4

"If you can't really love me," said Lulie Thayer—"and I know I've been a bad girl and don't deserve that you should—at least, will you allow me to go on loving you?"

She walked by Campbell's side, through the solitary, uncared-for park of Schloss Altenau. It was three weeks later in the year, and the spring feeling in the air stirred her blood. All round were signs and tokens of spring; in the busy gaiety of bird and insect life; in the purple flower-tufts which thickened the boughs of the ash trees; in the young green things pushing up pointed heads from amidst last season's dead leaves and grasses. The snow-wreaths, that had for so long decorated the distant hills, were shrinking perceptibly away beneath the strong March sunshine.

There was every invitation to spend one's time out of doors, and Campbell passed long mornings in the park, or wandering through the woods and the surrounding villages. Miss Thayer often accompanied him. He never invited her to do so, but when she offered him her company, he could not, or at least did not, refuse it.

"May I love you? Say," she entreated.

" 'Wenn ich Dich liebe, was geht's Dich an?' " he quoted lightly. "Oh, no, it's nothing to me, of course. Only don't expect me to believe you—that's all."

This disbelief of his was the recurring decimal of their conversation. No matter on what subject they began, they always ended thus. And the more sceptical he showed himself, the more eager she became. She exhausted herself in endeavours to convince him.

They had reached the corner in the park where the road to the Castle turns off at right angles from the road to Dürrendorf. The ground rises gently on the park-side to within three feet of the top of the boundary wall, although on the other side there is a drop of at least twenty feet. The broad wall-top makes a convenient seat. Campbell and the girl sat down on it. At his last words she wrung her hands together in her lap.

"But how can you disbelieve me?" she cried, "when I tell you I love you, I adore you? When I swear it to you? And can't you see for yourself? Why, everyone at the Castle sees it."

"Yes, you afford the Castle a good deal of unnecessary amusement; and that shows you don't understand what love really is. Real love is full of delicacy, of reticences, and would feel itself profaned if it became the jest of the servants' hall."

"It's not so much my love for you, as your rejection of it, which has made me talked about."

"Isn't it rather on accounts of the favours you've lavished on all my predecessors?"

She sprang to her feet, and walked up and down in agitation.

"But, after all, surely, mistakes of that sort are not to be counted against us? I did really think I was in love with Mr. March. Willie Anson doesn't count. He's an American too, and he understands things. Besides, he is only a boy. And how could I know I should love you before I had met you? And how can I help loving you now I have? You're so different from other men. You're good, you're honourable, you treat women with respect. Oh, I do love you so, I do love you! Ask Nannie if I don't."

The way in which Campbell shrugged his shoulders clearly expressed the amount of reliance he would place on any testimony from Miss Dodge. He could not forget her 'Why don't you make love to Lulie?' addressed to a married man. Such a want of principle argued an equal want of truth.

Lulie seemed on the brink of weeping.

"I wish I were dead," she struggled to say; "life's impossible if you won't believe me. I don't ask you any longer to love me. I know I've been a bad girl, and I don't deserve that you should; but if you won't believe that I love you, I don't want to live any longer."

Campbell confessed to himself that she acted admirably, but that the damnable iteration of the one idea became monotonous. He sought a change of subject. "Look there," he said, "close by the wall, what's that jolly little blue flower? It's the first I've seen this year."

He showed her where, at the base of the wall, a solitary blossom rose above a creeping stem and glossy dark green leaves.

Lulie, all smiles again, picked it with childlike pleasure. "Oh, if that's the first you've seen," she cried, "you can take a wish. Only you mustn't speak until someone asks you a question."

She began to fasten it in his coat. "It's just as blue as your eyes," she said. "You have such blue and boyish eyes, you know. Stop, stop, that's not a question," and seeing that he was about to speak, she laid her finger across his mouth. "You'll spoil the charm."

She stepped back, folded her arms, and seemed to dedicate herself to eternal silence; then relenting suddenly:

"Do you believe me?" she entreated.

"What's become of your ring?" Campbell answered beside the mark. He had noticed its absence from her finger while she had been fixing in the flower.

"Oh, my engagement's broken."

Campbell asked how the fiancé would like that.

"Oh, he won't mind. He knows I only got engaged because he

worried so. And it was always understood between us that I was to be free if I ever met anyone I liked better."

Campbell asked her what sort of fellow this accommodating fiancé was.

"Oh, he's all right. And he's very good too. But he's not a bit clever, and don't let us talk about him. He makes me tired."

"But you're wrong," Campbell told her, "to throw away a good, a sincere affection. If you really want to reform and turn over a new leaf, as you are always telling me you do, I should advise you to go home and marry him."

"What, when I'm in love with you?" she cried reproachfully. "Would that be right?"

"It's going to rain," said Campbell. "Didn't you feel a drop just then? And it's getting near lunch-time. Shall we go in?"

Their shortest way led through the little cemetery in which the departed Ritterhausens lay at peace, in the shadow of their sometime home.

"When I die the Baron has promised I shall be buried here," said Lulie pensively; "just here, next to his first wife. Don't you think it would be lovely to be buried in a beautiful, peaceful, baronial graveyard instead of in some horrid, crowded city cemetery?"

Mayne met them as they entered the hall. He noticed the flower in his friend's coat. "Ah, my dear chap, been treading the—periwinkle path of dalliance, I see? How many desirable young men have I not witnessed, led down the same broad way by the same seductive lady! Always the same thing; nothing changes but the flower according to the season."

When Campbell reached his room he took the poor periwinkle out of his coat, and threw it away into the stove.

And yet, had it not been for Mayne, Miss Thayer might have triumphed after all; might have convinced Campbell of her passion, or have added another victim to her long list. But Mayne had set himself as determinedly to spoil her game, as she was bent on winning it. He had always the cynical word, the apt reminiscence ready, whenever he saw signs on Campbell's part of surrender. He was very fond of Campbell. He did not wish him to fall a prey to the wiles of this little American siren. He had watched her conduct in the past with a dozen different men; he genuinely believed she was only acting in the present.

Campbell, for his part, began to experience an ever-increasing exasperation in the girl's presence. Yet he did not avoid it; he could not well avoid it, she followed him about so persistently: but his speech would overflow with bitterness towards her. He would say the cruellest things; then remembering them when alone, be ashamed of his brutalities. But nothing he said ever altered her sweetness of temper or weakened the tenacity of her purpose. His rebuffs made her beautiful eyes run over with tears, but the harshest of them never elicited the least sign of resentment. There would have been something touching as well as comic in this dog-like humility, which accepted everything as welcome at his hands, had he not been imbued with Mayne's conviction that it was all an admirable piece of acting. Or when for a moment he forgot the histrionic theory, then invariably there would come a chance word in her conversation which would fill him with cold rage. They would be talking of books, travels, sport, what not, and she would drop a reference to this man or to that. So-and-so had taken her to Bullier's, she had learned skating with this other; Duroy, the *prix de Rome* man, had painted her as Hebe, Franz Weber had tried to teach her German by means of Heine's poems. And he got glimpses of long vistas of amourettes played in every state in America, in every country of Europe, since the very beginning, when, as a mere child, elderly men, friends of her father's, had held her on their knee and fed her on sweetmeats and kisses. It was sickening to think of; it was pitiable. So much youth and beauty tarnished; the possibility for so much good thrown away. For if one could only blot out her record, forget it, accept her for what she chose to appear, a more endearing companion no man could desire.

5

It was a wet afternoon; the rain had set in at mid-day, with a grey determination, which gave no hopes of clearing. Nevertheless, Mayne had accompanied his wife and the Baroness into Hamelin. "To take up a servant's character, and expostulate with a recalcitrant dressmaker," he explained to Campbell, and wondered what women would do to fill up their days were it not for the perennial crimes of dressmakers and domestic servants. He himself was going to look in at the English Club; wouldn't Campbell come too? There was a fourth seat in the carriage. But Campbell was in no social mood; he felt his temper going all to pieces; a quarter of an hour of Mrs. Mayne's society would have brought on an explosion. He thought he must be alone; and yet when he had read for half an hour in his room he wondered vaguely what Lulie was doing; he had not seen her since luncheon. She always gave him her society when he could very well dispense with it, but on a wet day like this, when a little conversation would be tolerable, of course she stayed away. Then there came down the long Rittersaal the tapping of high heels, and a well-known knock at his door.

He went over and opened it. Miss Thayer, in the plush and lace tea-gown, fronted him serenely.

"Am I disturbing you?" she asked; and his mood was so capricious that, now she was standing there on his threshold, he thought he was annoyed at it. "It's so dull," she said persuasively: "Nannie's got a sick headache, and I daren't go downstairs, or the Baron will annex me to play Halma. He always wants to play Halma on wet days."

"And what do you want to do?" said Campbell, leaning against the doorpost, and letting his eyes rest on the strange piquant face in its setting of red hair.

"To be with you, of course."

"Well," said he, coming out and closing the door, "I'm at your service. What next?"

They strolled together through the room and listened to the falling rain. The Rittersaal occupies all the space on the first floor that the hall and four drawing-rooms do below. Wooden pillars support the ceiling, dividing the apartment lengthwise into a nave and two aisles. Down the middle are long tables, used for ceremonial banquets. Six windows look into the courtyard, and six out over the open country. The centre pane of each window is emblazoned with a Ritterhausen shield. Between the windows hang family portraits, and the sills are broad and low and cushioned in faded velvet.

"How it rains!" said Lulie, stopping before one of the south windows; "why, you can't see anything for the rain, and there's no sound at all but the rain either. I like it. It makes me feel as though we had the whole world to ourselves."

Then, "Say, what would you like to do?" she asked him. "Shall I fetch over my pistols, and we'll practise with them? You've no notion how well I can shoot. We couldn't hurt anything here, could we?"

Campbell thought they might practise there without inconvenience, and Lulie, bundling up the duchess tea-gown over one arm, danced off in very unduchess-like fashion to fetch the case. It was a charming little box of cedar-wood and mother-o'-pearl, lined with violet velvet; and two tiny revolvers lay inside, hardly more than six inches long, with silver engraved handles.

"I won them in a bet," she observed complacently, "with the Hon. Billie Thornton. He's an Englishman, you know, the son of Lord Thornton. I knew him in Washington two years ago last fall. He bet I couldn't hit a three-cent piece at twenty yards and I did. Aren't they perfectly sweet? Now, can't you contrive a target?"

Campbell went back to his room, drew out a rough diagram, and pasted it down on to a piece of cardboard. Then this was fixed up by means of a penknife driven into the wood of one of the pillars, and Campbell, with his walking-stick laid down six successive times, measured off the distance required, and set a chalk mark across the floor. Lulie took the first shot. She held the little weapon up at arm's length above her head, the first finger stretched out along the barrel; then dropping her hand sharply so that the finger pointed straight at the butt, she pulled the trigger with the third. There was a sharp report, the tiny smoke film—and when Campbell went up to examine results, he found she had only missed the very centre by a quarter of an inch.

Lulie was exultant. "I don't seem to have got out of practice any," she remarked. "I'm so glad, for I used to be a very good shot. It was Hiram P. Ladd who taught me. He's the crack shot of Montana. What, you don't know Hiram P.? Why, I should have supposed every-one must have heard of him. He had the next ranche to my Uncle Samuel's, where I used to go summers, and he made me do an hour's pistol practice every morning after bathing. It was he who taught me swimming too—in the river."

"Damnation," said Campbell under his breath, then shot in his turn, and shot wide. Lulie made another bull's-eye, and after that a white. She urged Campbell to continue, which he sullenly did, and again missed.

"You see I don't come up to your Hiram P. Ladd," he remarked savagely, and put the pistol down, and walked over to the window. He stood with one foot on the cushioned seat, staring out at the rain, and pulling moodily at his moustache.

Lulie followed him, nestled up to him, lifted the hand that hung passive by his side, put it round her waist and held it there. Campbell lost in thought, let it remain so for a second; then remembered how she had doubtless done this very same thing with other men in this very room. All her apparently spontaneous movements, he told himself, were but the oft-used pieces in the game she played so skilfully.

"Let go," he said, and flung himself down on the window-seat, looking up at her with darkening eyes.

She sitting meekly in the other corner folded her offending hands in her lap.

"Do you know, your eyes are not a bit nice when you're cross?" she said; "they seem to become quite black."

He maintained a discouraging silence.

She looked over at him meditatively.

"I never cared a bit for Hiram P., if that's what you mean," she remarked presently.

"Do you suppose I care a button if you did?"

"Then why did you leave off shooting, and why won't you talk to me?"

He vouchsafed no reply.

Lulie spent some moments immersed in thought. Then she sighed deeply, and recommenced on a note of pensive regret.

"Ah, if I'd only met you sooner in life, I should be a very different girl."

The freshness which her quaint, drawling enunciation lent to this time-dishonoured formula, made Campbell smile, till, remembering all its implications, his forehead set in frowns again.

Lulie continued her discourse. "You see," said she, "I never had anyone to teach me what was right. My mother died when I was quite a child, and my father has always let me do exactly as I pleased, so long as I didn't bother him. Then I've never had a home, but have always lived around in hotels and places: all winter in New York or Washington, and summers out at Longbranch or Saratoga. It's true we own a house at Detroit, on Lafayette Avenue, that we reckon as home, but we don't ever go there. It's a bad sort of life for a girl, isn't it?" she pleaded.

"Horrible," he said mechanically. His mind was at work. The loose threads of his angers, his irritations, his desires, were knitting

G

themselves together, weaving themselves into something over-mastering and definite.

The young girl meanwhile was moving up towards him along the seat, for the effect which his sharpest rebuke produced on her never lasted more than four minutes. She now again possessed herself of his hand, and holding it between her own, began to caress it in childlike fashion, pulling the fingers apart and closing them again, spreading it palm downwards on her lap, and laying her own little hand over it, to exemplify the differences between them. He let her be; he seemed unconscious of her proceedings.

"And then," she continued, "I've always known a lot of young fellows who've liked to take me round; and no one ever objected to my going with them, and so I went. And I enjoyed it, and there wasn't any harm in it, just kissing and making believe, and nonsense. But I never really cared for one of them—I can see that now, when I compare them with you; when I compare what I felt for them with what I feel for you. Oh, I do love you so much," she murmured; "don't you believe me?" She lifted his hand to her lips and covered it with kisses.

He pulled it roughly from her. "I wish you'd give over such fool's play," he told her, got up, walked to the table, came back again, stood looking at her with sombre eyes and dilating pupils.

"But I do love you," she repeated, rising and advancing towards him.

"For God's sake, drop that damned rot," he cried out with sudden fury. "It wearies me, do you hear, it sickens me. Love, love—my God, what do you know about it? Why, if you really loved me, really loved any man—if you had any conception of what the passion of love is, how beautiful, how fine, how sacred—the mere idea that you could not come to your lover fresh, pure, untouched, as a young girl should— that you had been handled, fondled, and God knows what besides, by this man and the other—would fill you with such horror for yourself, with such supreme disgust—you would feel yourself so unworthy, so polluted ... that ... that ... by God, you would take up that pistol there, and blow your brains out!"

Lulie seemed to find the idea quite entertaining. She picked the pistol up from where it lay in the window, examined it critically, with her pretty head drooping on one side. and then sent one of her long red-brown caressing glances up towards him.

"And suppose I were to," she asked lightly, "would you believe me then?"

"Oh, ... well ... then, perhaps! If you showed sufficient decency to kill yourself, perhaps I might," said he, with ironical laughter. His ebullition had relieved him; his nerves were calmed again. "But nothing short of that would ever make me."

With her little tragic air, which seemed to him so like a smile disguised, she raised the weapon to the bosom of her gown. There came a sudden, sharp crack, a tiny smoke film. She stood an instant swaying slightly, smiling certainly, distinctly outlined against the background of rain-washed window, of grey falling rain, the top of her head cutting in two the Ritterhausen escutcheon. Then all at once there was nothing at all between him and the window—he saw the coat of arms entire— but a motionless, inert heap of plush and lace, and fallen wine-red hair, lay at his feet upon the floor.

"Child, child, what have you done?" he cried with anguish, and kneeling beside her, lifted her up, and looked into her face.

When from a distance of time and place Campbell was at last able to look back with some degree of calmness on the catastrophe, the element in it which stung him most keenly was this: he could never convince himself that Lulie had really loved him after all. And the only two persons who had known them both, and the circumstances of the case, sufficiently well to have resolved his doubts one way or the other, held diametrically opposite views.

"Well, listen, then, and I'll tell you how it was," Miss Nannie Dodge had said to him impressively, the day before he left Schloss Altenau for ever. "Lulie was tremendously, terribly in love with you. And when she found that you wouldn't care about her, she didn't want to live any more. As to the way in which it happened, you don't need to reproach yourself for that. She'd have done it, anyhow. If not then, why later. But it's all the rest of your conduct to her that was so mean. Your cold, cruel complacent British unresponsiveness. I guess you'll never find another woman to love you as Lulie did. She was just the darlingest, the sweetest, the most loving girl in the world."

Mayne, on the other hand, summed it up in this way. "Of course, old chap, it's horrible to think of: horrible, horrible, horrible! I can't tell you how badly I feel about it. For she was a gorgeously beautiful creature. That red hair of hers! Good Lord! You won't come across such hair as that again in a lifetime. But, believe me, she was only fooling with you. Once she had you in her hunting-noose, once her buccaneering instincts satisfied, and she'd have chucked you as she did all the rest. As to her death, I've got three theories—no, two—for the first being that she compassed it in a moment of genuine emotion, we may dismiss, I think, as quite untenable. The second is, that it arose from pure misadventure. You had both been shooting, hadn't you? Well, she took up the pistol and pulled the trigger from mere mischief, to frighten you, and quite forgetting one barrel was still loaded. And the third is, it was just her histrionic sense of the fitness of things. The rôle she had played so long and so well now demanded a sensational finale in the centre of the stage. And it's the third theory I give the preference to. She was the most consummate little actress I ever met."

JOHN DAVIDSON

The Ballad of a Nun

From Eastertide to Eastertide
 For ten long years her patient knees
Engraved the stones—the fittest bride
 Of Christ in all the diocese.

She conquered every earthly lust;
 The abbess loved her more and more;
And, as a mark of perfect trust,
 Made her the keeper of the door.

High on a hill the convent hung
 Across a duchy looking down,
Where everlasting mountains flung
 Their shadows over tower and town.

The jewels of their lofty snows
 In constellations flashed at night;
Above their crests the moon arose;
 The deep earth shuddered with delight.

Long ere she left her cloudy bed,
  Still dreaming in the orient land,
On many a mountain's happy head
  Dawn lightly laid her rosy hand.

The adventurous sun took Heaven by storm;
  Clouds scattered largesses of rain;
The sounding cities rich and warm,
  Smouldered and glittered in the plain.

Sometimes it was a wandering wind,
  Sometimes the fragrance of the pine,
Sometimes the thought how others sinned,
  That turned her sweet blood into wine.

Sometimes she heard a serenade
  Complaining sweetly far away:
She said, "A young man woos a maid";
  And dreamt of love till break of day.

Then she would ply her knotted scourge
  Until she swooned; but evermore
She had the same red sin to purge,
  Poor passionate keeper of the door!

For still night's starry scroll unfurled,
  And still the day came like a flood:
It was the greatness of the world
  That made her long to use her blood.

In winter-time when Lent drew nigh,
  And hill and plain were wrapped in snow,
She watched beneath the frosty sky
  The nearest city nightly glow.

Like peals of airy bells outworn
  Faint laughter died above her head
In gusts of broken music borne:
  "They keep the Carnival", she said.

Her hungry heart devoured the town:
   "Heaven save me by a miracle,
Unless God sends an angel down,
   Thither I go though it were Hell."

She dug her nails deep in her breast,
   Sobbed, shrieked, and straight withdrew the bar:
A fledgling flying from the nest,
   A pale moth rushing to a star.

Fillet and veil in strips she tore;
   Her golden tresses floated wide;
The ring and bracelet that she wore
   As Christ's betrothed, she cast aside.

"Life's dearest meaning I shall probe;
   Lo! I shall taste of love at last!
Away!" She doffed her outer robe,
   And sent it sailing down the blast.

Her body seemed to warm the wind;
   With bleeding feet o'er ice she ran:
"I leave the righteous God behind;
   I go to worship sinful man."

She reached the sounding city's gate;
   No question did the warder ask:
He passed her in: "Welcome, wild mate"
   He thought her some fantastic mask.

Half-naked through the town she went;
   Each footstep left a bloody mark;
Crowds followed her with looks intent;
   Her bright eyes made the torches dark.

Alone and watching in the street
   There stood a grave youth nobly dressed;
To him she knelt and kissed his feet;
   Her face her great desire confessed.

Straight to his house the nun he led:
　"Strange lady, what would you with me?"
"Your love, your love, sweet lord," she said;
　"I bring you my virginity."

He healed her bosom with a kiss;
　She gave him all her passion's hoard;
And sobbed and murmured ever, "This
　Is life's great meaning, dear, my lord.

"I care not for my broken vow,
　Though God should come in thunder soon;
I am sister to the mountains now,
　And sister to the sun and moon."

Through all the towns of Belmarie,
　She made a progress like a queen.
"She is," they said, "what e'er she be,
　The strangest woman ever seen.

"From fairy land she must have come,
　Or else she is a mermaiden."
Some said she was a ghoul, and some
　A heathen goddess born again.

But soon her fire to ashes burned;
　Her beauty changed to haggardness;
Her golden hair to silver turned;
　The hour came of her last caress.

At midnight from her lonely bed
　She rose, and said, "I have had my will."
The old ragged robe she donned, and fled
　Back to the convent on the hill.

Half naked as she went before
　She hurried to the city wall,
Unnoticed in the rush and roar
　And splendour of the Carnival.

No question did the warder ask:
　Her ragged robe, her shrunken limb,
Her dreadful eyes, "It is no mask;
　It is a she-wolf, gaunt and grim!"

She ran across the icy plain;
　Her worn blood curdled in the blast;
Each footstep left a crimson stain;
　The white-faced moon looked on aghast.

She said between her chattering jaws,
　"Deep peace is mine, I cease to strive;
Oh, comfortable convent laws,
　That bury foolish nuns alive!

"A trowel for my passing-bell,
　A little bed within the wall,
A coverlet of stones; how well
　I there shall keep the Carnival."

Like tired bells chiming in their sleep,
　The wind faint peals of laughter bore;
She stopped her ears and climbed the steep,
　And thundered at the convent door.

It opened straight: she entered in,
　And at the wardress' feet fell prone:
"I come to purge away my sin,
　Bury me, close me up in stone."

The wardress raised her tenderly;
　She touched her wet and fast-shut eyes;
"Look, sister; sister, look at me;
　Look; can you see through my disguise?"

She looked and saw her own sad face,
　And trembled, wondering, "Who art thou?"
"God sent me down to fill your place:
　I am the Virgin Mary now."

And with the word, God's mother shone:
  The wanderer whispered, "Mary, hail!"
The vision helped her to put on
  Bracelet and fillet, ring and veil.

"You are sister to the mountains now,
  And sister to the day and night;
Sister to God;" and on the brow
  She kissed her thrice, and left her sight.

While dreaming in her cloudy bed,
  Far in the crimson orient land,
On many a mountain's happy head
  Dawn lightly laid her rosy hand.

LORD ALFRED DOUGLAS

The Dead Poet

I DREAMED of him last night, I saw his face
All radiant and unshadowed of distress,
And as of old, in music measureless,
I heard his golden voice and marked him trace
Under the common thing the hidden grace,
And conjure wonder out of emptiness,
Till mean things put on beauty like a dress
And all the world was an enchanted place.

And then methought outside a fast locked gate
I mourned the loss of unrecorded words,
Forgotten tales and mysteries half said,
Wonders that might have been articulate,
And voiceless thoughts like murdered singing birds.
And so I woke and knew that he was dead.

A Song

STEAL from the meadows, rob the tall green hills,
    Ravish my orchard's blossoms, let me bind
A crown of orchard flowers and daffodils,
    Because my love is fair and white and kind.

To-day the thrush has trilled her daintiest phrases,
    Flowers with their incense have made drunk the
        air,
God has bent down to gild the hearts of daisies,
    Because my love is kind and white and fair.

To-day the sun has kissed the rose-tree's daughter,
    And sad Narcissus, Spring's pale acolyte,
Hangs down his head and smiles into the water,
    Because my love is kind and fair and white.

The Travelling Companion

INTO the silence of the empty night
I went, and took my scornèd heart with me,
And all the thousand eyes of heaven were bright;
But Sorrow came and led me back to thee.

I turned my weary eyes towards the sun,
Out of the leaden East like smoke came he.
I laughed and said, "The night is past and done;"
But Sorrow came and led me back to thee.

I turned my face towards the rising moon,
Out of the south she came most sweet to see,
She smiled upon my eyes that loathed the noon;
But Sorrow came and led me back to thee.

I bent my eyes upon the summer land,
And all the painted fields were ripe for me,
And every flower nodded to my hand;
But Sorrow came and led me back to thee.

O Love! O Sorrow! O desired Despair!
I turn my feet towards the boundless sea,
Into the dark I go and heed not where,
So that I come again at last to thee.

If You Came Back

IF you came back, perhaps you would not find
The old enchantment, nor again discern
The altered face of love. The wheels yet turn
That clocked the wasted hours, the spirit's wind
Still fans the embers in the hidden mind.
But if I cried to you "Return! return!"
How could you come? How could you ever learn
The old ways you have left so far behind?

How sweetly, forged in sleep, come dreams that make
Swift wings and ships that sail the estranging seas,
Less roughly than blown rose-leaves in a bowl,
To harboured bliss. But oh! the pain to wake
In empty night seeking what may not be
Till the dead flesh set free the living soul.

ERNEST DOWSON

The Pierrot of the Minute

THE CHARACTERS	THE SCENE
A MOON MAIDEN, PIERROT	A glade in the Parc du Petit Trianon. In the centre a Doric temple with steps coming down the stage. On the left a little Cupid on a pedestal. Twilight.

[*Pierrot enters with his hands full of lilies. He is burdened with a little basket. He stands gazing at the Temple and the Statue.*]

PIERROT

My journey's end! This surely is the glade
Which I was promised: I have well obeyed!
A clue of lilies was I bid to find,
Where the green alleys most obscurely wind;
Where tall oaks darkliest canopy o'erhead,
And moss and violet make the softest bed;
Where the path ends, and leagues behind me lie
The gleaming courts and gardens of Versailles;
The lilies streamed before me, green and white:
I gathered, following; they led me right,
To the bright temple and the sacred grove:
This is, in truth, the very shrine of Love!

[*He gathers together his flowers and lays them at the foot of Cupid's
statue; then he goes timidly up the first steps of the temple and
stops.*]

PIERROT

It is so solitary, I grow afraid.
Is there no priest here, no devoted maid?
Is there no oracle, no voice to speak,
Interpreting to me the word I seek?

[*A very gentle music of lutes floats out from the temple. Pierrot starts
back; he shows extreme surprise; then he returns to the foreground, and crouches down in rapt attention until the music ceases.
His face grows puzzled and petulant.*]

PIERROT

Too soon! too soon! in that enchanting strain,
Days yet unlived, I almost lived again:
It almost taught me that I most would know—
Why am I here, and why am I Pierrot?

[*Absently he picks up a lily which had fallen to the ground, and repeats:*]

PIERROT

Why came I here, and why am I Pierrot?
That music and this silence both affright;
Pierrot can never be a friend of night.

I never felt my solitude before—
Once safe at home, I will return no more.
Yet the commandment of the scroll was plain;
While the light lingers let me read again.
[*He takes a scroll from his bosom and reads:*]

PIERROT
   "*He loves to-night who never loved before;*
Who ever loved, to-night shall love once more."
I never loved! I know not what love is.
I am so ignorant—but what is this?
   [*Reads:*]
   "*Who would adventure to encounter Love*
Must rest one night within this hallowed grove.
Cast down thy lilies, which have led thee on,
Before the tender feet of Cupidon."
Thus much is done, the night remains to me.
Well, Cupidon, be my security!
Here is more writing, but too faint to read.
   [*He puzzles for a moment, then casts the scroll down.*]

PIERROT
   Hence, vain old parchment. I have learnt thy rede!
   [*He looks round uneasily, starts at his shadow; then discovers his basket*
      with glee. He takes out a flask of wine, pours it into a glass, and
      drinks.]

PIERROT
   Courage, mon ami! I shall never miss
Society with such a friend as this.
How merrily the rosy bubbles pass,
Across the amber crystal of the glass.
I had forgotten you. Methinks this quest
Can wake no sweeter echo in my breast.
   [*Looks round at the statue, and starts.*]

PIERROT
   Nay, little god! forgive. I did but jest.
   [*He fills another glass, and pours it upon the statue.*]

PIERROT   This libation, Cupid, take,
                   With the lilies at thy feet;
                Cherish Pierrot for their sake:
                   Send him visions strange and sweet,
                While he slumbers at thy feet.
                   Only love kiss him awake!
                   Only love kiss him awake!
[*Slowly falls the darkness, soft music plays, while Pierrot gathers
together fern and foliage into a rough couch at the foot of the steps
which lead to the Temple d'Amour. Then he lies down upon it,
having made his prayer. It is night.*]

PERRIOT [*Softly.*]
     Music, more music, far away and faint:
It is an echo of mine heart's complaint.
Why should I be so musical and sad?
I wonder why I used to be so glad?
In single glee I chased blue butterflies,
Half butterfly myself, but not so wise,
For they were twain, and I was only one.
Ah me! how pitiful to be alone.
My brown birds told me much, but in mine ear
They never whispered this—I learned it here:
The soft wood sounds, the rustlings in the breeze,
Are but the stealthy kisses of the trees.
Each flower and fern in this enchanted wood
Leans to her fellow, and is understood;
The eglantine, in loftier station set,
Stoops down to woo the maidly violet.
In gracile pairs the very lilies grow:
None is companionless except Pierrot.
Music, more music! how its echoes steal
Upon my senses with unlooked for weal.
Tired am I, tired, and far from this lone glade
Seems mine old joy in rout and masquerade.
Sleep cometh over me, now will I prove,
By Cupid's grace, what is this thing called love.
          [*Sleeps.*]

*[There is more music of lutes for an interval, during which a bright
radiance, white and cold, streams from the temple upon the face
of Pierrot. Presently a Moon Maiden steps out of the temple;
she descends and stands over the sleeper.]*

THE LADY

        Who is this mortal
          Who ventures to-night
        To woo an immortal?
          Cold, cold the moon's light
        For sleep at this portal,
          Bold lover of night.

        Fair is the mortal
          In soft, silken white,
        Who seeks an immortal.
          Ah, lover of night,
        Be warned at the portal,
          And save thee in flight!
[She stoops over him: Pierrot stirs in his sleep.]

PIERROT
    [Murmuring.]
Forget not, Cupid. Teach me all thy lore:
"*He loves to-night who never loved before.*"

THE LADY
    Unwitting boy! when, be it soon or late,
What Pierrot ever has escaped his fate?
What if I warned him! He might yet evade,
Through the long windings of this verdant glade;
Seek his companions in the blither way,
Which, else, must be as lost as yesterday.
So might he still pass some unheeding hours
In the sweet company of birds and flowers.
How fair he is, with red lips formed for joy,
As softly curved as those of Venus' boy.

Methinks his eyes, beneath their silver sheaves,
Rest tranquilly like lilies under leaves.
Arrayed in innocence, what touch of grace
Reveals the scion of a courtly race?
Well, I will warn him, though, I fear, too late—
What Pierrot ever has escaped his fate?
But, see, he stirs, new knowledge fires his brain,
And Cupid's vision bids him wake again.
Dione's Daughter! but how fair he is,
Would it be wrong to rouse him with a kiss?
        [*She stoops down and kisses him, then withdraws into the shadow.*]

PIERROT

        [*Rubbing his eyes.*]
    Celestial messenger! remain, remain;
Or, if a vision, visit me again!
What is this light, and whither am I come
To sleep beneath the stars so far from home?
        [*Rises slowly to his feet.*]

PIERROT

    Stay, I remember this is Venus' Grove,
And I am hither come to encounter——

THE LADY

        [*Coming forward but veiled.*]

                                                    Love!

PIERROT

        [*In ecstasy, throwing himself at her feet.*]
    Then I have ventured and encountered Love?

THE LADY

    Not yet, rash boy! and, if thou wouldst be wise,
Return unknowing; he is safe who flies.

PIERROT

    Never, sweet lady, will I leave this place
Until I see the wonder of thy face.

Goddess or Naiad! Lady of this Grove,
Made mortal for a night to teach me love,
Unveil thyself, although thy beauty be
Too luminous for my mortality.

THE LADY
    [*Unveiling.*]
  Then, foolish boy, receive at length thy will:
Now knowest though the greatness of thine ill.

PIERROT
  Now have I lost my heart, and gained my goal.

THE LADY
  Didst thou not read the warning on the scroll?
    [*Picking up the parchment.*]

PIERROT
  I read it all, as on this quest I fared,
Save where it was illegible and hard.

THE LADY
  Alack! poor scholar, wast thou never taught
A little knowledge serveth less than naught?
Hadst thou perused—but, stay, I will explain
What was the writing which thou didst disdain.

    [*Reads:*]
"*Au Petit Trianon*, at night's full noon,
Mortal, beware the kisses of the moon!
Whoso seeks her she gathers like a flower—
He gives a life, and only gains an hour."

PIERROT
    [*Laughing recklessly.*]
Bear me away to thine enchanted bower,
All of my life I venture for an hour.

H

THE LADY

Take up thy destiny of short delight;
I am thy lady for a summer's night.
Lift up your viols, maidens of my train,
And work such havoc on this mortal's brain
That for a moment he may touch and know
Immortal things, and be full Pierrot.
White music, Nymphs! Violet and Eglantine!
To stir his tired veins like magic wine.
What visitants across his spirit glance,
Lying on lilies, while he watch me dance?
Watch, and forget all weary things of earth,
All memories and cares, all joy and mirth,
While my dance woos him, light and rhythmical,
And weaves his heart into my coronal.
Music, more music for his soul's delight:
Love is his lady for a summer's night.

[*Pierrot reclines, and gazes at her while she dances. The dance finished,
she beckons to him: he rises dreamily, and stands at her side.*]

PIERROT

Whence came, dear Queen, such magic melody?

THE LADY

Pan made it long ago in Arcady.

PIERROT

I heard it long ago, I know not where,
As I knew thee, or ever I came here.
But I forget all things—my name and race,
All that I ever knew except thy face.
Who art thou, lady? Breathe a name to me,
That I may tell it like a rosary.
Thou, whom I sought, dear Dryad of the trees,
How art thou designate—art thou Heart's-Ease?

THE LADY

Waste not the night in idle questioning,
Since Love departs at dawn's awakening.

PIERROT

    Nay, thou art right; what recks thy name or state,
Since thou art lovely and compassionate.
Play out thy will on me: I am thy lyre.

THE LADY

    I am to each the face of his desire.

PIERROT

    I am not Pierrot, but Venus' dove,
Who craves a refuge on the breast of love.

THE LADY

    What wouldst thou of the maiden of the moon?
Until the cock crow I may grant thy boon.

PIERROT

    Then, sweet Moon Maiden, in some magic car,
Wrought wondrously of many a homeless star—
Such must attend thy journeys through the skies,—
Drawn by a team of milk-white butterflies,
Whom, with soft voice and music of thy maids,
Thou urgest gently through the heavenly glades;
Mount me beside thee, bear me far away
From the low regions of the solar day;
Over the rainbow, up into the moon,
Where is thy palace and thine opal throne;
There on thy bosom——

THE LADY

                  Too ambitious boy!
I did not promise thee one hour of joy.
This tour thou plannest, with a heart so light,
Could hardly be completed in a night.
Hast thou no craving less remote than this?

PIERROT

    Would it be impudent to beg a kiss?

THE LADY

   I say not that: yet prithee have a care!
Often audacity has proved a snare.
How wan and pale do moon-kissed roses grow—
Dost thou not fear my kisses, Pierrot?

PIERROT

   As one who faints upon the Libyan plain
Fears the oasis which brings life again!

THE LADY

   Where far away green palm trees seem to stand
May be a mirage of the wreathing sand.

PIERROT

   Nay, dear enchantress, I consider naught,
Save mine own ignorance, which would be taught.

THE LADY

   Dost thou persist?

PIERROT

                 I do entreat this boon!
[*She bends forward, their lips meet: she withdraws with a petulant
shiver. She utters a peal of clear laughter.*]

THE LADY

   Why art thou pale, fond lover of the moon?

PIERROT

   Cold are thy lips, more cold than I can tell
Yet would I hang on them, thine icicle!
Cold is thy kiss, more cold than I could dream
Arcturus sits, watching the Boreal stream:
But with its frost such sweetness did conspire
That all my veins are filled with running fire;
Never I knew that life contained such bliss
As the divine completeness of a kiss.

THE LADY

Apt scholar! so love's lesson has been taught,
Warning, as usual, has gone for naught.

PIERROT

Had all my schooling been of this soft kind,
To play the truant I were less inclined.
Teach me again! I am a sorry dunce—
I never knew a task by conning once.

THE LADY

Then come with me! below this pleasant shrine
Of Venus we will presently recline,
Until birds' twitter beckon me away
To mine own home, beyond the milky-way.
I will instruct thee, for I deem as yet
Of Love thou knowest but the alphabet.

PIERROT

In its sweet grammer I shall grow most wise,
If all its rules be written in thine eyes.
[*The lady sits upon a step of the temple, and Pierrot leans upon his elbow at her feet, regarding her.*]

PIERROT

Sweet contemplation! how my senses yearn
To be thy scholar always, always learn.
Hold not so high from me thy radiant mouth,
Fragrant with all the spices of the South;
Nor turn, O sweet! thy golden face away,
For with it goes the light of all my day.
Let me peruse it, till I know by rote
Each line of it, like music, note by note;
Raise thy long lashes, Lady! smile again:
These studies profit me.
        [*Taking her hand.*]

THE LADY   Refrain, refrain!

PIERROT

[*With passion.*]
I am but studious, so do not stir;
Thou art my star, I thine astronomer!
Geometry was founded on thy lip.
[*Kisses her hand.*]

THE LADY

This attitude becomes not scholarship!
Thy zeal I praise; but, prithee, not so fast,
Nor leave the rudiments until the last.
Science applied is good, but 'twere a schism
To study such before the catechism,
Bear thee more modestly, while I submit
Some easy problems to conform thy wit.

PIERROT

In all humility my mind I pit
Against her problems which would test my wit.

THE LADY

[*Questioning him from a little book bound deliciously in vellum.*]
What is Love?
Is it a folly,
Is it mirth, or melancholy?
Joys above,
Are there many, or not any?
What is love?

PIERROT

[*Answering in a very humble attitude of scholarship.*]
If you please,
A most sweet folly!
Full of mirth and melancholy;
Both of these!
In its sadness worth all gladness,
If you please!

THE LADY

Prithee where,
Goes Love a-hiding?
Is he long in his abiding
Anywhere?
Can you bind him when you find him;
Prithee, where?

PIERROT

With spring days
Love comes and dallies:
Upon the mountains, through the valleys
Lie Love's ways.
Then he leaves you and deceives you
In spring days.

THE LADY

Thine answers please me: 'tis thy turn to ask
To meet thy questioning be now my task.

PIERROT

Since I know thee, dear Immortal,
Is my heart become a blossom,
To be worn upon thy bosom.
When thou turn me from this portal,
Whither shall I, hapless mortal,
Seek love out and win again
Heart of me that thou retain?

THE LADY

In and out the woods and valleys,
Circling, soaring like a swallow,
Love shall flee and thou shalt follow
Though he stops awhile and dallies,
Never shalt thou stay his malice!
Moon-kissed mortals seek in vain
To possess their hearts again!

PIERROT

Tell me, Lady, shall I never
Rid me of this grievous burden!
Follow Love and find his guerdon
In no maiden whatsoever?
Wilt thou hold my heart for ever?
Rather would I thine forget,
In some earthly Pierrette!

THE LADY

Thus thy fate, whate'er thy will is!
Moon-struck child, go seek my traces
Vainly in all mortal faces!
In and out among the lilies,
Court each rural Amaryllis:
Seek the signet of Love's hand
In each courtly Corisande!

PIERROT

Now, verily, sweet maid, of school I tire:
These answers are not such as I desire.

THE LADY

Why art thou sad?

PIERROT

I dare not tell.

THE LADY
[Caressingly.]

Come, say!

PIERROT

Is love all schooling, with no time to play?

THE LADY

Though all love's lessons be a holiday,
Yet I will humour thee: what wouldst thou play?

PIERROT

  What are the games that small moon-maids enjoy,
Or is their time all spent in staid employ?

THE LADY

  Sedate they are, yet games they much enjoy:
They skip with stars, the rainbow is their toy.

PIERROT

  That is too hard!

THE LADY

                      For mortal's play.

PIERROT

                        What then?

THE LADY

  Teach me some pastime from the world of men.

PIERROT

  I have it, maiden.

THE LADY

                Can it soon be taught?

PIERROT

  A simple game, I learnt it at the Court.
I sit by thee.

THE LADY

             But, prithee, not so near.

PIERROT

  That is essential, as will soon appear.
Lay here thine hand, which cold night dews anoint,
Washing its white —

THE LADY

Now is this to the point?

PIERROT

Prithee, forbear! Such is the game's design.

THE LADY

Here is my hand.

PIERROT

I cover it with mine.

THE LADY

What must I next?
[*They play.*]

PIERROT

Withdraw.

THE LADY

It goes too fast.
[*They continue playing, until Pierrot catches her hand.*]

PIERROT

[*Laughing.*]
'Tis done. I win my forfeit at the last.
[*He tries to embrace her. She escapes; he chases her round the stage, she eludes him.*]

THE LADY

Thou art not quick enough. Who hopes to catch
A moon-beam, must use twice as much despatch.

PIERROT

[*Sitting down sulkily.*]
I grow aweary, and my heart is sore,
Thou dost not love me; I will play no more.
[*He buries his face in his hands: the lady stands over him.*]

THE LADY
What is this petulance?

PIERROT

                                       'Tis quick to tell—
Thou hast but mocked me.

THE LADY

                                       Nay! I love thee well!

PIERROT
Repeat those words, for still within my breast
A whisper warns me they are said in jest.

THE LADY
I jested not: at daybreak I must go,
Yet loving thee far better than thou know.

PIERROT
Then, by this altar, and this sacred shrine,
Take my sworn troth, and swear thee wholly mine!
The Gods have wedded mortals long ere this.

THE LADY
There was enough betrothal in my kiss.
What need of further oaths?

PIERROT

                                    That bound not thee!

THE LADY
Peace! since I tell thee that it may not be.
But sit beside me whilst I soothe thy bale
With some moon fancy or celestial tale.

PIERROT
Tell me of thee, and that dim, happy place
Where lies thine home, with maidens of thy race!

THE LADY

[Seating herself.]

Calm is it yonder, very calm; the air
For mortal's breath is too refined and rare;
Hard by a green lagoon our palace rears
Its dome of agate through a myriad years.
A hundred chambers its bright walls enthrone,
Each one carved strangely from a precious stone.
Within the fairest, clad in purity,
Our mother dwelleth immemorially:
Moon-calm, moon-pale, with moon stones of her gown
The floor she treads with little pearls is sown;
She sits upon a throne of amethysts,
And orders mortal fortunes as she lists;
I, and my sisters, all around her stand,
And, when she speaks, accomplish her demand.

PIERROT

Methought grim Clotho and her sisters twain
With shrivelled fingers spun this web of bane!

THE LADY

Theirs and my mother's realm is far apart,
Hers is the lustrous kingdom of the heart,
And dreamers all, and all who sing and love,
Her power acknowledge, and her rule approve.

PIERROT

Me, even me, she hath led into this grove.

THE LADY

Yea, thou art one of hers! But, ere this night,
Often I watched my sisters take their flight
Down heaven's stairway of the clustered stars
To gaze on mortals through their lattice bars;
And some in sleep they woo with dreams of bliss
Too shadowy to tell, and some they kiss.

But all to whom they come, my sisters say,
Forthwith forget all joyance of the day,
Forget their laughter and forget their tears,
And dream away with singing all their years—
Moon-lovers always!
> [*She sighs.*]

PIERROT

                                   Why art sad, sweet Moon?
> [*Laughing.*]

THE LADY
For this, my story, grant me now a boon.

PIERROT
I am thy servitor.

THE LADY
                                   Would, then, I knew
More of the earth, what men and women do.

PIERROT
I will explain.

THE LADY
                         Let brevity attend
Thy wit, for night approaches to its end.

PIERROT
Once was I a page at Court, so trust in me:
That's the first lesson of society.

THE LADY
Society?

PIERROT
                    I mean the very best
Pardy! thou wouldst not hear about the rest.

I know it not, but am a *petit maître*
At rout and festival and *bal champêtre*.
But since example be instruction's ease,
Let's play the thing.—Now, Madame, if you please!
 [*He helps her to rise, and leads her forward: then he kisses her hand,
  bowing over it with a very courtly air.*]

THE LADY
 What am I, then?

PIERROT

          A most divine Marquise!
Perhaps that attitude hath too much ease.
  [*Passes her.*]
 Ah, that is better! To complete the plan,
Nothing is necessary save a fan.

THE LADY
 Cool is the night, what needs it?

PIERROT

            Madame, pray
Reflect, it is essential to our play.

THE LADY
 [*Taking a lily.*]
 Here is my fan!

PIERROT

        So, use it with intent:
The deadliest arm in beauty's armament!

THE LADY
 What do we next?

PIERROT

      We talk!

THE LADY   But what about?

PIERROT

    We quiz the company and praise the rout;
Are polished, petulant, malicious, sly,
Or what you will, so reputations die.
Observe the Duchess in Venetian lace,
With the red eminence.

THE LADY

                                  A pretty face!

PIERROT

    For something tarter set thy wits to search—
"She loves the churchman better than the church."

THE LADY

    Her blush is charming; would it were her own!

PIERROT

    Madame is merciless!

THE LADY

                             Is that the tone?

PIERROT

    The very tone: I swear thou lackest naught.
Madame was evidently bred at Court.

THE LADY

    Thou speakest glibly: 'tis not of thine age.

PIERROT

    I listened much, as best becomes a page.

THE LADY

    I like thy Court but little——

PIERROT

                         Hush! the Queen!
Bow, but now low—thou knowest what I mean.

THE LADY
  Nay, that I know not!

PIERROT
                    Though she wear a crown,
'Tis from La Pompadour one fears a frown.

THE LADY
  Thou art a child: thy malice is a game.

PIERROT
  A most sweet pastime—scandal is its name.

THE LADY
  Enough, it wearies me.

PIERROT
                    Then, rare Marquise,
Desert the crowd to wander through the trees.
  [*He bows low, and she curtsies; they move round the stage. When
      they pass before the Statue he seizes her hand and falls on his
      knee.*]

THE LADY
  What wouldst thou now?

PIERROT
                    Ah, prithee, what, save thee!

THE LADY
  Was this included in thy comedy?

PIERROT
  Ah, mock me not! In vain with quirk and jest
I strive to quench the passion in my breast;
In vain thy blandishments would make me play:
Still I desire far more than I can say.
My knowledge halts, ah, sweet, be piteous,

Instruct me still, while time remains to us,
Be what thou wist, Goddess, moon-maid, Marquise,
So that I gather from thy lips heart's ease,
Nay, I implore thee, think thee how time flies!

THE LADY

Hush! I beseech thee, even now night dies.

PIERROT

Night, day, are one to me for thy soft sake.
[*He entreats her with imploring gestures, she hesitates: then puts her
    finger on her lip, hushing him.*]

THE LADY

It is too late, for hark! the birds awake.

PIERROT

The birds awake! It is the voice of day!

THE LADY

Farewell dear youth! They summon me away.
[*The light changes, it grows daylight: and music imitates the twitter
    of the birds. They stand gazing at the morning: then Pierrot
    sinks back upon his bed, he covers his face in his hands.*]

THE LADY

          [*Bending over him.*]
Music, my maids! His weary senses steep
In soft untroubled and oblivious sleep,
With mandragore anoint his tirèd eyes,
That they may open on mere memories,
Then shall a vision seem his lost delight,
With love, his lady for a summer's night.
Dream thou hast dreamt all this, when thou awake,
Yet still be sorrowful, for a dream's sake.
I leave thee, sleeper! Yea, I leave thee now,
Yet take my legacy upon thy brow:
Remember me, who was compassionate,

I

And opened for thee once, the ivory gate.
I come no more, thou shalt not see my face
When I am gone to mine exalted place:
Yet all thy days are mine, dreamer of dreams,
All silvered over with the moon's pale beams:
Go forth and seek in each fair face in vain,
To find the image of thy love again.
All maids are kind to thee, yet never one
Shall hold thy truant heart till day be done.
Whom once the moón has kissed, loves long and late,
Yet never finds the maid to be his mate.
Farewell, dear sleeper, follow out thy fate.

[*The Moon Maiden withdraws: a song is sung from behind: it is full day.*]

THE MOON MAIDEN'S SONG.

Sleep! Cast thy canopy
　　Over this sleeper's brain,
Dim grow his memory,
　　When he awake again.

Love stays a summer night,
　　Till lights of morning come;
Then takes her wingèd flight
　　Back to her starry home.

Sleep! Yet thy days are mine;
　　Love's seal is over thee:
Far though my ways from thine,
　　Dim though thy memory.

Love stays a summer night,
　　Till lights of morning come;
Then takes her wingèd flight
　　Back to her starry home.

[*When the song is finished, the curtain falls upon Pierrot sleeping.*]

THE END

Non Sum qualis Eram Bonae sub Regno Cynarae

LAST night, ah, yesternight, betwixt her lips and mine
There fell thy shadow, Cynara! thy breath was shed
Upon my soul between the kisses and the wine;
And I was desolate and sick of an old passion,
    Yea, I was desolate and bowed my head:
I have been faithful to thee, Cynara! in my fashion.

All night upon mine heart I felt her warm heart beat,
Night-long within mine arms in love and sleep she lay;
Surely the kisses of her bought red mouth were sweet;
But I was desolate and sick of an old passion,
    When I awoke and found the dawn was gray:
I have been faithful to thee, Cynara! in my fashion.

I have forgot much, Cynara! gone with the wind,
Flung roses, roses riotously with the throng,
Dancing, to put thy pale, lost lilies out of mind;
But I was desolate and sick of an old passion,
    Yea, all the time, because the dance was long:
I have been faithful to thee, Cynara! in my fashion.

I cried for madder music and for stronger wine,
But when the feast is finished and the lamps expire,
Then falls thy shadow, Cynara! the night is thine;
And I am desolate and sick of an old passion,
    Yea, hungry for the lips of my desire:
I have been faithful to thee, Cynara! in my fashion.

GEORGE EGERTON

The Captain's Book

LET it be understood at the outset that this book was even more fateful
to its author than the forgotten pamphlet of one John Stubbs, Puritan,
whose right hand, with that of his publisher, was chopped off in the reign
of the great Queen, yclept virgin, "wich is writ sarkastic".

The Captain, by courtesy, for he had never really attained to more than lieutenant's rank, and that, too, was due to a page in the book blurred by a woman's tears and a comrade's hand-grip. It is not within my ken to say how the book was begotten, but I can vouch for the fact that it proved ever a barrier to the success of its author as a worth-while member of a tax-paying community.

It was with him as a laddie when he fished for troutlings in the mill-stream, or went birds'-nesting in the hedgerows. It floated as a nebulous magnetic spirit to lure him from set tasks in the dame school of his tender years, to play truant in pleasant meadows, with a stolen volume of forbidden lore in his satchel. It transformed every itinerant ballad-monger into a troubadour. It made the wooden-legged corporal who mended brogues between his drunken bouts, and told tales of the Peninsular and Waterloo, more wonderful than Prester John, and his feats greater than those of any hero of Northern Saga. It gave him, to the despair of tutor and parents, a leaning to the disreputable society of such members of gipsydom or the mummers' craft as paid flying visits with van or show to the town of his birth.

Was it begotten by the reading of his first romance, this desire that grew in him to write some day a great book, a book of which the world would ring, that would stir men's hearts to deeds of valour, and women's to vows of loyal love? Did it sleep in a cell of his brain at his birth, fateful inheritance of some roving ancestor, with a light touch on the harp and a genius of lying on his tongue?

When the dame school was abandoned for college, and the velvet cap with golden tassel and jean pantalettes with broidered frills ceded to cloth small-clothes with gilt button and college cap, it still grew apace; and when it crept between his dryer tasks and let duller boys snatch prizes from his grasp, he whispered to himself that some day he would let them know why he had failed to be an easy first.

Years fled, the choice of a career became imperative; but ever the golden book with its purple letters on fairest vellum, its clasps of jacinth and opal, its pageant of knights, ladies, courtiers and clowns; martial strains and dim cathedral choirs with mystic calls; its songs of the blood, leering satyrs, and the seven deadly sins in guise of maidens fair; whispered distractingly to his inner ear. Indecision blinked at him with restless eyes and whispered many callings: Art held up a pencil and said: You who can limn each passing face, who are affectable to every shade of colour, can quicken the inanimate world by the light of your fancy, if you follow me. I am an arbitrary mistress, but in the end I will lead you through the gate of the Temple of Fame! And he was about to follow, when the skirl of pipes and the echo of marching feet, the flutter of pennants and strains of a music that roused to imperative life the instincts of the fighting man, lulled to slumber by centuries of peace, made him pause again. Visions of foreign lands, gallant deeds for country and for fame, adventures by sea and shore that would serve for the pages of the marvellous book, decided him to abandon his true mistress and follow the jade of war.

It became so closely interwoven with the fibres of his being that often it was hard to distinguish the existing from the imagined, and every fact of life borrowed a colour from its inscribing therein; thus it came to pass, not seldom, that men listening to his narration of the happened by the light of their soberer reason, looked askance at his version and whispered to each other: "He is a liar"; and when the pain of their misunderstanding had ceased to sting he told himself: "They too will understand when they read the book."

One career after the other was tossed aside at the turn to success, and those who had watched the opening days of the brilliant lad with the many gifts, turned their faces away when they met him, for they could not afford to know a wastrel of the chances of life.

Yet the Captain was rarely unhappy, for he alone conned the pages of the magic book, ever present to him, a growing marvel, in manhood as in childhood. When the girl of his early love, weary of waiting for the home that was to harbour her, distrustful of promises as lightly made as broken, turned from a world of vanities and unsatisfied yearnings to take the veil as a Sister of Mercy, it was a keen wound, soon to be treasured as a melancholy sweet episode in the romance of the book. So years sped by. The Captain married, and little children came with reckless frequency, episodes of gay insouciance; materials of sorrow and pain, dark blots, with here and there a touch of shame accumulated to supply its tragedy and its truth.

Former schoolfellows, plodding boys of sparser talents who had kept a grip on the tool they had chosen, passed him in the race of life, and drove by his shabby lodgings in neat broughams, and forgot to greet him when they met.

What knew they of the witchery of the golden book, the hashish of its whisperings, the incidents crowding to fill it with all the experiences of humanity—a concordance of the soul of man? They merely looked upon him as belonging to the strange race of the sons of men who never work in the immediate present, but who lie in bed in the morning forming elaborate plans to catch a sea-serpent.

Debts increased, little children clamoured for food and raiment; yet the Captain, ever dreaming of his book, trod lightly and whistled through life, mellow in note as a blackbird; tired women stitching in narrow windows would lift their heads as they heard him pass, and think wistfully of bird-song and hazel-copse down country ways. Even when the wife of his choice, patient victim of his procrastinations, closed her tired eyes from sheer weariness, glad to be relieved of the burden of her sorrows, the Captain found solace in weaving her in as the central figure of his book—an apotheosis of heroic wifehood.

But the reaping must be as the sowing, and evil days must come with the ingathering: his clothes grew shabbier, his friends fewer, want rapped oftener at the door, gay romance gave place to sordid reality, and the sore places of life blotted the pages, as the plates in a book of surgery; dire necessity forced the Captain to woo the mistress he had jilted in early youth, but she laughed illusively. The old spirit had flown from the pencil, his fingers had lost their cunning, and younger men elbowed him out of the way; for a man who has spent his life in dreaming ever fails to grasp the "modern", the changeful spirit of the day. As time went on the book became a subject of jest to his children, of good-natured raillery to his friends; the boys and girls fought their separate ways, gathering educational manna from every bush; and became practical hard-headed men and women of the world, with a keen eye to the main chance, a grip of the essentials of life, as befits the offsping of a dreamer.

Something of scorn for his failures, of contempt for his ideals, impatience with his shiftlessness, tinged their attitude to him always, and, spreading wider, their attitude towards every one who bore not the hall-mark of the world's estimate of success. What is the good of it, how much will it bring? was their standard of worth.

Barney, who had become a successful stockbroker, occasionally found the former acquaintanceship of the old guv'nor with sundry families of noble breeding of signal service to him. He never failed to make capital of the "old Dad's" intimate knowledge of salmon-fishing, or the best places to go in search of big game and the easiest way to get there. "A fellow whose father is a crack shot and an authority on salmon-fishing can't be quite a cad, don't you know!" young De Vere would urge when asking his governor to send City Barney an invitation.

Barney, in return, paid for the Captain's cheap lodgings, and gave him a hint that the "missus" only cared to see people on invitation, as the chicks asked awkward questions before her folk as to why grandpa lived in such a little house. It didn't do! The Captain would curl his grey moustache fiercely and turn to his pipe and book, and lay the one as it burnt out as a marker in the half-read page of the other, and close his eyes with a vehemence of intention that boded ill for the performance, to map out the chapters of the wonderful book.

Dick, who had inherited his facile invention, astounding memory, and his adaptive mercurial temperament, without any of his tenderness of heart, had taken successfully to journalism as a stepping-stone to whatever might offer; and when the *Piccadilly Budget* treated all the clubs to a merry half-hour by its piquant details of the early life of the latest created military baronet, or told how the great porter-brewer's grandfather burnt the malt by accident and so laid the foundation to his fortune, or gave a most piquant version of an old scandal with modern touches as applicable to the newest woman-writer, brother-journalists were green with envy. Readers in the running said: "That's Dick O'Grady's pa.", and wondered where the deuce the fellow picked up his facts. And Dick smiled at acquaintances with the winning smile that too was an inheritance from the Captain, and stopped his hansom to greet a club-gossip useful to push him into the set he wished to enter, told him a rattling good story of the latest "star's" mother, whom he happened to know was a canteen woman in the Curragh in 1856, and was promised a card in return for Lady C.'s crush; sometimes, too, he found a modernized version of the Captain's chivalrous manner to women of almost miraculous effect in conciliating the esoteric petticoat influence of some leading daily; and, conscious of his debt he would order a new dress suit and send the old boy half a sovereign with a letter bemoaning the shortness of "oof", and asking three questions no one else in London could answer him. His Sunday afternoon with the Captain was always profitably spent; he gleaned stores of workable anecdotes, and if the stories he deftly drew out gained in malice as they lost in genial humanity, and the rennet of his cynicism turned sour the milk of human kindness that ran through the Captain's worst tale—well, he was the better latter-day journalist for that. No-wise deceived, the old man would pocket the stray shillings, and wash the taste of the interview down with a glass of his favourite Jamieson, swearing he would make that cub, with the mind of a journalising huckster, cry small when he published his book.

As the sons, so the daughters.

Mary, who married well and lived in Lancaster Gate, sometimes took the children in a cab to see him; but as her nurse's sister let apartments in the same terrace, she had to look after them herself, and that was too fatiguing for frequent repetition. Kitty, the black sheep of the family, who danced in burlesque, and showed her pretty limbs as Captain of the Guard, and her pretty teeth in her laughing song, stood to him best; but even she was frankly sceptical at mention of the golden book: "Chuck it, dad, and write naughty anecdotes of celebrities for *Modern Society* or some of the papers; nothing pays like scandal with just a grain of truth. Like some tickets for Thursday? No! Well, buy some baccy." And she would take her rustling petticoats and powdered, laughing face, and saucy eyes, into a hansom with ill-concealed relief.

They had all grown beyond him and his dreams. Their interests were frankly material; they were keenly alive to his faults, his subterfuges, his poor, sometimes mean, shifts to make ends meet; his silly reverence for everything that wore a gown, his wasted talents that might have served their advancement; they resented him as a failure, and they let him know it.

One thing solely they were blind to, Dick as well as Barney (which was the less excusable, seeing how like the chip was to the block), level-headed Mary as easy-going Kitty—that they themselves were the result of the very faults they condemned. Their acute sense of essentials, their world-insight, their calculating forethought, each of the very qualities that assured their success in the world of their desires was built up on the solid foundation of sordid experience his make-shift life had brought in its wake. His impecuniosity had taught them the value of money, his happy-go-lucky procrastination the need of immediate action; he had been an unconscious object lesson to them from their tenderest years, of the things to avoid unless a man wish to fail **in life.**

The Captain saw it clearly enough, and sometimes a tiny flame of his old spirit would flicker to life, and he would register a vow to begin the next day—perhaps he would make ready a couple of quills, dust his old desk, lay out some foolscap, and put away treasured letters from old comrades—his correspondence of late was infrequent—and whisper with a smile: "To-morrow!" He would cock his old hat jauntily and nod to Jeanet, his landlady's little daughter, and go on to the common with a paper and a pipe, and lose himself in a happy dream of a glorious first chapter; a marvel of psychological insight into the life of a child, in which youth and love, and the tender colours of hope and faith, would make young readers' eyes glow and old readers' eyes glisten. Later on, Jeanet, coming to seek him, would find him asleep with his chin on his stick. She was a wise little maid, with the worldliness that is such a pitiful side of London childhood, clever and practical, with a strange affection for the old gentleman who treated her so courteously and called her "My pretty Jane", and was a mine of wonderful lore. She was fiercely jealous of his stuck-up sons and daughters, and resented their treatment with the keen intuition and loyal devotion of childhood.

"Wake up, Captain; you shouldn't go to sleep like that!" with quaint reproof. "Supper is ready, and I've got a new book!"

"Have you, my pretty? I, too, was dreaming of my book, and to-morrow I must begin. 'I am growing old, Jeanette.' Lord, how divinely poor Paddy Blake used to sing that song. Yes, it's time to begin!"—with a sigh.

The child, a lanky, precocious thing of thirteen winters, in whom he alone had seen a promise of beauty, and whose rare intelligence he had striven to cultivate, was silent. Is it not of this book, his book, of which he has told her so often in the long evenings when they have sat together, when the mother has gone with Susie to a south-west music hall, that she has been thinking? Has she not learnt by heart the story of the youth and man, the lady—so wondrous a white lady surely never lived in fiction before—of the gentle nun tending wounded men in the wake of war and pestilence, of gallant "sojer" friends, witch-women with amber locks, little children buried at sea, and racy tales, expurgated for her hearing, of camp and bar? Is she not the only one who ever believed implicitly in its greatness and fulfilment? No wonder a plan grew in her little head, and now she has almost carried it to completion. She hurried the old man in, only to note with dismay how feeble his steps, how laboured his breathing had become; and from that day she redoubled her watchfulness of his needs.

Some days later, Dick, sauntering up the Strand from one of his numerous paper offices, was waylaid by an odd little maid with resentful eyes, who gave him a piece of her mind with the uncompromising bluntness of youth. She was too in earnest for him to resent it; besides, she interested him; he had been seeking a type of child-girl for a curtain-raiser, and she hit it off to the life. He watched each expressive gesture, each trick of emphasis and quaintness of idiom, noting them mentally for use; he talked of himself to draw her out.

"Don't you tell me you got to work 'ard"—in spite of the Captain's pains she lapses into her old ways of speech when strongly moved— "you go about in 'ansoms and wear expensive flowers in your button 'ole, an' the Captain 'e wants strengthenin' things 'e don't 'ave. I thought I'd tell you, if I was to be killed for it."

And Dick smiled and promised to send a cheque next day, honour bright!—in reply to her distrustful look, adding: "You'll write and tell me how he is!"

Jeanet waved her hand from the top of her 'bus, and Dick bared his head as to a duchess, and invented a lie on the spur of the moment in reply to the enthusiastic query of an artist friend who had seen the parting: "Who's the girl with the singular face?" Dick's lies were always entertaining, and he never made the mistake of lying about things that might be found out.

The cheque arrived, the Captain's spirits rose with his renewed health, and Jeanet came into his room one evening with an air of triumph. Her thin cheeks were flushed with eagerness, and she held something carefully wrapped up in tissue paper. The old man laid down his pipe and his well-thumbed Sterne with a sigh, and watched her with an amused twinkle in his faded old eyes. Jeanet undid it carefully, and displayed a gorgeous scarlet-bound book with gilt-edged leaves.

"See, Captain," handing it to him with a little air of solemnity, as if she were investing him with some strange order, "here it is!"

He, falling into her mood, took it solemnly, turned to the back— no title, just a square of gilt lines; opened it—clean unwritten pages.

Jeanet had been watching his face, and a delighted smile broke over hers at his look of wondering question.

"An album, Jeanette? I must do you a little sketch in it!"

"No, Captain, it is not for me; it is for you. *It's for the book.* I got it on purpose, my own self, from Sophy's young man—he's a book-binder; and now you must really and truly begin. I'm sorry it's not purple and gold, with those lovely clasps, you said; but afterwards, when it's written, you can have one like that." And, sliding up to his chair, and flicking a speck of dust off his shabby coat, "You'll begin it now, won't you? There is really a book inside your head; it isn't a fairy tale you made up just for me, is it? And you'll make a great name, and they'll put your picture in the papers, and all about you, and I'll cut out all the pieces and make an album, like Sophy does with her notices. She had a lovely one in the *Charing Cross Gazette.* The young man who wrote it owed mother rent, and she let him off for getting it in. And then when your sons know you have really made the book— they don't believe in it," with a note of scorn—"they'll want to take you away, but you won't forget as how little Jeanet gave you the book to write it in, will you?"

The Captain blew his nose and wiped his glasses, and kissed the little maid, and patted her head, and called her his little comfort, and promised her a whole chapter to herself; and to-morrow he would begin—without fail, to-morrow. Then he invited Jeanet to supper, and they decided upon fried fish and baked potatoes, and Jeanet laid the table-cloth, and he put on his threadbare overcoat and she her hat, and they went out joyous as only children at heart can be. The Captain chaffed the busy stout women frying the pieces a golden brown, and insisted on carrying the basket. Jeanet was careful not to get re-roasted potatoes, and gave the old man a wise little lecture because he bade a rogue of a news-boy to keep the half-penny change from an evening paper; and he bought her a bunch of ragged bronze-brown chrysanthe-mums, and she tried hard to see that they were prettier than the close magenta ones.

They supped merrily, and whilst she mixed his punch for him he unlocked an old workbox, and found her a little silver fish, with a waggling tail, that had once served the dear white lady as a tape-measure; and then she sat at his feet and he told her more wonderful stories of bygone days, but he lost the thread of his story at times, and names bothered him; sometimes, too, the tears welled up and his lips trembled under his old grey moustache, and his hand shook as he rubbed his glasses, and though the fires had not long begun nor the chestnut-roasters taken up their winter places, and it seemed only a few weeks back that delicate spirals of smoke rose up from all the squares, with a pungent smell of burning leaves—surest London token of the coming of the fall—the old man sat huddled over the fire. His little friend, who had seen most of the serious sides of life, observed him anxiously as she whispered good-bye with her good-night.

"For I am going to Aunt Sarah's for a week, and I wish I wasn't going, Captain dear, but I'll write to you. I've filled the inkpot fresh and put a hassock for your feet, and told Bessie to mind your fire, and when I come back you'll read me all you have written in the book."

The old man, seeing her face clouded, promised her with forced gaiety to work like a Trojan, and kissed her little red hand with a touch of old-time grace.

Five days later Jeanet got a shakily written letter in reply to hers, with a comical little sketch of the Captain surrounded by icebergs, with icicles hanging from his beard; he wrote that he missed her, felt seedy, but to-morrow surely he would be better, and then he would write. Jeanet declared resolutely she must go home, and the next day when the shadows were gathering thickly and the lamp-lighter trotted from street to street, and the tinkle of the muffin-bell told the hour of tea, the little maid surprised her family by her advent:

"How is the Captain?" was her first question.

"Indeed he's only middlin'. Bessy took him some gruel at dinner-time and made up the fire, for he said he was going to write, an' he asked about you. La, she do make a fuss about the Captain," she added to a crony, in for a gossip.

Jeanet stole upstairs, paused outside the door with a strange disinclination to enter. She knocked twice with caught breath; no sound reached her from inside. She entered; the cheap coal had burnt out to slate and grey white ash; the shadows filled the room, accentuating the strange quiet. The Captain sat a little to one side with his chin sunk on his breast and his old hands folded on the closed book; the quill pen shone whitely on the floor where it had dropped to his feet. Some sudden spell of awe kept Jeanet from touching the silent figure, and checked the cry of "Captain" on her lips. She went out, fetched in the lamp from the bracket on the landing and turned it up to its full height—gave one look, and uttered a long cry that brought them hurrying up from below, and woke the lodger's baby on the floor above.

And whilst they clustered round his chair and felt his heart and talked volubly of doctor and telegrams, Jeanet took the book reverently from under his hand, and hugging it to her breast burst into tears—to her alone it was of signification, had not his own always made a jest of it?

"He would get up, the pore gentleman, he was fair set on writin' in his book; I left 'im sittin' with the pen in 'is 'and," cried the girl.

When the ghastly details had been carried out and the Captain lay with a restful smile on his face, and sons and daughters had been and gone, and the undertaker's young man was talking it over in the kitchen, Jeanet stole with swollen lids and pinched features to the bedside of her best friend—to open the book. It had escaped everyone's thought, but she had lain awake all night thinking of the wonderful tale it must hold, for the Captain, Bessy said, had sat with it upon his knee each day since her departure. How she regretted having gone away, her dear Captain—well, as the lips that had told her many of its wonders were for ever silenced, she would read it here, at his side, before they laid him away for ever.

She bolted the door and knelt down with a light on her face of faith and devotion. She opened the wonderful book—paused at the title with a look of surprise—turned the pages with eager fingers—all fair, all unsullied—and read in trembling letters across the title-page of the golden book, that had been alike the dream of his life and its fate—his own name.

MICHAEL FIELD[1]

A Fête Champêtre

(Watteau: Dresden Gallery)

A LOVELY, animated group
That picnic on a marble seat,
Where flaky boughs of beeches droop,
Where gowns in woodland sunlight glance,
Where shines each coy, lit countenance;

[1] The pseudonym adopted by Catharine Harris Bradley (d. 1914) and her niece, Edith Emma Cooper (d. 1913).

While sweetness rules the air, most sweet
          Because the day
Is deep within the year that shall decay.

They group themselves around their queen,
This lady in the yellow dress,
With bluest knots of ribbon seen
Upon her breast and yellow hair;
But the reared face proclaims *Beware!*
To him who twangs his viol less
          To speak his joy
That her soon-flattered choiceness to annoy.

Beside her knee a damsel sits,
In petticoat across whose stripes
Of delicate decision flits
The wind that shows them blue and white
And primrose round a bodice tight—
As grey as is the peach that ripes:
          Her hair was spun
For Zephyrus among the threads to run.

She on love's varying theme is launched—
Ah, youth!—behind her, roses lie,
The latest, artless roses, blanched
Around a hectic centre. Two
Protesting lovers near her sue
And quarrel, Cupid knows not why:
          Withdrawn and tart,
One gallant stands in reverie apart.

Proud of his silk and velvet, each
Plum-tinted, of his pose that spurns
The company, his eyes impeach
A Venus on an ivied bank,
Who rests her rigorous, chill flank
Against a water-jet and turns
          Her face from those
Who wanton in the coloured autumn's close.

Ironical he views her shape of stone
And the harsh ivy and grey mound;
Then sneers to think she treats her own
Enchanted couples with contempt,
As though her bosom were exempt
From any care, while tints profound
          Touch the full trees
And there are warning notes in every breeze.

The coldness of mere pleasure when
Its hours are over cuts his heart:
That Love should rule the earth and men
For but a season year by year
And then must straightway disappear,
Even as the summer weeks depart,
          Has thrilled his brain
With icy anger and censorious pain.

Alas, the arbour-foliage now,
As cornfields when they lately stood
Awaiting harvest, bough on bough
Is saffron. Yonder to the left
A straggling rose-bush is bereft
Of the last roses of the wood:
          For one or two
Still flicker where the balmy dozens grew.

On the autumnal grass the pairs
Of lovers couch themselves and raise
A facile merriment that dares
Surprise the vagueness of the sun
October to a veil has spun
About the heads and forest-ways—
          Delicious light
Of gold so pure it half-refines to white.

Yet Venus from this world of love,
Of haze and warmth has turned: as yet

None feels it save the trees above,
The roses in their soft decline
And one ill-humoured libertine.
Soon shall all hearts forget
         The vows they swore,
And the leaves strew the glade's untrodden
   floor.

NORMAN GALE

A Love Song

O to think, O to think as I see her stand there
With the rose that I plucked in her glorious hair,
      In the robe that I love,
      So demure and so neat,
I am lord of her lips and her eyes and her feet!

O to think, O to think when the last hedge is leapt,
When the blood is awakened that dreamingly slept,
      I shall make her heart throb
      In its cradle of lace,
As the lord of her hair and her breast and her face!

O to think, O to think when our wedding-bells ring,
When our love's at the summer but life's at the spring,
      I shall guard her asleep
      As my hound guards her glove,
Being lord of her life and her heart and her love!

Threescore and Ten

SILENT he sits from day to day,
With eyes as dull as smoky glass,
And wonders in a childish way
At shadows on the grass.

Or else the spark of memory
Lights to his chair, now quick, now slow,
The shades of what he used to be,
The ghosts of Long Ago!

Remembrances of velvet cheeks
And blushes that are Cupid's spies,
Revealing what a shy heart speaks
To lovers' burning eyes!

And as they glide in dumb review
He stretches out his withered hand,
Desiring you, O Joy, and you,
O Love, to hear and stand.

"Once more," he cries to Time, "once more
To rise at dawn and swiftly start
To find my milkmaid as of yore
And press against her heart!

"Again," he cries to Time, "again
To swing my boy upon my knee,
And kiss the scented cherry-stain
On lips upraised to me!

"Again to call for Joan, and hear
Her steps obedient to the call;
But not again the depthless fear,
The one thing worst of all—

"The narrow coffin and the face
Cold, comfortless, and sightless there,
And whiter than the filmy lace
Her breast was wont to bear!"

Ah, Life, that dost begin so fair
With eager heart and tender kiss
And strokings of Love's golden hair,
That thou shouldst come to this—

K

This—that a broken man should watch
And pray for just one day—one more—
While Death is trifling with the latch,
And fumbling at the door!

KENNETH GRAHAME

The Headswoman

I

IT was a bland sunny morning of a mediæval May—an old-style May
of the most typical quality; and the Council of the little town of St.
Radegonde were assembled, as was their wont at that hour, in the
picturesque upper chamber of the Hotel de Ville, for the dispatch of the
usual municipal business. Though the date was early sixteenth century,
the members of this particular town-council possessed some resemblance
to those of similar assemblies in the seventeenth, eighteenth, and even
the nineteenth centuries, in a general absence of any characteristic at
all—unless a pervading hopeless insignificance can be considered as
such. All the character, indeed, in the room seemed to be concentrated
in the girl who stood before the table, erect, yet at her ease, facing the
members in general and Mr. Mayor in particular; a delicate-handed,
handsome girl of some eighteen summers, whose tall, supple figure was
well set off by the quiet, though tasteful mourning in which she was
clad.

"Well, gentlemen," the Mayor was saying; "this little business
appears to be—er—quite in order, and it only remains for me to—er—
review the facts. You are aware that the town has lately had the
misfortune to lose its executioner—a gentleman who, I may say,
performed the duties of his office with neatness and dispatch, and gave
the fullest satisfaction to all with whom he—er—came in contact.
But the Council has already, in a vote of condolence, expressed its sense
of the—er—striking qualities of the deceased. You are doubtless also
aware that the office is hereditary, being secured to a particular family
in this town, so long as any one of its members is ready and willing to
take it up. The deed lies before me, and appears to be—er—quite in

order. It is true that on this occasion the Council might have been called upon to consider and examine the title of the claimant, the late lamented official having only left a daughter—she who now stands before you; but I am happy to say that Jeanne—the young lady in question—with what I am bound to call great good-feeling on her part, has saved us all trouble in that respect, by formally applying for the family post, with all its—er—duties, privileges, and emoluments; and her application appears to be—er—quite in order. There is therefore, under the circumstances, nothing left for us to do but to declare the said applicant duly elected. I would wish, however, before I—er—sit down, to make it quite clear to the—er—fair petitioner, that if a laudable desire to save the Council trouble in the matter has led her to a—er—hasty conclusion, it is quite open to her to reconsider her position. Should she determine not to press her claim, the succession to the post would then apparently devolve upon her cousin Enguerrand, well known to you all as a practising advocate in the courts of this town. Though the youth has not, I admit, up to now proved a conspicuous success in the profession he has chosen, still there is no reason why a bad lawyer should not make an excellent executioner; and in view of the close friendship—may I even say attachment?—existing between the cousins, it is possible that this young lady may, in due course, practically enjoy the solid emoluments of the position without the necessity of discharging its (to some girls) uncongenial duties. And so, though not the rose herself, she would still be—er—near the rose!" And the Mayor resumed his seat, chuckling over his little pleasantry, which the keener wits of the Council proceeded to explain at length to the more obtuse.

"Permit me, Mr. Mayor," said the girl, quietly, "first to thank you for what was evidently the outcome of a kindly though misdirected feeling on your part; and then to set you right as to the grounds of my application for the post to which you admit my hereditary claim. As to my cousin, your conjecture as to the feeling between us is greatly exaggerated; and I may further say at once, from my knowledge of his character, that he is little qualified either to adorn or to dignify an important position such as this. A man who has achieved such indifferent success in a minor and less exacting walk of life, is hardly likely to shine in an occupation demanding punctuality, concentration, judgment—all the qualities, in fine, that go to make a good business man. But this is beside the question. My motives, gentlemen, in demanding what is my due, are simple and (I trust) honest, and I desire that you should know them. It is my wish to be dependent on no one. I am both willing and able to work, and I only ask for what is the common right of humanity—admission to the labour market. How many poor toiling women would simply jump at a chance like this which fortune lays open to me! And shall I, from any false deference to that conventional voice which proclaims this thing as 'nice,' and that thing as 'not nice,' reject a handicraft which promises me both artistic satisfaction and a competence? No, gentlemen; my claim is a small one—only a fair day's wage for a fair day's work. But I can accept nothing less, nor consent to forgo my rights, even for any contingent remainder of possible cousinly favour!"

There was a touch of scorn in her fine contralto voice as she finished speaking; the Mayor himself beamed approval. He was not wealthy, and had a large family of daughters; so Jeanne's sentiments seemed to him entirely right and laudable.

"Well, gentlemen," he began, briskly, "then all we've got to do, is to——"

"Beg pardon, your worship," put in Master Robinet, the tanner, who had been sitting with a petrified, Bill-the-Lizard sort of expression during the speechifying; "but are we to understand as how this here young lady is going to be the public executioner?"

"Really, neighbour Robinet," said the Mayor somewhat pettishly, "you've got ears like the rest of us, I suppose; and you know the contents of the deed; and you've had my assurance that it's—er—quite in order; and as it's getting towards lunch-time——",

"But it's unheard-of," protested honest Robinet. "There hasn't ever been no such thing—leastways not as I've heard tell."

"Well, well, well," said the Mayor, "everything must have a beginning, I suppose. Times are different now, you know. There's the march of intellect, and—er—all that sort of thing. We must advance with the times—don't you see, Robinet?—advance with the times!"

"Well I'm——" began the tanner.

But no one heard, on this occasion, the tanner's opinion as to his condition, physical or spiritual; for the clear contralto cut short his obtestations.

"If there's really nothing more to be said, Mr. Mayor," she remarked, "I need not trespass longer on your valuable time. I propose to take up the duties of my office to-morrow morning, at the usual hour. The salary will, I assume, be reckoned from the same date; and I shall make the customary quarterly application for such additional emoluments as may have accrued to me during that period. You see I am familiar with the routine. Good morning, gentlemen!" And as she passed from the Council chamber, her small head held erect, even the tanner felt that she took with her a large portion of the May sunshine which was condescending that morning to gild their deliberations.

2

One evening, a few weeks later, Jeanne was taking a stroll on the ramparts of the town, a favourite and customary walk of hers when business cares were over. The pleasant expanse of country that lay spread beneath her—the rich sunset, the gleaming sinuous river, and the noble old château that dominated both town and pasture from its adjacent height—all served to stir and bring out in her those poetic impulses which had lain dormant during the working day; while the cool evening breeze smoothed out and obliterated any little jars or worries which might have ensued during the practice of a profession in which she was still something of a novice. This evening she felt fairly happy and content. True, business was rather brisk, and her days had been fully occupied; but this mattered little so long as her modest efforts were appreciated, and she was now really beginning to feel that, with practice, her work was creditably and artistically done. In a satisfied, somewhat dreamy mood, she was drinking in the various sweet influences of the evening, when she perceived her cousin approaching.

"Good evening, Enguerrand," cried Jeanne pleasantly; she was thinking that since she had begun to work for her living, she had hardly seen him—and they used to be such good friends. Could anything have occurred to offend him?

Enguerrand drew near somewhat moodily, but could not help relaxing his expression at sight of her fair young face, set in its framework of rich brown hair, wherein the sunset seemed to have tangled itself and to cling, reluctant to leave it.

"Sit down, Enguerrand," continued Jeanne, "and tell me what

you've been doing this long time. Been very busy, and winning forensic fame and gold?"

"Well, not exactly," said Enguerrand, moody once more. "The fact is, there's so much interest required nowadays at the courts, that un-assisted talent never gets a chance. And you, Jeanne?"

"Oh, I don't complain," answered Jeanne, lightly. "Of course it's fair-time just now, you know, and we're always busy then. But work will be lighter soon, and then I'll get a day off, and we'll have a delight-ful ramble and picnic in the woods, as we used to do when we were children. What fun we had in those old days, Enguerrand! Do you remember when we were quite little tots, and used to play at executions in the back-garden, and you were a bandit and a buccaneer, and all sorts of dreadful things, and I used to chop off your head with a paper-knife? How pleased dear father used to be!"

"Jeanne," said Enguerrand, with some hesitation, "you've touched upon the very subject that I came to speak to you about. Do you know, dear, I can't help feeling—it may be unreasonable, but still the feeling is there—that the profession you have adopted is not quite—is just a little——"

"Now, Enguerrand!" said Jeanne, an angry flash sparkling in her eyes. She was a little touchy on this subject, the word she most affected to despise being also the one she most dreaded—the adjective "un-ladylike."

"Don't misunderstand me, Jeanne," went on Enguerrand, im-ploringly: "You may naturally think that, because I should have succeeded to the post, with its income and perquisites, had you re-linquished your claim, there is therefore some personal feeling in my remonstrances. Believe me, it is not so. My own interests do not weigh with me for a moment. It is on your own account, Jeanne, and yours alone, that I ask you to consider whether the higher æsthetic qualities, which I know you possess, may not become cramped and thwarted by 'the trivial round, the common task,' which you have lightly under-taken. However laudable a professional life may be, one always feels that with a delicate organism such as woman, some of the bloom may possibly get rubbed off the peach."

"Well, Enguerrand," said Jeanne, composing herself with an effort, though her lips were set hard, "I will do you the justice to believe that personal advantage does not influence you, and I will try to reason calmly with you, and convince you that you are simply hide-bound by old-world prejudice. Now, take yourself, for instance, who come here to instruct me: what does *your* profession amount to, when all's said and done? A mass of lies, quibbles, dodges, and tricks, that would make any self-respecting executioner blush! And even with the dirty weapons at your command, you make but a poor show of it. There was that wretched fellow you defended only two days ago. (I was in court during the trial—professional interest, you know.) Well, he had his regular *alibi* all ready, as clear as clear could be; only you must needs go and mess and bungle the thing up, so that, as I expected all along, he was passed on to me for treatment in due course. You may like to have his opinion—that of a shrewd, though unlettered person. 'It's a real pleasure, miss,' he said, 'to be handled by you. You *knows* your work, and you *does* your work—though p'raps I ses it as shouldn't. If that blooming fool of a mouthpiece of mine'—he was referring to you, dear, in your capacity of advocate—'had known his business half as well as you do yours, I shouldn't a bin here now!' And you know, Enguerrand, he was perfectly right."

"Well, perhaps he was," admitted Enguerrand. "You see, I had been working at a sonnet the night before, and I couldn't get the rhymes right, and they would keep coming into my head in court and mixing themselves up with the *alibi*. But look here, Jeanne, when you saw I was going off the track, you might have given me a friendly hint, you know—for old times' sake, if not for the prisoner's!"

"I daresay," replied Jeanne, calmly: "perhaps you'll tell me why I should sacrifice my interests because you're unable to look after yours. You forget that I receive a bonus, over and above my salary, upon each exercise of my functions!"

"True," said Enguerrand, gloomily: "I did forget that. I wish I had your business aptitudes, Jeanne."

"I daresay you do," remarked Jeanne. "But you see, dear, how all your arguments fall to the ground. You mistake a prepossession for a logical base. Now if I had gone, like that Clairette you used to dangle after, and been waiting-woman to some grand lady in a château—a thin-blooded compound of drudge and sycophant—then, I suppose, you'd have been perfectly satisfied. So feminine! So genteel!"

"She's not a bad sort of girl, little Claire," said Enguerrand, reflectively (thereby angering Jeanne afresh): "but putting her aside—of course you could always beat me at argument, Jeanne; you'd have made a much better lawyer than I. But you know, dear, how much I care about you; and I did hope that on that account even a prejudice, however unreasonable, might have some little weight. And I'm not alone, let me tell you, in my views. There was a fellow in court only to-day, who was saying that yours was only a *succès d'estime*, and that woman, as a naturally talkative and hopelessly unpunctual animal, could never be more than a clever amateur in the profession you have chosen."

"That will do, Enguerrand," said Jeanne, proudly; "it seems that when argument fails, you can stoop so low as to insult me through my sex. You men are all alike—steeped in brutish masculine prejudice. Now go away, and don't mention the subject to me again till you're quite reasonable and nice."

3

Jeanne passed a somewhat restless night after her small scene with her cousin, waking depressed and unrefreshed. Though she had carried matters with so high a hand, and had scored so distinctly all around, she had been more agitated than she had cared to show. She liked Enguerrand; and more especially did she like his admiration for her; and that chance allusion to Clairette contained possibilities that were alarming. In embracing a professional career, she had never thought for a moment that it could militate against that due share of admiration to which, as a girl, she was justly entitled; and Enguerrand's views seemed this morning all the more narrow and inexcusable. She rose languidly, and as soon as she was dressed sent off a little note to the Mayor, saying that she had a nervous headache and felt out of sorts, and begging to be excused from attendance on that day; and the missive reached the Mayor just as he was taking his usual place at the head of the Board.

"Dear, dear," said the kind-hearted old man, as soon as he had read the letter to his fellow-councilmen: "I'm very sorry. Poor girl! Here, one of you fellows, just run round and tell the gaoler there won't be any business to-day. Jeanne's seedy. It's put off till to-morrow. And now, gentlemen, the agenda———"

"Really, your worship," exploded Robinet, "this is simply ridiculous!"

"Upon my word, Robinet," said the Mayor, "I don't know what's the matter with you. Here's a poor girl unwell—and a more hard-working girl isn't in the town—and instead of sympathising with her, and saying you're sorry, you call it ridiculous! Suppose you had a headache yourself! You wouldn't like——"

"But it *is* ridiculous," maintained the tanner stoutly. "Who ever heard of an executioner having a nervous headache? There's no precedent for it. And 'out of sorts,' too! Suppose the criminals said they were out of sorts, and didn't feel up to being executed?"

"Well, suppose they did," replied the Mayor, "we'd try and meet them halfway, I daresay. They'd have to be executed some time or other, you know. Why on earth are you so captious about trifles? The prisoners won't mind, and *I* don't mind: nobody's inconvenienced, and everybody's happy!"

"You're right there, Mr. Mayor," put in another councilman. "This executing business used to give the town a lot of trouble and bother; now it's all as easy as kiss-your-hand. Instead of objecting, as they used to do, and wanting to argue the point and kick up a row, the fellows as is told off for execution come skipping along in the morning, like a lot of lambs in Maytime. And then the fun there is on the scaffold! The jokes, the back-answers, the repartees! And never a word to shock a baby! Why, my little girl, as goes through the market-place every morning—on her way to school, you know—she says to me only yesterday, she says, 'Why, father,' she says, 'it's as good as the play-actors,' she says."

"There again," persisted Robinet, "I object to that too. They ought to show a properer feeling. Playing at mummers is one thing, and being executed is another, and people ought to keep 'em separate. In my father's time, that sort of thing wasn't thought good taste, and I don't hold with new-fangled notions."

"Well, really, neighbour," said the Mayor, "I think you're out of sorts yourself to-day. You must have got out of bed the wrong side this morning. As for a little joke, more or less, we all know a maiden loves a merry jest when she's certain of having the last word! But I'll tell you what I'll do, if it'll please you; I'll go round and see Jeanne myself on my way home, and tell her—quite nicely, you know—that once in a way doesn't matter, but that if she feels her health won't let her keep regular business hours, she mustn't think of going on with anything that's bad for her. Like that, don't you see? And now gentlemen let's read the minutes!"

Thus it came about that Jeanne took her usual walk that evening with a ruffled brow and a swelling heart; and her little hand opened and shut angrily as she paced the ramparts. She couldn't stand being found fault with. How could she help having a headache? Those clods of citizens didn't know what a highly-strung sensitive organization was. Absorbed in her reflections, she had taken several turns up and down the grassy footway, before she became aware that she was not alone. A youth, of richer dress and more elegant bearing than the general run of the Radegundians, was leaning in an embrasure, watching the graceful figure with evident interest.

"Something has vexed you, fair maiden?" he observed, coming forward deferentially as soon as he perceived he was noticed; "and care sits but awkwardly on that smooth young brow."

"Nay, it is nothing, kind sir," replied Jeanne; "we girls who work for our living must not be too sensitive. My employers have been somewhat exigent, that is all. I did wrong to take it to heart."

"'Tis the way of the bloated capitalist," rejoined the young man lightly, as he turned to walk by her side. "They grind us, they grind us; perhaps some day they will come under your hands in turn, and then you can pay them out. And so you toil and spin, fair lily! And yet methinks those delicate hands show little trace of labour?"

"You wrong me, indeed, sir," replied Jeanne merrily. "These hands of mine, that you are so good as to admire, do great execution!"

"I can well believe that your victims are numerous," he replied; "may I be permitted to rank myself among the latest of them?"

"I wish you a better fortune, kind sir," answered Jeanne demurely.

"I can imagine no more delightful one," he replied; "and where do you ply your daily task, fair mistress? Not entirely out of sight and access, I trust?"

"Nay, sir," laughed Jeanne, "I work in the market-place most mornings, and there is no charge for admission; and access is far from difficult. Indeed, some complain—but that is no business of mine. And now I must be wishing you a good evening. Nay"—for he would have detained her—"it is not seemly for an unprotected maiden to tarry in converse with a stranger at this hour. *Au revoir*, sir! If you should happen to be in the market-place any morning"——And she tripped lightly away. The youth, gazing after her retreating figure, confessed himself strangely fascinated by this fair unknown, whose particular employment, by the way, he had forgotten to ask; while Jeanne, as she sped homewards, could not help reflecting that for style and distinction, this new acquaintance threw into the shade all the Enguerrands and others she had met hitherto—even in the course of business.

4

The next morning was bright and breezy, and Jeanne was early at her post, feeling quite a different girl. The busy little market-place was full of colour and movement, and the gay patches of flowers and fruit, the strings of fluttering kerchiefs, and the piles of red and yellow pottery, formed an artistic setting to the quiet impressive scaffold which they framed. Jeanne was in short sleeves, according to the etiquette of her office, and her round graceful arms showed snowily against her dark blue skirt and scarlet tight-fitting bodice. Her assistant looked at her with admiration.

"Hope you're better, miss," he said respectfully. "It was just as well you didn't put yourself out to come yesterday; there was nothing particular to do. Only one fellow, and he said *he* didn't care; anything to oblige a lady!"

"Well, I wish he'd hurry up now, to oblige a lady," said Jeanne, swinging her axe carelessly to and fro: "ten minutes past the hour; I shall have to talk to the Mayor about this."

"It's a pity there ain't a better show this morning," pursued the assistant, as he leant over the rail of the scaffold and spat meditatively into the busy throng below. "They do say as how the young Seigneur arrived at the Château yesterday—him as has been finishing his education in Paris, you know. He's as likely as not to be in the market-place to-day; and if he's disappointed, he may go off to Paris again, which would be a pity, seeing the Château's been empty so long. But he may go to Paris, or anywheres else he's a mind to, he won't see better workmanship than in this here little town!"

"Well, my good Raoul," said Jeanne, colouring slightly at the obvious compliment, "quality, not quantity, is what we aim at here, you know. If a Paris education has been properly assimilated by the Seigneur, he will not fail to make all the necessary allowances. But see, the prison-doors are opening at last!"

They both looked across the little square to the prison, which fronted the scaffold; and sure enough, a small body of men, the Sheriff at their head, was issuing from the building, conveying, or endeavouring to convey, the tardy prisoner to the scaffold. That gentlemen, however, seemed to be in a different and less obliging frame of mind from that of the previous day; and at every pace one or other of the guards was shot violently into the middle of the square, propelled by a vigorous kick or blow from the struggling captive. The crowd, unaccustomed of late to such demonstrations of feeling, and resenting the prisoner's want of taste, hooted loudly; but it was not until that ingenious mediæval arrangement known as *la marche aux crapauds* had been brought to bear on him, that the reluctant convict could be prevailed upon to present himself before the young lady he had already so unwarrantably detained.

Jeanne's profession had both accustomed her to surprises and taught her the futility of considering her clients as drawn from any one particular class: yet she could hardly help feeling some astonishment on recognising her new acquaintance of the previous evening. That, with all his evident amiability of character, he should come to this end, was not in itself a special subject for wonder; but that he should have been conversing with her on the ramparts at the hour when—after courteously excusing her attendance on the scaffold—he was cooling his heels in prison for another day, seemed hardly to be accounted for, at first sight. Jeanne, however, reflected that the reconciling of apparent contradictions was not included in her official duties.

The Sheriff, wiping his heated brow, now read the formal *procès* delivering over the prisoner to the executioner's hands; "and a nice job we've had to get him here," he added on his own account. And the young man, who had remained perfectly tractable since his arrival, stepped forward and bowed politely.

"Now that we have been properly introduced," said he courteously, "allow me to apologise for any inconvenience you have been put to by my delay. The fault was entirely mine, and these gentlemen are in no way to blame. Had I known whom I was to have the pleasure of meeting, wings could not have conveyed me swiftly enough."

"Do not mention, I pray, the word inconvenience," replied Jeanne with that timid grace which so well became her: "I only trust that any slight discomfort it may be my duty to cause you before we part, will be as easily pardoned. And now—for the morning, alas! advances—any little advice or assistance that I can offer is quite at your service; for the situation is possibly new, and you may have had but little experience."

"Faith, none worth mentioning," said the prisoner, gaily. "Treat me as a raw beginner. Though our acquaintance has been but brief, I have the utmost confidence in you."

"Then, sir," said Jeanne, blushing, "suppose I were to assist you in removing this gay doublet, so as to give both of us more freedom and less responsibility?"

"A perquisite of the office?" queried the prisoner with a smile, as he slipped one arm out of the sleeve.

A flush came over Jeanne's fair brow. "That was ungenerous," she said.

"Nay, pardon me, sweet one," said he, laughing: "'twas but a poor jest of mine—in bad taste, I willingly admit."

"I was sure you did not mean to hurt me," she replied kindly, while her fingers were busy in turning back the collar of his shirt. It was composed, she noticed, of the finest point lace; and she could not help a feeling of regret that some slight error—as must, from what she knew, exist somewhere—should compel her to take a course so at variance with her real feelings. Her only comfort was that the youth himself seemed entirely satisfied with his situation. He hummed the last air from Paris during her ministrations, and when she had quite finished, kissed the pretty fingers with a metropolitan grace.

"And now, sir," said Jeanne, "if you will kindly come this way: and please to mind the step—so. Now, if you will have the goodness to kneel here—nay, the sawdust is perfectly clean; you are my first client this morning. On the other side of the block you will find a nick, more or less adapted to the human chin, though a perfect fit cannot of course be guaranteed in every case. So! Are you pretty comfortable?"

"A bed of roses," replied the prisoner. "And what a really admirable view one gets of the valley and the river, from just this particular point!"

"Charming, is it not?" replied Jeanne. "I'm so glad you do justice to it. Some of your predecessors have really quite vexed me by their inability to appreciate that view. It's worth coming here to see it. And now, to return to business for one moment—would you prefer to give the word yourself? Some people do; it's a mere matter of taste. Or will you leave yourself entirely in my hands?"

"Oh, in your fair hands," replied her client, "which I beg you to consider respectfully kissed once more by your faithful servant to command."

Jeanne, blushing rosily, stepped back a pace, moistening her palms as she grasped her axe, when a puffing and blowing behind caused her to turn her head, and she perceived the Mayor hastily ascending the scaffold.

"Hold on a minute, Jeanne, my girl,' he gasped. "Don't be in a hurry. There's been some little mistake."

Jeanne drew herself up with dignity. "I'm afraid I don't quite understand you, Mr. Mayor," she replied in freezing accents. "There's been no little mistake on my part that I'm aware of."

"No, no, no," said the Mayor, apologetically; "but on somebody else's there has. You see it happened in this way: this here young fellow was going round the town last night; and he'd been dining, I should say, and he was carrying on rather free. I will only say so much in your presence, that he was carrying on decidedly free. So the town-guard happened to come across him, and he was very high and very haughty, he was, and wouldn't give his name nor yet his address—as a gentleman should, you know, when he's been dining and carrying on free. So our fellows just ran him in—and it took the pick of them all their time to do it, too. Well, then, the other chap who was in prison—the gentleman who obliged you yesterday, you know—what does he do but slip out and run away in the middle of all the row and confusion; and very inconsiderate and ungentlemanly it was of him to take advantage of us in that mean way, just when we wanted a little sympathy and forbearance. Well, the Sheriff comes this morning to fetch out his man for execution, and he knows there's only one man to execute, and he sees there's only one man in prison, and it all seems as simple as A B C—he never was much of a mathematician, you know—so he fetches our friend here along, quite gaily. And—and that's how it came about, you see; *hinc illæ lachrymæ*, as the Roman poet has it. So now I shall just give this young fellow a good talking to, and discharge him with a caution; and we shan't require you any more to-day, Jeanne, my girl."

"Now, look here, Mr. Mayor," said Jeanne severely, "you utterly fail to grasp the situation in its true light. All these little details may be interesting in themselves, and doubtless the press will take note of them; but they are entirely beside the point. With the muddleheadedness of your officials (which I have frequently remarked upon) I have nothing whatever to do. All I know is, that this young gentleman has been formally handed over to me for execution, with all the necessary legal requirements; and executed he has got to be. When my duty has been performed, you are at liberty to re-open the case if you like; and any 'little mistake' that may have occurred through your stupidity you can then rectify at your leisure. Meantime, you've no *locus standi* here at all; in fact, you've no business whatever lumbering up my scaffold. So shut up and clear out."

"Now, Jeanne, do be reasonable," implored the Mayor. "You women are so precise. You never will make any allowance for the necessary margin of error in things."

"If I were to allow the necessary margin for all *your* errors, Mayor," replied Jeanne, coolly, "the edition would have to be a large-paper one, and even then the text would stand a poor chance. And now, if you don't allow me the necessary margin to swing my axe, there may be another 'little mistake'——"

But at this point a hubbub arose at the foot of the scaffold, and Jeanne, leaning over, perceived sundry tall fellows, clad in the livery of the Seigneur, engaged in dispersing the municipal guard by the agency of well-directed kicks, applied with heartiness and anatomical knowledge. A moment later, there strode on to the scaffold, clad in black velvet, and adorned with his gold chain of office, the stately old seneschal of the Château, evidently in a towering passion.

"Now, mark my words, you miserable little bladder-o'-lard," he roared at the Mayor (whose bald head certainly shone provokingly in the morning sun), "see if I don't take this out of your skin presently!" And he passed on to where the youth was still kneeling, apparently quite absorbed in the view.

"My lord," he said, firmly though respectfully, "your hairbrained folly really passes all bounds. Have you entirely lost your head?"

"Faith, nearly," said the young man, rising and stretching himself. "Is that you, old Thibault? Ow, what a crick I've got in my neck! But that view of the valley was really delightful!"

"Did you come here simply to admire the view, my lord?" inquired Thibault severely.

"I came because my horse would come," replied the young Seigneur lightly: "that is, these gentlemen here were so pressing; they would not

hear of any refusal; and besides, they forgot to mention what my attendance was required in such a hurry for. And when I got here, Thibault,
old fellow, and saw that divine creature—nay, a goddess, *dea certé*—so
graceful, so modest, so anxious to acquit herself with credit—— Well,
you know my weakness; I never could bear to disappoint a woman. She
had evidently set her heart on taking my head; and as she had my
heart already——"

"I think, my lord," said Thibault with some severity, "you had better
let me escort you back to the Château. This appears to be hardly a safe
place for light-headed and susceptible persons!"

Jeanne, as was natural, had the last word. "Understand me, Mr.
Mayor," said she, "these proceedings are entirely irregular. I decline
to recognise them, and when the quarter expires I shall claim the usual
bonus!"

5

When, an hour or two later, an invitation arrived—courteously
worded, but significantly backed by an escort of half-a-dozen tall
archers—for both Jeanne and the Mayor to attend at the Château
without delay, Jeanne for her part received it with neither surprise nor
reluctance. She had felt it especially hard that the only two interviews
fate had granted her with the one man who had made some impression
on her heart, should be hampered, the one by considerations of propriety,
the other by the conflicting claims of her profession and its duties. On
this occasion, now, she would have an excellent chaperon in the Mayor;
and business being over for the day, they could meet and unbend on a
common social footing. The Mayor was not at all surprised either,
considering what had gone before; but he was exceedingly terrified, and
sought some consolation from Jeanne as they proceeded together to
the Château. That young lady's remarks, however, could hardly be
called exactly comforting.

"I always thought you'd put your foot in it some day, Mayor," she
said. "You are so hopelessly wanting in system and method. Really,
under the present happy-go-lucky police arrangements, I never know
whom I may not be called upon to execute. Between you and my cousin
Enguerrand, life is hardly safe in this town. And the worst of it is, that
we other officials on the staff have to share in the discredit."

"What do you think they'll do to me, Jeanne?" whimpered the Mayor, perspiring freely.

"Can't say, I'm sure," pursued the candid Jeanne. "Of course, if it's anything in the *rack* line of business, I shall have to superintend the arrangements, and then you can feel sure you're in capable hands. But probably they'll only fine you pretty smartly, give you a month or two in the dungeons, and dismiss you from your post; and you will hardly grudge any slight personal inconvenience resulting from an arrangement so much to the advantage of the town."

This was hardly reassuring, but the Mayor's official reprimand of the previous day still rankled in this unforgiving young person's mind.

On their reaching the Château, the Mayor was conducted aside, to be dealt with by Thibault; and from the sounds of agonised protestation and lament which shortly reached Jeanne's ears, it was evident that he was having a *mauvais quart d'heure*. The young lady was shown respectfully into a chamber apart, where she had hardly had time to admire sufficiently the good taste of the furniture and the magnificence of the tapestry with which the walls were hung, when the Seigneur entered and welcomed her with a cordial grace that put her entirely at her ease.

"Your punctuality puts me to shame, fair mistress," he said, "considering how unwarrantably I kept you waiting this morning, and how I tested your patience by my ignorance and awkwardness."

He had changed his dress, and the lace round his neck was even richer than before. Jeanne had always considered one of the chief marks of a well-bred man to be a fine disregard for the amount of his washing-bill; and then with what good taste he referred to recent events—putting himself in the wrong, as a gentleman should!

"Indeed, my lord," she replied modestly, "I was only too anxious to hear from your own lips that you bore me no ill-will for the part forced on me by circumstances in our recent interview. Your lordship has sufficient critical good sense, I feel sure, to distinguish between the woman and the official."

"True, Jeanne," he replied, drawing nearer; "and while I shrink from expressing, in their fulness, all the feelings that the woman inspires in me, I have no hesitation—for I know it will give you pleasure—in acquainting you with the entire artistic satisfaction with which I watched you at your task!"

"But, indeed" said Jeanne, "you did not see me at my best. In fact, I

L

can't help wishing—it's ridiculous, I know, because the thing is hardly practicable—but if I could only have carried my performance quite through, and put the last finishing touches to it, you would not have been judging me now by the mere 'blocking-in' of what promised to be a masterpiece!"

"Yes, I wish it could have been arranged somehow," said the Seigneur reflectively; "but perhaps it's better as it is. I am content to let the artist remain for the present on trust, if I may only take over, fully paid up, the woman I adore!"

Jeanne felt strangely weak. The official seemed oozing out at her fingers and toes, while the woman's heart beat even more distressingly.

"I have one little question to ask," he murmured (his arm was about her now). "Do I understand that you still claim your bonus?"

Jeanne felt like water in his strong embrace; but she nerved herself to answer faintly but firmly: "Yes!"

"Then so do I," he replied, as his lips met hers.

*   *   *   *   *

Executions continued to occur in St. Radegonde; the Radegundians being conservative and very human. But much of the innocent enjoyment that formerly attended them departed after the fair Chatelaine had ceased to officiate. Enguerrand, on succeeding to the post, wedded Clairette, she being (he was heard to say) a more suitable match in mind and temper than others of whom he would name no names. Rumour had it, that he found his match and something over; while as for temper —and mind (which she gave him in bits)—— But the domestic trials of high-placed officials have a right to be held sacred. The profession, in spite of his best endeavours, languished nevertheless. Some said that the scaffold lacked its old attraction for criminals of spirit; others, more unkindly, that the headsman was the innocent cause, and that Enguerrand was less fatal in his new sphere than formerly, when practising in the criminal court as advocate for the defence.

JOHN GRAY

Les Demoiselles De Sauve

BEAUTIFUL ladies through the orchard pass;
Bend under crutched-up branches, forked and low;
Trailing their samet palls o'er dew-drenched grass.

Pale blossoms, looking on proud Jacqueline,
Blush to the colour of her finger tips,
And rosy knuckles, laced with yellow lace.

High-crested Berthe discerns, with slant, clinched eyes,
Amid the leaves pink faces of the skies;
She locks her plaintive hands Sainte-Margot-wise.

Ysabeau follows last, with languorous pace;
Presses, voluptuous, to her bursting lips,
With backward stoop, a branch of eglantine.

Courtly ladies through the orchard pass;
Bow low, as in lords' halls; and springtime grass
Tangles a snare to catch the tapering toe.

The Ox

The holy night that Christ was born
    The ox stood reverently apart,
Both ruminating eaten corn,
    And pondering within his heart.

There be (he pondered) certain beasts,
    Which stand about Jehovah's throne,
Which hearken to the Lord's behests,
    Which have no thought but Him alone.

Now I am surely one of these.
    And, since he comes to my abode,
'Tis fitting I should bow my knees
    Before the Holy Child of God.

I hold it for a solemn troth
    I shall no more be sacrificed.
For when to prophethood He groweth,
    I cease to symbolise the Christ,

Who is the noble Holocaust
As anciently himself did plan
Himself to be the Holy Host
To feed and succour fallen man.

I cannot tell the Mother dear
My joy; but softly if I low,
The noble Infant Christ will hear
His bullock praise Him. He will know.

HENRY HARLAND

Castles near Spain

I

THAT HE should not have guessed it from the beginning seems odd, if
you like, until one stops to consider the matter twice; then, I think,
one sees that after all there was no shadow of a reason why he should
have done so—one sees, indeed, that even had a suspicion of the truth
at any time crossed his mind, he would have had the best of reasons for
scouting it as nonsense. It is obvious to us from the first word, because
we know instinctively that otherwise there would be no story; it is
that which knits a mere sequence of incidents into a coherent, com-
municable whole. But, to his perceptions, the thing never presented
itself as a story at all. It wasn't an anecdote which somebody had
buttonholed him to tell; it was an adventure in which he found himself
launched, an experience to be enjoyed bit by bit, as it befell, but in no
wise suggestive of any single specific climax. What earthly hint had he
received from which to infer the identity of the two women? On the
contrary, weren't the actions of the one totally inconsistent with what
everybody assured him was the manner of life—with what the necessities
of the case led him to believe, would be the condition of spirit—of the
other? If the tale were to be published the fun would lie, not in attempting to mystify the reader, but in watching with him the mystification
of the hero—in showing how he played at hoodman-blind with his

destiny, and how surprised he was, when, the bandage stripped from
his eyes, he saw whom he had caught.

2

ON THAT first morning—the first after his arrival at Saint-Graal,
and the first, also, of the many on which they encountered each other
in the forest—he was bent upon a sentimental pilgrimage to Granjolaye. He was partly obeying, partly seeking, an emotion. His mind,
inevitably, was full of old memories; the melancholy by which they
were attended he found distinctly pleasant, and was inclined to nurse.
To revisit the scene of their boy-and-girl romance, would itself be
romantic. In a little while he would come to the park gates, and could
look up the long, straight avenue to the château—there where, when
they were children, twenty years ago, he and she had played so earnestly
at being married, burning for each other with one of those strange,
inarticulate passions that almost every childhood knows; and where
now, worse than widowed, she withheld herself, in silent, mysterious,
tragical seclusion.

And then he heard the rhythm of a horse's hoofs; and looking forward,
down the green pathway, between the two walls of forest, he saw a
lady cantering towards him.

In an instant she had passed; and it took a little while for the blur of
black and white that she had flashed upon his retina to clear into an
image—which even then, from under-exposure, was obscure and
piecemeal: a black riding-habit, of some flexile stuff, that fluttered in a
multitude of pretty curves and folds; a small black hat, a *toque*, set
upon a loosely-fastened mass of black hair; a face intensely white—a
softly-rounded face, but intensely white; soft full lips, singularly
scarlet; and large eyes, very dark.

It was not much, certainly, but it persisted. The impression, defective as I give it, had been pleasing; an impression of warm femininity,
of graceful motion. It had had the quality, besides, of the unexpected
and the fugitive, and the advantage of a sylvan background. Anyhow,
it pursued him. He went on to his journey's end; stopped before the
great gilded grille, with its multiplicity of scrolls and flourishes, its
coronets and interlaced initials; gazed up the shadowy aisle of plane-
trees to the bit of castle gleaming in the sun at the end; remembered the

child Hélène, and how he and she had loved each other there, a hundred years ago; and thought of the exiled, worse than widowed woman immured there now: but it was mere remembering, mere thinking, it was mere cerebration. The emotion he had looked for did not come. An essential part of him was elsewhere—following the pale lady in the black riding-habit, trying to get a clearer vision of her face, blaming him for his inattention when she had been palpable before him, wondering who she was.

"If she should prove to be a neighbour, I shan't bore myself so dreadfully down here after all," he thought. "I wonder if I shall meet her again as I go home." She would very likely be returning the way she had gone. But, though he loitered, he did not meet her again. He met nobody. It was, in some measure, the attraction of that lonely forest lane, that one almost never did meet anybody in it.

3

At Saint-Graal André was waiting to lunch with him.

"When we were children," Paul wrote in a letter to Mrs. Winchfield, "André, our gardener's son, and I were as intimate as brothers, he being the only companion of my sex and age the neighbourhood afforded. But now, after a separation of twenty years, André, who has become our curé, insists upon treating me with distance. He won't waive the fact that I am the lord of the manor, and calls me relentlessly Monsieur. I've done everything to entice him to unbend, but his backbone is of granite. From the merriest of mischief-loving youngsters, he has hardened into the solemnest of square-toes, with *such* a long upper-lip, and manners as stiff as the stuff of his awful best cassock, which he always buckles on prior to paying me a visit. Whatever is a poor young man to do? At our first meeting, after my arrival, I fell upon his neck, and thee-and-thou'd him, as of old time; he repulsed me with a *vous* italicised. At last I demanded reason. 'Why *will* you treat me with this inexorable respect? What have I done to deserve it? What can I do to forfeit it?' *Il devint cramoisi* (in the traditional phrase) and stared. —This is what it is to come back to the home of your infancy."

André, in his awful best cassock, was waiting on the terrace. It was on the terrace that Paul had ordered luncheon to be served. The terrace at Saint-Graal is a very jolly place. It stretches the whole length of the southern façade of the house, and is generously broad. It is paved with great lozenge-shaped slabs of marble, stained in delicate pinks and greys with lichens; and a marble balustrade borders it, overgrown, the columns half uprooted and twisted from the perpendicular, by an aged wistaria-vine, with a trunk as stout as a tree's. Seated there, one can look off over miles of richly-timbered country, dotted with white-walled villages, and traversed by the Nive and the Adour, to the wry masses of the Pyrenees, purple curtains hiding Spain.

Here, under an awning, the table was set, gay with white linen and glistening glass and silver, a centrepiece of flowers and jugs of red and yellow wine. The wistaria was in blossom, a world of colour and fragrance, shaken at odd moments by the swift dartings of innumerable lizards. The sun shone hot and clear; the still air, as you touched it, felt like velvet.

"Oh, what a heavenly place, what a heavenly day," cried Paul; "it only needs a woman." And then, meeting André's eye, he caught himself up, with a gesture of contrition. "I beg a thousand pardons. I forgot your cloth. If you," he added, "would only forget it too, what larks we might have together. *Allons, à table.*"

And they sat down.

If Paul had sincerely wished to forfeit André's respect, he could scarcely have employed more efficacious means to do so, than his speech and conduct throughout the meal that followed. You know how flippant, how "fly-away", he can be when the mood seizes him, how whole-heartedly he can play the fool. To-day he really behaved outrageously; and, since the priest maintained a straight countenance, I think the wonder is that he didn't excommunicate him.

"I remember you were a teetotaller, André, when you were young," his host began, pushing a decanter towards him.

"That, monsieur, was because my mother wished it, and my father was a drunkard," André answered bluntly. "Since my father's death, I have taken wine in moderation." He filled his glass.

"I remember once I cooked some chestnuts over a spirit-stove, and you refused to touch them, on the ground that they were alcoholic."

"That would have been from a confusion of thought," the curé explained, with never a smile. "But it was better to err on the side of scrupulosity than on that of self-indulgence."

"Ah, that depends. That depends on whether the pleasure you got from your renunciation equalled that you might have got from the chestnuts."

"You're preaching pure Paganism."

"Oh, I'm not denying I'm a Pagan—in my amateurish way. Let me give you some asparagus. Do you think a man can be saved who smokes cigarettes between the courses?"

"Saved?" questioned André. "What have cigarettes to do with a man's salvation?"

"It's a habit I learned in Russia. I feared it might relate itself in some way to the Schism." And he lit a cigarette. "I'm always a rigid Catholic when I'm in France."

"And when you're in England?"

"Oh, one goes in for local colour, for picturesqueness, don't you know. The Church of England's charmingly overgrown with ivy. And besides, they're going to disestablish it. One must make the most of it while it lasts. Tell me—why can you never get decent *brioches* except in Catholic countries?"

"Is that a fact?"

"I swear it."

"It's very singular," said André.

"It's only one of the many odd things a fellow learns from travel. Hush! Wait a moment."

He rose hastily, and made a dash with his hand at the tail of a lizard, that was hanging temptingly out from a bunch of wistaria leaves. But the lizard was too quick for him. With a whisk, it had disappeared. He sank back into his chair, sighing. "It's always like that. They'll never keep still long enough to let me catch them. What's the use of a university education and a cosmopolitan culture, if you can't catch lizards? Do you think they have eyes in the backs of their heads?"

André stared.

"Oh, I see. You think I'm frivolous," Paul said plaintively. "But you ought to have seen me an hour or two ago."

André's eyes asked, "Why?"

"Oh, I was plunged in all the most appropriate emotions—shedding floods of tears over my lost childhood and my misspent youth. Don't you like to have a good cry now and then? Oh, I don't mean literal tears, of course; only spiritual ones. For the letter killeth, but the spirit giveth life. I walked over to Granjolaye."

André looked surprised. "To Granjolaye? Have you—were you—"

He hesitated, but Paul understood. "Have you heard from her? Were you invited?" "Oh, dear, no," he answered. "No such luck. Not to the Château, only to the gates—the East Gate." (The principal entrance to the home park of Granjolaye is the South Gate, which opens upon the Route Départementale.) "I stood respectfully outside, and looked through the grating of the grille. I walked through the forest, by the Sentier des Contrebandiers."

"Ah," said André.

"And on my way what do you suppose I met?"

"A—a viper," responded André. "The hot weather is bringing them out. I killed two in my garden yesterday."

"Oh, you cruel thing! What did you want to kill the poor young creatures for? And then to boast of it!—But no, not a viper. A lady."

"A lady?"

"Yes—a real lady; she wore gloves. She was riding. I hope you won't think I'm asking impertinent questions, but I wonder if you can tell me who she is."

"A lady riding in the Sentier des Contrebandiers?" André repeated incredulously.

"She looked like one. Of course I may have been deceived. I didn't hear her speak. Do you think she was a cook?"

"I didn't know anyone ever rode in the Sentier des Contrebandiers."

"Oh, for that, I give you my word of honour. A lady—or say a female—in a black riding-habit; dark hair and eyes; very pale, with red lips and things. Oh, I'm not trying to impose upon you. It was about half a mile this side of where the path skirts the road."

"You might stop in the Sentier des Contrebandiers from January to December and not meet a soul," said André.

"Ah, I see. There's no convincing you. Sceptic! And yet, twenty years ago, you'd have been pretty sure to meet a certain couple of small boys there, wouldn't you?"

"*Si fait*," assented André. "We went there a good deal. But we were privileged. The only boys in this country now are peasants' children, and they have no leisure for wandering in the wood. When they're not at school, they're working in the fields. As for their elders, the path is rough and circuitous; the high road's smoother and shorter, no

matter where you're bound. Since our time, I doubt if twenty people
have passed that way."

"That argues ill for people's taste· The place is lovely. Underfoot,
it's quite overgrown with mosses; and the branches interlace overhead.
Where the sun filters through, you get adorable effects of light and
shadow. It's fearfully romantic; perfect for making love in, and that
sort of thing. Oh, if all the women hereabouts hadn't such hawk-like
noses! You see, the Duke of Wellington was here in 1814—No?
He wasn't? I thought I'd read he was. Ah, well, he was just over the
border. But my lady of this morning hadn't a hawk-like nose. I can't
quite remember what style of nose she did have, but it wasn't hawk-like.
I say, frankly, as between old friends, have you any notion who she
was?"

"What kind of horse had she?"

"Ah, there!" cried Paul, with a despairing gesture. "You've touched
my vulnerable point. I never shall have any memory for horses. I
think it was black—no, brown—no, grey—no, green. Oh, what am I
saying? I can't remember. Do—do you make it an essential?"

"She might have been from Bayonne."

"Who rides from Bayonne? Fancy a Bayonnaise on a horse! They're
all busy in their shops."

"You forget the military. She may have been the wife of an
officer."

"Oh, horror! Do you really think so? Then she must have been
frowsy and provincial, after all; and I thought her so smart and distin-
guished-looking and everything."

"Or perhaps an Englishwoman from Biarritz. They sometimes
ride out as far as this."

"Dear André, if she were English, I should have known it at a glance
—and there the matter would have rested. I have at least a practised
eye for English women. I haven't lived half my life in England without
learning something."

"Well, there are none but English at Biarritz at this season."

"She was never English. Don't try to bully me. Besides, she evidently
knew the country. Otherwise, how could she have found the Sentier
des Contrebandiers?—She wasn't from Granjolaye?"

"There's no one at Granjolaye save the Queen herself."

"Deceiver! Manuela told me last night. She has her little Court, her maids-of-honour. I think my *inconnue* looked like a maid-of-honour."

"She has her aunt, old Mademoiselle Henriette, and a couple of German women, countesses or baronesses or something, with unpronounceable names."

"I can't believe she's German. Still, I suppose there are *some* Christian Germans. Perhaps . . ."

"They're both middle-aged. Past fifty, I should think."

"Oh! Ah, well, that disposes of them. But how do you know her Majesty hasn't a friend, a guest, staying with her?"

"It's possible, but most unlikely, seeing the close retirement in which she lives. She's never once gone beyond her garden, since she came back there, three, four, years ago; nor received any visitors. *Personne*—not the Bishop of Bayonne nor the Sous-Préfet, not even *feu* Monsieur le Comte, though they all called as a matter of civility. She has her private chaplain. If a guest had arrived at Granjolaye, the whole country would know it and talk of it."

"Oh, I see what you're trying to insinuate," cried Paul. "You're trying to insinuate that she came from Château Yroulte." That was the next nearest country-house.

"Nothing of the sort," said André. "Château Yroulte has been shut up and uninhabited these two years—ever since the death of old Monsieur Raoul. It was bought by a Spanish Jew; but he's never lived in it and never let it."

"Well, then, where *did* she come from? Not out of the Fourth Dimension? Who *was* she? Not a wraith, an apparition? Why *will* you entertain such weird conjectures?"

"She must have come from Bayonne. An officer's wife, beyond a doubt."

"Oh, you're perfectly remorseless," sighed Paul, and changed the subject. But he was unconvinced. Officers' wives, in garrison-towns like Bayonne, had, in his experience, always been, as he expressed it, frowsy and provincial.

4

ONE WOULD think, by this time, the priest, poor man, had earned a moment of mental rest; but Paul's thirst for knowledge was insatiable.

He began to ply him with questions about the Queen. And though André could tell him very little, and though he had heard all that the night before from Manuela, it interested him curiously to hear it repeated.

It amounted to scarcely more than a single meagre fact. A few months after the divorce, she had returned to Granjolaye, and she had never once been known to set her foot beyond the limits of her garden from that day to this. She had arrived at night, attended by her two German ladies-in-waiting. A carriage had met her at the railway station at Bayonne, and set her down at the doors of her Château, where her aunt, old Mademoiselle Henriette, awaited her. What manner of life she led there, nobody had the poorest means of discovering. Her own servants (tongue-tied by fear or love) could not be got to speak; and from the eyes of all outsiders she was sedulously screened. Paul could imagine her, in her great humiliation, solitary among the ruins of her high destiny, hiding her wounds; too sensitive to face the curiosity, too proud to brook the pity, of the world. She seemed to him a very grandiose and tragic figure, and he lost himself musing of her—her with whom he had played at being married, when they were children here, so long, so long ago. She was the daughter, the only child and heiress, of the last Duc de la Granjolaye de Ravanches— the same nobleman of whom it was told that when Louis Napoléon, meaning to be gracious, said to him, "You bear a great name, Monsieur," he had answered sweetly, "The greatest of all, I think." It is certain he was the head of one of the most illustrious houses in the noblesse of Europe, descended directly and legitimately, through the Bourbons, from Saint Louis of France; and, to boot, he was immensely rich, owning (it was said) half the iron mines in the north of Spain, as well as a great part of the city of Bayonne. Paul's grandmother, the Comtesse de Louvance, was his next neighbour. Paul remembered him vaguely as a tall, drab, mild-mannered man, with a receding chin, and a soft, rather piping voice, who used to tip him, and have him over a good deal to stay at Granjolaye.

On the death of Madame de Louvance, the property of Saint-Graal had passed to her son, Edmond—André's *feu* Monsieur le Comte. Edmond rarely lived there, and never asked his sister or her boy there; whence, twenty years ago, at the respective ages of thirteen and eleven, Paul and Hélène had vanished from each other's ken. But Edmond never married, either; and when, last winter, he died, he left a will making Paul his heir. Of Hélène's later history Paul knew as much as all the world knows, and no more—so much, that is, as one could gather from newspapers and public rumour. He knew of her father's death, whereby she had become absolute mistress of his enormous fortune. He knew of her princely marriage, and of her elevation by the old king to her husband's rank of Royal Highness. He knew of that swift series of improbable deaths which had culminated in her husband's accession to the throne, and how she had been crowned Queen-Consort. And then he knew that three or four years afterwards she had sued for and obtained a Bull of Separation from the Pope, on the plea of her husband's infidelity and cruelty. The infidelity, to be sure, was no more than, as a Royalty, if not as a woman, she might have bargained for and borne with; but everybody remembers the stories of the king's drunken violence that got bruited about at the time. Everybody will remember, too, how, the Papal Separation once pronounced, he had retaliated upon her with a decree of absolute divorce, and a sentence of perpetual banishment, voted by his own parliament. Whither she had betaken herself after these troubles Paul had never heard—until, yesterday, arriving at Saint-Graal, they told him she was living cloistered like a nun at Granjolaye.

News travels fast and penetrates everywhere in that lost corner of garrulous Gascony. The news that Paul had taken up his residence at Saint-Graal could scarcely fail to reach the Queen. Would she remember their childish intimacy? Would she make him a sign? Would she let him see her, for old sake's sake? Oh, in all probability, no. Most certainly, no. And yet—and yet, he couldn't forbid a little furtive hope to flicker in his heart.

5

IT WAS only April, but the sun shone with midsummer strength.
After André left him, he went down into the garden.

From a little distance the house, against the sky, looked insubstantial, a water-colour, painted in grey and amber on a field of luminous blue. If he had wished it, he could have bathed himself in flowers; hyacinths, crocuses, jonquils, camellias, roses, grew round him everywhere, sending up a symphony of warm odours; further on, in the grass, violets, anemones, celandine; further still, by the margins of the pond, narcissi, and tall white flowers-de-luce; and, in the shrubberies, satiny azaleas; and overhead, the magnolia trees, drooping with their freight of ivory cups. The glass doors of the orangery stood open, a cloud of sweetness hanging heavily before them. In the park, the chestnuts were in full leaf; and surely a thousand birds were twittering and piping amongst their branches.

"Oh, bother! How it cries out for a woman," said Paul. "It's such a waste of good material."

The beauty went to one's head. One craved a sympathetic companion to share it with, a woman on whom to lavish the ardours it enkindled. "If I don't look out I shall become sentimental," the lone man told himself. "Nature's so fearfully lacking in tact. Fancy her singing an epithalamium in a poor fellow's ears, when he doesn't know a single human woman nearer than Paris." To make matters worse, the day ended in a fiery sunset, and then there was a full moon; and in the rosery a nightingale performed its sobbing serenade. "Please go out and give that bird a penny, and tell him to go away," Paul said to a servant. It was all very well to jest, but at every second breath he sighed profoundly. I'm afraid he *had* become sentimental. It seemed a serious pity that what his heart was full of should spend itself on the incapable air. His sense of humour was benumbed. And when, presently, the frogs in the pond, a hundred yards away, set up their monotonous plaintive concert, he laid down his arms. "It's no use, I'm in for it," he confessed. After all, he was out of England. He was in Gascony, the borderland between amorous France and old romantic Spain.

I don't know whom his imagination dwelt the more fondly with: the stricken Queen, beyond there, alone in the darkness and the silence, where the night lay on the forest of Granjolaye; or the horse-woman of the morning.

But surely, as yet, he had no ghost of a reason for dreaming that the two were one and the same.

6

"Now LET's be logical," he said next morning. "Let's be logical and hopeful—yet not too hopeful, not utopian. Let's look the matter courageously in the face. Since she rode there once, why may she not ride again in the Sentier des Contrebandiers? Why mayn't she ride there often—even daily? I think that's logical. Don't *you* think that's logical?"

The person he addressed, a tall, slender young man, with a fresh-coloured skin, a straight nose, and rather a ribald eye, was vigorously brushing a head of yellowish hair in the looking-glass before him.

"Tush! But of course *you* think so," Paul went on. "You always think as I do. If you knew how I despise a sycophant! And yet—— you're not bad looking. No, I'll be hanged if I can honestly say that you're bad looking. You've got nice hair, and plenty of it; and there's a weakness about your mouth and chin that goes to my heart. I hate firm people.—What? So do you? I thought so.—Ah well my poor friend, you're booked for a shocking long walk this morning. You must summon your utmost fortitude.—*Under the greenwood tree, who loves to lie with me?*" he carolled forth to Marzials's tune. "But come! I say! That's anticipating."

And he set forth for the Smugglers' Pathway—where sure enough, she rode again. As she passed him, her eyes met his: at which he was conscious of a good deal of interior commotion. "By Jove, she's magnificent, she's really stunning," he exclaimed to himself. He perceived that she was rather a big woman, tall, with finely-rounded, smoothly-flowing lines. Her hair—velvety blue-black in its shadows—where the light caught it was dully iridescent. Her features were irregular enough to give her face a high degree of individuality, yet by no means to deprive it of delicacy or attractiveness. She had a superb white throat, and a soft voluptuous chin; and "As I live, I never saw such a mouth," said Paul.

Where did she come from? Bayonne? Never. André might have been mistaken about Château Yroulte; the Spanish Jew had perhaps sold it, or found a tenant. Or, further afield, there were Châteaux Labenne, Saumuse, d'Orthevielle. Or else the Queen had a guest.

"Anyhow," he mused, when he got home, "that makes five, six miles that you have tramped, to enjoy an instant's glimpse of her. Fortunately they say walking is good for the constitution. It only shows what extremities a country life may drive one to."

The next day, not only did her eyes meet his, but he could have sworn that she almost smiled. Oh, a very furtive smile, the mere transitory suggestion of a smile. But the inner commotion was more marked.

The next day (the fourth) she undoubtedly did smile, and slightly inclined her head. He removed his hat, and went home, and waited impatiently for twenty-four hours to wear away. "She smiled—she bowed," he kept repeating. But, alas, he couldn't forget that in that remote countryside it is very much the fashion for people who meet in the roads and lanes to bow as they pass.

On the fifth, sixth, seventh, and eighth days she bowed and smiled.

"I fairly wonder at myself—to walk that distance for a bow and smile," said Paul. "To-morrow I'm going to speak. *Faut brusquer les choses.*"

And he penetrated into the forest, firmly determined to speak. "Only I can't seem to think of anything very pat to say," he sighed. "Hello! She's off her horse."

She was off her horse, standing beside it, holding the loose end of a strap in her hand.

Providence was favouring him. Here was his obvious chance. Something was wrong. He could offer his assistance. And yet, that inner commotion was so violent, he felt a little bewildered about the *mot juste.* He approached her gradually, trying to compose himself and collect his wits.

She looked up, and said in French "I beg your pardon. Something has come undone. Can you help me?"

Her voice was delicious, cool and smooth as ivory. His heart pounded. He vaguely bowed, and murmured, "I should be delighted."

She stood aside a little, and he took her place. He bent over the strap that was loose, and bit his lips, and cursed his embarrassments. "Come, I mustn't let her think me quite an ass." He was astonished at himself. That he should still be capable of so strenuous a sensation! "And I had thought I was blasé!" He was intensely conscious of the silence, of the solitude and dimness of the forest, and of their isolation there, so near to each other, that superb pale woman and himself. But his eyes were bent on the misbehaving strap, which he held helplessly between his fingers.

At last she looked up at her. "How warm and beautiful and fragrant she is," he thought. "With her white face, with her dark eyes, with those red lips and that splendid figure—what an heroic looking woman!"

"This is altogether disgraceful," he said, "and I assure you I'm covered with confusion. But I won't dissemble. I haven't the remotest

notion what needs to be done. I'm afraid this is the first time in my life
I have ever touched anything belonging to a horse."

He said it with a pathetic drawl, and she laughed.—"And yet
you're English."

"Oh, I dare say I'm English enough. Though I don't see how you
knew it. Don't tell me you knew it from my accent."

"*Oh, non pas,*" she hastened to protest. "But you're the new owner
of Saint-Graal. Everybody of the country knows, of course, that the
new owner of Saint-Graal, Mr. Warringwood, is English."

"Ah, then she's of the country," was Paul's mental note.

"And I thought all Englishmen were horsemen," she went on.

"Oh, there are a few bright exceptions—there's a little scattered
remnant. It's the study of my life to avoid being typical."

"Ah, well, then give *me* the strap."

He gave her the strap, and in the twinkling of an eye had snapped the
necessary buckle. Then she looked up at him and smiled oddly. It
occurred to him that the entire comedy of the strap had perhaps been
invented as an excuse for opening a conversation; and he was at once
flattered and disappointed. "Oh, if she's that sort . . ." he thought.

"I'm heart-broken not to have been able to serve you," he said.

"You can help me to mount," she answered.

And, before he quite knew how it was done, he had helped her to
mount, and she was galloping down the path. The firm grasp of her
warm gloved hand on his shoulder accompanied him to Saint-Graal.
"It's amazing how she sticks in my mind," he said. He really couldn't
fix his attention on any other subject. "I wonder who the deuce she is.
She's giving me my money's worth in walking. That business of the
strap was really brazen. Still, one mustn't quarrel with the means if
one desires the end. I hope she *isn't* that sort."

7

On the tenth, eleventh, and twelfth days, she passed him with a bow
and a good-morning.

"This is too much!" he groaned, in the silence of his chamber.
"She's doing it with malice. I'll not be trifled with. I—I'll do something desperate. I'll pretend to faint, andshe'll have to get down and
bandage up my wounds."

M

On the thirteenth day, as they met, she stopped her horse.

"You're at least typically English in one respect," she said.

"Oh, unkind lady! To announce it to me in this sudden way. Then my life's a failure."

"I mean in your fondness for long walks."

"Ah, then you're totally in error. I hate long walks."

"But it's a good ten kilometres to and from your house; and you do it every morning."

"That's only because there aren't any omnibuses or cabs or things. And" (he reminded himself that if she was that sort, he might be bold) "I'm irresistibly attracted here."

"It's very pretty," she admitted, and rode on.

He looked after her, grinding his teeth. *Was* she that sort? "One never can tell. Her face is so fine—so noble even."

The next day, "Yes, I suppose it's very pretty. But I wasn't thinking of Nature," he informed her, as she approached.

She drew up.

"Oh, it has its human interest too, no doubt." She glanced in the direction of the Château of Granjolaye.

"The Queen," said he. "But one never sees her."

"That adds the charm of mystery, don't you feel? To think of that poor young exiled woman, after so grand a beginning, ending so desolately—shut up alone in her mysterious castle! It's like a legend."

"Then you're not of her Court?"

"I? Of her Court? *Mais quelle idée!*"

"It was only a hypothesis. Of course, you know I'm devoured by curiosity. My days are spent in wondering who you are."

She laughed. "You must have a care, or you'll be typical," she warned him.

"I never said I wasn't human," he called after her, as she cantered away.

8

The next day still (the fifteenth), "Haven't I heard you lived at Saint-Graal when you were a child?" she asked.

"If you have, for once in a way rumour has told the truth. I lived at Saint-Graal till I was thirteen."

"Then perhaps you knew her?"

"Her?"

"The Queen. Mademoiselle de la Granjolaye de Ravanches."

"Oh, I knew her very well—when we were children."

"Tell me all about her."

"It would be a long story."

She leaped from her horse; then, raising her riding whip, and looking the animal severely in the eye, "Bézigue! Attention," she said impressively. "You're to stop exactly where you are and not play any tricks. Entendu? Bien." She moved a few steps down the pathway, and stopped at an opening among the trees, where the ground was a cushion of bright green moss. "By Jove, she is at her ease," thought Paul, who followed her. "How splendidly she walks—what undulations!" From the French point of view, as she must be aware, the situation gave him all sorts of rights.

She sank softly, gracefully, upon the moss.

"It's a long story. Tell it me," she commanded, and pointed to the earth. He sat down facing her, at a little distance.

"It's odd you should have chosen this place," said he.

"Odd? Why?" She looked at him inquiringly. For a moment their eyes held each other; and all at once the blood swept through him with suffocating violence. She was so beautiful, so sumptuous, so warmly and richly feminine; and surely the circumstances were not anodyne. Her softly rounded face, its very pallor, the curve and colour of her lips, her luminous dark eyes, the smooth modulations of her voice, and then her loose abundance of black hair, and the swelling lines of her breast, the fluent contour of her waist and hips, under the fine black cloth of her dress—all these, with the silence of the forest, the heat of the southern day, the woodland fragrances of which the air was full, and the sense of being intimately alone with her, set up within him a turbulent vibration, half of delight, half of pained suspense. And the complaisant informality with which she met him played a sustaining counterpoint. "What luck, what luck, what luck," were the words which shaped themselves to the strong beating of his pulses. What would happen next? Whither would it lead? He had savoured the bouquet, he was famished to taste the wine. And yet, so complicated are our human feelings he was obscurely vexed. Only two kinds of woman, he would have maintained yesterday, could conceivably do a thing like this: an ingénue or "that sort". She wasn't an ingénue. Something, at

the same time, half assured him that she wasn't "that sort", either. But
—the circumstances! The situation!

"Why odd?" she repeated.

"Oh, I don't want to talk about the Queen," he said in a smothered
voice.

"The oddity relates itself to the Queen?"

"Oh, this is where we used to waste half our lives when we were
children. That's all. This was our favourite nook."

"Perfect then for the story you're going to tell me."

"What story?"

"You said it was a long story."

"There's really no story at all." His eyes were fastened upon her
hands, small and tapering, in their tan gauntlets. The point of a
patent-leather boot glanced from the edge of her skirt. A short gold
watch-chain dangled from her breast, a cluster of charms at the end.

"You said it was a long story," she repeated sternly.

"It would be a dull one. We knew each other when we were infants,
and used to play together. That is all."

"But what was she like? Describe her to me. I adore *souvenirs
d'enfance.*" Her eyes were bright with eagerness.

"Oh, she was very pretty. The prettiest little girl I've ever seen.
She had the most wonderful eyes—deep, deep, into which you could
look a hundred miles; you know the sort; dreamy, poetical, sad; oh,
lovely eyes. And she used to wear her hair down her back; it was very
long, and soft—soft as smoke, almost; almost impalpable. She always
dressed in white—short white frocks, with broad sashes, red or blue.
That was the fashion then for little girls. Perhaps it is still—I've never
noticed."

"Yes. Don't stop. Go on."

"Dear me, I don't know what to say. I used to see her a good deal,
because they were our neighbours. Her father used to ask me over to
stay at Granjolaye. She needed a playmate, and I was the only one
available. Sometimes she would come and spend a day at Saint-Graal.
Do you know Granjolaye? The castle? It's worth going over. It
used to belong to the Kings of Navarre, you know. We used to play
together in the great audience chamber, and chase each other through
the secret passages in the walls. At Saint-Graal we confined ourselves
to the garden. Her head was full of the queerest romantic notions.

You couldn't persuade her that the white irises that grew about our pond weren't enchanted princesses. One day we filled a bottle with holy water at the Church, and then she sprinkled them with it, pronouncing an incantation. 'If ye were born as ye are, remain as ye are; but if ye were born otherwise, resume your original shapes.' They remained as they were; but that didn't shake her faith. Something was amiss with the holy water, or with the form of her incantation."

She laughed softly. "Then she was nice? You liked her?" she asked.

"Oh, I was passionately in love with her. All children are passionately in love with somebody, aren't they? A real *grande passion*. It began when I was about ten." He broke off to laugh. "Do you care for love stories? I'm a weary, wayworn man; but upon my word, I've never in all my life felt any such intense emotion for a woman, anything that so nearly deserved to be called *love*, as I felt for Hélène de la Granjolaye when I was an infant. Night after night I used to lie awake thinking how I loved her—longing to tell her so—planning how I would, next day—composing tremendous declarations—imagining her response—and waiting in a fever of impatience for the day to come. But then, when I met her, I didn't dare. Bless me, how I used to thrill at sight of her, with love, with fear. How I used to look at her face, and pine to kiss her. If her hand touched mine, I almost fainted. It's very strange that children before their teens should be able to experience the whole gamut of the spiritual side of love; and yet it's certain."

She was looking at him with intent eyes, her lips parted a little. "But you did tell her at last, I hope?" she said, anxiously.

He had got warmed to his subject, and her interest inspired him. "Oh, at last! It was here—in this very spot. I had picked a lot of celandine, and stuck them about in her hair, where they shone like stars. Oh, the joy of being allowed to touch her hair! It made utterance a necessity. I fumbled and stammered, and blushed and thrilled, and almost choked. And at last I blurted it out. 'I love you so. I love you so.' That—after the eloquent declarations I had composed overnight!"

"And she?"

"She answered quite simply, 'Et moi, je t'aime tant, aussi.' And then she began to cry. And when I asked her what she was crying for, she explained that I oughtn't to have left her in doubt for so long; she had been so unhappy from fear that I didn't 'love her so'. She was quite unfemininely frank, you see. Oh, the ecstasy of that hour! The ecstasy of our first kiss! From that time on it was 'mon petit mari' and 'ma petite femme'. The greatest joy in life for me, for us, was to sit together, holding each other's hands, and repeating from time to time, 'J' t'aime tant, j' t'aime tant'. Now and then we would vary it with a fugue upon our names—'Hélène!'—'Paul!'" He laughed. "Children, with their total lack of humour, are the drollest of created beings, aren't they?"

"Oh, I don't think it's droll. I know, all children have those desperate love affairs. But they seem to me pathetic. How did it go on?"

"Oh, for two or three years we lived in Paradise. There were no other boys in the neighbourhood, so she was constant."

"For three years? And then?"

"Then my grandmother died, and I was carried off to Paris. She remained here. And so it ended."

"And when did you meet her next? After you were grown up?"

"I have never met her since."

"You must have followed her career with a special interest, though?"

"*Ah, quant á ça!*"

"Her marriage, her coronation, her divorce. Poor woman! What she must have suffered. Have you made any attempt to see her since you came back to Saint-Graal?"

"*Ah, merci, non!* If she wanted to see me, she'd send for me."

"She sees no one, everybody says. But I should think she'd like to see you—her old playmate. If she *should* send for you—— But I suppose I mustn't ask you to tell me about it afterwards? Of course, like everybody else in her neighbourhood, I'm awfully interested in her."

There was a moment's silence. She looked at the moss beneath her, and stroked it lightly with a finger-tip. Paul looked at her.

"You're horribly unkind," he said at last.

"Unkind?" She raised wide eyes of innocent surprise.

"You know I'm in an agony of curiosity."

"About what?"

"About you."

"Me?"

"Yourself."

She lifted the cluster of charms at the end of her watch-chain. One of them was a tiny golden whistle. On this she blew, and Bézigue came trotting up. She mounted him to-day without Paul's assistance. Smiling down on the young man, she said, "Oh, after the reckless way in which I've cast the conventions to the winds, you really can't expect me to give you my name and address." And before he could answer, she was gone.

He walked about for the rest of the day in a great state of excitement. "My dear," he told himself, "if you're not careful, something serious will happen to you."

9

When he woke up he saw that it was raining; and in that part of the world it really never does rain but it pours. Needless to touch upon the impatient ennui with which he roamed the house. He sent for André to lunch with him.

"André, can't you do something to stop this rain?" he asked; but André stared. "Oh, I was thinking of the priests of Baal," Paul explained. "I beg your pardon." And after the coffee, "Let's go up and play in the garret," he proposed: at which André stared harder still. "We always used to play in the garret on rainy days," Paul reminded him. "Mais, ma foi, monsieur, nous ne sommes plus des gosses," André answered.

"Is there any news about the Queen?" Paul asked.

"There's never any news from Granjolaye," said André.

"And the lady I met in the forest? Have you any new theory who she is?"

"An officer's wife from Ba——"

"André!" cried Paul. "If you say that again, I shall write to the Pope and ask him to unfrock you."

The next day was fine; but, though he spent the entire morning in the Smuggler's Pathway, he did not meet her. "It's because the ground's still wet," he reasoned. "Oh, why don't things dry quicker?"

The next day he did meet her—and she passed him with a bow. He shook his fist at her unsuspecting back.

The next day he perceived Bézigue riderless near the opening among the trees. The horse neighed, as he drew near. She was seated on the moss. He stood still, and bowed tentatively from the path. "Are you disengaged? May I come in?" he asked.

"Oh, do," she answered. "And—won't you take a seat?"

"Thank you," and he placed himself beside her.

"Tell me about your life afterwards," she said.

"My life afterwards? After what?"

"After you were carried off to Paris."

"What earthly interest can *that* have?"

"I want to know."

"It was the average life of the average youth whose family is in average circumstances."

"You went to school?"

"What makes you doubt it? Do I seem so illiterate?"

"Where? In England? Eton? Harrow?"

"No, in Paris. The Lycée Louis le Grand. Oh, I have received an education—no expense was spared. I forget how many years I passed *à faire mon droit* in the Latin Quarter. You'd be surprised if you were to discover what a lot I know. Shall I prove to you that the sum of the angles of a right-angled triangle is equal to two right angles? Or conjugate the verb *amo*? Or give you a brief summary of the doctrines of Aristotle? Or an account of the life and works of Gustavus Adolphus?"

"When did you go to England?"

"Not till Necessity drove me there. I had to eke out a meagre patrimony. I went to England to seek my fortune."

"Did you find it?"

"I never had the knack of finding things. When my father used to send me into the library to fetch a book, or my mother into her dressing-room to fetch her scissors, I could never find them. I looked for it everywhere, but I couldn't find it."

"What did you do?"

"I lived by my wits. *Chevalier d'industrie.*"

"*Ah, non. Je ne crois pas.*"

"You don't believe my wits were sufficient to the task? I was like the London hospitals—practically unendowed; only they wouldn't support me by voluntary contributions. So—I wrote for the newspapers, I'm afraid."

"For the newspapers?"

"Oh, I admit, it's scandalous. But you may as well know the worst.

A penny-a-liner! But I shan't do so any more, now that I have stepped into the shoes of my uncle. You'll never catch me fatiguing myself with work, now that I've got enough to live on!"

"Lazy!"

"Oh, I'm everything that's reprehensible."

"And you never married?"

"I don't think so."

"Aren't you sure?"

"As sure as one can be of anything in this doubtful world."

"But why didn't you?"

"*Pas si bête.* Marriage is such a bore. I never met a woman I could bear the thought of passing all my life with."

"Conceited!"

"I daresay. If you like false modesty better, I'll try to meet your wishes. What woman would have had a poor devil like me?"

"Still, marriage is, after all, very much in vogue."

"Yes, but it's mad. Either you must love the woman you marry, or you mustn't love her. But if you marry a woman without loving her, I hope you'll not deny you're doing a very shocking thing. If, on the contrary, you do love her, *raison de plus* for not marrying her. Fancy marrying a woman you love; and then, day by day, watching the beautiful wild flower of love fatten into a domestic cabbage! Isn't that a syllogism?"

"You have been in love then?"

"Never."

"Never?"

"Oh, I've made a fool of myself occasionally, of course. But I've never been in love."

"Except with Hélène de la Granjolaye?"

"Oh, yes, I was in love with her—when I was ten."

"Till you were . . .?"

"Till I was . . .?"

"How long did it take you to get over it, I mean?"

"I don't know. It wore away gradually. The tooth of time."

"You're not at all in love with her any more?"

"After twenty years? And she a Queen? I hope I know my place."

"But if you were to meet her again?"

"I should probably suffer a horrible disillusion."

"But you have found, at any rate, that 'first love is best'?"

"First and last. The last shall be first," he said oracularly.

"Don't you smoke?" she asked.

"Oh, one by one you drag my vices from me. Let me own, *en bloc*, that I have them all."

"Then you may light a cigarette and give me one."

He gave her a cigarette, and held a match while she lit it. Then he lit one for himself. Her manner of smoking was leisurely, luxurious. She inhaled the smoke, and let it escape slowly in a slender spiral. He looked at her through the thin cloud, and his heart closed in a convulsion. "How big and soft and rich—how magnificent she is—like some great splendid flower, heavy with sweetness!" he thought. He had to breathe deep to overcome a feeling of suffocation; he was trembling in every nerve, and he wondered if she perceived it. He divined the smooth perfection of her body, through the supple cloth that moulded it; he noticed vaguely that the dress she wore to-day was blue, not black. He divined the warmth of her round white throat, the perfume of her skin. "And how those lips could kiss!" his imagination shouted wildly. Again, the silence, the solitude and dimness of the forest, their intimate seclusion there, the great trees, the sky, the bright green cushion of moss, the few detached sounds—bird-notes, rustling leaves, snapping twigs—by which the silence was intensified; again all these lent an acuteness to his sensations. Her dark eyes were smiling lustrously, languidly, at the smoke curling in the air before her, as if they saw a vision in it.

"You're adorable at moments," he said at last.

"At moments! Thank you." She laughed.

"Oh, you can't expect me to pretend that I find you adorable always. There are times when I could fall upon you and exterminate you."

"Why?"

"When you passed me yesterday with a nod."

"'Twas your own fault. You didn't look amusing yesterday."

"When you baffle my perfectly innocent desire to know whom I have the honour of addressing."

"Shall I summon Bézigue?" she asked, touching her bunch of charms.

He acted his despair.

"Besides, what does it matter? I know who *you* are," she went on. "Let that console you."

"Did I say you were adorable? You're hateful."

"What's in a name? Nothing but the power to compromise. Would you have me compromise myself more than I've done already? A woman who makes a man's acquaintance without an introduction, and talks about love, and smokes cigarettes, with him!" She gave a little shudder. "How horrible it sounds when you state it baldly."

"One must never state things baldly. One must qualify. It's the difference between Truth and mere Fact. Truth is Fact qualified. You must add that the woman knew the man by common report to be of the highest possible respectability, and that she saw for herself he was (alas!) altogether harmless. And then you must explain that the affair took place in the country, in the spring; and that the cigarettes were the properest conceivable sort of cigarettes, having been rolled by hand in England."

"You wouldn't believe me if I said I had never done such a thing before? They all say that, don't they?"

"Yes, they all say that. But, oddly enough, I do believe you."

"Then you're not entirely lost to grace, not thoroughly a cynic."

"Oh, there are *some* good women."

"And some good men?"

"Possibly. I've never happened to meet one."

"The eye of the beholder!"

"If you like. But I don't know. There are such things, no doubt, as cynics by temperament; congenital cynics. Then, indeed, you may cry: The eye of the beholder. But others become cynics, are driven into cynicism, by sad experience. I started in life with the rosiest faith in my fellow-man. If I've lost it, it's because he's always behaved shabbily to me, soon or late; always taken some advantage. The struggle for existence! We're all beasts, who take part in it; we must be, or we're devoured. Women for the most part are out of it. Anyhow, *plus je vois les hommes, plus j'aime les femmes.*"

"Are you a beast too?"

"Oh, yes. But I don't bite. I'm the kind of beast that runs away. I lie by the fire and purr, but at the first sign of trouble I jump for the open door. That's why the other fellows always got the better of me. They knew I was a coward, and profited by the knowledge. If my dear good uncle hadn't died, I don't know how I should have lived."

"I'm afraid you have 'lived' too much."

"That was uncalled for."

"Or else your looks belie you."

"My looks?"

"You're so dissipated-looking."

"Dissipated-looking? I? Horror!"

"You've got such a sophisticated eye, if that suits you better. You look *blasé*."

"You're a horrid, rude, uncomplimentary thing."

"Oh, if you're going to call names, I must summon my natural protector." She blew on her golden whistle, and up trotted the obedient Bézigue.

That evening Paul said to himself, "I vastly fear that something serious *has* happened to you. No, she's everything you like, but she *isn't* that sort."

He was depressed, dejected; the reaction, no doubt, from the excitement of her presence. "She's married, of course; and of course she's got a lover. And of course she'll never care a pin for the likes of me. And of course she sees what's the matter with me, and is laughing in her sleeve. And I had thought myself impervious. Oh, damn all women."

10

"Don't stop; ride on," he called out to her, next morning, "I shan't be amusing to-day. I'm frightfully low in my mind."

"Perhaps it will amuse me to study you in a new aspect," she said. "You can entertain me with the story of your griefs."

"Bare my wounds to make a lady smile. Oh, anything to oblige you."

She leapt lightly from Bézigue, and sank upon the moss.

"What is it all about?"

"Oh, not what you imagine," said he. "It's about my debts."

"I had hoped it was about your sins."

"*My* sins! I'm kept awake at night by the thought of *yours*."

"Your conscience is too sensitive. Mine are but peccadillos."

"You say that because you've no sense of moral proportion. Are cruelty and dissimulation peccadillos?"

"They may be even virtues. It all depends. Discipline and reserve!"

"I'll forgive you everything if you'll tell me your name."

"Oh, I have debts, as well as you."

"What have debts to do with the question?"

"I owe something to my reputation."

"If we're going to consider our reputations, what of mine?"

"Yours has preceded you into the country," she said, and drew from her pocket a small, thin volume, bound in grey cloth, with a gilt design.

"Oh, heavens!" cried Paul. "This is how one's past finds one out."

"Oh, some of them aren't bad," she said. "Wait, I'll read you one."

"Then you know English?"

"A leetle. Bot the one I shall read is in Franch."

And then she read out, in an enchanting voice, one of his own French sonnets. "That isn't bad," she added. "Do you think it hopelessly bad?"

"It shows promise, perhaps—when *you* read it."

"It is strange, though, that it should have been written by a man who had never been in love."

"Imagination! Upon my word, I never had been. Besides, the idea is stolen. It's almost a literal translation from Rossetti. What with a little imagination and a little ingenuity, one can do wonderfully well on other people's experience."

"I don't believe you. You have been in love a hundred times."

"Never."

"Never? Not even with Hélène de la Granjolaye de Ravanches?"

"Oh, I don't count my infancy. Never with anybody else."

"Never."

"It's very strange," she said. "Tell me some more about her."

"Oh, bother her."

"I suppose when they carried you off to Paris you had a tearful parting? Did you kick and scream and say you wouldn't go?"

"Why do you always make me talk about the Queen?"

"She interests me. And when you talk about the Queen, I rather like you. It is nice to see that there *was* a time when you were capable of an emotion."

"You fancy I'm incapable now?"

"Tell me about your leave-taking, your farewells."

"Bother our farewells."

"They must have been heart-rending?"

"Probably."

"Don't you remember?"

"Oh, yes, I remember."

"Go on. Don't make me drag it from you by inches. Tell it to me in a pretty melodious narrative. . Either that, or—" she touched her whistle.

"That's barefaced intimidation."

She raised the whistle to her lips.

"Stay, stay!" he cried, "I yield."

"I wait," she answered.

He bent his brows for an instant, then looked up smiling. "If it puts you to sleep, you'll know whom to blame."

"Yes, yes, go on," she said impatiently.

"Dear me, there's nothing worth telling. It was a few weeks after my grandmother's death. We were going to Paris the next day. Her father drove over, with her, to say good-bye. Whilst he was with my people in the drawing-room, she and I walked in the garden.—I say, this is going to become frightfully sentimental, you know. Sure you want it?"

"Go on. Go on."

"Well, we walked in the garden; and she was crying, and I was beseeching her not to cry. She wore one of her white frocks, with a red sash, and her fair fell down her back below her waist. I was holding her hand. 'Don't cry, don't cry. I'll come back as soon as I'm a man, and marry you in real earnest!' I promised her." He paused and laughed.

"Go on. And she?"

" 'Oh, aren't we married in real earnest now?' she asked. I explained that we weren't. 'You have to have the Notary over from Bayonne, and go to Church. I know, because that's how it was when my cousin Elodie was married. We're only married in play.' Then she asked if that wasn't just as good. 'Things one does in play are always so much nicer than real things,' she said."

"Out of the mouths of babes and sucklings! She had a prophetic soul."

"Hadn't she? I admitted that that was true. But I added that perhaps when people were grown-up and could do exactly as they pleased, it was different—perhaps real things would come to be pleasant too."

"Have you found them so?"

"I suppose I can't be quite grown-up, for I've never yet had a chance to do exactly as I pleased."

"Poor young man. Go on."

"And, besides, I reminded her, all the married people we knew were really married, my father and mother, André's father and mother, my cousin Elodie. Hélène's mother was dead, so her parents didn't count. And I argued that we might be sure they found it fun to be really married, or else they wouldn't keep it up. 'Oh, well, then, I suppose we'll have to be really married too,' she consented. 'But it seems as though it never could be as nice as this. If only you weren't going away!' Whereupon I promised again to come back, if she'd promise to wait for me, and never love anybody else, and never, never, never allow another boy to kiss her. 'Oh, never, never, never,'' she assured me. Then her father called her, and they drove away."

"And you went to Paris and forgot her. Why were you false to your engagement?"

"Oh, she had allowed another boy to kiss her. She had married a German prince. Besides, I received a good deal of discouragement from my family. The next day, in the train, I confided our understanding to my mother. My mother seemed to doubt whether her father would like me as a son-in-law. I was certain he would; he was awfully good-natured; he had given me two louis as a parting tip. 'But do you think he'll care to let his daughter marry a bourgeois?' my mother asked. 'A what?' cried I. 'A bourgeois,' said my mother. 'I ain't a bourgeois,' I retorted indignantly. 'What are you then?' pursued my mother. I explained that my grandmother had been a countess, and my uncle was a count; so how could I be a bourgeois? 'But what is your father?' my mother asked. Oh, my father was 'only an Englishman'. But that didn't make me a bourgeois? 'Yes, it does,' my mother said. 'Just because my father's English?' 'Because he's a commoner, because he isn't noble.' 'But then—then what did you go and marry him for?' I stammered. 'Where would you have been if I hadn't?' my mother enquired. That puzzled me for a moment, but then I answered, 'Well, if you'd married a Frenchman, a Count or a Duke or something, I shouldn't have been a bourgeois;' and my mother confessed that that was true enough. 'I don't care if I *am* a bourgeois,' I said at last. 'When I'm big I'm going back to Saint-Graal; and if her father won't let me really marry her, because I'm a bourgeois, then we'll just go on making believe we're married.' "

She laughed. "And now you are big, and you've come back to Saint-Graal, and your lady-love is at Granjolaye. Why don't you call on her and offer to redeem your promise?"

"Why doesn't she send for me—bid me to an audience?"

"Perhaps her prophetic soul warns her how you'd disappoint her.'

"Do you think she'd be disappointed in me?"

"Aren't you disappointed in yourself?"

"Oh, dear, no; I think I'm very nice."

"*I* should be disappointed in myself, if I were a man who had been capable of such an innocent, sweet affection as yours for Hélène de la Granjolaye, and had then gone and soiled myself with the mud of what they call life." She spoke earnestly; her face was grave and sad.

He was surprised, and a little alarmed. "Do you mean by that that you think I'm a bad lot?" he asked.

"You said the other day—yesterday was it?—that you had made a fool of yourself on various occasions."

"Well?"

"Did the process not generally involve making a fool of a woman too?"

"Reciprocity? Perhaps."

"And what was it you always said to them?"

"Oh, I suppose I did."

"You told them you loved them?"

"I'm afraid so."

"And was it true?"

"No."

"Well, then!"

"Ah, but they weren't deceived; they never believed it. That's only a convention of the game, a necessary formula, like the 'Dear' at the beginning of a letter."

"You have 'lived'; you have 'lived'. You'd have been so unique, so rare, so much more interesting, if instead of going and 'living' like other men, you had remained true to the ideal passion of your childhood."

"I had the misfortune to be born into the world, and not into a fairy tale, you see. But it's a perfectly gratuitous assumption, that I have 'lived'."

"Can you honestly tell me you haven't?" she asked, very soberly, with something like eagerness; her pale face intent.

"As a matter of fact . . . Oh, the worst of it is . . . I can't honestly say that I've never . . . But then, what do you want to rake up such matters for? It's not my fault if I've accepted the traditions of my century. Well, anyhow, you see I can't lie to you."

"You appear to find it difficult," she assented, rising.

"Well, what do you infer from that?"

She blew her whistle. "That—that you're out of training," she said lightly, as she mounted her horse.

"Oh," he groaned, "you're——"

"What?"

"You beggar language."

She laughed and rode away.

"There, I've spoiled everything," Paul said, and went home, and passed a sleepless night.

II

"I'll bet you sixpence she won't turn up to-day," he said to his friend in the glass, next morning; nevertheless he went into the forest, and there she was. But she did not offer to dismount.

"Isn't there another inference to be drawn from my inability to lie to you?" he asked.

She smiled on him from her saddle. "Oh, perhaps there are a hundred."

"Don't you think a reasonable inference is that—I love you?"

She laughed.

"You know I love you," he persisted.

"Oh, the conventions of the game! the necessary formula, like 'Dear' at the beginning of a letter!" she cried.

"You don't believe me?"

"*Qui m'aime me suive*," she said, spurring Bézigue into a rapid trot.

12

But the next day he found her already installed in their nook among the trees.

N

"I hate people who doubt my word," he said.

"Oh, now you hate me?"

"I love you. I love you."

She drew away a little.

"Oh, you needn't be afraid. I shan't touch you. Why won't you believe me?"

"Do men always glare savagely like that at women they love?"

"Why won't you believe me?"

"How long have you known me?"

"All my life. A fortnight—three weeks. But that's a lifetime."

"And what do you know about me?"

"Everything. I know that you're adorable. And I adore you."

"Adorable—at moments. Do you know whether I am—married, for example?"

"I know that if you are, I should like to kill your husband. Are you? Tell me. Put me out of suspense. Let me go home and open a vein."

"Have I the air of a *jeune fille*?"

"Thank goodness, no. But there are such things as widows."

"And what more do you know about me?"

"Tell me—*are* you married?"

"You may suppose that I'm a widow."

"Thank God!"

She laughed.

"Will you marry me?" he asked.

"Oh, marriage is such a bore," she reminded him.

"Will you marry me?"

"No," she said. "But you may give me a cigarette."

And for a while they smoked without speaking.

"I hope at any rate you believe me now," he said.

"Because you've offered to make the crowning sacrifice? By the bye, what is my number?"

"Oh, don't," he cried. "You're the only woman I've ever cared a straw for; and I care so much for you that I'd—I'd—" He stammered, seeking for a thing to say he'd do.

"You'd go to the length of marrying me. Only fancy!"

"Oh, you may laugh. But I love you."

"Do you love me as much as you used to love Hélène?"

"I love you as much as it's possible for a man to love a woman."

"Do you know what I think?"

"No. What?"

"If she were to send for you, one of these days I think you'd forget me utterly. Your old love would come back at sight of her. They say she's very good-looking."

"Nonsense."

"I should like to try you."

"I shouldn't fear the trial."

"*Il ne faut jamais dire à la fontaine, je ne boirai pas de ton eau.*"

"But when one's thirst is for wine?"

"It shows that there's some relation between psychology and geography after all," she said.

"What do you mean?"

"Oh, the influences of places. It is here that you and she used to play a fugue on each other's names. The spot raises ghosts. Ghosts of your old emotions. And I'm conveniently at hand."

"If you could see yourself, you'd understand that the influence of places is superfluous. If you could look into my heart you'd recognize that my emotion is scarcely a ghost."

"There's one thing I *should* like to see," she said. "I should very much like to look into your garden at Saint-Graal."

"Would you?" he cried eagerly. "When will you come?"

"Whenever you like."

"Now. At once."

"No. To-morrow."

"To-morrow morning?"

"Yes. You can await me at your park-gates at eleven."

"Then you'll lunch with me?"

"No. . . . Perhaps."

"You're an angel!"

And he trudged home on the air. "If a woman will listen!" his heart sang. "If a woman will come to see your garden!"

13

That evening a servant handed him a letter.

"A footman has brought it from Granjolaye, and is waiting for an answer."

The letter ran thus:

"Monsieur:

"I am directed by Her Majesty the Queen Hélène to request the pleasure of your company at the Château de Granjolaye to-morrow at eleven. Her Majesty desires me to add that she has only to-day learned of your presence in the country.

"Agréez, Monsieur, l'assurance de mes sentiments distingués.

"CTESSE. DE WOLFENBACH."

"Oh, this is staggering," cried Paul. "What to do?" He walked backwards and forwards, pondering his reply. "I believe the only excuse that will pass with Royalty is illness or death. Shall I send word that I died suddenly this morning. Ah, well, here goes for a thumping lie."

And he wrote: "Madame, I am unspeakably honoured by her Majesty's command, and in despair that the state of my health makes it impossible for me to obey it. I am confined to my bed by a severe attack of bronchitis. Pray express to her Majesty my most respectful thanks as well as my profound regret. I shall hope to be able to leave my room at the week's end, when, if her Majesty can be prevailed upon again to accord me an audience, I shall be infinitely grateful."

"There!" he muttered. "I have perjured my soul for you, and made myself appear ridiculous into the bargain. Bronchitis! But—à demain! Good—good Lord! if she shouldn't come!"

14

She came, followed by a groom. She greeted Paul with a smile that made his heart leap with a wild hope. Her groom led Bézigue away to the stables.

"Thank you," said Paul.

"For what?"

"For everything. For coming. For that smile."

"Oh."

They walked about the garden. "It is lovely. The prettiest garden of the neighbourhood," she said. "Show me where the irises grow, by the pond." And when they had arrived there, "They do look like princesses, don't they? Your little friend had some perceptions. Show me where you and she used to sit down. I am tired."

He led her into a corner of the rosery. She sank upon the turf.

"It is nice here," she said, "and quite shut in. One would never know there was a house so near."

She had taken off one of her gloves. Her soft white hand lay languidly in her lap. Suddenly Paul seized it, and kissed it—furiously—again and again. She yielded it. It was sweet to smell, and warm. "My God, how I love you, how I love you!" he murmured.

When he looked up, she was smiling. "Oh, you are radiant! You are divine!" he cried. And then her eyes filled with tears. "What is it? What is it? You are unhappy?"

"Oh, no," she said. "But to think—to think that after all these years of misery, of heartbreak, it should end like this, here."

"Here?" he questioned.

"I am glad your bronchitis is better, but you *can* invent the most awful fibs," she said.

He looked at her, while the universe whirled round him.

"Hélène!"

"Paul!"

15

Her divorce didn't carry with it the right to marry again. But she said, "We can go on making believe we're married. Things one does in play are always so much nicer than real things." And when he spoke of the "world", she answered, "I have nothing to fear or to hope from the world. It has done its worst by me already."

As they walked back to the house for luncheon, Paul looked into her face, and said, "I can't believe my eyes, you know."

She smiled and took his arm. "J' t' aime tant," she whispered.

"And now I can't believe my ears!"

And this would appear to be the end, but I suppose it can't be, for everybody says nowadays that nothing ever ends happily here below.

FRANK HARRIS

Montes the Matador

"YES! I'm better, and the doctor tells me I've escaped once more—as if I cared! . . . And all through the fever you came every day to see me, so my niece says, and brought me the cool drink that drove the heat away and gave me sleep. You thought, I suppose, like the doctor, that I'd escape you, too. Ha! ha! And that you'd never hear old Montes tell what he knows of bull-fighting and you don't. . . . Or perhaps it was kindness; though, why you, a foreigner and a heretic, should be kind to me, God knows. . . . The doctor says I've not got much more life in me, and you're going to leave Spain within the week—within the week, you said, didn't you? . . . Well, then, I don't mind telling you the story.

"Thirty years ago I wanted to tell it often enough, but I knew no one I could trust. After that fit passed, I said to myself I'd never tell it; but as you're going away, I'll tell it to you, if you swear by the Virgin you'll never tell it to anyone, at least until I'm dead. You'll swear, will you, easily enough! They all will; but as you're going away, it's much the same. Besides, you can do nothing now; no one can do anything; they never could have done anything. Why, they wouldn't believe you if you told it to them, the fools! . . . My story will teach you more about bull-fighting than Frascuelo or Mazzantini, or—yes, Lagartijo knows. Weren't there Frascuelos and Mazzantinis in my day? Dozens of them. You could pick one Frascuelo out of every thousand labourers if you gave him the training and the practice, and could keep him away from wine and women. But a Montes is not to be found every day, if you searched all Spain for one. . . . What's the good of bragging? I never bragged when I was at work: the deed talks —louder than any words. Yet I think no one has ever done the things I used to do; for I read in a paper once an account of a thing I often did, and the writer said it was incredible. Ha, ha, incredible to the Frascuelos and Mazzantinis and the rest, who can kill bulls and are called *espadas*. Oh, yes, bulls so tired out they can't lift their heads. You didn't guess when you were telling me about Frascuelo and Mazzantini that I knew them. I knew all about both of them before you told me. I know their work, though I've not been within sight of a ring for more than thirty years. . . . Well, I'll tell you my story: I'll tell you my story—if I can."

The old man said the last words as if to himself in a low voice, then sank back in the armchair, and for a time was silent.

Let me say a word or two about myself and the circumstances which led me to seek out Montes.

I had been in Spain off and on a good deal, and had taken from the first a great liking to the people and country; and no one can love Spain and the Spaniards without becoming interested in the bull-ring—the sport is so characteristic of the people, and in itself so enthralling. I set myself to study it in earnest, and when I came to know the best bull-fighters, Frascuelo, Mazzantini, and Lagartijo, and heard them talk of their trade, I began to understand what skill and courage, what qualities of eye and hand and heart, this game demands. Through my love of the sport, I came to hear of Montes. He had left so great a name that thirty years after he had disappeared from the scene of his triumphs, he was still spoken of not infrequently. He would perhaps have been better remembered, had the feats attributed to him been less astounding. It was Frascuelo who told me that Montes was still alive:

"Montes," he cried out in answer to me; "I can tell you about Montes. You mean the old *espada* who, they say, used to kill the bull in its first rush into the ring—as if anyone could do that! I can tell you about him. He must have been clever; for an old *aficionado* I know, swears no one of us is fit to be in his *cuadrilla*. Those old fellows are all like that, and I don't believe half they tell about Montes. I daresay he was good enough in his day, but there are just as good men now as ever there were. When I was in Ronda, four years ago, I went to see Montes. He lives out of the town in a nice little house all alone, with one woman to attend to him, a niece of his, they say. You know he was born in Ronda; but he would not talk to me; he only looked at me and laughed—the little, lame, conceited one!"

"You don't believe then, in spite of what they say, that he was better than Lagartijo or Mazzantini," I asked.

"No, I don't," Frascuelo replied. "Of course, he may have known more than they do, and that wouldn't be difficult, for neither of them knows much. Mazzantini is a good *matador* because he's very tall and strong—that's his advantage. For that, too, the women like him, and when he makes a mistake and has to try again, he gets forgiven.

It wasn't so when I began. There were *aficionados* then, and if you
made a mistake they began to jeer, and you were soon pelted out of the
ring. Now the crowd knows nothing and is no longer content to
follow those who do know. Lagartijo? Oh! he's very quick and daring,
and the women and boys like that, too. But he's ignorant: he knows
nothing about a bull. Why, he's been wounded oftener in his five years
than I in my twenty. And that's a pretty good test. Montes must
have been clever; for he's very small and I shouldn't think he was
ever very strong, and then he was lame almost from the beginning, I've
heard. I've no doubt he could teach the business to Mazzantini or
Lagartijo, but that's not saying much. . . . He must have made a lot
of money, too, to be able to live on it ever since. And they didn't pay
as high then or even when I began as they do now."

So much I knew about Montes when, in the spring of 188—, I
rode from Seville to Ronda, fell in love with the place at first sight, and
resolved to stop at Polos' inn for some time. Ronda is built, as it were,
upon an island tableland high above the sea-level, and is ringed about
by still higher mountain ranges. It is one of the most peculiar and
picturesque places in the world. A river runs almost all round it; and
the sheer cliffs fall in many places three or four hundred feet, from the
tableland to the water, like a wall. No wonder that the Moors held
Ronda after they had lost every other foot of ground in Spain. Taking
Ronda as my headquarters, I made almost daily excursions, chiefly on
foot, into the surrounding mountains. On one of these I heard again
of Montes. A peasant with whom I had been talking and who was
showing me a short cut back to the town, suddenly stopped and said,
pointing to a little hut perched on the mountain-shoulder in front of us,
"From that house you can see Ronda. That's the house where Montes,
the great *matador*, was born," he added, evidently with some pride.
Then and there the conversation with Frascuelo came back to my
memory, and I made up my mind to find Montes out and have a talk
with him. I went to his house, which lay just outside the town, next
day with the *alcalde*, who introduced me to him and then left us. The
first sight of the man interested me. He was short—about five feet
three or four, I should think—of well-knit, muscular frame. He
seemed to me to have Moorish blood in him. His complexion was very
dark and tanned; the features clean-cut; the nose sharp and inquisitive;
the nostrils astonishingly mobile; the chin and jaws square, boney—

resolute. His hair and thick moustache were snow-white, and this, together with the deep wrinkles on the forehead and round the eyes and mouth, gave him an appearance of great age. He seemed to move, too, with extreme difficulty, his lameness, as he afterwards told me, being complicated with rheumatism. But when one looked at his eyes, the appearance of age vanished. They were large and brown, usually inexpressive, or rather impenetrable, brooding wells of unknown depths. But when anything excited him, the eyes would suddenly flash to life and become intensely luminous. The effect was startling. It seemed as if all the vast vitality of the man had been transmuted into those wonderful gleaming orbs: they radiated courage, energy, intellect. Then as his mood changed, the light would die out of the eyes, and the old, wizened, wrinkled face would settle down into its ordinary, ill-tempered, wearied expression. There was evidently so much in the man—courage, melancholy, keen intelligence—that in spite of an anything but flattering reception I returned again and again to the house. One day his niece told me that Montes was in bed, and from her description I decided that he was suffering from an attack of malarial fever. The doctor who attended him, and whom I knew, confirmed this. Naturally enough I did what I could for the sufferer, and so it came about that after his recovery he received me with kindness, and at last made up his mind to tell me the story of his life.

"I may as well begin at the beginning," Montes went on. "I was born near here about sixty years ago. You thought I was older. Don't deny it. I saw the surprise in your face. But it's true: in fact, I am not yet, I think, quite sixty. My father was a peasant with a few acres of land of his own and a cottage."

"I know it," I said. "I saw it the other day."

"Then you may have seen on the further side of the hill the pasture-ground for cattle which was my father's chief possession. It was good pasture; very good. My mother was of a better class than my father; she was the daughter of the chemist in Ronda; she could read and write, and she did read, I remember, whenever she could get the chance, which wasn't often, with her four children to take care of—three girls and a boy—and the house to look after. We all loved her, she was so gentle; besides, she told us wonderful stories; but I think I was her favourite. You see I was the youngest and a boy, and women are like that. My father was hard—at least, I thought him so, and feared rather than loved him; but the girls got on better with him. He never talked to me as he did to them. My mother wanted me to go to school and become a priest; she had taught me to read and write by the time I was six. But my father would not hear of it. "If you had had three boys and one girl," I remember him saying to her once, "you could have done what you liked with this one. But as there is only one boy, he must work and help me." So by the time I was nine I used to go off down to the pasture and watch the bulls all day long. For though the herd was a small one—only about twenty head—it required to be constantly watched. The cows were attended to in an enclosure close to the house. It was my task to mind the bulls in the lower pasture. Of course I had a pony, for such bulls in Spain are seldom approached, and cannot be driven by a man on foot. I see you don't understand. But it's simple enough. My father's bulls were of good stock, savage and strong; they were always taken for the ring, and he got high prices for them. He generally managed to sell three *novillos* and two bulls of four years old each year. And there was no bargaining, no trouble; the money was always ready for that class of animal. All day long I sat on my pony, or stood near it, minding the bulls. If any of them strayed too far, I had to go and get him back again. But in the heat of the day they never moved about much, and that time I turned to use by learning the lessons my mother gave me. So a couple of years passed. Of course in that time I got to know our bulls pretty well; but it was a remark of my father which first taught me that each bull had an individual character and which first set me to watch them closely. That must have been in my twelfth year; and in that summer I learned more than in the two previous years. My father, though he said nothing to me, must have noticed that I had gained confidence in dealing with the bulls; for one night, when I was in bed, I heard him say to my mother—'The little fellow is as good as a man now.' I was proud of his praise, and from that time on, I set to work to learn everything I could about the bulls.

"By degrees I came to know every one of them—better far than I ever got to know men or women later. Bulls, I found, were just like men, only simpler and kinder; some were good-tempered and honest, others were sulky and cunning. There was a black one which was wild and hot-tempered, but at bottom good, while there was one almost as black, with light horns and flanks, which I never trusted. The other

bulls didn't like him. I could see they didn't; they were all afraid of
him. He was cunning and suspicious, and never made friends with
any of them; he would always eat by himself far away from the others—
but he had courage, too; I knew that as well as they did. He was sold
that very summer with the black one for the ring in Ronda. One
Sunday night, when my father and eldest sister (my mother would
never go to *los toros*) came back from seeing the game in Ronda, they
were wild with excitement, and began to tell the mother how one of
our bulls had caught the *matador* and tossed him, and how the *chulos*
could scarcely get the *matador* away. Then I cried out—'I know;
'twas Judas' (so I had christened him), and as I saw my father's look of
surprise I went on confusedly, 'The bull with the white horns I mean.
Juan, the black one, wouldn't have been clever enough.' My father
only said, 'The boy's right'; but my mother drew me to her and kissed
me, as if she were afraid. . . . Poor mother! I think even then she knew
or divined something of what came to pass later. . . .

"It was the next summer, I think, that my father first found out
how much I knew about the bulls. It happened in this way. There
hadn't been much rain in the spring, the pasture, therefore, was thin,
and that, of course, made the bulls restless. In the summer the weather
was unsettled—spells of heat and then thunderstorms—till the animals
became very excitable. One day, there was thunder in the air I remember, they gave me a great deal of trouble and that annoyed me, for I
wanted to read. I had got to a very interesting tale in the story-book my
mother had given me on the day our bulls were sold. The story was
about Cervantes—ah, you know who I mean, the great writer. Well,
he was a great man, too. The story told how he escaped from the prison
over there in Algiers and got back to Cadiz, and how a widow came to
him to find out if he knew her son, who was also a slave of the Moors.
And when she heard that Cervantes had seen her son working in chains,
she bemoaned her wretchedness and ill-fortune, until the heart of the
great man melted with pity, and he said to her, 'Come, mother, be
hopeful, in one month your son shall be here with you.' And then the
book told how Cervantes went back to slavery, and how glad the Bey
was to get him again, for he was very clever; and how he asked the Bey,
as he had returned of his free will, to send the widow's son home in his
stead; and the Bey consented. That Cervantes was a man! . . . Well,
I was reading the story and I believed every word of it, as I do still,

for no ordinary person could invent that sort of tale; and I grew very much excited and wanted to know all about Cervantes. But as I could only read slowly and with difficulty, I was afraid the sun would go down before I could get to the end. While I was reading as hard as ever I could, my father came down on foot and caught me. He hated to see me reading—I don't know why; and he was angry and struck at me. As I avoided the blow and got away from him, he pulled up the picket line, and got on my pony to drive one of the bulls back to the herd. I have thought since, he must have been very much annoyed before he came down and caught me. For though he knew a good deal about bulls, he didn't show it then. My pony was too weak to carry him easily, yet he acted as if he had been well mounted. For, as I said, the bulls were hungry and excited, and my father should have seen this and driven the bull back quietly and with great patience. But no; he wouldn't let him feed even for a moment. At last the bull turned on him. My father held the goad fairly against his neck, but the bull came on just the same, and the pony could scarcely get out of the way in time. In a moment the bull turned and prepared to rush at him again. My father sat still on the little pony and held the goad; but I knew that was no use; he knew it too; but he was angry and wouldn't give in. At once I ran in between him and the bull, and then called to the bull, and went slowly up to him where he was shaking his head and pawing the ground. He was very angry, but he knew the difference between us quite well, and he let me come close to him without rushing at me, and then just shook his head to show me he was still angry, and soon began to feed quietly. In a moment or two I left him and went back to my father. He had got off the pony and was white and trembling, and he said,

" 'Are you hurt?'

"And I said laughing, 'No: he didn't want to hurt me. He was only showing off his temper.'

"And my father said, 'There's not a man in all Spain that could have done that! You know more than I do—more than anybody.'

"After that he let me do as I liked, and the next two years were very happy ones. First came the marriage of my second sister; then the eldest one was married, and they were both good matches. And the bulls sold well, and my father had less to do, as I could attend to the whole herd by myself. Those were two good years. My mother seemed to love me more and more every day, or I suppose I noticed it more, and she praised me for doing the lessons she gave me; and I had more and more time to study as the herd got to know me better and better.

"My only trouble was that I had never seen the bulls in the ring. But when I found my father was willing to take me, and it was mother who wanted me not to go, I put up with that, too, and said nothing, for I loved her greatly. Then of a sudden came the sorrow. It was in late winter, just before my fifteenth birthday. I was born in March, I think. In January my mother caught cold, and as she grew worse my father fetched the doctor, and then her father and mother came to see her, but nothing did any good. In April she died. I wanted to die too.

"After her death my father took to grumbling about the food and house and everything. Nothing my sister could do was right. I believe she only married in the summer because she couldn't stand his constant blame. At any rate she married badly, a good-for-nothing who had twice her years, and who ill-treated her continually. A month or two later my father, who must have been fifty, married again, a young woman, a labourer's daughter without a *duro*. He told me he was going to do it, for the house needed a woman. I suppose he was right. But I was too young then to take such things into consideration, and I had loved my mother. When I saw his new wife I did not like her, and we did not get on well together.

"Before this, however, early in the summer that followed the death of my mother, I went for the first time to see a bull-fight. My father wanted me to go, and my sister, too; so I went. I shall never forget that day. The *chulos* made me laugh, they skipped about so and took such extra-good care of themselves; but the *banderilleros* interested me. Their work required skill and courage, that I saw at once; but after they had planted the *banderillas* twice, I knew how it was done, and felt I could do it just as well or better. For the third or fourth *banderillero* made a mistake! He didn't even know with which horn the bull was going to strike; so he got frightened, and did not plant the *banderillas* fairly—in fact, one was on the side of the shoulder and the other didn't even stick in. As for the *picadores*, they didn't interest me at all. There was no skill or knowledge in their work. It was for the crowd, who liked to see blood and who understand nothing. Then came the turn of the *espada*. Ah, that seemed splendid to me. He knew his work

I thought at first, and his work evidently required knowledge, skill, courage, strength—everything. I was intensely excited, and when the bull, struck to the heart, fell prone on his knees and the blood gushed from his nose and mouth, I cheered and cheered till I was hoarse. But before the games were over, that very first day, I saw more than one *matador* make a mistake. At first I thought I must be wrong, but soon the event showed I was right. For the *matador* hadn't even got the bull to stand square when he tried his stroke and failed. Ah, I see you don't know what that means—'to stand square'."

"I do partly," I replied, "but I don't see the reason of it. Will you explain?"

"Well," Montes answered, "it's very simple. You see, so long as the bull's standing with one hoof in front of the other, his shoulder-blades almost meet, as when you throw your arms back and your chest out; that is, they don't meet, but the space between them is not as regular, and, therefore, not as large as it is when their front hooves are square. Now, the space between the shoulder-blades is none too large at any time, for you have to strike with force to drive the sword through the inch-thick hide, and through a foot of muscle, sinew, and flesh besides to the heart. Nor is the stroke a straight one. Then, too, there's always the backbone to avoid. And the space between the backbone and the nearest thick gristle of the shoulder-blade is never more than an inch and a half. So if you narrow this space by even half an inch you increase your difficulty immensely. And that's not your object. Well, all this I've been telling you, I divined at once. Therefore, when I saw the bull wasn't standing quite square I knew the *matador* was either a bungler or else very clever and strong indeed. In a moment he proved himself to be a bungler, for his sword turned on the shoulder-blade, and the bull, throwing up his head, almost caught him on his horns. Then I hissed and cried, 'Shame!' And the people stared at me. That butcher tried five times before he killed the bull, and at last even the most ignorant of the spectators knew I had been right in hissing him. He was one of your Mazzantinis, I suppose."

"Oh, no!" I replied, "I've seen Mazzantini try twice, but never five times. That's too much!"

"Well," Montes continued quietly, "the man who tries once and fails ought never to be allowed in a ring again. But to go on. That first day taught me I could be an *espada*. The only doubt in my mind was in regard to the nature of the bulls. Should I be able to understand new bulls—bulls, too, from different herds and of different race, as well as I understood our bulls? Going home that evening I tried to talk to my father, but he thought the sport had been very good, and when I wanted to show him the mistakes the *matadores* had made, he laughed at me, and, taking hold of my arm, he said, 'Here's where you need the gristle before you could kill a bull with a sword, even if he were tied for you." My father was very proud of his size and strength, but what he said had reason in it, and made me doubt myself. Then he talked about the gains of the *matadores*. A fortune, he said, was given for a single day's work. Even the pay of the *chulos* seemed to me to be extravagant, and a *banderillero* got enough to make one rich for life. That night I thought over all I had seen and heard, and fell asleep and dreamt I was an *espada*, the best in Spain, and rich, and married to a lovely girl with golden hair—as boys do dream.

"Next day I set myself to practise with our bulls. First I teased one till he grew angry and rushed at me; then, as a *chulo*, I stepped aside. And after I had practised this several times, I began to try to move aside as late as possible and only just as far as was needful; for I soon found out the play of horn of every bull we had. The older the bull the heavier his neck and shoulders become, and, therefore, the sweep of horns in an old bull is much smaller than a young one's. Before the first morning's sport was over I knew that with our bulls at any rate I could beat any *chulo* I had seen the day before. Then I set myself to quiet the bulls, which was a little difficult, and after I had succeeded I went back to my pony to read and dream. Next day I played at being a *banderillero*, and found out at once that my knowledge of the animal was all important. For I knew always on which side to move to avoid the bull's rush. I knew how he meant to strike by the way he put his head down. To plant the *banderillas* perfectly would have been child's play to me, at least with our bulls. The *matador's* work was harder to practise. I had no sword; besides, the bull I wished to pretend to kill, was not tired and wouldn't keep quiet. Yet I went on trying. The game had a fascination for me. A few days later, provided with a make-shift red *capa*, I got a bull far away from the others. Then I played with him till he was tired out. First I played as a *chulo*, and avoided his rushes by an inch or two only; then, as *banderillero*, I escaped his stroke, and, as I did so, struck his neck with two sticks. When he was tired I approached him with the *capa* and found I could make him do what I pleased, stand crooked or square in a moment, just as I liked. For I learned at once that as a rule the bull rushes at the *capa* and not at the man who holds it. Some bulls, however, are clever enough to charge the man. For weeks I kept up this game, till one day my father expressed his surprise at the thin and wretched appearance of the bulls. No wonder! The pasture ground had been a ring to them and me for many a week.

"After this I had to play matador—the only part which had any interest for me—without first tiring them. Then came a long series of new experiences, which in time made me what I was, a real *espada*, but which I can scarcely describe to you.

"For power over wild animals comes to a man, as it were, by leaps and bounds. Of a sudden one finds he can make a bull do something which the day before he could not make him do. It is all a matter of intimate knowledge of the nature of the animal. Just as the shepherd, as I've been told, knows the face of each sheep in a flock of a thousand, though I can see no difference between the faces of sheep, which are all alike stupid to me, so I came to know bulls, with a complete understanding of the nature and temper of each one. It's just because I can't tell you how I acquired this part of my knowledge that I was so long-winded in explaining to you my first steps. What I knew more than I have told you, will appear as I go on with my story, and that you must believe or disbelieve as you think best."

"Oh," I cried, "you've explained everything so clearly, and thrown light on so many things I didn't understand, that I shall believe whatever you tell me."

Old Montes went on as if he hadn't heard my protestation:

"The next three years were intolerable to me: my stepmother repaid my dislike with interest and found a hundred ways of making me uncomfortable, without doing anything I could complain of and so get altered. In the spring of my nineteenth year I told my father I intended to go to Madrid and become an *espada*. When he found he couldn't induce me to stay, he said I might go. We parted, and I walked to Seville; there I did odd jobs for a few weeks in connection with the bull-ring, such as feeding the bulls, helping to separate them, and so forth; and there I made an acquaintance who was afterwards a friend. Juan Valdera was one of the *cuadrilla* of Girvalda, a *matador* of the ordinary type. Juan was from Estramadura, and we could scarcely understand each other at first; but he was kindly and careless and I took a great liking to him. He was a fine man; tall, strong and handsome, with short, dark, wavy hair and dark moustache, and great black eyes. He liked me, I suppose, because I admired him and because I never wearied of hearing him tell of his conquests among women and even great ladies. Of course I told him I wished to enter the ring, and he promised to help me to get a place in Madrid where he knew many of the officials. 'You may do well with the *capa*,' I remember he said condescendingly, 'or even as a *banderillero*, but you'll never go further. You see, to be an *espada*, as I intend to be, you must have height and strength,' and he stretched his fine figure as he spoke. I acquiesced humbly enough. I felt that perhaps he and my father were right, and I didn't know whether I should ever have strength enough for the task of an *espada*. To be brief, I saved a little money, and managed to get to Madrid late in the year, too late for the bull-ring. Thinking over the matter I resolved to get work in a blacksmith's shop, and at length succeeded. As I had thought, the labour strengthened me greatly, and in the spring of my twentieth year, by Juan's help, I got employed on trial one Sunday as a *chulo*.

* * * * * * *

"I suppose," Montes went on, after a pause, "I ought to have been excited and nervous on that first Sunday—but I wasn't; I was only eager to do well in order to get engaged for the season. The blacksmith, Antonio, whom I had worked with, had advanced me the money for my costume, and Juan had taken me to a tailor and got the things made, and what I owed Antonio and the tailor weighed on me. Well, on that Sunday I was a failure at first. I went in the procession with the rest, then with the others I fluttered my *capa*; but when the bull rushed at me, instead of running away, like the rest, I wrapped my *capa* about me and, just as his horns were touching me, I moved aside—not half a pace. The spectators cheered me, it is true, and I thought I had done very well, until Juan came over to me, and said:

" 'You mustn't show off like that. First of all, you'll get killed if you play that game; and then you fellows with the *capa* are there to make the bull run about, to tire him out so that we *matadores* may kill him.'

"That was my first lesson in professional jealousy. After that I

O

ran about like the rest, but without much heart in the sport. It seemed to me stupid. Besides, from Juan's anger and contempt, I felt sure I shouldn't get a permanent engagement. Bit by bit, however, my spirits rose again with the exercise, and when the fifth or sixth bull came in I resolved to make him run. It was a good, honest bull; I saw that at once; he stood in the middle of the ring, excited, but not angry, in spite of the waving of the *capas* all round him. As soon as my turn came, I ran forward, nearer to him than the others had considered safe, and waved the challenge with my *capa*. At once he rushed at it, and I gave him a long run, half round the circle, and ended it by stopping and letting him toss the *capa* which I held not quite an arm's length from my body. As I did this I didn't turn round to face him. I knew he'd toss the *capa* and not me, but the crowd rose and cheered as if the thing were extraordinary. Then I felt sure I should be engaged, and I was perfectly happy. Only Juan said to me a few minutes later

" 'You'll be killed, my boy, one of these fine days if you try those games. Your life will be a short one if you begin by trusting a bull.'

"But I didn't mind what he said. I thought he meant it as a friendly warning, and I was anxious only to get permanently engaged. And sure enough, as soon as the games were over, I was sent for by the director. He was kind to me, and asked me where I had played before. I told him that was my first trial.

" 'Ah!' he said, turning to a gentleman who was with him, 'I knew it, Senor Duque; such courage always comes from—want of experience, let me call it.'

" 'No,' replied the gentleman, whom I afterwards knew as the Duke of Medina Celi, the best *aficionado*, and one of the noblest men in Spain; 'I'm not so sure of that. Why,' he went on, speaking now to me, 'did you keep your back turned to the bull?'

" 'Senor,' I answered, 'it was an honest bull, and not angry, and I knew he'd toss the *capa* without paying any attention to me.'

" 'Well,' said the Duke, 'if you know that much, and aren't afraid to risk your life on your knowledge, you'll go far. I must have a talk with you some day, when I've more time; you can come and see me. Send in your name; I shall remember.' And as he said this, he nodded to me and waved his hand to the director, and went away.

"Then and there the director made me sign an engagement for the season, and gave me one hundred *duros* as earnest money in advance of my pay. What an evening we had after that! Juan, the tailor, Antonio the blacksmith, and I. How glad and proud I was to be able to pay my debts and still have sixty *duros* in my pocket after entertaining my friends. If Juan had not hurt me every now and then by the way he talked of my foolhardiness, I should have told them all I knew; but I didn't. I only said I was engaged at a salary of a hundred *duros* a month.

" 'What!' said Juan. 'Come, tell the truth; make it fifty.'

" 'No,' I said; 'it was a hundred,' and I pulled out the money.

" 'Well,' he said, 'that only shows what it is to be small and young and foolhardy! Here am I, after six years' experience, second, too, in the *cuadrilla* of Girvalda, and I'm not getting much more than that.'

"Still, in spite of such little drawbacks, in spite, too, of the fact that Juan had to go away early, to meet 'a lovely creature,' as he said, that evening was one of the happiest I ever spent.

"All that summer through I worked every Sunday, and grew in favour with the Madrilenos, and with the Madrilenas, though not with these in Juan's way. I was timid and young; besides, I had a picture of a woman in my mind, and I saw no one like it. So I went on studying the bulls, learning all I could about the different breeds, and watching them in the ring. Then I sent money to my sister and to my father, and was happy.

"In the winter I was a good deal with Antonio; every day I did a spell of work in his shop to strengthen myself, and he, I think, got to know that I intended to become an *espada*. At any rate, after my first performance with the *capa*, he believed I could do whatever I wished. He used often to say God had given him strength and me brains, and he only wished he could exchange some of his muscle for some of my wits. Antonio was not very bright, but he was good-tempered, kind, and hard-working, the only friend I ever had. May Our Lady give his soul rest!

"Next spring when the director sent for me, I said that I wanted to work as a *banderillero*. He seemed to be surprised, told me I was a favourite with the *capa*, and had better stick to that for another season at least. But I was firm. Then he asked me whether I had ever used the *banderillas* and where? The director always believed I had been employed in some other ring before I came to Madrid. I told him I was confident I could do the work. 'Besides,' I added, 'I want more pay,' which was an untruth; but the argument seemed to him decisive, and he engaged me at two hundred *duros* a month, under the condition that, if the spectators wished it, I should work now and then with the *capa* as well. It didn't take me long to show the *aficionados* in Madrid that I was as good with the *banderillas* as I was with the *capa*. I could plant them when and where I liked. For in this season I found I could make the bull do almost anything. You know how the *banderillero* has to excite the bull to charge him before he can plant the darts. He does that to make the bull lower his head well, and he runs towards the bull partly so that the bull may not know when to toss his head up, partly because he can throw himself aside more easily when he's running fairly fast. Well, again and again I made the bull lower his head and then walked to him, planted the *banderillas*, and as he struck upwards swayed aside just enough to avoid the blow. That was an infinitely more difficult feat than anything I had ever done with the *capa*, and it gave me reputation among the *aficionados* and also with the *espadas*; but the ignorant herd of spectators preferred my trick with the *capa*. So the season came and went. I had many a carouse with Juan, and gave him money from time to time, because women always made him spend more than he got. From that time, too, I gave my sister fifty *duros* a month, and my father fifty. For before the season was half over my pay was raised to four hundred *duros* a month, and my name was always put on the bills. In fact I was rich and a favourite of the public.

"So time went on, and my third season in Madrid began, and with it came the beginning of the end. Never was anyone more absolutely content than I when we were told *los toros* would begin in a fortnight. On the first Sunday I was walking carelessly in the procession beside Juan, though I could have been next to the *espadas* had I wished, when he suddenly nudged me, saying:

" 'Look up! there on the second tier; there's a face for you.'

"I looked up, and saw a girl with the face of my dreams, only much more beautiful. I suppose I must have stopped, for Juan pulled me by the arm crying: 'You're moon-struck, man; come on!' and on I went —love-struck in heart and brain and body. What a face it was! The golden hair framed it like a picture, but the great eyes were hazel, and the lips scarlet, and she wore the *mantilla* like a queen. I moved forward like a man in a dream, conscious of nothing that went on round me, till I heard Juan say:

" 'She's looking at us. She knows we've noticed her. All right, pretty one, we'll make friends afterwards.'

" 'But how?' I asked, stupidly.

" 'How!' he replied, mockingly. 'I'll just send someone to find out who she is, and then you can send her a box for next Sunday, and pray for her acquaintance, and the thing's done. I suppose that's her mother sitting behind her,' he went on. 'I wonder if the other girl next to her is the sister. She's as good-looking as the fair-haired one, and easier to win, I'd bet. Strange how all the timid ones take to me.' And again he looked up.

"I said nothing; nor did I look up at the place where she was sitting; but I worked that day as I had never worked before. Then, for the first time, I did something that has never been done since by anyone. The first bull was honest and kindly: I knew the sort. So, when the people began to call for *El Pequeno* (the little fellow)—that was the nickname they had given me—I took up a *capa*, and, when the bull chased me, I stopped suddenly, faced him, and threw the *capa* round me. He was within six paces of me before he caught my look, and began to stop; but before he came to a standstill his horns were within a foot of me. He tossed his head once or twice as if he would strike me, and then went off. The people cheered and cheered as if they would never stop. Then I looked up at her. She must have been watching me, for she took the red rose from her hair and threw it into the ring towards me, crying, 'Bien! Muy bien! El Pequeno!'

"As I picked up the rose, pressed it to my lips, and hid it in my breast, I realized all that life holds of triumphant joy! . . Then I made up my mind to show what I could do, and everything I did that day seemed to delight the public. At last, as I planted the *banderillas*, standing in front of the bull, and he tried twice in quick succession to strike me and failed, the crowd cheered and cheered and cheered, so that, even when I went away after bowing, and stood among my fellows, ten minutes passed before they would let the game go on. I didn't look up again. No! I wanted to keep the memory of what she looked like when she threw me the rose.

"After the games were over, I met her, that same evening. Juan had brought it about, and he talked easily enough to the mother and daughter and niece, while I listened. We all went, I remember, to a restaurant in the Puerta del Sol, and ate and drank together. I said

little or nothing the whole evening. The mother told us they had just
come from the north: Alvareda was the family name; her daughter
was Clemencia, the niece, Liberata. I heard everything in a sort of
fever of hot pulses and cold fits of humility, while Juan told them all
about himself, and what he meant to do and to be. While Clemencia
listened to him, I took my fill of gazing at her. At last Juan invited
them all to *los toros* on the following Sunday, and promised them
the best *palco* in the ring. He found out, too, where they lived, in a little
street running parallel to the Alcala, and assured them of our visit
within the week. Then they left, and as they went out of the door
Liberata looked at Juan, while Clemencia chatted with him and teased
him.

" 'That's all right,' said Juan, turning to me when they were gone,
'and I don't know which is the more taking, the niece or Clemencia.
Perhaps the niece; she looks at one so appealingly; and those who talk
so with their eyes are always the best. I wonder have they any money
One might do worse than either with a good portion.'

" 'Is that your real opinion?' I asked hesitatingly.

" 'Yes,' he answered; 'why?'

" 'Because, in that case leave Clemencia to me. Of course you could
win her if you wanted to. But it makes no difference to you, and to me
all the difference. If I cannot marry her, I shall never marry.'

" 'Jesus!' he cried, 'how fast you go, but I'd do more than that for
you; and besides, the niece really pleases me better.'

"So the matter was settled between us.

"Now, if I could tell you all that happened, I would. But much
escaped me at the time that I afterwards remembered, and many things
that then seemed to me to be as sure as a straight stroke, have since
grown confused. I only know that Juan and I met them often, and
that Juan paid court to the niece, while I from time to time talked
timidly to Clemencia.

"One Sunday after another came and went, and we grew to know
each other well. Clemencia did not chatter like other women: I liked
her the better for it, and when I came to know she was very proud, I
liked that, too. She charmed me, why, I can scarcely tell. I saw her
faults gradually, but even her faults appeared to me fascinating. Her
pride was insensate. I remember one Sunday afternoon after the games,
I happened to go into a restaurant, and found her sitting there with her

mother. I was in costume and carried in my hand a great nosegay of roses that a lady had thrown me in the ring. Of course as soon as I saw Clemencia I went over to her and—you know it is the privilege of the *matadores* in Spain, even if they do not know the lady—taking a rose from the bunch I presented it to her as the fairest of the fair. Coming from the cold North, she didn't know the custom and scarcely seemed pleased. When I explained it to her, she exclaimed that it was monstrous; she'd never allow a mere *matador* to take such a liberty unless she knew and liked him. Juan expostulated with her laughingly; I said nothing; I knew what qualities our work required, and didn't think it needed any defence. I believe in that first season, I came to see that her name Clemencia wasn't very appropriate. At any rate she had courage and pride, that was certain. Very early in our friendship she wanted to know why I didn't become an *espada*.

" 'A man without ambition,' she said, 'was like a woman without beauty.'

"I laughed at this and told her my ambition was to do my work well, and advancement was sure to follow in due course. For love of her seemed to have killed ambition in me. But no. She wouldn't rest content in spite of Juan's telling her my position already was more brilliant than that of most of the *espadas*.

" 'He does things with the *capa* and the *banderillas* which no *espada* in all Spain would care to imitate. And that's position enough. Besides, to be an *espada* requires height and strength.' "

"As he said this she seemed to be convinced, but it annoyed me a little, and afterwards as we walked together, I said to her,

" 'If you want to see me work as an *espada*, you shall.'

" 'Oh, no!' she answered half carelessly; 'if you can't do it, as Juan says, why should you try? To fail is worse than to lack ambition.'

" 'Well,' I answered, 'you shall see.'

"And then I took my courage in both hands and went on:

" 'If you cared for me I should be the first *espada* in the world next season.'

"She turned and looked at me curiously and said,

" 'Of course I'd wish it if you could do it.'

"And I said, 'See, I love you as the priest loves the Virgin; tell me to be an *espada* and I shall be one for the sake of your love.'

" 'That's what all men say, but love doesn't make a man tall and strong.'

" 'No; nor do size and strength take the place of heart and head. Do you love me? That's the question.'

" 'I like you, yes. But love—love, they say, comes after marriage.'

" 'Will you marry me?'

" 'Become an *espada* and then ask me again,' she answered coquettishly.

"The very next day I went to see the Duke of Medina Celi; the servants would scarcely let me pass till they heard my name and that the Duke had asked me to come. He received me kindly. I told him what I wanted.

" 'But,' he said, 'have you ever used the sword? Can you do it? You see we don't want to lose the best man with *capa* and *banderillas* ever known, to get another second-class *espada*.'

"And I answered him,

" 'Senor Duque, I have done better with the *banderillas* than I could with the *capa*. Believe me, I shall do better with the *espada* than with the *banderillas*.'

" 'You little fiend!' he laughed, 'I believe you; but now for the means. All the *espadas* are engaged; it'll be difficult. . . . But early in July the Queen has asked me to superintend the sports, and then I shall give you your chance. Will that do? In the meantime, astonish us all with *capa* and *banderillas*, so that men may not think me mad when I put your name first on the bill.'

"I thanked him from my heart, as was his due, and after a little more talk I went away to tell Clemencia the news. She only said:

" 'I'm glad. Now you'll get Juan to help you.'

"I stared at her.

" 'Yes!' she went on, a little impatiently; 'he has been trained to the work; he's sure to be able to teach you a great deal.'

"I said not a word. She was sincere, I saw, but then she came from the North and knew nothing. I said to myself, 'That's how women are!'

"She continued, 'Of course you're clever with the *capa* and *banderillas*, and now you must do more than ever, as the Duke said, to deserve your chance.' And then she asked carelessly, 'Couldn't you bring the Duke and introduce him to us some time or other? I should like to thank him.'

"And I, thinking it meant our betrothal, was glad, and promised. And I remember I did bring him once to the box and he was kind in a way, but not cordial as he always was when alone with me, and he told Clemencia that I'd go very far, and that any woman would be lucky to get me for a husband, and so on. And after a little while he went away. But Clemencia was angry with him and said he put on airs, and, indeed, I had never seen him so cold and reserved; I could say little or nothing in his defence.

"Well, all that May I worked as I had never done. The Director told me he knew I was to use the *espada* on the first Sunday in July, and he seemed to be glad; and one or two of the best *espadas* came to me and said they'd heard the news and should be glad to welcome me among them. All this excited me, and I did better and better. I used to pick out the old prints of Goya, the great painter—you know his works are in the Prado—and do everything the old *matadores* did, and invent new things. But nothing 'took' like my trick with the *capa*. One Sunday, I remember, I had done it with six bulls, one after the other, and the people cheered and cheered. But the seventh was a bad bull, and, of course, I didn't do it. And afterwards Clemencia asked me why I didn't, and I told her. For you see I didn't know then that women rate high what they don't understand. Mystery is everything to them. As if the explanation of such a thing makes it any easier. A man wins great battles by seizing the right moment and using it—the explanation is simple. One must be great in order to know the moment, that's all. But women don't see that it is only small men who exaggerate the difficulties of their work. Great men find their work easy and say so, and, therefore, you'll find that women underrate great men and overpraise small ones. Clemencia really thought I ought to learn the *espada's* work from Juan. Ah, women are strange creatures. . . . Well, after that Sunday she was always bothering me to do the *capa* trick with every bull.

" 'If you don't,' she used to say, 'you won't get the chance of being an *espada*.' And when she saw I laughed and paid no attention to that, she became more and more obstinate.

" 'If the people get to know you can only do it with some bulls, they won't think much of you. Do it with every bull, then they can't say anything.'

"And I said 'No, and I shouldn't be able to say anything either.'

" 'If you love me you will do as I say!'

"And when I didn't do as she wished—it was madness—she grew cold to me, and sneered at me, and then urged me again, till I half yielded. Really, by that time I hardly knew what I couldn't do, for each day I seemed to get greater power over the bulls. At length a Sunday came, the first, I think, in June, or the last in May. Clemencia sat with her mother and cousin in the best *palco*; I had got it from the Director, who now refused me nothing. I had done my *capa* trick with three bulls, one after the other, then the fourth came in. As soon as I saw him, I knew he was bad, cunning I mean, and with black rage in the heart of him. The other men stood aside to let me do the trick, but I wouldn't. I ran away like the rest, and let him toss the *capa*. The people liked me, and so they cheered just the same, thinking I was tired; but suddenly Clemencia called out: 'The *capa* round the shoulders; the *capa* trick!' and I looked up at her; and she leaned over the front of the *palco*, and called out the words again.

"Then rage came into me, rage at her folly and cold heart; I took off my cap to her, and turned and challenged the bull with the *capa*, and, as he put down his head and rushed, I threw the *capa* round me and stood still. I did not even look at him. I knew it was no use. He struck me here on the thigh, and I went up into the air. The shock took away my senses. As I came to myself they were carrying me out of the ring, and the people were all standing up; but, as I looked towards the *palco*, I saw she wasn't standing up: she had a handkerchief before her face. At first I thought she was crying, and I felt well, and longed to say to her, 'It doesn't matter, I'm content;' then she put down the handkerchief and I saw she wasn't crying; there wasn't a tear in her eyes. She seemed surprised merely and shocked. I suppose she thought I could work miracles, or rather she didn't care much whether I was hurt or not. That turned me faint again. I came to myself in my bed, where I spent the next month. The doctor told the Duke of Medina Celi—he had come to see me the same afternoon—that the shock hadn't injured me, but I should be lame always, as the bull's horn had torn the muscles of my thigh from the bone. 'How he didn't bleed to death,' he said, 'is a wonder; now he'll pull through, but no more play with the bulls for him.' I knew better than the doctor but I said nothing to him, only to the Duke I said:

" 'Senor, a promise is a promise; I shall use the *espada* in your show in July.'

"And he said, 'Yes, my poor boy, if you wish it, and are able to; but how came you to make such a mistake?'

" 'I made no mistake, Senor.'

" 'You knew you'd be struck?'

"I nodded. He looked at me for a moment, and then held out his hand. He understood everything I'm sure; but he said nothing to me then.

"Juan came to see me in the evening, and next day Clemencia and her mother. Clemencia was sorry, that I could see, and wanted me to forgive her. As if I had anything to forgive when she stood there so lithe and straight, with her flower-like face and the appealing eyes. Then came days of pain while the doctors forced the muscles back into their places. Soon I was able to get up, with a crutch, and limp about. As I grew better, Clemencia came seldomer, and when she came her mother never left the room. I knew what that meant. She had told her mother not to go away; for, though the mother thought no one good enough for her daughter, yet she pitied me and would have left us alone—sometimes. She had a woman's heart. But no, not once. Then I set myself to get well soon. I would show them all, I said to myself, that a lame Montes was worth more than other men. And I got better, so the doctor said with surprising speed. . . . One day, towards the end of June, I said to the servant of the Duke—he sent a servant every day to me with fruit and flowers—that I wished greatly to see his master. And the Duke came to see me, the very same day.

"I thanked him first for all his kindness to me, and then asked:

" 'Senor, have you put my name on the bills as *espada?*'

" 'No,' he replied; 'you must get well first, and, indeed, if I were in your place, I should not try anything more till next season.'

"And I said, 'Senor Duque, it presses. Believe me, weak as I am, I can use the sword.'

"And he answered my very thought: 'Ah! She thinks you can't. And you want to prove the contrary. I shouldn't take the trouble, if I were you; but there! Don't deceive yourself or me; there is time yet for three or four days: I'll come again to see you, and if you wish to have your chance you shall. I give you my word.' As he left the room

I had tears in my eyes; but I was glad, too, and confident: I'd teach the false friends a lesson. Save Antonio, the blacksmith, and some strangers, and the Duke's servant, no one had come near me for more than a week. Three days afterwards I wrote to the Duke asking him to fulfil his promise, and the very next day Juan, Clemencia, and her mother all came to see me together. They all wanted to know what it meant. My name as *espada* for the next Sunday, they said, was first on the bills placarded all over Madrid, and the Duke had put underneath it—'By special request of H.M. the Queen.' I said nothing but that I was going to work; and I noticed that Clemencia wouldn't meet my eyes.

"What a day that was! That Sunday I mean. The Queen was in her box with the Duke beside her as our procession saluted them, and the great ring was crowded tier on tier, and she was in the best box I could get. But I tried not to think about her. My heart seemed to be frozen. Still I know now that I worked for her even then. When the first bull came in and the *capa* men played him, the people began to shout for me—'El Pequeno! El Pequeno! El Pequeno!'—and wouldn't let the games go on. So I limped forward in my *espada's* dress and took a *capa* from a man and challenged the bull, and he rushed at me—the honest one; I caught his look and knew it was all right, so I threw the *capa* round me and turned my back upon him. In one flash I saw the people rise in their places, and the Duke lean over the front of the *palco*; then, as the bull hesitated and stopped and they began to cheer, I handed back the *capa*, and, after bowing, went again among the *espadas*. Then the people christened me afresh—'El Cojo!' (The Cripple!)—and I had to come forward and bow again and again, and the Queen threw me a gold cigarette case. I have it still. There it is. . . . I never looked up at Clemencia, though I could see her always. She threw no rose to me that day. . . . Then the time came when I should kill the bull. I took the *muleta* in my left hand and went towards him with the sword uncovered in my right. I needed no trick. I held him with my will, and he looked up at me. 'Poor brute,' I thought, 'you are happier than I am.' And he bowed his head with the great, wondering, kindly eyes, and I struck straight through to the heart. On his knees he fell at my feet, and rolled over dead, almost without a quiver. As I put my sword in the *muleta* and turned away, the people found their voices, 'Well done, The Cripple! Well done!' When I left the ring that day I left it as the first *espada* in Spain. So the Duke said, and he knew—none better. After one more Sunday the sports were over for the year, but that second Sunday I did better than the first, and I was engaged for the next season as first *espada*, with fifty thousand *duros* salary. Forty thousand I invested as the Duke advised— I have lived on the interest ever since—the other ten thousand I kept by me.

* * * * * * *

"I had resolved never to go near Clemencia again, and I kept my resolve for weeks. One day Juan came and told me Clemencia was suffering because of my absence. He said:

" 'She's proud, you know, proud as the devil, and she won't come and see you or send to you, but she loves you. There's no doubt of that: she loves you. I know them, and I never saw a girl so gone on a man. Besides they're poor now, she and her mother; they've eaten up nearly all they had, and you're rich and could help them.'

"That made me think. I felt sure she didn't love me. That was plain enough. She hadn't even a good heart, or she would have come and cheered me up when I lay wounded—because of her obstinate folly. No! It wasn't worth while suffering any more on her account. That was clear. But if she needed me, if she were really poor? Oh, that I couldn't stand. I'd go to her. 'Are you sure?' I asked Juan, and when he said he was, I said:

" 'Then I'll visit them to-morrow.'

"And on the next day I went. Clemencia received me as usual: she was too proud to notice my long absence, but the mother wanted to know why I had kept away from them so long. From that time on the mother rather seemed to like me. I told her I was still sore—which was the truth—and I had had much to do.

" 'Some lady fallen in love with you, I suppose,' said Clemencia half scoffingly—so that I could hardly believe she had wanted to see me.

" 'No,' I answered, looking at her, 'one doesn't get love without seeking for it, sometimes not even then—when one's small and lame as I am.'

"Gradually the old relations established themselves again. But I had grown wiser, and watched her now with keen eyes as I had never done formerly. I found she had changed—in some subtle way had become different. She seemed kinder to me, but at the same time her character appeared to be even stronger than it had been. I remember noticing one peculiarity in her I had not remarked before. Her admiration of the physique of men was now keen and outspoken. When we went to the theatre (as we often did) I saw that the better-looking and more finely-formed actors had a great attraction for her. I had never noticed this in her before. In fact she had seemed to me to know nothing about virile beauty, beyond a girl's vague liking for men who were tall and strong. But now she looked at men critically. She had changed; that was certain. What was the cause? . . . I could not divine. Poor fool that I was! I didn't know then that good women seldom or never care much for mere bodily qualities in a man; the women who do are generally worthless. Now, too, she spoke well of the men of Southern Spain; when I first met her she professed to admire the women of the South, but to think little of the men. Now she admired the men, too; they were warmer-hearted, she said; had more love and passion in them, and were gentler with women than those of the North. Somehow I hoped that she referred to me, that her heart was beginning to plead for me, and I was very glad and proud, though it all seemed too good to be true.

"One day in October, when I called with Juan, we found them packing their things. They had to leave, they said, and take cheaper lodgings. Juan looked at me, and some way or other I got him to take Clemencia into another room. Then I spoke to the mother: Clemencia, I hoped, would soon be my wife; in any case I couldn't allow her to want for anything; I would bring a thousand *duros* the next day, and they must not think of leaving their comfortable apartments. The mother cried and said, I was good: 'God makes few such men,' and so forth. The next day I gave her the money, and it was arranged between us without saying anything to Clemencia. I remember about this time, in the early winter of that year, I began to see her faults more clearly, and I noticed that she had altered in many ways. Her temper had changed. It used to be equable though passionate. It had become uncertain and irritable. She had changed greatly. For now, she would let me kiss her without remonstrance, and sometimes almost as if she didn't notice the kiss, whereas before it used always to be a matter of importance. And when I asked her when she would marry me she would answer half-carelessly, 'Sometime, I suppose,' as she used to do, but her manner was quite different. She even sighed once as she spoke.

Certainly she had changed. What was the cause? I couldn't make it out, therefore I watched, not suspiciously, but she had grown a little strange to me—a sort of puzzle, since she had been so unkind when I lay wounded. And partly from this feeling, partly from my great love for her, I noticed everything. Still I urged her to marry me. I thought as soon as we were married, and she had a child to take care of and to love, it would be all right with both of us. Fool that I was!

"In April, which was fine, I remember, that year in Madrid—you know how cold it is away up there, and how keen the wind is; as the Madrilenos say, 'It won't blow out a candle, but it'll kill a man'— Clemencia began to grow pale and nervous. I couldn't make her out; and so, more than ever, pity strengthening love in me, I urged her to tell me when she would marry me; and one day she turned to me, and I saw she was quite white as she said:

"'After the season, perhaps.'

"Then I was happy, and ceased to press her. Early in May the games began—my golden time. I had grown quite strong again, and was surer of myself than ever. Besides, I wanted to do something to deserve my great happiness. Therefore, on one of the first days when the Queen and the Duke and Clemencia were looking on, I killed the bull with the sword immediately after he entered the ring, and before he had been tired at all. From that day on the people seemed crazy about me. I couldn't walk in the streets without being cheered; a crowd followed me wherever I went; great nobles asked me to their houses, and their ladies made much of me. But I didn't care, for all the time Clemencia was kind, and so I was happy.

"One day suddenly she asked me why I didn't make Juan an *espada*. I told her I had offered him the first place in my *cuadrilla*; but he wouldn't accept it. She declared that it was natural of him to refuse when I had passed him in the race; but why didn't I go to the Duke and get him made an *espada*? I replied laughingly that the Duke didn't make men *espadas*, but God or their parents. Then her brows drew down, and she said she hadn't thought to find such mean jealousy in me. So I answered her seriously that I didn't believe Juan would succeed as an *espada*, or else I should do what I could to get him appointed. At once she came and put her arms on my shoulders, and said it was like me, and she would tell Juan; and after that I could do nothing but kiss her. A little later I asked Juan about it, and he told me he thought he could do the work at least as well as Girvalda, and if I got him the place, he would never forget my kindness. So I went to the Director and told him what I wished. At first he refused, saying Juan had no talent, he would only get killed. When I pressed him he said all the *espadas* were engaged, and made other such excuses. So at last I said I'd work no more unless he gave Juan a chance. Then he yielded after grumbling a great deal.

"Two Sundays later Juan entered the ring for the first time as an *espada*. He looked the part to perfection. Never was there a more splendid figure of a man, and he was radiant in silver and blue. His mother was in the box that day with Clemencia and her mother. Just before we all parted as the sports were about to begin, Clemencia drew me on one side, and said, 'You'll see that he succeeds, won't you?' And I replied, 'Yes, of course I will. Trust me; it'll be all right.' And it was, though I don't think it would have been, if she hadn't spoken. I remembered my promise to her, and when I saw that the bull which Juan ought to kill was vicious, I told another *espada* to kill him, and so got Juan an easy bull, which I took care to have tired out before I told him the moment had come. Juan wasn't a coward—no! but he hadn't the peculiar nerve needed for the business. The *matador's* spirit should rise to the danger, and Juan's didn't rise. He was white, but determined to do his best. That I could see. So I said to him, 'Go on, man! Don't lose time, or he'll get his wind again. You're all right; I shall be near you as one of your *cuadrilla*.' And so I was, and if I hadn't been, Juan would have come to grief. Yes, he'd have come to grief that very first day.

"Naturally enough we spent the evening together. It was a real *tertulia*, Senora Alvareda said; but Clemencia sat silent with the great, dark eyes turned in upon her thoughts, and the niece and myself were nearly as quiet, while Juan talked for every one, not forgetting himself. As he had been depressed before the trial so now he was unduly exultant, forgetting altogether, as it seemed to me, not only his nervousness but also that it had taken him two strokes to kill the bull. His first attempt was a failure, and the second one, though it brought the bull to his knees, never reached his heart. But Juan was delighted and seemed never to weary of describing the bull and how he had struck him, his mother listening to him the while adoringly. It was past midnight when we parted from our friends; and Juan, as we returned to my rooms, would talk of nothing but the salary he expected to get. I was out of sorts; he had bragged so incessantly I had scarcely got a word with Clemencia, who could hardly find time to tell me she had a bad headache. Juan would come up with me; he wanted to know whether I'd go on the morrow to the Director to get him a permanent engagement. I got rid of him, at last, by saying I was tired to death, and it would look better to let the Director come and ask for his services. So at length we parted. After he left me I sat for some time wondering at Clemencia's paleness. She was growing thin too! And what thoughts had induced that rapt expression of face?

"Next morning I awoke late and had so much to do that I resolved to put off my visit to Clemencia till the afternoon, but in the meantime the Director spoke to me of Juan as rather a bungler, and when I defended him, agreed at last to engage him for the next four Sundays. This was a better result than I had expected, so as soon as I was free I made off to tell Juan the good news. I met his mother at the street door where she was talking with some women; she followed me into the *patio* saying Juan was not at home.

"'Never mind,' I replied carelessly, 'I have good news for him, so I'll go upstairs to his room and wait.'

"'Oh!' she said, 'you can't do that; you mustn't; Juan wouldn't like it.'

"Then I laughed outright. Juan wouldn't like it—oh, no! It was amusing to say that when we had lived together like brothers for years, and had had no secrets from one another. But she persisted and grew strangely hot and excited. Then I thought to myself—there you are again; these women understand nothing. So I went away, telling her to send Juan to me as soon as he came in. At this she seemed hugely relieved and became voluble in excuses. In fact her manner altered so entirely that before I had gone fifty yards down the street, it forced me to wonder. Suddenly my wonder changed to suspicion. Juan wasn't out! Who was with him I mustn't see?

"As I stopped involuntarily, I saw a man on the other side of the street who bowed to me. I went across and said:

"'Friend, I am Montes, the matador. Do you own this house?'

"He answered that he did, and that everyone in Madrid knew me.

"So I said, 'Lend me a room on your first-floor for an hour; *cosa de mujer*. A lady's in the case, you understand.'

P

"At once he led me upstairs and showed me a room from the windows of which I could see the entrance to Juan's lodging. I thanked him, and when he left me I stood near the window and smoked and thought. What could it all mean? . . . Had Clemencia anything to do with Juan? She made me get him his trial as *espada*; charged me to take care of him. He was from the South, too, and she had grown to like Southern men: 'they were passionate and gentle with women.' Curses on her! Her paleness occured to me, her fits of abstraction. As I thought, every memory fitted into its place, and what had been mysterious grew plain to me; but I wouldn't accept the evidence of reason. No! I'd wait and see. Then I'd—at once I grew quiet. But again the thoughts came— like the flies that plague the cattle in summer-time—and again I brushed them aside, and again they returned.

"Suddenly I saw Juan's mother come into the street wearing altogether too careless an expression. She looked about at haphazard as if she expected someone. After a moment or two of this she slipped back into the *patio* with mystery in her sudden decision and haste. Then out came a form I knew well, and, with stately, even step, looking neither to the right hand nor the left, walked down the street. It was Clemencia, as my heart had told me it would be. I should have known her anywhere even had she not—just below the window where I was watching—put back her *mantilla* with a certain proud grace of movement which I had admired a hundred times. As she moved her head to feel that the *mantilla* draped her properly I saw her face; it was drawn and set like one fighting against pain. That made me smile with pleasure.

"Five minutes later Juan swung out of the doorway in the full costume of an *espada*—he seemed to sleep in it now—with a cigarette between his teeth. Then I grew sad and pitiful. We had been such friends. I had meant only good to him always. And he was such a fool! I understood it all now; knew, as if I had been told, that the intimacy between them dated from the time when I lay suffering in bed. Thinking me useless and never having had any real affection for me, Clemencia had then followed her inclination and tried to win Juan. She had succeeded easily enough, no doubt, but not in getting him to marry her. Later, she induced me to make Juan an *espada*, hoping against hope that he'd marry her when his new position had made him rich. On the other hand he had set himself to cheat me because of the money I had given her mother, which relieved him from the necessity of helping them, and secondly, because it was only through my influence that he could hope to become an *espada*. Ignoble beasts! And then jealousy seized me as I thought of her admiration of handsome men, and at once I saw her in his arms. Forthwith pity, and sadness, and anger left me, and, as I thought of him swaggering past the window, I laughed aloud. Poor weak fools! I, too, could cheat.

"He had passed out of the street. I went downstairs and thanked the landlord for his kindness to me. 'For your good-nature,' I said, 'you must come and see me work from a box next Sunday. Ask for me, I won't forget.' And he thanked me with many words and said he had never missed a Sunday since he had first seen me play with the *capa* three years before. I laughed and nodded to him and went my way homewards, whither I knew Juan had gone before me.

"As I entered my room, he rose to meet me with a shadow as of doubt or fear upon him. But I laughed cheerfully, gaily enough to deceive even so finished an actor as he was, and told him the good news. 'Engaged,' I cried, slapping him on the shoulder. 'The Director engages you for four Sundays certain.' And that word 'certain' made me laugh louder still—jubilantly. Then afraid of overdoing my part, I sat quietly for some time and listened to his expressions of fatuous self-satisfaction. As he left me to go and trumpet the news from *café* to *café*, I had to choke down my contempt for him by recalling that picture, by forcing myself to see them in each other's arms. Then I grew quiet again and went to call upon my betrothed.

"She was at home and received me as usual, but with more kindness than was her wont. 'She feels a little remorse at deceiving me,' I said to myself, reading her now as if her soul were an open book. I told her of Juan's engagement and she let slip 'I wish I had known that sooner!' But I did not appear to notice anything. It amused me now to see how shallow she was and how blind I had been. And then I played with her as she had often, doubtless, played with me. 'He will go far, will Juan,' I said, 'now that he has begun—very far, in a short time.' And within me I laughed at the double meaning as she turned startled eyes upon me. And then, 'His old loves will mourn for the distance which must soon separate him from them. Oh, yes, Juan will go far and leave them behind.' I saw a shade come upon her face, and, therefore, added: 'But no one will grudge him his success. He's so good-looking and good-

tempered, and kind and true.' And then she burst into tears, and I
went to her and asked as if suspiciously, 'Why, what's the matter?
Clemencia!' Amid her sobs, she told me she didn't know, but she felt
upset, out of sorts, nervous: she had a headache. 'Heartache,' I laughed
to myself, and bade her go and lie down; rest would do her good; I'd
come again on the morrow. As I turned to leave the room she called
me back and put her arms round my neck and asked me to be patient
with her; she was foolish, but she'd make it up to me yet. . . . And I
comforted her, the poor, shallow fool, and went away.

"In some such fashion as this the days passed; each hour—now my
eyes were opened—bringing me some new amusement; for, in spite
of their acting, I saw that none of them were happy. I knew everything.
I guessed that Juan, loving his liberty, was advising Clemencia to make
up to me, and I saw how badly she played her part. And all this had
escaped me a few days before; I laughed at myself more contemptuously
than at them. It amused me, too, to see that Liberata had grown
suspicious. She no longer trusted Juan's protestations implicitly.
Every now and then, with feminine bitterness, she thrust the knife of
her own doubt and fear into Clemencia's wound. 'Don't you think,
Montes, Clemencia is getting pale and thin?' she'd ask; 'it is for love
of you, you know. She should marry soon.' And all the while she
cursed me in her heart for a fool, while I laughed to myself. The
comedy was infinitely amusing to me, for now I held the cards in my
hand, and knew I could drop the curtain and cut short the acting just
when I liked. Clemencia's mother too, would sometimes set to work
to amuse me as she went about with eyes troubled, as if anxious for the
future, and yet stomach-satisfied with the comforts of the present.
She, too, thought it worth while, now and then, to befool me, when
fear came upon her—between meals. That did not please me! When
she tried to play with me, the inconceivable stupidity of my former
blind trust became a torture to me. Juan's mother I saw but little of;
yet I liked her. She was honest at least, and deceit was difficult to her.
Juan was her idol; all he did was right in her eyes; it was not her fault
that she couldn't see he was like a poisoned well. All these days Juan
was friendly to me as usual, with scarcely a shade of the old condes-
cension in his manner. He no longer showed envy by remarking upon
my luck. Since he himself had been tested, he seemed to give me as
much respect as his self-love could spare. Nor did he now boast, as he

used to do, of his height and strength. Once, however, on the Friday evening, I think it was, he congratulated Clemencia on my love for her, and joked about our marriage. Then I felt the time had come to drop the curtain and make an end.

"On the Saturday I went to the ring and ordered my *palco* to be filled with flowers. From there I went to the Duke of Medina Celi. He received me as always, with kindness, thought I looked ill, and asked me whether I felt the old wound still. "No,' I replied, 'no, Senor Duque, and if I come to you now it is only to thank you once more for all your goodness to me.'

"And he said after a pause—I remember each word; for he meant well:

"'Montes, there's something very wrong.' And then, 'Montes, one should never adore a woman; they all want a master. My hairs have grown grey in learning that. . . . A woman, you see, may look well and yet be cold-hearted and—not good. But a man would be a fool to refuse nuts because one that looked all right was hollow.'

"'You are wise,' I said, 'Senor Duque, and I have been foolish. I hope it may be well with you always; but wisdom and folly come to the same end at last.'

"After I left him I went to Antonio and thanked him, and gave him a letter to be opened in a week. There were three enclosure in it—one for himself, one for the mother of Juan, and one for the mother of Clemencia, and each held three thousand *duros*. As they had cheated me for money, money they should have—with my contempt. Then I went back to the ring, and as I looked up to my *palco* and saw that the front of it was one bed of white and scarlet blossoms, I smiled. 'White for purity,' I said, 'and scarlet for blood, a fit show!' And I went home and slept like a child.

"Next day in the ring I killed two bulls, one on his first rush, and the other after the usual play. Then another *espada* worked, and then came the turn of Juan. As the bull stood panting I looked up at the *palco*. There they all were, Clemencia with hands clasped on the flowers and fixed, dilated eyes, her mother half asleep behind her. Next to Clemencia, the niece with flushed cheeks, and leaning on her shoulder his mother. Juan was much more nervous than he had been on the previous Sunday. As his bull came into the ring he asked me hurriedly: 'Do you think it's an easy one?' I told him carelessly that all bulls were easy and he seemed to grow more and more nervous. When the bull was ready for him he turned to me, passing his tongue feverishly over his dry lips.

" 'You'll stand by me, won't you, Montes?'

"And I asked with a smile:

" 'Shall I stand by you as you've stood by me?'

" 'Yes, of course, we've always been friends.'

" 'I shall be as true to you as you have been to me!' I said. And I moved to his right hand and looked at the bull. It was a good one; I couldn't have picked a better. In his eyes I saw courage that would never yield and hate that would strike in the death-throe, and I exulted and held his eyes with mine, and promised him revenge. While he bowed his horns to the *muleta*, he still looked at me and I at him; and as I felt that Juan had levelled his sword, and was on the point of striking, I raised my head with a sweep to the side, as if I had been the bull; and as I swung, so the brave bull swung too. And then—then all the ring swam round with me, and yet I had heard the shouting and seen the spectators spring to their feet.

"I was in the street close to the Alvaredas'. The mother met me at the door; she was crying and the tears were running down her fat, greasy cheeks. She told me Clemencia had fainted and had been carried home, and Juan was dead—ripped open—and his mother distracted, and it was a pity, for he was so handsome and kind and good-natured, and her best dress was ruined. and *los toros* shouldn't be allowed and— as I brushed past her in disgust—that Clemencia was in her room crying.

"I went upstairs and entered the room. There she sat with her elbows on the table and her hair all round her face and down her back, and her fixed eyes stared at me. As I closed the door and folded my arms and looked at her, she rose, and her stare grew wild with surprise and horror, and then, almost without moving her lips, she said:

" 'Holy Virgin! You did it! I see it in your face!'

"And my heart jumped against my arms for joy, and I said in the same slow whisper, imitating her:

" 'Yes; I did it.'

"As I spoke she sprang forward with hate in her face, and poured out a stream of loathing and contempt on me. She vomited abuse as from her very soul: I was low and base and cowardly; I was—God knows what all. And he was handsome and kind, with a face like a king. . . . And I had thought she could love me, me, the ugly, little, lame cur, while he was there. And she laughed. She'd never have let my lips touch her if it hadn't been that her mother liked me and to please him. And now I had killed him, the best friend I had. Oh, it was horrible! Then she struck her head with her fists and asked how God, God, God could allow me to kill a man whose finger was worth a thousand lives such as mine!

"Then I laughed and said:

" 'You mistake. You killed him. You made him an *espada*— you!'

"As I spoke her eyes grew fixed and her mouth opened, and she seemed to struggle to speak, but she only groaned—and fell face forwards on the floor.

"I turned and left the room as her mother entered it." After a long pause Montes went on:

"I heard afterwards that she died next morning in premature child-birth. I left Madrid that night and came here, where I have lived ever since, if this can be called living. . . . Yet at times now fairly content, save for one thing—Remorse? Yes!"—And the old man rose to his feet, while his great eyes blazing with passion held me—"Remorse! That I let the bull kill him. I should have torn his throat out with my own hands."

W. E. HENLEY

O, Time and Change

O, Time and Change, they range and range
    From sunshine round to thunder!
They gleam and go as the great winds blow
    And the best of our dreams drive under:
For Time and Change estrange, estrange—
    And now, they have looked and seen us.
O, we that were dear we are all too near
    With the thick of the world between us.

O, Death and Time, they chime and chime
Like bells at sunset falling!
They end the song, they right the wrong,
They set the old echoes calling:
For Death and Time bring out the prime
Of God's own chosen weather,
And we lie in the peace of the Great Release
As once in the grass together.

Ballade of Antique Dances

BEFORE the town had lost its wits,
And scared the bravery from the beaux,
When money-grubs were merely cits,
And verse was crisp and clear as prose,
Ere Chloe and Strephon came to blows
For votes, degrees, and cigarettes,
The world rejoiced to point its toes
In Gigues, Gavottes, and Minuets.

The solemn fiddlers touch their kits;
The tinkling clavichord o'erflows
With contrapuntal quirks and hits;
And, with all measure and repose,
Through figures grave as royal shows,
With noble airs and pirouettes,
They move to rhythms Handel knows,
In Gigues, Gavottes, and Minuets.

O Fans and Swords, O Sacques and Mits,
That was the better part you chose
You knew not how those gamesome chits
Waltz, Polka and Schottische arose,
Nor how quadrille—a kind of doze
In time and tune—the dance besets;
You aired your fashion to the close
In Gigues, Gavottes, and Minuets.

ENVOY

Muse of the many-twinkling hose,
Terpsichore, O teach your pets
The charm that shines, the grace that glows
In Gigues, Gavottes, and Minuets.

The Ways of Death

THE WAYS of Death are soothing and serene,
And all the words of Death are grave and sweet.
From camp and church, the fireside and the street,
She beckons forth, and strife and song have been.

A summer night descending, cool and green
And dark, on daytime's dust and stress and heat,
The ways of Death are soothing and serene,
And all the words of Death are grave and sweet.

O glad and sorrowful, with triumphant mien
And radiant faces look upon and greet
This last of all your lovers, and to meet
Her kiss, the Comforter's, your spirit lean . . .
The ways of Death are soothing and serene.

HERBERT P. HORNE[1]

A Question and an Answer

THE QUESTION

WHAT IS Love? Is Love in this,
That flies between us, in a kiss?
Nay, what is Love? Is Love the zest,
That wakes, when I unloose my breast?
But what is Love? Say now: who knows,
Or where he lurks, or how he shows?

[1] He was not only a poet, but a practising architect as well, and the author of a monumental work on Botticelli. He was also an expert in book production, and designed founts of type for printing. The Lion colophon of the Chiswick Press at the end of this volume is his work.

THE ANSWER

Dearest, Truth is stern, I fear:
Love, as yet, can scarce be here.

Love is poor; nay, Love is sorry;
    Tears, not kisses, chiefly stay him:
His sad weeds best tell his story;
    Vain delights befool, bewray him.

Truth, alas, is hard to bear:
Know, as yet, Love is not here.

But, when the evil days are come,
    If those same lips, which kiss you now,
Still make your tearful eyes their home,
    And chide the sorrow from your brow;

Then say to your own heart, my Dear:
Abide, poor heart, for Love is here.

Love is a light, in darkened ways;
    Love is a path, in pathless lands;
Love is a fire, in winter days;
    A staff in chill, unsteady hands.

Speak to your heart, my own, my Dear;
Say: this is Love, and Love is here.

Et Sunt Commercia Coeli

I DID NOT raise my eyes to hers,
    Although I knew she passed me near:
I said, "Her shadow round me stirs;
    It is enough, that she is here,
And that, for once, my way is hers."

I did not look upon her face,
    I knew with whom her heart confers;
For more, that moment had no place:
    I did not raise my eyes to hers,
    I did not look upon her face.

Paradise Walk

SHE IS living in Paradise Walk,
With the dirt and the noise of the street;
And heaven flies up, if she talk,
With Paradise down at her feet.

She laughs through a summer of curls;
She moves in a garden of grace:
Her glance is a treasure of pearls,
How saved from the deeps of her face!

And the magical reach of her thigh
Is the measure, with which God began
To build up the peace of the sky,
And fashion the pleasures of man.

With Paradise down at her feet,
While heaven flies up if she talk;
With the dirt and the noise of the street,
She is living in Paradise Walk.

A. E. HOUSMAN

Four Poems from "A Shropshire Lad"[1]

I

IN summer time on Bredon
    The bells they sound so clear;
Round both the shires they ring them
    In steeples far and near,
    A happy noise to hear.

[1] First published in 1895, twenty-seven years were to elapse before its
successor, "Last Poems", appeared.

Here of a Sunday morning
  My love and I would lie,
And see the coloured counties,
  And hear the larks so high
  About us in the sky.

The bells would ring to call her
  In valleys miles away:
"Come all to church, good people;
  Good people, come and pray."
  But here my love would stay.

And I would turn and answer
  Among the springing thyme,
"Oh, peal upon our wedding,
  And we will hear the chime,
  And come to church in time."

But when the snows at Christmas
  On Bredon top were strown,
My love rose up so early
  And stole out unbeknown
  And went to church alone.

They tolled the one bell only,
  Groom there was none to see,
The mourners followed after,
  And so to church went she,
  And would not wait for me.

The bells they sound on Bredon,
  And still the steeples hum.
"Come all to church, good people,"—
  Oh, noisy bells, be dumb;
  I hear you, I will come.

2

THIS time of year a twelvemonth past,
  When Fred and I would meet,
We needs must jangle, till at last
  We fought and I was beat.

So then the summer fields about,
   Till rainy days began,
Rose Harland on her Sundays out
   Walked with the better man.

The better man she walks with still,
   Though now 'tis not with Fred:
A lad that lives and has his will
   Is worth a dozen dead.

Fred keeps the house all kinds of weather,
   And clay's the house he keeps;
When Rose and I walk out together
   Stock-still lies Fred and sleeps.

3

Along the field as we came by
A year ago, my love and I,
The aspen over stile and stone
Was talking to itself alone.
"Oh who are these that kiss and pass?
A country lover and his lass;
Two lovers looking to be wed;
And time shall put them both to bed,
But she shall lie with earth above,
And he beside another love."

And sure enough beneath the tree
There walks another love with me,
And overhead the aspen heaves
Its rainy-sounding silver leaves;
And I spell nothing in their stir,
But now perhaps they speak to her,
And plain for her to understand
They talk about a time at hand
When I shall sleep with clover clad,
And she beside another lad.

4

"Is my team ploughing,
   That I was used to drive
And hear the harness jingle
   When I was man alive?"

Ay, the horses trample,
   The harness jingles now;
No change though you lie under
   The land you used to plough.

"Is football playing
   Along the river shore,
With lads to chase the leather,
   Now I stand up no more?"

Ay, the ball is flying,
   The lads play heart and soul;
The goal stands up, the keeper
   Stands up to keep the goal.

"Is my girl happy,
   That I thought hard to leave,
And has she tired of weeping
   As she lies down at eve?"

Ay, she lies down lightly,
   She lies not down to weep:
Your girl is well contented.
   Be still, my lad, and sleep.

"Is my friend hearty,
   Now I am thin and pine,
And has he found to sleep in
   A better bed than mine?"

Yes, lad, I lie easy,
   I lie as lads would choose;
I cheer a dead man's sweetheart,
   Never ask me whose.

LIONEL JOHNSON

The Church of a Dream

SADLY the dead leaves rustle in the whistling wind,
Around the weather-worn, gray church, low down the vale:
The Saints in golden vesture shake before the gale;
The glorious windows shake, where still they dwell enshrined;
Old Saints by long dead, shrivelled hands, long since designed:
There still, although the world autumnal be, and pale,
Still in their golden vesture the old saints prevail;
Alone with Christ, desolate else, left by mankind.

Only one ancient Priest offers the Sacrifice,
Murmuring holy Latin immemorial:
Swaying with tremulous hands the old censer full of spice,
In gray, sweet incense clouds; blue, sweet clouds mystical:
To him, in place of men, for he is old, suffice
Melancholy remembrances and vesperal.

By the Statue of King Charles at Charing Cross

SOMBRE and rich, the skies;
Great glooms, and starry plains.
Gently the night wind sighs;
Else a vast silence reigns.

The splendid silence clings
Around me: and around
The saddest of all kings
Crowned and again discrowned.

Comely and calm, he rides
Hard by his own Whitehall:
Only the night wind glides:
No crowds, nor rebels, brawl.

Gone, too, his Court: and yet,
The stars his courtiers are:
Stars in their stations set;
And every wandering star.

Alone he rides, alone,
The fair and fatal king:
Dark night is all his own,
That strange and solemn thing.

Which are more full of fate:
The stars; or those sad eyes?
Which are more still and great:
Those brows; or the dark skies?

Although his whole heart yearn
In passionate tragedy:
Never was face so stern
With sweet austerity.

Vanquished in life, his death
By beauty made amends:
The passing of his breath
Won his defeated ends.

Brief life, and hapless? Nay:
Through death, life grew sublime
Speak after sentence? Yea:
And to the end of time.

Armoured he rides, his head
Bare to the stars of doom:
He triumphs now, the dead,
Beholding London's gloom.

Our wearier spirit faints,
Vexed in the world's employ:
His soul was of the saints;
And art to him was joy.

King, tried in fires of woe!
Men hunger for thy grace:
And through the night I go,
Loving thy mournful face.

Yet, when the city sleeps;
When all the cries are still:
The stars and heavenly deeps
Work out a perfect will.

Nihilism

AMONG immortal things not made with hands:
Among immortal things dead hands have made:
Under the Heavens, upon the Earth, there stands
Man's life, my life: of life I am afraid.

Where silent things, and unimpassioned things,
Where things of naught, and things decaying are:
I shall be calm soon, with the calm death brings.
The skies are gray there, without any star.

Only the rest, the rest! Only the gloom,
Soft and long gloom! The pausing from all thought.
My life I cannot taste: the eternal tomb
Brings me the peace which life has never brought.

For all the things I do, and do not well:
All the forced drawings of a mortal breath:
Are as the hollow music of a bell,
That times the slow approach of perfect death.

RICHARD LE GALLIENNE

A Ballad of London

AH, LONDON! London! our delight,
Great flower that opens but at night,
Great City of the midnight sun,
Whose day begins when day is done.

Q

Lamp after lamp against the sky
Opens a sudden beaming eye,
Leaping alight on either hand,
The iron lilies of the Strand.

Like dragonflies, the hansoms hover,
With jewelled eyes, to catch the lover,
The streets are full of lights and loves,
Soft gowns, and flutter of soiled doves.

Upon thy petals butterflies,
But at thy root, some say, there lies
A world of weeping trodden things,
Poor worms that have not eyes or wings.

From out corruption of their woe
Springs this bright flower that charms us so,
Men die and rot deep out of sight
To keep this jungle-flower bright.

Paris and London, World-Flowers twain
Wherewith the World-Tree blooms again,
Since Time hath gathered Babylon
And withered Rome still withers on.

Sidon and Tyre were such as ye,
How bright they shone upon the tree!
But Time hath gathered, both are gone,
And no man sails to Babylon.

Ah, London! London! our delight,
For thee, too, the eternal night,
And Circe Paris hath no charm
To stay Time's unrelenting arm.

An Ode to Spring

Is it the Spring?
    Or are the birds all wrong
That play on flute and viol,
    A thousand strong.

In minstrel galleries
     Of the long deep wood,
Epiphanies
     Of bloom and bud.

Grave minstrels those,
     Of deep responsive chant;
But see how yonder goes,
     Dew-drunk, with giddy slant,
Yon Shelley-lark,
     And hark !
Him on the giddy brink
     Of pearly heaven
His fairy anvil clink.

Or watch, in fancy,
     How the brimming note
Falls, like a string of pearls,
     From out his heavenly throat;
Or like a fountain
     In Hesperides,
Raining its silver rain,
     In gleam and chime,
On backs of ivory girls—
     Twice happy rhyme!
Ah, none of these
     May make it plain,
No image we may seek
     Shall match the magic of his gurgling beak.

And many a silly thing
     That hops and cheeps,
And perks his tiny tail,
     And sideway peeps,
And flitters little wing,
     Seems in his consequential way
To tell of Spring.

The river warbles soft and runs
  With fuller curve and sleeker line,
Though on the winter-blackened hedge
  Twigs of unbudding iron shine,
And trampled still the river sedge.

And O the Sun!
  I have no friend so generous as this Sun
That comes to meet me with his big warm hands.
  And O the Sky!
There is no maid, how true,
  Is half so chaste
As the pure kiss of greening willow wands
  Against the intense pale blue
Of this sweet boundless overarching waste.

And see!—dear Heaven, but it is the Spring!
  See yonder, yonder, by the river there,
Long glittering pearly fingers flash
  Upon the warm bright air:
Why, 'tis the heavenly palm,
  The Christian tree,
Whose budding is a psalm
  Of natural piety:
Soft silver notches up the smooth green stem—
  Ah, Spring must follow them,
It is the Spring!

O Spirit of Spring,
  Whose strange instinctive art
Makes the birds sing,
  And brings the buds again;
O in my heart
  Take up thy heavenly reign,
And from its deeps
  Draw out the hidden flower,
And where it sleeps,
  Throughout the winter long,
O sweet mysterious power
  Awake the slothful song!

What of the Darkness?

What of the darkness? Is it very fair?
Are there great calms and find ye silence there?
Like soft-shut lilies all your faces glow
With some strange peace our faces never know,
With some great faith our faces never dare.
Dwells it in Darkness? Do you find it there?

Is it a Bosom where tired heads may lie?
Is it a Mouth to kiss our weeping dry?
Is it a Hand to still the pulse's leap?
Is it a Voice that holds the runes of sleep?
Day shows us not such comfort anywhere.
Dwells it in Darkness? Do you find it there?

Out of the Day's deceiving light we call,
Day that shows man so great and God so small,
That hides the stars and magnifies the grass;
O is the Darkness too a lying glass,
Or, undistracted, do you find truth there?
What of the Darkness? Is it very fair?

EUGENE LEE-HAMILTON
Meeting the Ghosts

When years have passed, is't wise to meet again?
   Body and Mind have changed; and is it wise
   To take old Time, the Alterer, by surprise,
And see how he has worked in human grain?
We think that what once was, must still remain;
   Ourself a ghost, we bid a ghost arise;
   Two spectres look into each other's eyes,
And break the image that their hearts contain.

Mix not the Past and Present: let the Past
   Remain in peace within its jewelled shrine,
And drag it not into the hum and glare;
Mix not two faces in the thoughts that last;
   The one thou knewest, fair in every line,
And one unknown, which may be far from fair.

ARTHUR MACHEN

The Three Impostors

PROLOGUE

"AND MR. JOSEPH WALTERS is going to stay the night?" said the smooth, clean-shaven man to his companion, an individual not of the most charming appearance, who had chosen to make his ginger-coloured moustache merge into a pair of short chin-whiskers.

The two stood at the hall door, grinning evilly at each other; and presently a girl ran quickly down the stairs and joined them. She was quite young, with a quaint and piquant rather than a beautiful face, and her eyes were of a shining hazel. She held a neat paper parcel in one hand, and laughed with her friends.

"Leave the door open," said the smooth man to the other, as they were going out. "Yes, by ——," he went on with an ugly oath, "we'll leave the front door on the jar. He may like to see company, you know."

The other man looked doubtfully about him.

"Is it quite prudent, do you think, Davies?" he said, pausing with his hand on the mouldering knocker. "I don't think Lipsius would like it. What do you say, Helen?"

"I agree with Davies. Davies is an artist, and you are commonplace, Richmond, and a bit of a coward. Let the door stand open, of course. But what a pity Lipsius had to go away! He would have enjoyed himself."

"Yes," replied the smooth Mr. Davies, "that summons to the west was very hard on the doctor."

The three passed out, leaving the hall door, cracked and riven with frost and wet, half open, and they stood silent for a moment under the ruinous shelter of the porch.

"Well," said the girl, "it is done at last. We shall hurry no more on the track of the young man with spectacles."

"We owe a great deal to you," said Mr. Davies politely; "the doctor said so before he left. But have we not all three some farewells to

make? I, for my part, propose to say good-bye here, before this picturesque but mouldy residence, to my friend, Mr. Burton, dealer in the
antique and curious," and the man lifted his hat with an exaggerated
bow.

"And I," said Richmond, "bid adieu to Mr. Wilkins, the private
secretary, whose company has, I confess, become a little tedious."

"Farewell to Miss Lally, and to Miss Leicester also," said the girl,
making as she spoke a delicious curtsy. "Farewell to all occult adventure; the farce is played."

Mr. Davies and the lady seemed full of grim enjoyment, but
Richmond tugged at his whiskers nervously.

"I feel a bit shaken up," he said. "I've seen rougher things in the
States, but that crying noise he made gave me a sickish feeling."

The three friends moved away from the door, and began to walk
slowly up and down what had been a gravel path, but now lay green
and pulpy with damp mosses. It was a fine autumn evening, and a
faint sunlight shone on the yellow walls of the old deserted house, and
showed the patches of gangrenous decay, the black drift of rain from
the broken pipes, the scabrous blots where the bare bricks were exposed,
the green weeping of a gaunt laburnum that stood beside the porch,
and ragged marks near the ground where the reeking clay was gaining
on the worn foundations. It was a queer, rambling old place, the centre
perhaps two hundred years old, with dormer windows sloping from
the tiled roof, and on each side there were Georgian wings; bow
windows had been carried up to the first floor, and two dome-like
cupolas that had once been painted a bright green were now grey and
neutral. Broken urns lay upon the path, and a heavy mist seemed to
rise from the unctuous clay; the neglected shrubberies, grown all
tangled and unshapen, smelt dank and evil, and there was an atmosphere
all about the deserted mansion that proposed thoughts of an open grave.
The three friends looked dismally at the rough grasses and the nettles
that grew thick over lawn and flower-beds; and at the sad water-pool
in the midst of the weeds. There, above green and oily scum, instead of
lilies, stood a rusting Triton on the rocks, sounding a dirge through
a shattered horn; and beyond, beyond the sunk fence and the far
meadows the sun slid down and shone red through the bars of the elm
trees.

Richmond shivered and stamped his foot.

"We had better be going soon," he said; "there is nothing else to be done here."

"No," said Davies; "it is finished at last. I thought for some time we should never get hold of the gentleman with the spectacles. He was a clever fellow, but, Lord! he broke up badly at last. I can tell you, he looked white at me when I touched him on the arm in the bar. But where could he have hidden the thing? We can all swear it was not on him."

The girl laughed, and they turned away, when Richmond gave a violent start.

"Ah!" he cried, turning to the girl, "what have you got there? Look, Davies, look; it's all oozing and dripping."

The young woman glanced down at the little parcel she was carrying, and partially unfolded the paper.

"Yes, look, both of you," she said; "it's my own idea. Don't you think it will do nicely for the doctor's museum? It comes from the right hand, the hand that took the Gold Tiberius."

Mr. Davies nodded with a good deal of approbation, and Richmond lifted his ugly high-crowned bowler, and wiped his forehead with a dingy handkerchief.

"I'm going," he said; "you two can stay if you like."

The three went round by the stable-path, past the withered wilderness of the old kitchen-garden, and struck off by a hedge at the back, making for a particular point in the road.

About five minutes later two gentlemen, whom idleness had led to explore these forgotten outskirts of London, came sauntering up the shadowy carriage-drive. They had spied the deserted house from the road, and as they observed all the heavy desolation of the place, they began to moralize in the great style, with considerable debts to Jeremy Taylor.

"Look, Dyson," said the one, as they drew nearer; "look at those upper windows; the sun is setting, and, though the panes are dusty, yet—

'The grimy sash an oriel burns.' "

"Phillipps," replied the elder and (it must be said) the more pompous of the two, "I yield to fantasy; I cannot withstand the influence of the grotesque. Here, where all is falling into dimness and dissolution, and we walk in cedarn gloom, and the very air of heaven goes mouldering to the lungs, I cannot remain commonplace. I look at that deep glow on the panes, and the house lies all enchanted; that very room, I tell you, is within all blood and fire."

ADVENTURE OF THE GOLD TIBERIUS

THE acquaintance between Mr. Dyson and Mr. Charles Phillipps arose from one of those myriad chances which are every day doing their work in the streets of London. Mr. Dyson was a man of letters, and an unhappy instance of talents misapplied. With gifts that might have placed him in the flower of his youth among the most favoured of Bentley's favourite novelists, he had chosen to be perverse; he was, it is true, familiar with scholastic logic, but he knew nothing of the logic of life, and he flattered himself with the title of artist, when he was in fact but an idle and curious spectator of other men's endeavours. Amongst many delusions, he cherished one most fondly, that he was a strenuous worker; and it was with a gesture of supreme weariness that he would enter his favourite resort, a small tobacco-shop in Great Queen Street, and proclaim to any one who cared to listen that he had seen the rising and setting of two successive suns. The proprietor of the shop, a middle-aged man of singular civility, tolerated Dyson partly out of good nature, and partly because he was a regular customer. He was allowed to sit on an empty cask, and to express his sentiments on literary and artistic matters till he was tired, or the time for closing came; and if no fresh customers were attracted, it is believed that none was turned away by his eloquence. Dyson was addicted to wild experiments in tobacco; he never wearied of trying new combinations; and one evening he had just entered the shop, and given utterance to his last preposterous formula, when a young fellow of about his own age, who had come in a moment later, asked the shopman to duplicate the order on his account, smiling politely, as he spoke, to Mr. Dyson's address. Dyson felt profoundly flattered, and after a few phrases the two entered into conversation, and in an hour's time the tobacconist saw the new friends sitting side by side on a couple of casks, deep in talk.

"My dear sir," said Dyson, "I will give you the task of the literary man in a phrase. He has got to do simply this—to invent a wonderful story, and to tell it in a wonderful manner."

"I will grant you that," said Mr. Phillips, "but you will allow me to insist that in the hands of the true artist in words all stories are marvellous and every circumstance has its peculiar wonder. The matter is of little consequence; the manner is everything. Indeed, the highest skill is shown in taking matter apparently commonplace and transmuting it by the high alchemy of style into the pure gold of art."

"That is indeed a proof of great skill, but it is great skill exerted foolishly, or at least unadvisedly. It is as if a great violinist were to show us what marvellous harmonies he could draw from a child's banjo."

"No, no, you are really wrong. I see you take a radically mistaken view of life. But we must thresh this out. Come to my rooms; I live not far from here."

It was thus that Mr. Dyson became the associate of Mr. Charles Phillipps, who lived in a quiet square not far from Holborn. Thenceforth they haunted each other's rooms at intervals, sometimes regular, and occasionally the reverse, and made appointments to meet at the shop in Queen Street, where their talk robbed the tobacconist's profit of half its charm. There was a constant jarring of literary formulas, Dyson exalting the claims of the pure imagination; while Phillipps, who was a student of physical science and something of an ethnologist, insisted that all literature ought to have a scientific basis. By the mistaken benevolence of deceased relatives both young men were placed out of reach of hunger, and so, meditating high achievements, idled their time pleasantly away, and revelled in the careless joys of a Bohemianism devoid of the sharp seasoning of adversity. One night in June Mr. Phillipps was sitting in his room in the calm retirement of Red Lion Square. He had opened the window, and was smoking placidly, while he watched the movement of life below. The sky was clear, and the afterglow of sunset had lingered long about it. The flushing twilight of a summer evening vied with the gas-lamps in the square, and fashioned a chiaroscuro that had in it something unearthly; and the children, racing to and fro upon the pavement, the lounging idlers by the public-house, and the casual passers-by rather flickered and hovered in the plat of lights than stood out substantial things. By degrees in the houses opposite one window after another leapt out a square of light; now and again a figure would shape itself against a blind and vanish, and to all this semi-theatrical magic the runs and flourishes of brave Italian opera played a little distance off on a piano-organ seemed an appropriate accompaniment, while the deep-muttered bass of the traffic of Holborn never ceased. Phillipps enjoyed the scene and its effects; the light in the sky faded and turned to darkness, and the square gradually grew silent, and still he sat dreaming at the window, till the sharp peal of the house-bell roused him, and looking at his watch, he found that it was past ten o'clock. There was a knock at the door, and his friend Mr. Dyson entered, and, according to his custom, sat down in an arm-chair and began to smoke in silence.

"You know, Phillipps," he said at length, "that I have always battled for the marvellous. I remember your maintaining in that chair that one has no business to make use of the wonderful, the improbable, the odd coincidence in literature, and you took the ground that it was wrong to do so, because as a matter of fact the wonderful and the im- probable don't happen, and men's lives are not really shaped by odd coincidence. Now, mind you, if that were so, I would not grant your conclusion, because I think the "criticism-of-life" theory is all non- sense; but I deny your premiss. A most singular thing has happened to me to-night."

"Really, Dyson, I am very glad to hear it. Of course, I oppose your argument, whatever it may be; but if you would be good enough to tell me of your adventure, I should be delighted."

"Well, it came about like this. I have had a very hard day's work; indeed I have scarcely moved from my old bureau since seven o'clock last night. I wanted to work out that idea we discussed last Tuesday, you know, the notion of the fetish-worshipper?"

"Yes, I remember. Have you been able to do anything with it?"

"Yes; it came out better than I expected; but there were great difficulties, the usual agony between the conception and the execution. Anyhow, I got it done about seven o'clock to-night, and I thought I should like a little of the fresh air. I went out and wandered rather aimlessly about the streets; my head was full of my tale, and I didn't much notice where I was going. I got into those quiet places to the north of Oxford Street as you go west, the genteel residential neigh- bourhood of stucco and prosperity. I turned east again without knowing it, and it was quite dark when I passed along a sombre little by-street, ill-lighted and empty. I did not know at the time in the least where I was, but I found out afterwards that it was not very far from Tottenham

Court Road. I strolled idly along, enjoying the stillness; on one side there seemed to be the back premises of some great shop; tier after tier of dusty windows lifted up into the night, with gibbet-like contrivances for raising heavy goods, and below large doors, fast closed and bolted, all dark and desolate. Then there came a huge pantechnicon warehouse; and over the way a grim blank wall, as forbidding as the wall of a gaol, and then the headquarters of some volunteer regiment, and afterwards a passage leading to a court where waggons were standing to be hired; it was, one might almost say, a street devoid of inhabitants, and scarce a window showed the glimmer of a light. I was wondering at the strange peace and dimness there, where it must be close to some roaring main artery of London life, when suddenly I heard the noise of dashing feet tearing along the pavement at full speed, and from a narrow passage, a mews or something of that kind, a man was discharged as from a catapult under my very nose, and rushed past me, flinging something from him as he ran. He was gone, and down another street in an instant, almost before I knew what had happened; but I didn't much bother about him, I was watching something else. I told you he had thrown something away; well, I watched what seemed a line of flame flash through the air and fly quivering over the pavement, and in spite of myself I could not help tearing after it. The impetus lessened, and I saw something like a bright halfpenny roll slower and slower, and then deflect towards the gutter, hover for a moment on the edge, and dance down into a drain. I believe I cried out in positive despair, though I hadn't the least notion what I was hunting; and then, to my joy, I saw that, instead of dropping into a sewer, it had fallen flat across two bars. I stooped down and picked it up and whipped it into my pocket, and I was just about to walk on when I heard again that sound of dashing footsteps. I don't know why I did it, but as a matter of fact I dived down into the mews, or whatever it was, and stood as much in the shadow as possible. A man went by with a rush a few paces from where I was standing, and I felt uncommonly pleased that I was in hiding. I couldn't make out much feature, but I saw his eyes gleaming and his teeth showing, and he had an ugly-looking knife in one hand, and I thought things would be very unpleasant for gentleman number one if the second robber, or robbed, or what you like, caught him up. I can tell you, Phillipps, a fox-hunt is exciting enough, when the horn blows clear on a winter morning, and the hounds give tongue, and the red-coats charge away, but it's nothing to a man-hunt, and that's what I had a slight glimpse of to-night. There was murder in the fellow's eyes as he went by, and I don't think there was much more than fifty seconds between the two. I only hope it was enough."

Dyson leant back in his arm-chair, relit his pipe, and puffed thoughtfully. Phillipps began to walk up and down the room, musing over the story of violent death fleeting in chase along the pavement, the knife shining in the lamplight, the fury of the pursuer, and the terror of the pursued.

"Well," he said at last, "and what was it, after all, that you rescued from the gutter?"

Dyson jumped up, evidently quite startled. "I really haven't a notion. I didn't think of looking. But we shall see."

He fumbled in his waistcoat pocket, drew out a small and shining object, and laid it on the table. It glowed there beneath the lamp with the radiant glory of rare old gold; and the image and the letters stood out in high relief, clear and sharp, as if it had but left the mint a month before. The two men bent over it, and Phillipps took it up and examined it closely.

"Imp. Tiberius Cæsar Augustus," he read the legend, and then looking at the reverse of the coin, he stared in amazement, and at last turned to Dyson with a look of exultation.

"Do you know what you have found?" he said.

"Apparently a gold coin of some antiquity," said Dyson coolly.

"Quite so, a gold Tiberius. No, that is wrong. You have found *the* gold Tiberius. Look at the reverse."

Dyson looked and saw the coin was stamped with the figure of a faun standing amidst reeds and flowing water. The features, minute as they were, stood out in delicate outline; it was a face lovely and yet terrible, and Dyson thought of the well-known passage of the lad's playmate, gradually growing with his growth and increasing with his stature, till the air was filled with the rank fume of the goat.

"Yes," he said, "it is a curious coin. Do you know it?"

"I know about it. It is one of the comparatively few historical objects in existence; it is all storied like those jewels we have read of. A whole cycle of legend has gathered round the thing; the tale goes that it formed part of an issue struck by Tiberius to commemorate an infamous excess. You see the legend on the reverse: "Victoria." It is said that by an extraordinary accident the whole issue was thrown into the melting-pot, and that only this one coin escaped. It glints through history and legend, appearing and disappearing, with intervals of a hundred years in time, and continents in place. It was "discovered" by an Italian humanist, and lost and rediscovered. It had not been heard of since 1727, when Sir Joshua Byrde, a Turkey merchant, brought it home from Aleppo, and vanished with it a month after he had shown it to the virtuosi, no man knew or knows where. And here it is!"

"Put it into your pocket, Dyson," he said, after a pause. "I would not let anyone have a glimpse of the thing if I were you. I would not talk about it. Did either of the men you saw see you?"

"Well, I think not. I don't think the first man, the man who was vomited out of the dark passage, saw anything at all; and I am sure that the second could not have seen me."

"And you didn't really see them. You couldn't recognize either the one or the other if you met him in the street to-morrow?"

"No, I don't think I could. The street, as I said, was dimly lighted, and they ran like madmen."

The two men sat silent for some time, each weaving his own fancies of the story; but lust of the marvellous was slowly overpowering Dyson's more sober thoughts.

"It is all more strange than I fancied," he said at last. "It was queer enough what I saw; a man is sauntering along a quiet, sober, everyday London street, a street of grey houses and blank walls, and there, for a moment, a veil seems drawn aside, and the very fume of the pit steams up through the flagstones, the ground glows, red-hot, beneath his feet, and he seems to hear the hiss of the infernal caldron. A man flying in mad terror for his life, and furious hate pressing hot on his steps with knife drawn ready; here, indeed, is horror; but what is all that to what you have told me? I tell you, Phillipps, I see the plot thicken; our steps will henceforth be dogged with mystery, and the most ordinary incidents will teem with significance. You may stand out against it, and shut your eyes, but they will be forced open; mark my words, you will have to yield to the inevitable. A clue, tangled if you like, has been placed by chance in our hands; it will be our business to follow it up. As for the guilty person or persons in this strange case, they will be unable to escape us, our nets will be spread far and wide over this great city, and suddenly, in the streets and places of public resort, we shall in some way or other be made aware that we are in touch with the unknown criminal. Indeed I almost fancy I see him slowly approaching this quiet square of yours; he is loitering at street corners, wandering, apparently without aim, down far-reaching thoroughfares, but all the while coming nearer and nearer, drawn by an irresistible magnetism, as ships were drawn to the Loadstone Rock in the Eastern tale."

"I certainly think," replied Phillipps, "that if you pull out that coin and flourish it under people's noses as you are doing at the present moment, you will very probably find yourself in touch with the criminal, or a criminal. You will undoubtedly be robbed with violence. Otherwise, I see no reason why either of us should be troubled. No one saw you secure the coin, and no one knows you have it. I, for my part, shall sleep peacefully, and go about my business with a sense of security and a firm dependence on the natural order of things. The events of the evening, the adventure in the street, have been odd, I grant you, but I resolutely decline to have any more to do with the matter, and, if necessary, I shall consult the police. I will not be enslaved by a gold Tiberius, even though it swims into my ken in a manner which is somewhat melodramatic."

"And I, for my part," said Dyson, "go forth like a knight-errant in search of adventure. Not that I shall need to seek; rather adventure will seek me; I shall be like a spider in the midst of his web, responsive to every movement, and ever on the alert."

Shortly afterwards Dyson took his leave, and Mr. Phillipps spent the rest of the night in examining some flint arrow-heads which he had purchased. He had every reason to believe that they were the work of a modern and not a palæolithic man; still he was far from gratified when a close scrutiny showed him that his suspicions were well founded. In his anger at the turpitude which would impose on an ethnologist, he completely forgot Dyson and the gold Tiberius; and when he went to bed at first sunlight, the whole tale had faded utterly from his thoughts.

THE ENCOUNTER OF THE PAVEMENT

MR. DYSON, walking leisurely along Oxford Street, and staring with bland inquiry at whatever caught his attention, enjoyed in all its rare flavours the sensation that he was really very hard at work. His observation of mankind, the traffic, and the shop windows tickled his faculties with an exquisite bouquet; he looked serious, as one looks on whom charges of weight and moment are laid; and he was attentive in his glances to right and left, for fear lest he should miss some circumstance of more acute significance. He had narrowly escaped being run over at a crossing by a charging van, for he hated to hurry his steps, and indeed the afternoon was warm; and he had just halted by a place of popular refreshment, when the astounding gestures of a well-dressed individual on the opposite pavement held him enchanted and gasping like a fish. A treble line of hansoms, carriages, vans, cabs, and omnibuses was tearing east and west, and not the most daring adventurer of the crossings would have cared to try his fortune; but the person who had attracted Dyson's attention seemed to rage on the very edge of the pavement, now and then darting forward at the hazard of instant death, and at each repulse absolutely dancing with excitement, to the rich amusement of the passers-by. At last a gap that would have tried the courage of a street-boy appeared between the serried lines of vehicles, and the man rushed across in a frenzy, and escaping by a hair's-breadth, pounced upon Dyson as a tiger pounces on her prey. "I saw you looking about you," he said, sputtering out his words in his intense eagerness; "would you mind telling me this! Was the man who came out of the Aerated Bread Shop and jumped into the hansom three minutes ago a youngish-looking man with dark whiskers and spectacles? Can't you speak, man? For heaven's sake, can't you speak? Answer me; it's a matter of life and death."

The words bubbled and boiled out of the man's mouth in the fury of his emotion, his face went from red to white, and the beads of sweat stood out on his forehead; he stamped his feet as he spoke, and tore with his hand at his coat, as if something swelled and choked him, stopping the passage of his breath.

"My dear sir," said Dyson, "I always like to be accurate. Your observation was perfectly correct. As you say, a youngish man—a man, I should say, of somewhat timid bearing—ran rapidly out of the shop here, and bounced into a hansom that must have been waiting for him, as it went eastwards at once. Your friend also wore spectacles, as you say. Perhaps you would like me to call a hansom for you to follow the gentleman?"

"No, thank you; it would be a waste of time." The man gulped down something which appeared to rise in his throat, and Dyson was alarmed to see him shaking with hysterical laughter; he clung hard to a lamp-post, and swayed and staggered like a ship in a heavy gale.

"How shall I face the doctor?" he murmured to himself. "It is too hard to fail at the last moment." Then he seemed to recollect himself; he stood straight again, and looked quietly at Dyson.

"I owe you an apology for my violence," he said at last. "Many men would not be so patient as you have been. Would you mind adding to your kindness by walking with me a little way? I feel a little sick; I think it's the sun."

Dyson nodded assent, and devoted himself to a quiet scrutiny of this strange personage as they moved on together. The man was dressed in quiet taste, and the most scrupulous observer could find nothing amiss with the fashion or make of his clothes; yet, from his hat to his boots, everything seemed inappropriate. His silk hat, Dyson thought, should have been a high bowler of odious pattern, worn with a baggy morning-coat, and an instinct told him that the fellow did not commonly carry a clean pocket-handkerchief. The face was not of the most agreeable pattern, and was in no way improved by a pair of bulbous chin-whiskers of a ginger hue, into which moustaches of like colour merged imperceptibly. Yet, in spite of these signals hung out by nature, Dyson felt that the individual beside him was something more than compact of vulgarity. He was struggling with himself, holding his feelings in check; but now and again passion would mount black to his face, and it was evidently by a supreme effort that he kept himself from raging like a madman. Dyson found something curious, and a little terrible, in the spectacle of an occult emotion thus striving for the mastery, and threatening to break out at every instant with violence; and they had gone some distance before the person whom he had met by so odd a hazard was able to speak quietly.

"You are really very good," he said. "I apologize again; my rudeness was really must unjustifiable. I feel my conduct demands an explanation, and I shall be happy to give it to you. Do you happen to know of any place near here where one could sit down? I should really be very glad."

"My dear sir," said Dyson solemnly, "the only café in London is close by. Pray do not consider yourself as bound to offer me any

R

explanation, but at the same time I should be most happy to listen to you. Let us turn down here."

They walked down a sober street and turned into what seemed a narrow passage past an iron-barred gate thrown back. The passage was paved with flagstones, and decorated with handsome shrubs in pots on either side, and the shadow of the high walls made a coolness which was very agreeable after the hot breath of the sunny street. Presently the passage opened out into a tiny square, a charming place, a morsel of France transplanted into the heart of London. High walls rose on either side, covered with glossy creepers, flower-beds beneath were gay with nasturtiums and marigolds and odorous mignonette, and in the centre of the square a fountain, hidden by greenery, sent a cool shower continually plashing into the basin beneath. Chairs and tables were disposed at convenient intervals, and at the other end of the court broad doors had been thrown back; beyond was a long, dark room, and the turmoil of traffic had become a distant murmur. Within the room one or two men were sitting at the tables, writing and sipping, but the courtyard was empty.

"You see, we shall be quiet," said Dyson. "Pray sit down here, Mr. ——?"

"Wilkins. My name is Henry Wilkins."

"Sit here, Mr. Wilkins. I think you will find that a comfortable seat. I suppose you have not been here before? This is the quiet time; the place will be like a hive at six o'clock, and the chairs and tables will overflow into that little alley there."

A waiter came in response to the bell; and after Dyson had politely inquired after the health of M. Annibault, the proprietor, he ordered a bottle of the wine of Champigny.

"The wine of Champigny," he observed to Mr. Wilkins, who was evidently a good deal composed by the influence of the place, "is a Tourainian wine of great merit. Ah, here it is; let me fill your glass. How do you find it?"

"Indeed," said Mr. Wilkins, "I should have pronounced it fine Burgundy. The bouquet is very exquisite. I am fortunate in lighting upon such a good Samaritan as yourself: I wonder you did not think me mad. But if you knew the terrors that assailed me, I am sure you would no longer be surprised at conduct which was certainly most unjustifiable."

He sipped his wine, and leant back in his chair, relishing the drip and trickle of the fountain, and the cool greenness that hedged in this little port of refuge.

"Yes," he said at last, "that is indeed an admirable wine. Thank you; you will allow me to offer you another bottle?"

The waiter was summoned, and descended through a trap-door in the floor of the dark apartment and brought up the wine. Mr. Wilkins lit a cigarette, and Dyson pulled out his pipe.

"Now," said Mr. Wilkins, "I promised to give you an explanation of my strange behaviour. It is rather a long story, but I see, sir, that you are no mere cold observer of the ebb and flow of life. You take, I think, a warm and an intelligent interest in the chances of your fellow-creatures, and I believe you will find what I have to tell not devoid of interest."

Mr. Dyson signified his assent to these propositions; and though he thought Mr. Wilkins's diction a little pompous, prepared to interest himself in his tale. The other, who had so raged with passion half an hour before, was now perfectly cool, and when he had smoked out his cigarette, he began in an even voice to relate

THE NOVEL OF THE DARK VALLEY

I am the son of a poor but learned clergyman in the west of England —but I am forgetting, these details are not of special interest. I will briefly state, then, that my father, who was, as I have said, a learned man, had never learnt the specious arts by which the great are flattered, and would never condescend to the despicable pursuit of self-advertisement. Though his fondness for ancient ceremonies and quaint customs, combined with a kindness of heart that was unequalled and a primitive and fervent piety, endeared him to his moorland parishioners, such were not the steps by which clergy then rose in the Church, and at sixty my father was still incumbent of the little benefice he had accepted in his thirtieth year. The income of the living was barely sufficient to support life in the decencies which are expected of the Anglican parson; and when my father died a few years ago, I, his only child, found myself thrown upon the world with a slender capital of less than a hundred pounds, and all the problem of existence before me. I felt that there was nothing for me to do in the country, and as usually happens in such cases, London drew me like a magnet. One day in August, in the early morning, while the dew still glittered on the turf, and on the high green banks of the lane, a neighbour drove me to the railway station, and I bade good-bye to the land of the broad moors and unearthly battlements of the wild tors. It was six o'clock as we neared London; the faint, sickly fume of the brickfields about Acton came in puffs through the open window, and a mist was rising from the ground. Presently the brief view of successive streets, prim and uniform, struck me with a sense of monotony; the hot air seemed to grow hotter; and when we had rolled beneath the dismal and squalid houses, whose dirty and neglected backyards border the line near Paddington, I felt as if I should be stifled in this fainting breath of London. I got a hansom and drove off, and every street increased my gloom; grey houses with blinds drawn down, whole thoroughfares almost desolate, and the foot-passengers who seemed to stagger wearily along rather than walk, all made me feel a sinking at heart. I put up for the night at a small hotel in a street leading from the Strand, where my father had stayed on his few brief visits to town; and when I went out after dinner, the real gaiety and bustle of the Strand and Fleet Street could cheer me but little, for in all this great city there was no single human being whom I could claim even as an acquaintance. I will not weary you with the history of the next year, for the adventures of a man who sinks are too trite to be worth recalling. My money did not last me long; I found that I must be neatly dressed, or no one to whom I applied would so much as listen to me; and I must live in a street of decent reputation if I wished to be treated with common civility. I applied for various posts, for which, as I now see, I was completely devoid of qualification; I tried to become a clerk without having the smallest notion of business habits; and I found, to my cost, that a general knowledge of literature and an execrable style of penmanship are far from being looked upon with favour in commercial circles. I had read one of the most charming of the works of a famous novelist of the present day, and I frequented the Fleet Street taverns in the hope of making literary friends, and so getting the introductions which I understood were indispensable in the career of letters. I was disappointed; I once or twice ventured to address gentlemen who were sitting in adjoining boxes, and I was answered, politely indeed, but in a manner that told me my advances were unusual. Pound by pound, my small resources melted; I could no longer think of appearances; I migrated to a shy quarter, and my meals became mere observances. I went out at one and returned to my room at two, but nothing but a mere milk-cake had occurred in the interval. In short, I became acquainted with misfortune; and as I sat amidst slush and ice on a seat in Hyde Park, munching a piece of bread, I realized the bitterness of poverty, and the feelings of a gentleman reduced to something far below the condition of a vagrant. In spite of all discouragement I did not desist in my efforts to earn a living. I consulted advertisement columns, I kept my eyes open for a chance, I looked in at the windows of stationers' shops, but all in vain. One evening I was sitting in a Free Library, and I saw an advertisement in one of the papers. It was something like this: "Wanted by a gentleman a person of literary taste and abilities as secretary and amanuensis. Must not object to travel." Of course I knew that such an advertisement would have answers by the hundred, and I thought my own chances of securing the post extremely small; however, I applied at the address given, and wrote to Mr. Smith, who was staying at a large hotel at the West End. I must confess that my heart gave a jump when I received a note a couple of days later, asking me to call at the Cosmopole at my earliest convenience. I do not know, sir, what your experiences of life may have been, and so I cannot tell whether you have known such moments. A slight sickness, my heart beating rather more rapidly than usual, a choking in the throat, and a difficulty of utterance; such were my sensations as I walked to the Cosmopole; I had to mention the name twice before the hall porter could understand me, and as I went upstairs my hands were wet. I was a good deal struck by Mr. Smith's appearance; he looked younger than I did, and there was something mild and hesitating about his expression. He was reading when I came in, and he looked up when I gave my name. "My dear sir," he said, "I am really delighted to see you. I have read very carefully the letter you were good enough to send me. Am I to understand that this document is in your own handwriting?" He showed me the letter I had written, and I told him I was not so fortunate as to be able to keep a secretary myself. "Then, sir," he went on, "the post I advertised is at your service. You have no objection to travel, I presume?" As you may imagine, I closed pretty eagerly with the offer he made, and thus I entered the service of Mr. Smith. For the first few weeks I had no special duties; I had received a quarter's salary, and a handsome allowance was made me in lieu of board and lodging. One morning, however, when I called at the hotel according to instructions, my master informed me that I must hold myself in readiness for a sea-voyage, and, to spare unnecessary detail, in the course of a fortnight we had landed at New York. Mr. Smith told me that he was engaged on a work of a special nature, in the compilation of which some peculiar researches had to be made; in short, I was given to understand that we were to travel to the far West.

After about a week had been spent in New York we took our seats in the cars, and began a journey tedious beyond all conception. Day after day, and night after night, the great train rolled on, threading its way through cities the very names of which were strange to me, passing at slow speed over perilous viaducts, skirting mountain-ranges and pine-forests, and plunging into dense tracts of wood, where mile after mile and hour after hour the same monotonous growth of brushwood met the eye, and all along the continual clatter and rattle of the wheels upon the ill-laid lines made it difficult to hear the voices of our fellow-passengers. We were a heterogeneous and ever-changing company; often I woke up in the dead of night with a sudden grinding jar of the brakes, and looking out found that we had stopped in the shabby street of some frame-built town, lighted chiefly by the flaring windows of the saloon. A few rough-looking fellows would often come out to stare at the cars, and sometimes passengers got down, and sometimes there was a party of two or three waiting on the wooden sidewalk to get on board. Many of the passengers were English; humble households torn up from the moorings of a thousand years, and bound for some problematical paradise in the alkali desert or the Rockies. I heard the men talking to one another of the great profits to be made on the virgin soil of America, and two or three, who were mechanics, expatiated on the wonderful wages given to skilled labour on the railways and in the factories of the States. This talk usually fell dead after a few minutes, and I could see a sickness and dismay in the faces of these men as they looked at the ugly brush or at the desolate expanse of the prairie, dotted here and there with frame-houses, devoid of garden or flowers or trees, standing all alone in what might have been a great grey sea frozen into stillness. Day after day the waving sky-line, and the desolation of a land without form or colour or variety, appalled the hearts of such of us as were Englishmen, and once in the night as I lay awake I heard a woman weeping and sobbing and asking what she had done to come to such a place. Her husband tried to comfort her in the broad speech of Gloucestershire, telling her the ground was so rich that one had only to plough it up and it would grow sunflowers of itself, but she cried for her mother and their old cottage and the bee-hives like a little child. The sadness of it all overwhelmed me, and I had no heart to think of other matters; the question of what Mr. Smith could have to do in such a country, and of what manner of literary research could be carried on in the wilderness, hardly troubled me. Now and again my situation struck me as peculiar; I had been engaged as a literary assistant at a handsome salary, and yet my master was still almost a stranger to me; sometimes he could come to where I was sitting in the cars and make a few banal remarks about the country, but for the most part of the journey he sat by himself, not speaking to anyone, and so far as I could judge, deep in his thoughts. It was, I think, on the fifth day from New York when I received the intimation that we should shortly leave the cars; I had been watching some distant mountains which rose wild and savage before us, and I was wondering if there were human beings so unhappy as to speak of home in con-nection with those piles of lumbered rock, when Mr. Smith touched me lightly on the shoulder. "You will be glad to be done with the cars, I have no doubt, Mr. Wilkins," he said. "You were looking at the mountains, I think? Well, I hope we shall be there to-night. The train stops at Reading, and I daresay we shall manage to find our way."

A few hours later the brakesman brought the train to a standstill at the Reading depôt, and we got out. I noticed that the town, though of course built almost entirely of frame-houses, was larger and busier than any we had passed for the last two days. The depôt was crowded; and as the bell and whistle sounded, I saw that a number of persons were preparing to leave the cars, while an even greater number were waiting to get on board. Besides the passengers, there was a pretty dense crowd of people, some of whom had come to meet or to see off their friends and relatives, while others were mere loafers. Several of our English fellow-passengers got down at Reading, but the confusion was so great that they were lost to my sight almost immediately. Mr. Smith beckoned to me to follow him, and we were soon in the thick of the mass; and the continual ringing of bells, the hubbub of voices, the shrieking of whistles, and the hiss of escaping steam, confused my senses, and I wondered dimly, as I struggled after my employer, where we were going, and how we should be able to find our way through an unknown country.

Mr. Smith had put on a wide-brimmed hat, which he had sloped over his eyes, and as all the men wore hats of the same pattern, it was with some difficulty that I distinguished him in the crowd. We got free at last, and he struck down a side street, and made one or two sharp turns to right and left. It was getting dusk, and we seemed to be passing through a shy portion of the town; there were few people about in the ill-lighted streets, and these few were men of the most unprepossessing pattern. Suddenly we stopped before a corner house. A man was standing at the door, apparently on the look-out for someone, and I noticed that he and Smith gave sharp glances one to the other.

"From New York City, I expect, mister?"

"From New York."

"All right; they're ready, and you can have 'em when you choose. I know my orders, you see, and I mean to run this business through."

"Very well, Mr. Evans, that is what we want. Our money is good, you know. Bring them round."

I had stood silent, listening to this dialogue and wondering what it meant. Smith began to walk impatiently up and down the street, and the man Evans was still standing at his door. He had given a sharp whistle, and I saw him looking me over in a quiet, leisurely way, as if to make sure of my face for another time. I was thinking what all this could mean, when an ugly slouching lad came up a side passage, leading two raw-boned horses.

"Get up, Mr. Wilkins, and be quick about it," said Smith; "we ought to be on our way."

We rode off together into the gathering darkness, and before long I looked back and saw the far plain behind us, with the lights of the town glimmering faintly; and in front rose the mountains. Smith guided his horse on the rough track as surely as if he had been riding along Piccadilly, and I followed him as well as I could. I was weary and exhausted, and scarcely took note of anything; I felt that the track was a gradual ascent, and here and there I saw great boulders by the road. The ride made but little impression on me. I have a faint recollection of passing through a dense black pine forest, where our horses had to pick their way among the rocks, and I remember the peculiar effect of the rarefied air as we kept still mounting higher and higher. I think I must have been half asleep for the latter half of the ride, and it was with a shock that I heard Smith saying—

"Here we are, Wilkins. This is Blue Rock Park. You will enjoy the view to-morrow. To-night we will have something to eat, and then go to bed."

A man came out of a rough-looking house and took the horses, and we found some fried steak and coarse whisky awaiting us inside. I had come to a strange place. There were three rooms—the room in which we had supper, Smith's room, and my own. The deaf old man who did the work slept in a sort of shed, and when I woke up the next morning and walked out I found that the house stood in a sort of hollow amongst the mountains; the clumps of pines and some enormous bluish-grey rocks that stood here and there between the trees had given the place the name of Blue Rock Park. On every side the snow-covered mountains surrounded us, the breath of the air was as wine, and when I climbed the slope and looked down, I could see that, so far as any human fellowship was concerned, I might as well have been wrecked on some small island in mid-Pacific. The only trace of man I could see was the rough log-house where I had slept, and in my ignorance I did not know that there were similar houses within comparatively easy distance, as distance is reckoned in the Rockies. But at the moment, the utter, dreadful loneliness rushed upon me, and the thought of the great plain and the great sea that parted me from the world I knew caught me by the throat, and I wondered if I should die there in that mountain hollow. It was a terrible instant, and I have not yet forgotten it. Of course, I managed to conquer my horror; I said I should be all the stronger for the experience, and I made up my mind to make the best of everything. It was a rough life enough, and rough enough board and lodging. I was left entirely to myself. Smith I scarcely ever saw, nor did I know when he was in the house. I have often thought he was far away, and have been surprised to see him walking out of his room, locking the door behind him, and putting the key in his pocket; and on several occasions, when I fancied he was busy in his room, I have seen him come in with his boots covered with dust and dirt. So far as work went I enjoyed a complete sinecure; I had nothing to do but to walk about the valley, to eat, and to sleep. With one thing and another I grew accustomed to the life, and managed to make myself pretty comfortable, and by degrees I began to venture farther away from the house, and to explore the country. One day I had contrived to get into a neighbouring valley, and suddenly I came upon a group of men sawing timber. I went up to them, hoping that perhaps some of them might be Englishmen; at all events, they were human beings, and I should hear articulate speech; for the old man I have mentioned, besides being half-blind and stone-deaf, was wholly dumb so far as I was concerned. I was prepared to be welcomed in a rough and ready fashion, without much of the forms of politeness, but the grim glances and the short, gruff answers I received astonished me. I saw the men glancing oddly at each other; and one of them, who had stopped work, began fingering a gun, and I was obliged to return on my path uttering curses on the fate which had brought me into a land where men were more brutish than the very brutes. The solitude of the life began to oppress me as with a nightmare, and a few days later I determined to walk to a kind of station some miles distant, where a rough inn was kept for the accommodation of hunters and tourists. English gentlemen occasionally stopped there for the night, and I thought I might perhaps fall in with someone of better manners than the inhabitants of the country. I found, as I had expected, a group of men lounging about the door of the log-house that served as a hotel, and as I came nearer I could see that heads were put together and looks interchanged, and when I walked up the six or seven trappers stared at me in stony ferocity, and with something of the disgust that one eyes a loathsome and venomous snake. I felt that I could bear it no longer, and I called out—

"Is there such a thing as an Englishman here, or any one with a little civilization?"

One of the men put his hand to his belt, but his neighbour checked him, and answered me—

"You'll find we've got some of the resources of civilization before very long, mister, and I expect you'll not fancy them extremely. But, any way, there's an Englishman tarrying here, and I've no doubt he'll be glad to see you. There you are; that's Mr. D'Aubernoun."

A young man, dressed like an English country squire, came and stood at the door, and looked at me. One of the men pointed to me and said—

"That's the individual we were talking about last night. Thought you might like to have a look at him, squire, and here he is."

The young fellow's good-natured English face clouded over, and he glanced sternly at me, and turned away with a gesture of contempt and aversion.

"Sir," I cried, "I do not know what I have done to be treated in this manner. You are my fellow-countryman, and I expected some courtesy."

He gave me a black look and made as if he would go in, but he changed his mind and faced me.

"You are rather imprudent, I think, to behave in this manner. You must be counting on a forbearance which cannot last very long, which may last a very short time indeed. And let me tell you this, sir, you may call yourself an Englishman, and drag the name of England through the dirt, but you need not count on any English influence to help you. If I were you, I would not stay here much longer."

He went into the inn, and the men quietly watched my face as I stood there, wondering whether I was going mad. The woman of the house came out and stared at me as if I were a wild beast or a savage, and I turned to her, and spoke quietly—

"I am very hungry and thirsty. I have walked a long way. I have plenty of money. Will you give me something to eat and drink?"

"No, I won't," she said. "You had better quit this."

I crawled home like a wounded beast, and lay down on my bed. It was all a hopeless puzzle to me; I knew nothing but rage, and shame, and terror, and I suffered little more when I passed by a house in an adjacent valley, and some children who were playing outside ran from me shrieking. I was forced to walk to find some occupation; I should have died if I had sat down quietly in Blue Rock Park and looked all day at the mountains; but wherever I saw a human being I saw the same glance of hatred and aversion, and once as I was crossing a thick brake I heard a shot and the venomous hiss of a bullet close to my ear.

One day I heard a conversation which astounded me; I was sitting behind a rock resting, and two men came along the track and halted. One of them had got his feet entangled in some wild vines, and swore fiercely, but the other laughed, and said they were useful things sometimes .

"What the hell do you mean?"

"Oh, nothing much. But they're uncommon tough, these here vines, and sometimes rope is skerse and dear."

The man who had sworn chuckled at this, and I heard them sit down and light their pipes.

"Have you seen him lately?" asked the humorist.

"I sighted him the other day, but the darned bullet went high. He's got his master's luck I expect, sir, but it can't last much longer. You heard about him going to Jinks's and trying his brass, but the young Britisher downed him pretty considerable, I can tell you."

"What the devil is the meaning of it?"

"I don't know, but I believe it'll have to be finished, and done in the old style too. You know how they fix the niggers?"

"Yes, sir, I've seen a little of that. A couple of gallons of kerosene 'll cost a dollar at Brown's store, but I should say it's cheap anyway."

They moved off after this, and I lay still behind the rock, the sweat pouring down my face. I was so sick that I could barely stand, and I walked home as slowly as an old man, leaning on my stick. I knew that the two men had been talking about me, and I knew that some terrible death was in store for me. That night I could not sleep; I tossed on the rough bed and tortured myself to find out the meaning of it all. At last, in the very dead of night, I rose from the bed and put on my clothes, and went out. I did not care where I went, but I felt that I must walk till I had tired myself out. It was a clear moonlight night, and in a couple of hours I found I was approaching a place of dismal reputation in the mountains, a deep cleft in the rocks, known as Black Gulf Canyon. Many years before an unfortunate party of Englishmen and English women had camped here and had been surrounded by Indians. They were captured, outraged, and put to death with almost inconceivable tortures, and the roughest of the trappers or woodsmen gave the canyon a wide berth even in the daytime. As I crushed through the dense brushwood which grew above the canyon I heard voices; and wondering who could be in such a place at such a time, I went on, walking more carefully, and making as little noise as possible. There was a great tree growing on the very edge of the rocks, and I lay down and looked out from behind the trunk. Black Gulf Canyon was below me, the moonlight shining bright into its very depths from mid-heaven, and casting shadows as black as death from the pointed rock, and all the sheer rock on the other side, overhanging the canyon, was in darkness. At intervals a light veil obscured the moonlight, as a filmy cloud fleeted across the moon, and a bitter wind blew shrill across the gulf. I looked down, as I have said, and saw twenty men standing in a semi-circle round a rock; I counted them one by one, and knew most of them. They were the very vilest of the vile, more vile than any den in

London could show, and there was murder, worse than murder, on the heads of not a few. Facing them and me stood Mr. Smith, with the rock before him, and on the rock was a great pair of scales, such as are used in the stores. I heard his voice ringing down the canyon as I lay beside the tree, and my heart turned cold as I heard it.

"Life for gold," he cried, "a life for gold. The blood and the life of an enemy for every pound of gold."

A man stepped out and raised one hand, and with the other flung a bright lump of something into the pan of the scales, which clanged down, and Smith muttered something in his ear. Then he cried again—

"Blood for gold, for a pound of gold, the life of an enemy. For every pound of gold upon the scales, a life."

One by one the men came forward, each lifting up his right hand; and the gold was weighed in the scales, and each time Smith leant forward and spoke to each man in his ear. Then he cried again—

"Desire and lust for gold on the scales. For every pound of gold enjoyment of desire."

I saw the same thing happen as before; the uplifted hand and the metal weighed, and the mouth whispering, and black passion on every face.

Then, one by one, I saw the men again step up to Smith. A muttered conversation seemed to take place. I could see that Smith was explaining and directing, and I noticed that he gesticulated a little as one who points out the way, and once or twice he moved his hands quickly as if he would show that the path was clear and could not be missed. I kept my eyes so intently on his figure that I noted little else, and at last it was with a start that I realized that the canyon was empty. A moment before I thought I had seen the group of villainous faces, and the two standing, a little apart, by the rock; I had looked down a moment, and when I glanced again into the canyon there was no one there. In dumb terror I made my way home, and I fell asleep in an instant from exhaustion. No doubt I should have slept on for many hours, but when I woke up the sun was only rising, and the light shone in on my bed. I had started up from sleep with the sensation of having received a violent shock; and as I looked in confusion about me, I saw, to my amazement, that there were three men in the room. One of them had his hand on my shoulder, and spoke to me—

"Come, mister, wake up. Your time's up now, I reckon, and the boys are waiting for you outside, and they're in a big hurry. Come on; you can put on your clothes; it's kind of chilly this morning."

I saw the other two men smiling sourly at each other, but I understood nothing. I simply pulled on my clothes and said I was ready.

"All right; come on, then. You go first, Nichols, and Jim and I will give the gentleman an arm."

They took me out into the sunlight, and then I understood the meaning of a dull murmur that had vaguely perplexed me while I was dressing. There were about two hundred men waiting outside, and some women too, and when they saw me there was a low muttering growl. I did not know what I had done, but that noise made my heart beat and the sweat come out on my face. I saw confusedly, as through a veil, the tumult and tossing of the crowd, discordant voices were speaking, and amongst all those faces there was not one glance of mercy, but a fury of lust that I did not understand. I found myself presently walking in a sort of procession up the slope of the valley, and on every side of me there were men with revolvers in their hands. Now and then a voice struck me, and I heard words and sentences of which I could form no connected story. But I understood that there was one sentence of execration; I heard scraps of stories that seemed strange and improbable. Someone was talking of men, lured by cunning devices from their homes and murdered with hideous tortures, found writhing like wounded snakes in dark and lonely places, only crying for someone to stab them to the heart, and so end their anguish; and I heard another voice speaking of innocent girls who had vanished for a day or two, and then had come back and died, blushing red with shame even in the agonies of death. I wondered what it all meant, and what was to happen; but I was so weary that I walked on in a dream, scarcely longing for anything but sleep. At last we stopped. We had reached the summit of the hill overlooking Blue Rock Valley, and I saw that I was standing beneath a clump of trees where I had often sat. I was in the midst of a ring of armed men, and I saw that two or three men were very busy with piles of wood, while others were fingering a rope. Then there was a stir in the crowd, and a man was pushed forward. His hands and feet were tightly bound with cord; and though his face was unutterably villainous, I pitied him for the agony that worked his features and twisted his lips. I knew him; he was amongst those that had gathered round Smith in Black Gulf Canyon. In an instant he was unbound and stripped naked, borne beneath one of the trees, and his neck encircled by a noose that went around the trunk. A hoarse voice gave some kind of order; there was a rush of feet, and the rope tightened; and there before me I saw the blackened face and the writhing limbs and the shameful agony of death. One after another half a dozen men, all of whom I had seen in the canyon the night before, were strangled before me, and their bodies were flung forth on the ground. Then there was a pause, and the man who had roused me a short while before came up to me, and said—

"Now, mister, it's your turn. We give you five minutes to cast up your accounts, and when that's clocked, by the living God, we will burn you alive at that tree."

It was then I awoke and understood. I cried out—

"Why, what have I done? Why should you hurt me? I am a harmless man; I never did you any wrong." I covered my face with my hands; it seemed so pitiful, and it was such a terrible death.

"What have I done?" I cried again. "You must take me for some other man. You cannot know me."

"You black-hearted devil," said the man at my side, "we know you well enough. There's not a man within thirty miles of this that won't curse Jack Smith when you are burning in hell."

"My name is not Smith," I said, with some hope left in me. "My name is Wilkins. I was Mr. Smith's secretary, but I knew nothing of him."

"Hark at the black liar," said the man. "Secretary be damned! You were clever enough, I dare say, to slink out at night and keep your face in the dark, but we've tracked you out at last. But your time's up. Come along."

I was dragged to the tree and bound to it with chains; I saw the piles of wood heaped all about me, and shut my eyes. Then I felt myself drenched all over with some liquid, and looked again, and a woman grinned at me. She had just emptied a great can of petroleum over me and over the wood. A voice shouted, "Fire away!" and I fainted, and knew nothing more.

When I opened my eyes I was lying on a bed in a bare, comfortless room. A doctor was holding some strong salts to my nostrils, and a gentleman standing by the bed, whom I afterwards found to be the sheriff, addressed me.

"Say, mister," he began, "you've had an uncommon narrow squeak for it. The boys were just about lighting up when I came along with the posse, and I had as much as I could do to bring you off, I can tell you. And, mind you, I don't blame them; they had made up their minds, you see, that you were the head of the Black Gulf gang, and at first nothing I could say would persuade them you weren't Jack Smith. Luckily, a man from here named Evans, that came along with us, allowed he had seen you with Jack Smith, and that you were yourself. So we brought you along and gaoled you, but you can go if you like when you're through with this faint turn."

I got on the cars the next day, and in three weeks I was in London; again almost penniless. But from that time my fortune seemed to change; I made influential friends in all directions; bank directors courted my company, and editors positively flung themselves into my arms. I had only to choose my career, and after a while I determined that I was meant by nature for a life of comparative leisure. With an ease that seemed almost ridiculous, I obtained a well-paid position in connection with a prosperous political club. I have charming chambers in a central neighbourhood, close to the parks, the club chef exerts himself when I lunch or dine, and the rarest vintages in the cellar are always at my disposal. Yet, since my return to London, I have never known a day's security or peace; I tremble when I awake lest Smith should be standing at my bed, and every step I take seems to bring me nearer to the edge of the precipice. Smith, I knew, had escaped free from the raid of the Vigilantes, and I grew faint at the thought that he would in all probability return to London, and that suddenly and unprepared I should meet him face to face. Every morning as I left my house I would peer up and down the street, expecting to see that dreaded figure awaiting me; I have delayed at street-corners, my heart in my mouth, sickening at the thought that a few quick steps might bring us together; I could not bear to frequent the theatres or music-halls, lest by some bizarre chance he should prove to be my neighbour. Sometimes I have been forced, against my will, to walk out at night, and then in silent squares the shadows have made me shudder, and in the medley of meetings in the crowded thoroughfares I have said to myself, "It must come sooner or later; he will surely return to London, and I shall see him when I feel most secure." I scanned the newspapers for hint or intimation of approaching danger, and no small type nor report of trivial interest was allowed to pass unread. Especially I read and re-read the advertisement columns, but without result; months passed by, and I was undisturbed till, though I felt far from safe, I no longer suffered from the intolerable oppression of instant and ever-present terror. This afternoon, as I was walking quietly along Oxford Street, I raised my eyes and looked across the road, and then at last I saw the man who had so long haunted my thoughts.

Mr. Wilkins finished his wine, and leant back in his chair, looking sadly at Dyson; and then, as if a thought struck him, fished out of an inner pocket a leather letter-case, and handed a newspaper cutting across the table.

Dyson glanced closely at the slip, and saw that it had been extracted from the columns of an evening paper. It ran as follows:

WHOLESALE LYNCHING

SHOCKING STORY

"A Dalziel telegram from Reading (Colorado) states that advices received there from Blue Rock Park report a frightful instance of popular vengeance. For some time the neighbourhood has been terrorized by the crimes of a gang of desperadoes, who, under the cover of a carefully planned organization, have perpetrated the most infamous cruelties on men and women. A Vigilance Committee was formed, and it was found that the leader of the gang was a person named Smith, living in Blue Rock Park. Action was taken, and six of the worst in the band were summarily strangled in the presence of two or three hundred men and women. Smith is said to have escaped."

"This is a terrible story," said Dyson; "I can well believe that your days and nights are haunted by such fearful scenes as you have described. But surely you have no need to fear Smith? He has much more cause to fear you. Consider: you have only to lay your information before the police, and a warrant would be immediately issued for his arrest. Besides, you will, I am sure, excuse me for what I am going to say."

"My dear sir," said Mr. Wilkins, "I hope you will speak to me with perfect freedom."

"Well, then, I must confess that my impression was that you were rather disappointed at not being able to stop the man before he drove

S

off. I thought you seemed annoyed that you could not get across the street."

"Sir, I did not know what I was about. I caught sight of the man, but it was only for a moment, and the agony you witnessed was the agony of suspense. I was not perfectly certain of the face, and the horrible thought that Smith was again in London overwhelmed me. I shuddered at the idea of this incarnate fiend, whose soul is black with shocking crimes, mingling free and unobserved amongst the harmless crowds, meditating perhaps a new and more fearful cycle of infamies. I tell you, sir, that an awful being stalks through the streets, a being before whom the sunlight itself should blacken, and the summer air grow chill and dank. Such thoughts as these rushed upon me with the force of a whirlwind; I lost my senses."

"I see. I partly understand your feelings, but I would impress on you that you have nothing really to fear. Depend upon it, Smith will not molest you in any way. You must remember he himself has had a warning; and indeed, from the brief glance I had of him, he seemed to me to be a frightened-looking man. However, I see it is getting late, and if you will excuse me, Mr. Wilkins, I think I will be going. I daresay we shall often meet here."

Dyson walked off smartly, pondering the strange story chance had brought him, and finding on cool reflection that there was something a little strange in Mr. Wilkins's manner, for which not even so weird a catalogue of experiences could altogether account.

ADVENTURE OF THE MISSING BROTHER

MR. CHARLES PHILLIPPS was, as has been hinted, a gentleman of pronounced scientific tastes. In his early days he had devoted himself with fond enthusiasm to the agreeable study of biology, and a brief monograph on the Embryology of the Microscopic Holothuria had formed his first contribution to the *belles lettres*. Later he had somewhat relaxed the severity of his pursuits, and had dabbled in the more frivolous subjects of palæontology and ethnology; he had a cabinet in his sitting-room whose drawers were stuffed with rude flint implements, and a charming fetish from the South Seas was the dominant note in the decorative scheme of the apartment. Flattering himself

with the title of materialist, he was in truth one of the most credulous
of men, but he required a marvel to be neatly draped in the robes of
Science before he would give it any credit, and the wildest dreams took
solid shape to him if only the nomenclature were severe and irreproachable. He laughed at the witch, but quailed before the powers of the
hypnotist, lifting his eyebrows when Christianity was mentioned, but
adoring protyle and the ether. For the rest, he prided himself on a
boundless scepticism; the average tale of wonder he heard with nothing
but contempt, and he would certainly not have credited a word or
syllable of Dyson's story of the pursuer and pursued, unless the gold
coin had been produced as visible and tangible evidence. As it was, he
half suspected that Dyson had imposed on him; he knew his friend's
disordered fancies, and his habit of conjuring up the marvellous to
account for the entirely commonplace; and, on the whole, he was
inclined to think that the so-called facts in the odd adventure had been
gravely distorted in the telling. Since the evening on which he had
listened to the tale he had paid Dyson a visit, and had delivered himself
of some serious talk on the necessity of accurate observation, and the
folly, as he put it, of using a kaleidoscope instead of a telescope in the
view of things, to which remarks his friend had listened with a smile
that was extremely sardonic. "My dear fellow," Dyson had remarked
at last, "you will allow me to tell you that I see your drift perfectly.
However, you will be astonished to hear that I consider you to be the
visionary, while I am a sober and serious spectator of human life. You
have gone round the circle; and while you fancy yourself far in the
golden land of new philosophies, you are in reality a dweller in a metaphorical Clapham; your scepticism has defeated itself and become a
monstrous credulity; you are, in fact, in the position of the bat or owl, I
forget which it was, who denied the existence of the sun at noonday,
and I shall be astonished if you do not one day come to me full of contrition for your manifold intellectual errors, with a humble resolution
to see things in their true light for the future." This tirade had left
Mr. Phillipps unimpressed; he considered Dyson as hopeless, and he
went home to gloat over some primitive stone implements that a friend
had sent him from India. He found that his landlady, seeing them displayed in all their rude formlessness upon the table, had removed the
collection to the dustbin, and had replaced it by lunch; and the afternoon
was spent in malodorous research. Mrs. Brown hearing these stones

spoken of as very valuable knives, had called him in his hearing "poor Mr. Phillipps", and between rage and evil odours he spent a sorry afternoon. It was four o'clock before he had completed his work of rescue; and, overpowered with the flavours of decaying cabbage leaves, Phillipps felt that he must have a walk to gain an appetite for the evening meal. Unlike Dyson he walked fast, with his eyes on the pavement, absorbed in his thoughts, and oblivious of the life around him; and he could not have told by what streets he had passed, when he suddenly lifted up his eyes and found himself in Leicester Square. The grass and flowers pleased him, and he welcomed the opportunity of resting for a few minutes, and glancing round, he saw a bench which had only one occupant, a lady, and as she was seated at one end, Phillipps took up a position at the other extremity, and began to pass in angry review the events of the afternoon. He had noticed as he came up to the bench that the person already there was neatly dressed, and to all appearance young; her face he could not see, as it was turned away in apparent contemplation of the shrubs, and, moreover, shielded with her hand; but it would be doing wrong to Mr. Phillipps to imagine that his choice of a seat was dictated by any hopes of an affair of the heart, he had simply preferred the company of one lady to that of five dirty children, and having seated himself, was immersed directly in thoughts of his misfortunes. He had meditated changing his lodgings; but now, on a judicial review of the case in all its bearings, his calmer judgment told him that the race of landladies is like to the race of the leaves, and that there was but little to choose between them. He resolved, however, to talk to Mrs. Brown, the offender, very coolly and yet severely, to point out the extreme indiscretion of her conduct, and to express a hope for better things in the future. With this decision registered in his mind, Phillipps was about to get up from the seat and move off, when he was intensely annoyed to hear a stifled sob, evidently from the lady, who still continued her contemplation of the shrubs and flower-beds. He clutched his stick desperately, and in a moment would have been in full retreat, when the lady turned her face towards him, and with a mute entreaty bespoke his attention. She was a young girl with a quaint and piquant rather than a beautiful face, and she was evidently in the bitterest distress. Mr. Phillipps sat down again, and cursed his chances heartily. The young lady looked at him with a pair of charming eyes of a shining hazel, which showed no trace of tears, though a handkerchief was in her hand; she bit her lip, and seemed to struggle with some overpowering grief, and her whole attitude was all-beseeching and imploring. Phillipps sat on the edge of the bench gazing awkwardly at her, and wondering what was to come next, and she looked at him still without speaking.

"Well, madam," he said at last, "I understood from your gesture that you wished to speak to me. Is there anything I can do for you? Though, if you will pardon me, I cannot help saying that that seems highly improbable."

"Ah, sir," she said in a low, murmuring voice, "do not speak harshly to me. I am in sore straits, and I thought from your face that I could safely ask your sympathy, if not your help."

"Would you kindly tell me what is the matter?" said Phillipps. "Perhaps you would like some tea?"

"I knew I could not be mistaken," the lady replied. "That offer of refreshment bespeaks a generous mind. But tea, alas! is powerless to console me. If you will let me, I shall endeavour to explain my trouble."

"I should be glad if you would."

"I shall do so, and I shall try to be brief, in spite of the numerous complications which have made me, young as I am, tremble before what seems the profound and terrible mystery of existence. Yet the grief which now racks my very soul is but too simple; I have lost my brother."

"Lost your brother! How on earth can that be?"

"I see I must trouble you with a few particulars. My brother, then, who is by some years my elder, is a tutor in a private school in the extreme north of London. The want of means deprived him of the advantages of a University education; and lacking the stamp of a degree, he could not hope for that position which his scholarship and his talents entitled him to claim. He was thus forced to accept the post of classical master at Dr. Saunderson's Highgate Academy for the Sons of Gentlemen, and he has performed his duties with perfect satisfaction to his principal for some years. My personal history need not trouble you; it will be enough if I tell you that for the last month I have been governess in a family residing at Tooting. My brother and I have always cherished the warmest mutual affection; and though circumstances into which I need not enter have kept us apart for some time, yet we have never lost sight of one another. We made up our minds that unless one of us was

absolutely unable to rise from a bed of sickness, we should never let a
week pass by without meeting, and some time ago we chose this square
as our rendezvous on account of its central position and its convenience
of access. And indeed, after a week of distasteful toil, my brother felt
little inclination for much walking, and we have often spent two or
three hours on this bench, speaking of our prospects and of happier
days, when we were children. In the early spring it was cold and chilly;
still we enjoyed the short respite, and I think that we were often taken
for a pair of lovers, as we sat close together, eagerly talking. Saturday
after Saturday we have met each other here; and though the doctor told
him it was madness, my brother would not allow the influenza to break
the appointment. That was some time ago; last Saturday we had a
long and happy afternoon, and separated more cheerfully than usual,
feeling that the coming week would be bearable, and resolving that our
next meeting should be if possible still more pleasant. I arrived here
at the time agreed upon, four o'clock, and sat down and watched for my
brother, expecting every moment to see him advancing towards me
from that gate at the north side of the square. Five minutes passed by,
and he had not arrived, I thought he must have missed his train, and the
idea that our interview would be cut short by twenty minutes, or perhaps half an hour, saddened me; I had hoped we should be so happy
together to-day. Suddenly, moved by I know not what impulse, I
turned abruptly round, and how can I describe to you my astonishment
when I saw my brother advancing slowly towards me from the southern
side of the square, accompanied by another person? My first thought, I
remember, had in it something of resentment that this man, whoever
he was, should intrude himself into our meeting; I wondered who it
could possibly be, for my brother had, I may say, no intimate friends.
Then as I looked still at the advancing figures, another feeling took
possession of me; it was a sensation of bristling fear, the fear of the
child in the dark, unreasonable and unreasoning, but terrible, clutching
at my heart as with the cold grip of a dead man's hands. Yet I over-
came the feeling, and looked steadily at my brother, waiting for him to
speak, and more closely at his companion. Then I noticed that this
man was leading my brother rather than walking arm-in-arm with
him; he was a tall man, dressed in quite ordinary fashion. He wore a
high bowler hat, and, in spite of the warmth of the day, a plain black
overcoat, tightly buttoned, and I noticed his trousers, of a quiet black

and grey stripe. The face was commonplace too, and indeed I cannot recall any special features, or any trick of expression; for though I looked at him as he came near, curiously enough his face made no impression on me—it was as though I had seen a well-made mask. They passed in front of me, and to my unutterable astonishment, I heard my brother's voice speaking to me, though his lips did not move, nor his eyes look into mine. It was a voice I cannot describe, though I knew it, but the words came to my ears as if mingled with plashing water and the sound of a shallow brook flowing amidst stones. I heard, then, the words, "I cannot stay," and for a moment the heavens and the earth seemed to rush together with the sound of thunder, and I was thrust forth from the world into a black void without beginning and without end. For, as my brother passed me, I saw the hand that held him by the arm, and seemed to guide him, and in one moment of horror I realized that it was as a formless thing that has mouldered for many years in the grave. The flesh was peeled in strips from the bones, and hung apart dry and granulated, and the fingers that encircled my brother's arm were all unshapen, claw-like things, and one was but a stump from which the end had rotted off. When I recovered my senses I saw the two passing out by that gate. I paused for a moment, and then with a rush as of fire to my heart I knew that no horror could stay me, but that I must follow my brother and save him, even though all hell rose up against me. I ran out, and looked up the pavement, and saw the two figures walking amidst the crowd. I ran across the road, and saw them turn up that side street, and I reached the corner a moment later. In vain I looked to right and left, for neither my brother nor his strange guardian was in sight; two elderly men were coming down arm-in-arm, and a telegraph boy was walking lustily along whistling. I remained there a moment horror-struck, and then I bowed my head and returned to this seat, where you found me. Now, sir, do you wonder at my grief? Oh, tell me what has happened to my brother, or I feel I shall go mad!"

Mr. Phillipps, who had listened with exemplary patience to this tale, hesitated a moment before he spoke.

"My dear madam," he said at length, "you have known how to engage me in your service, not only as a man, but as a student of science. As a fellow-creature I pity you most profoundly; you must have suffered extremely from what you saw, or rather from what you fancied you saw. For, as a scientific observer, it is my duty to tell you the plain truth, which, indeed, besides being true, must also console you. Allow me to ask you then to describe your brother."

"Certainly," said the lady eagerly; "I can describe him accurately. My brother is a somewhat young-looking man; he is pale, has small black whiskers, and wears spectacles. He has rather a timid, almost a frightened expression, and looks about him nervously from side to side. Think, think! Surely you must have seen him. Perhaps you are an habitué of this engaging quarter; you may have met him on some previous Saturday. I may have been mistaken in supposing that he turned up that side street; he may have gone on, and you may have passed each other. Oh, tell me, sir, whether you have not seen him!"

"I am afraid I do not keep a very sharp look-out when I am walking," said Phillipps, who would have passed his mother unnoticed; "but I am sure your description is admirable. And now will you describe the person who, you say, held your brother by the arm?"

"I cannot do so. I told you his face seemed devoid of expression or salient feature. It was like a mask."

"Exactly; you cannot describe what you have never seen. I need hardly point out to you the conclusion to be drawn; you have been the victim of an hallucination. You expected to see your brother, you were alarmed because you did not see him, and unconsciously, no doubt, your brain went to work, and finally you saw a mere projection of your own morbid thoughts—a vision of your absent brother, and a mere confusion of terrors incorporated in a figure which you can't describe. Of course your brother had been in some way prevented from coming to meet you as usual. I expect you will hear from him in a day or two."

The lady looked seriously at Mr. Phillipps, and then for a second there seemed almost a twinkling as of mirth about her eyes, but her face clouded sadly at the dogmatic conclusions to which the scientist was led so irresistibly.

"Ah!" she said, "you do not know. I cannot doubt the evidence of my waking senses. Besides, perhaps I have had experiences even more terrible. I acknowledge the force of your arguments, but a woman has intuitions which never deceive her. Believe me, I am not hysterical; feel my pulse, it is quite regular."

She stretched out her hand with a dainty gesture, and a glance that enraptured Phillipps in spite of himself. The hand held out to him was soft and white and warm, and as, in some confusion, he placed his fingers on the purple vein, he felt profoundly touched by the spectacle of love and grief before him.

"No," he said, as he released her wrist, "as you say, you are evidently quite yourself. Still, you must be aware that living men do not possess dead hands. That sort of thing doesn't happen. It is, of course, barely possible that you did see your brother with another gentleman, and that important business prevented him from stopping. As for the wonderful hand, there may have been some deformity, a finger shot off by accident, or something of that sort."

The lady shook her head mournfully.

"I see you are a determined rationalist," she said. "Did you not hear me say that I have had experiences even more terrible? I too was once a sceptic, but after what I have known I can no longer affect to doubt."

"Madam," replied Mr. Phillipps, "no one shall make me deny my faith. I will never believe, nor will I pretend to believe, that two and two make five, nor will I on any pretences admit the existence of two-sided triangles."

"You are a little hasty," rejoined the lady. "But may I ask you if you ever heard the name of Professor Gregg, the authority on ethnology and kindred subjects?"

"I have done much more than merely hear of Professor Gregg," said Phillipps. "I always regarded him as one of our most acute and clear-headed observers; and his last publication, the *Textbook of Ethnology*, struck me as being quite admirable in its kind. Indeed, the book had but come into my hands when I heard of the terrible accident which cut short Gregg's career. He had, I think, taken a country house in the West of England for the summer, and is supposed to have fallen into a river. So far as I remember, his body was never recovered."

"Sir, I am sure that you are discreet. Your conversation seems to declare as much, and the very title of that little work of yours which you mentioned assures me that you are no empty trifler. In a word, I feel that I may depend on you. You appear to be under the impression that Professor Gregg is dead; I have no reason to believe that that is the case."

"What?" cried Phillipps, astonished and perturbed. "You do not hint that there was anything disgraceful? I cannot believe it. Gregg was a man of clearest character; his private life was one of great benevolence; and though I myself am free from delusions, I believe him to have been a sincere and devout Christian. Surely you cannot mean to insinuate that some disreputable history forced him to flee the country?"

"Again you are in a hurry," replied the lady. "I said nothing of all this. Briefly, then, I must tell you that Professor Gregg left his house one morning in full health both of mind and body. He never returned, but his watch and chain, a purse containing three sovereigns in gold, and some loose silver, with a ring that he wore habitually, were found three days later on a wild and savage hillside, many miles from the river. These articles were placed beside a limestone rock of fantastic form; they had been wrapped into a parcel with a kind of rough parchment which was secured with gut. The parcel was opened, and the inner side of the parchment bore an inscription done with some red substance; the characters were undecipherable, but seemed to be a corrupt cuneiform."

"You interest me intensely," said Phillipps. "Would you mind continuing your story? The circumstance you have mentioned seems to me of the most inexplicable character, and I thirst for an elucidation."

The young lady seemed to meditate for a moment, and she then proceeded to relate

THE NOVEL OF THE BLACK SEAL

I must now give you some fuller particulars of my history. I am the daughter of a civil engineer, Steven Lally by name, who was so unfortunate as to die suddenly at the outset of his career, and before he had accumulated sufficient means to support his wife and her two children.

My mother contrived to keep the small household going on resources which must have been incredibly small; we lived in a remote country village, because most of the necessaries of life were cheaper than in a town, but even so we were brought up with the severest economy. My father was a clever and well-read man, and left behind him a small but select collection of books, containing the best Greek, Latin, and English classics, and these books were the only amusement we possessed. My brother, I remember, learnt Latin out of Descartes' *Meditationes*, and I, in place of the little tales which children are usually told to read, had nothing more charming than a translation of the *Gesta Romanorum*. We grew up thus, quiet and studious children, and in course of time my brother provided for himself in the manner I have mentioned. I continued to live at home; my poor mother had become an invalid, and demanded my continual care, and about two years ago she died after many months of painful illness. My situation was a terrible one; the shabby furniture barely sufficed to pay the debts I had been forced to contract, and the books I dispatched to my brother, knowing how he would value them. I was absolutely alone; I was aware how poorly my brother was paid; and though I came up to London in the hope of finding employment, with the understanding that he would defray my expenses, I swore it should only be for a month, and that if I could not in that time find some work, I would starve rather than deprive him of the few miserable pounds he had laid by for his day of trouble. I took a little room in a distant suburb, the cheapest that I could find; I lived on bread and tea, and I spent my time in vain answering of advertisements, and vainer walks to addresses I had noted. Day followed on day, and week on week, and still I was unsuccessful, till at last the term I had appointed drew to a close, and I saw before me the grim prospect of slowly dying of starvation. My landlady was good-natured in her way; she knew the slenderness of my means, and I am sure that she would not have turned me out of doors; it remained for me then to go away, and to try to die in some quiet place. It was winter then, and a thick white fog gathered in the early part of the afternoon, becoming more dense as the day wore on; it was a Sunday, I remember, and the people of the house were at chapel. At about three o'clock I crept out and walked away as quickly as I could, for I was weak from abstinence. The white mist wrapped all the streets in silence, a hard frost had gathered thick upon the bare branches of the trees, and frost crystals glittered on the wooden fences, and on the cold, cruel ground beneath my feet. I walked on, turning to right and left in utter haphazard, without caring to look up at the names of the streets, and all that I remember of my walk on that Sunday afternoon seems but the broken fragments of an evil dream. In a confused vision I stumbled on, through roads half town and half country, grey fields melting into the cloudy world of mist on one side of me, and on the other comfortable villas with a glow of firelight flickering on the walls, but all unreal; red brick walls and lighted windows, vague trees, and glimmering country, gas-lamps beginning to star the white shadows, the vanishing perspectives of the railway line beneath high embankments, the green and red of the signal lamps—all these were but momentary pictures flashed on my tired brain and senses numbed by hunger. Now and then I would hear a quick step ringing on the iron road, and men would pass me well wrapped up, walking fast for the sake of warmth and no doubt eagerly foretasting the pleasures of a glowing hearth, with curtains tightly drawn about the frosted panes, and the welcomes of their friends; but as the early evening darkened and night approached, foot-passengers got fewer and fewer, and I passed through street after street alone. In the white silence I stumbled on, as desolate as if I trod the streets of a buried city; and as I grew more weak and exhausted, something of the horror of death was folding thickly round my heart. Suddenly, as I turned a corner, some one accosted me courteously beneath the lamp-post, and I heard a voice asking if I could kindly point the way to Avon Road. At the sudden shock of human accents I was prostrated, and my strength gave way; I fell all huddled on the sidewalk, and wept and sobbed and laughed in violent hysteria. I had gone out prepared to die, and as I stepped across the threshold that had sheltered me, I consciously bade adieu to all hopes and all remembrances; the door clanged behind me with the noise of thunder, and I felt that an iron curtain had fallen on the brief passages of my life, that henceforth I was to walk a little way in a world of gloom and shadow; I entered on the stage of the first act of death. Then came my wandering in the mist, the whiteness wrapping all things, the void streets, and muffled silence, till when that voice spoke to me it was as if I had died and life returned to me. In a few minutes I was able to compose my feelings, and as I rose I saw that I was confronted by a middle-aged gentleman of pleasing appearance, neatly and correctly dressed. He looked at me with an expression of great pity, but before I could stammer out my ignorance of the neighbourhood, for indeed I had not the slightest notion of where I had wandered, he spoke.

"My dear madam," he said, "you seem in some terrible distress. You cannot think how you alarmed me. But may I inquire the nature of your trouble? I assure you that you can safely confide in me."

"You are very kind," I replied, "but I fear there is nothing to be done. My condition seems a hopeless one."

"Oh, nonsense, nonsense! You are too young to talk like that.

Come, let us walk down here, and you must tell me your difficulty.
Perhaps I may be able to help you."

There was something very soothing and persuasive in his manner,
and as we walked together I gave him an outline of my story, and told
of the despair that had oppressed me almost to death.

"You were wrong to give in so completely," he said, when I was
silent. "A month is too short a time in which to feel one's way in
London. London, let me tell you, Miss Lally, does not lie open and
undefended; it is a fortified place, fossed and double-moated with
curious intricacies. As must always happen in large towns, the conditions of life have become hugely artificial; no mere simple palisade
is run up to oppose the man or woman who would take the place by
storm, but serried lines of subtle contrivances, mines, and pitfalls
which it needs a strange skill to overcome. You, in your simplicity,
fancied you had only to shout for these walls to sink into nothingness,
but the time is gone for such startling victories as these. Take courage;
you will learn the secret of success before very long."

"Alas! sir," I replied, "I have no doubt your conclusions are correct,
but at the present moment I seem to be in a fair way to die of starvation.
You spoke of a secret; for heaven's sake tell it me, if you have any pity
for my distress."

He laughed genially. "There lies the strangeness of it all. Those
who know the secret cannot tell it if they would; it is positively as
ineffable as the central doctrine of Freemasonry. But I may say this,
that you yourself have penetrated at least the outer husk of the mystery,"
and he laughed again.

"Pray do not jest with me," I said. "What have I done, *que sais-je?*
I am so far ignorant that I have not the slightest idea of how my next
meal is to be provided."

"Excuse me. You ask what you have done. You have met me.
Come, we will fence no longer. I see you have self-education, the only
education which is not infinitely pernicious, and I am in want of a
governess for my two children. I have been a widower for some years;
my name is Gregg. I offer you the post I have named, and shall we say a
salary of a hundred a year?"

I could only stutter out my thanks, and slipping a card with his
address, and a banknote by way of earnest, into my hand, Mr. Gregg
bade me goodbye, asking me to call in a day or two.

Such was my introduction to Professor Gregg, and can you wonder that the remembrance of despair and the cold blast that had blown from the gates of death upon me made me regard him as a second father? Before the close of the week I was installed in my new duties. The professor had leased an old brick manor-house in a western suburb of London, and here, surrounded by pleasant lawns and orchards, and soothed with the murmur of ancient elms that rocked their boughs above the roof, the new chapter of my life began. Knowing as you do the nature of the professor's occupations, you will not be surprised to hear that the house teemed with books, and cabinets full of strange, and even hideous, objects filled every available nook in the vast low rooms. Gregg was a man whose one thought was for knowledge, and I too before long caught something of his enthusiasm, and strove to enter into his passion for research. In a few months I was perhaps more his secretary than the governess of the two children, and many a night I have sat at the desk in the glow of the shaded lamp while he, pacing up and down in the rich gloom of the firelight, dictated to me the substance of his *Textbook of Ethnology*. But amidst these more sober and accurate studies I always detected a something hidden, a longing and desire for some object to which he did not allude; and now and then he would break short in what he was saying and lapse into reverie, entranced, as it seemed to me, by some distant prospect of adventurous discovery. The textbook was at last finished, and we began to receive proofs from the printers, which were entrusted to me for a first reading, and then underwent the final revision of the professor. All the while his weariness of the actual business he was engaged on increased, and it was with the joyous laugh of a schoolboy when term is over that he one day handed me a copy of the book. "There," he said, "I have kept my word; I promised to write it, and it is done with. Now I shall be free to live for stranger things; I confess it, Miss Lally, I covet the renown of Columbus; you will, I hope, see me play the part of an explorer."

"Surely," I said, "there is little left to explore. You have been born a few hundred years too late for that."

"I think you are wrong," he replied; "there are still, depend upon it, quaint, undiscovered countries and continents of strange extent. Ah, Miss Lally! believe me, we stand amidst sacraments and mysteries full of awe, and it doth not yet appear what we shall be. Life, believe me, is no simple thing, no mass of grey matter and congeries of veins and

muscles to be laid naked by the surgeon's knife; man is the secret which
I am about to explore, and before I can discover him I must cross over
weltering seas indeed, and oceans and the mists of many thousand years.
You know the myth of the lost Atlantis; what if it be true, and I am
destined to be called the discoverer of that wonderful land?"

I could see excitement boiling beneath his words, and in his face
was the heat of the hunter; before me stood a man who believed himself summoned to tourney with the unknown. A pang of joy possessed
me when I reflected that I was to be in a way associated with him
in the adventure, and I too burned with the lust of the chase, not
pausing to consider that I knew not what we were to unshadow.

The next morning Professor Gregg took me into his inner study,
where, ranged against the wall, stood a nest of pigeon-holes, every
drawer neatly labelled, and the results of years of toil classified in a few
feet of space.

"Here," he said, "is my life; here are all the facts which I have
gathered together with so much pains, and yet it is all nothing. No,
nothing to what I am about to attempt. Look at this"; and he took me
to an old bureau, a piece fantastic and faded, which stood in a corner
of the room. He unlocked the front and opened one of the drawers.

"A few scraps of paper," he went on, pointing to the drawer, "and a
lump of black stone, rudely annotated with queer marks and scratches
—that is all that drawer holds. Here you see is an old envelope with the
dark red stamp of twenty years ago, but I have pencilled a few lines at
the back; here is a sheet of manuscript, and here some cuttings from
obscure local journals. And if you ask me the subject-matter of the
collection, it will not seem extraordinary—a servant-girl at a farmhouse,
who disappeared from her place and has never been heard of, a child
supposed to have slipped down some old working on the mountains,
some queer scribbling on a limestone rock, a man murdered with a blow
from a strange weapon; such is the scent I have to go upon. Yes, as
you say, there is a ready explanation for all this; the girl may have run
away to London, or Liverpool, of New York; the child may be at the
bottom of the disused shaft; and the letters on the rock may be the idle
whims of some vagrant. Yes, yes, I admit all that; but I know I hold
the true key. Look!" and he held out a slip of yellow paper.

Characters found inscribed on a limestone rock on the Grey Hills, I
read, and then there was a word erased, presumably the name of a

county, and a date some fifteen years back. Beneath was traced a number of uncouth characters, shaped somewhat like wedges or daggers, as strange and outlandish as the Hebrew alphabet.

"Now the seal," said Professor Gregg, and he handed me the black stone, a thing about two inches long, and something like an old-fashioned tobacco-stopper, much enlarged.

I held it up to the light, and saw to my surprise the characters on the paper repeated on the seal.

"Yes," said the professor, "they are the same. And the marks on the limestone rock were made fifteen years ago, with some red substance. And the characters on the seal are four thousand years old at least. Perhaps much more."

"Is it a hoax?" I said.

"No, I anticipated that. I was not to be led to give my life to a practical joke. I have tested the matter very carefully. Only one person besides myself knows of the mere existence of that black seal. Besides, there are other reasons which I cannot enter into now."

"But what does it all mean?" I said. "I cannot understand to what conclusion all this leads."

"My dear Miss Lally, that is a question I would rather leave unanswered for some little time. Perhaps I shall never be able to say what secrets are held here in solution; a few vague hints, the outlines of village tragedies, a few marks done with red earth upon a rock, and an ancient seal. A queer set of data to go upon? Half a dozen pieces of evidence, and twenty years before even so much could be got together; and who knows what mirage or *terra incognita* may be beyond all this? I look across deep waters, Miss Lally, and the land beyond may be but a haze after all. But still I believe it is not so, and a few months will show whether I am right or wrong."

He left me, and alone I endeavoured to fathom the mystery, wondering to what goal such eccentric odds and ends of evidence could lead. I myself am not wholly devoid of imagination, and I had reason to respect the professor's solidity of intellect; yet I saw in the contents of the drawer but the materials of fantasy, and vainly tried to conceive what theory could be founded on the fragments that had been placed before me. Indeed, I could discover in what I had heard and seen but the first chapter of an extravagant romance; and yet deep in my heart I burned with curiosity, and day after day I looked eagerly in Professor Gregg's face for some hint of what was to happen.

It was one evening after dinner that the word came.

"I hope you can make your preparations without much trouble," he said suddenly to me. "We shall be leaving here in a week's time."

"Really!" I said in astonishment. "Where are we going?"

"I have taken a country house in the west of England, not far from Caermaen, a quiet little town, once a city, and the headquarters of a Roman legion. It is very dull there, but the country is pretty, and the air is wholesome."

I detected a glint in his eyes, and guessed that this sudden move had some relation to our conversation of a few days before.

"I shall just take a few books with me," said Professor Gregg, "that is all. Everything else will remain here for our return. I have got a holiday," he went on, smiling at me, "and I shan't be sorry to be quit for a time of my old bones and stones and rubbish. Do you know," he went on, "I have been grinding away at facts for thirty years; it is time for fancies."

The days passed quickly; I could see that the professor was all quivering with suppressed excitement, and I could scarce credit the eager appetence of his glance as we left the old manor-house behind us and began our journey. We set out at midday, and it was in the dusk of the evening that we arrived at a little country station. I was tired and excited, and the drive through the lanes seems all a dream. First the deserted streets of a forgotten village, while I heard Professor Gregg's voice talking of the Augustan Legion and the clash of arms, and all the tremendous pomp that followed the eagles; then the broad river swimming to full tide with the last afterglow glimmering duskily in the yellow water, the wide meadows, the cornfields whitening, and the deep lane winding on the slope between the hills and the water. At last we began to ascend, and the air grew rarer. I looked down and saw the pure white mist tracking the outline of the river like a shroud, and a vague and shadowy country; imaginations and fantasy of swelling hills and hanging woods, and half-shaped outlines of hills beyond, and in the distance, the glare of the furnace fire on the mountain, growing by turns a pillar of shining flame and fading to a dull point of red. We were slowly mounting a carriage drive, and then there came to me the cool breath and the secret of the great wood that was above.

T

us; I seemed to wander in its deepest depths, and there was the sound of trickling water, the scent of the green leaves, and the breath of the summer night. The carriage stopped at last, and I could scarcely distinguish the form of the house as I waited a moment at the pillared porch. The rest of the evening seemed a dream of strange things bounded by the great silence of the wood and the valley and the river.

The next morning, when I awoke and looked out of the bow window of the big, old-fashioned bedroom, I saw under a grey sky a country that was still all mystery. The long, lovely valley, with the river winding in and out below, crossed in mid-vision by a medieval bridge of vaulted and buttressed stone, the clear presence of the rising ground beyond, and the woods that I had only seen in shadow the night before, seemed tinged with enchantment, and the soft breath of air that sighed in at the opened pane was like no other wind. I looked across the valley, and beyond, hill followed on hill as wave on wave, and here a faint blue pillar of smoke rose still in the morning air from the chimney of an ancient grey farmhouse, there was a rugged height crowned with dark firs, and in the distance I saw the white streak of a road that climbed and vanished into some unimagined country. But the boundary of all was a great wall of mountain, vast in the west, and ending like a fortress with a steep ascent and a domed tumulus clear against the sky.

I saw Professor Gregg walking up and down the terrace path below the windows, and it was evident that he was revelling in the sense of liberty, and the thought that he had for a while bidden goodbye to task-work. When I joined him there was exultation in his voice as he pointed out the sweep of valley and the river that wound beneath the lovely hills.

"Yes," he said, "it is a strangely beautiful country; and to me, at least, it seems full of mystery. You have not forgotten the drawer I showed you, Miss Lally? No; and you have guessed that I have come here not merely for the sake of the children and the fresh air?"

"I think I have guessed as much as that," I replied; "but you must remember I do not know the mere nature of your investigations; and as for the connection between the search and this wonderful valley, it is past my guessing."

He smiled queerly at me. "You must not think I am making a mystery for the sake of mystery," he said. "I do not speak out because, so far, there is nothing to be spoken, nothing definite, I mean, nothing that can be set down in hard black and white, as dull and sure and irreproachable as any blue-book. And then I have another reason. Many years ago a chance paragraph in a newspaper caught my attention, and focused in an instant the vagrant thoughts and half-formed fancies of many idle and speculative hours into a certain hypothesis. I saw at once that I was treading on a thin crust; my theory was wild and fantastic in the extreme, and I would not for any consideration have written a hint of it for publication. But I thought that in the company of scientific men like myself, men who knew the course of discovery, and were aware that the gas that blazes and flares in the gin-palace was once a wild hypothesis—I thought that with such men as these I might hazard my dream—let us say Atlantis, or the philosopher's stone, or what you like—without danger of ridicule. I found I was grossly mistaken; my friends looked blankly at me and at one another, and I could see something of pity, and something also of insolent contempt, in the glances they exchanged. One of them called on me next day, and hinted that I must be suffering from overwork and brain exhaustion. "In plain terms," I said, "you think I am going mad. I think not"; and I showed him out with some little appearance of heat. Since that day I vowed that I would never whisper the nature of my theory to any living soul; to no one but yourself have I ever shown the contents of that drawer. After all, I may be following a rainbow; I may have been misled by the play of coincidence; but as I stand here in this mystic hush and silence amidst the woods and wild hills, I am more than ever sure that I am hot on the scent. Come, it is time we went in."

To me in all this there was something both of wonder and excitement; I knew how in his ordinary work Professor Gregg moved step by step, testing every inch of the way, and never venturing on assertion without proof that was impregnable. Yet I divined more from his glance and the vehemence of his tone than from the spoken word, that he had in his every thought the vision of the almost incredible continually with him; and I, who was with some share of imagination no little of a sceptic, offended at a hint of the marvellous, could not help asking myself whether he were cherishing a monomania, and barring out from this one subject all the scientific method of his other life.

Yet, with this image of mystery haunting my thoughts, I surrendered wholly to the charm of the country. Above the faded house on the hillside began the great forest—a long, dark line seen from the opposing hills, stretching above the river for many a mile from north to south, and yielding in the north to even wilder country, barren and savage hills, and ragged commonland, a territory all strange and unvisited, and more unknown to Englishmen than the very heart of Africa. The space of a couple of steep fields alone separated the house from the wood, and the children were delighted to follow me up the long alleys of undergrowth, between smooth pleached walls of shining beech, to the highest point in the wood, whence one looked on one side across the river and the rise and fall of the country to the great western mountain wall, and on the other over the surge and dip of the myriad trees of the forest, over level meadows and the shining yellow sea to the faint coast beyond. I used to sit at this point on the warm sunlit turf which marked the track of the Roman Road, while the two children raced about hunting for the whinberries that grew here and there on the banks. Here beneath the deep blue sky and the great clouds rolling, like olden galleons with sails full-bellied, from the sea to the hills, as I listened to the whispered charm of the great and ancient wood, I lived solely for delight, and only remembered strange things when we would return to the house and find Professor Gregg either shut up in the little room he had made his study, or else pacing the terrace with the look, patient and enthusiastic, of the determined seeker.

One morning, some eight or nine days after our arrival, I looked out of my window and saw the whole landscape transmuted before me. The clouds had dipped low and hidden the mountain in the west; a southern wind was driving the rain in shifting pillars up the valley, and the little brooklet that burst the hill below the house now raged, a red torrent, down the river. We were perforce obliged to keep snug within-doors; and when I had attended to my pupils, I sat down in the morning-room where the ruins of a library still encumbered an old-fashioned bookcase. I had inspected the shelves once or twice, but their contents had failed to attract me; volumes of eighteenth-century sermons, an old book on farriery, a collection of *Poems* by "persons of quality", Prideaux's *Connection*, and an odd volume of Pope, were the boundaries of the library, and there seemed little doubt that everything of interest or value had been removed. Now however, in desperation, I began to re-examine the musty sheepskin and calf bindings, and found, much to my delight, a fine old quarto printed by the Stephani, containing the three books of Pomponius Mela, *De Situ Orbis*, and other of the ancient geographers. I knew enough of Latin to steer my way through an ordinary sentence, and I soon became absorbed in the odd mixture of fact and fancy—light shining on a little of the space of the world, and beyond, mist and shadow and awful forms. Glancing over the clear-printed pages, my attention was caught by the heading of a chapter in Solinus, and I read the words:

"Mira de intimis gentibus libyae, de lapide Hexecontalitho,"

—"The wonders of the people that inhabit the inner parts of Libya, and of the stone called Sixtystone."

The odd title attracted me, and I read on: "Gens ista avia et secreta habitat, in montibus horrendis fœda mysteria celebrat. De hominibus nihil aliud illi praeferunt quam figuram, ab humano ritu prorsus exulant, oderunt deum lucis. Strident potius quam loquuntur; vox absona nec sine horrore auditur. Lapide quodam gloriantur, quem Hexecontalithon vocant; dicunt enim hunc lapidem sexaginta notas ostendere. Cujus lapidis nomen secretum ineffabile colunt: quod Ixaxar."

"This folk," I translated to myself, "dwells in remote and secret places, and celebrates foul mysteries on savage hills. Nothing have they in common with men save the face, and the customs of humanity are wholly strange to them; and they hate the sun. They hiss rather than speak; their voices are harsh, and not to be heard without fear. They boast of a certain stone, which they call Sixtystone; for they say that it displays sixty characters. And this stone has a secret unspeakable name; which is Ixaxar."

I laughed at the queer inconsequence of all this, and thought it fit for *Sinbad the Sailor*, or other of the supplementary Nights. When I saw Professor Gregg in the course of the day, I told him of my find in the bookcase, and the fantastic rubbish I had been reading. To my surprise he looked up at me with an expression of great interest.

"That is really very curious," he said. "I have never thought it worth while to look into the old geographers, and I daresay I have missed a good deal. Ah, that is the passage, is it? It seems a shame to rob you of your entertainment, but I really think I must carry off the book."

The next day the professor called me to come to the study. I found him sitting at a table in the full light of the window, scrutinizing something very attentively with a magnifying glass.

"Ah, Miss Lally," he began, "I want to use your eyes. This glass is pretty good, but not like my old one that I left in town. Would you mind examining the thing yourself, and telling me how many characters are cut on it?"

He handed me the object in his hand. I saw that it was the black seal he had shown me in London, and my heart began to beat with the thought that I was presently to know something. I took the seal, and, holding it up to the light, checked off the grotesque dagger-shaped characters one by one.

"I make sixty-two," I said at last.

"Sixty-two? Nonsense; it's impossible. Ah, I see what you have done, you have counted that and that," and he pointed to two marks which I had certainly taken as letters with the rest.

"Yes, yes," Professor Gregg went on, "but those are obvious scratches, done accidentally; I saw that at once. Yes, then that's quite right. Thank you very much, Miss Lally."

I was going away, rather disappointed at my having been called in merely to count the number of marks on the black seal, when suddenly there flashed into my mind what I had read in the morning.

"But, Professor Gregg," I cried, breathless, "the seal, the seal Why, it is the stone Hexecontalithos that Solinus writes of; it is Ixaxar."

"Yes," he said, "I suppose it is. Or it may be a mere coincidence. I never does to be too sure, you know, in these matters. Coincidence killed the professor."

I went away puzzled by what I had heard, and as much as ever at loss to find the ruling clue in this maze of strange evidence. For three days the bad weather lasted, changing from driving rain to a dense mist, fine and dripping, and we seemed to be shut up in a white cloud that veiled all the world away from us. All the while Professor Gregg wa darkling in his room, unwilling, it appeared, to dispense confidences o talk of any kind, and I heard him walking to and fro with a quick impatient step, as if he were in some way wearied of inaction. Th fourth morning was fine, and at breakfast the professor said briskly—

"We want some extra help about the house; a boy of fifteen or six teen, you know. There are a lot of little odd jobs that take up the maids time which a boy could do much better."

"The girls have not complained to me in any way," I replied. "Indeed, Anne said there was much less work than in London, owing to there being so little dust."

"Ah, yes, they are very good girls. But I think we shall do much better with a boy. In fact, that is what has been bothering me for the last two days."

"Bothering you?" I said in astonishment, for as a matter of fact the professor never took the slightest interest in the affairs of the house.

"Yes," he said, "the weather, you know. I really couldn't go out in that Scotch mist; I don't know the country very well, and I should have lost my way. But I am going to get the boy this morning."

"But how do you know there is such a boy as you want anywhere about?"

"Oh, I have no doubt as to that. I may have to walk a mile or two at the most, but I am sure to find just the boy I require."

I thought the professor was joking, but though his tone was airy enough there was something grim and set about his features that puzzled me. He got his stick, and stood at the door looking meditatively before him, and as I passed through the hall he called to me.

"By the way, Miss Lally, there was one thing I wanted to say to you. I daresay you may have heard that some of these country lads are not over bright; idiotic would be a harsh word to use, and they are usually called 'naturals', or something of the kind. I hope you won't mind if the boy I am after should turn out not too keen-witted; he will be perfectly harmless, of course, and blacking boots doesn't need much mental effort."

With that he was gone, striding up the road that led to the wood, and I remained stupefied; and then for the first time my astonishment was mingled with a sudden note of terror, arising I knew not whence, and all unexplained even to myself, and yet I felt about my heart for an instant something of the chill of death, and that shapeless, formless dread of the unknown that is worse than death itself. I tried to find courage in the sweet air that blew up from the sea, and in the sunlight after rain, but the mystic woods seemed to darken around me; and the vision of the river coiling between the reeds, and the silver grey of the ancient bridge, fashioned in my mind symbols of vague dread, as the mind of a child fashions terror from things harmless and familiar.

Two hours later Professor Gregg returned. I met him as he came down the road, and asked quietly if he had been able to find a boy.

"Oh, yes," he answered; "I found one easily enough. His name is Jervase Cradock, and I expect he will make himself very useful. His father has been dead for many years, and the mother, whom I saw, seemed very glad at the prospect of a few shillings extra coming in on Saturday nights. As I expected, he is not too sharp, has fits at times, the mother said; but as he will not be trusted with the china, that doesn't much matter, does it? And he is not in any way dangerous, you know, merely a little weak."

"When is he coming?"

"To-morrow morning at eight o'clock. Anne will show him what he has to do, and how to do it. At first he will go home every night, but perhaps it may ultimately turn out more convenient for him to sleep here, and only go home for Sundays."

I found nothing to say to all this; Professor Gregg spoke in a quiet tone of matter-of-fact, as indeed was warranted by the circumstance; and yet I could not quell my sensation of astonishment at the whole affair. I knew that in reality no assistance was wanted in the house-work, and the professor's prediction that the boy he was to engage might prove a little "simple", followed by so exact a fulfilment, struck me as bizarre in the extreme. The next morning I heard from the housemaid that the boy Cradock had come at eight, and that she had been trying to make him useful. "He doesn't seem quite all there, I don't think, miss," was her comment, and later in the day I saw him helping the old man who worked in the garden. He was a youth of about fourteen, with black hair and black eyes and an olive skin, and I saw at once from the curious vacancy of his expression that he was mentally weak. He touched his forehead awkwardly as I went by, and I heard him answering the gardener in a queer, harsh voice that caught my attention; it gave me the impression of some one speaking deep below under the earth, and there was a strange sibilance, like the hissing of the phonograph as the pointer travels over the cylinder. I heard that he seemed anxious to do what he could, and was quite docile and obedient, and Morgan the gardener, who knew his mother, assured me he was perfectly harmless. "He's always been a bit queer," he said, "and no wonder, after what his mother went through before he was born. I did know his father, Thomas Cradock, well, and a very fine workman he was too, indeed. He got something wrong with his lungs owing to working in the wet woods, and never got over it, and went off quite sudden like. And they do say as how Mrs. Cradock was quite off her head; anyhow, she was found by Mr. Hillyer, Ty Coch, all crouched up on the Grey Hills, over there, crying and weeping like a lost soul. And Jervase, he was born about eight months afterwards, and as I was saying, he was a bit queer always; and they do say when he could scarcely walk he would frighten the other children into fits with the noises he would make."

A word in the story had stirred up some remembrance within me, and, vaguely curious, I asked the old man where the Grey Hills were.

"Up there," he said, with the same gesture he had used before; you go past the 'Fox and Hounds', and through the forest, by the old ruins. It's a good five mile from here, and a strange sort of a place. The poorest soil between this and Monmouth, they do say, though it's good feed for sheep. Yes, it was a sad thing for poor Mrs. Cradock."

The old man turned to his work, and I strolled on down the path between the espaliers, gnarled and gouty with age, thinking of the story I had heard, and groping for the point in it that had some key to my memory. In an instant it came before me; I had seen the phrase, "Grey Hills" on the slip of yellowed paper that Professor Gregg had taken from the drawer in his cabinet. Again I was seized with pangs of mingled curiosity and fear. I remembered the strange characters copied from the limes one rock, and then again their identity with the inscription on the age-old seal, and the fantastic fables of the Latin geographer. I saw beyond doubt that, unless coincidence had set all the scene and disposed all these bizarre events with curious art, I was to be a spectator of things far removed from the usual and customary traffic and jostle of life. Professor Gregg I noted day by day; he was hot on his trail, growing lean with eagerness; and in the evenings, when the sun was swimming on the verge of the mountain, he would pace the terrace to and fro with his eyes on the ground, while the mist grew white in the valley and the stillness of the evening brought far voices near, and the blue smoke rose a straight column from the diamond-shaped chimney of the grey farmhouse, just as I had seen it on the first morning. I have told you I was of sceptical habit; but though I understood little or nothing, I began to dread, vainly proposing to myself the iterated dogmas of science that all life is material, and that in the system of things there is no undiscovered land, even beyond the remotest stars, where the supernatural can find a footing. Yet there struck in on this the thought that matter is as really awful and unknown as spirit, that science itself but dallies on the threshold, scarcely gaining more than a glimpse of the wonders of the inner place.

There is one day that stands up from amidst the others as a grim red beacon, betokening evil to come. I was sitting on a bench in the garden, watching the boy Cradock weeding, when I was suddenly alarmed by a harsh and choking sound, like the cry of a wild beast in anguish, and I was unspeakably shocked to see the unfortunate lad standing in full view before me, his whole body quivering and shaking at short intervals as though shocks of electricity were passing through him, his teeth grinding, foam gathering on his lips, and his face all swollen and blackened to a hideous mask of humanity. I shrieked with terror, and Professor Gregg came running; and as I pointed to Cradock, the boy with one convulsive shudder fell face forward, and lay on the wet earth, his body writhing like a wounded blind-worm, and an inconceivable babble of sounds bursting and rattling and hissing from his lips. He seemed to pour forth an infamous jargon, with words, or what seemed words, that might have belonged to a tongue dead since untold ages, and buried deep beneath Nilotic mud, or in the inmost recesses of the Mexican forest. For a moment the thought passed through my mind, as my ears were still revolted with that infernal clamour, "Surely this is the very speech of hell," and then I cried out again and again, and ran away shuddering to my inmost soul. I had seen Professor Gregg's face as he stooped over the wretched boy and raised him, and I was appalled by the glow of exultation that shone on every lineament and feature. As I sat in my room with drawn blinds, and my eyes hidden in my hands, I heard heavy steps beneath, and I was told afterwards that Professor Gregg had carried Cradock to his study, and had locked the door. I heard voices murmur indistinctly, and I trembled to think of what might be passing within a few feet of where I sat; I longed to escape to the woods and sunshine, and yet I dreaded the sights that might confront me on the way; and at last, as I held the handle of the door nervously, I heard Professor Gregg's voice calling to me with a cheerful ring. "It's all right now, Miss Lally," he said. "The poor fellow has got over it, and I have been arranging for him to sleep here after tomorrow. Perhaps I may be able to do something for him."

"Yes," he said later, "it was a very painful sight, and I don't wonder you were alarmed. We may hope that good food will build him up a little, but I am afraid he will never be really cured," and he affected the dismal and conventional air with which one speaks of hopeless illness; and yet beneath it I detected the delight that leapt up rampant within him, and fought and struggled to find utterance. It was as if one glanced down on the even surface of the sea, clear and immobile, and saw beneath raging depths and a storm of contending billows. It was indeed to me a torturing and offensive problem that this man, who had so bounteously rescued me from the sharpness of death, and showed himself in all the relations of life full of benevolence, and pity, and kindly forethought, should so manifestly be for once on the side of the demons, and take a ghastly pleasure in the torments of an afflicted fellow-creature. Apart, I struggled with the horned difficulty, and strove to find the solution; but without the hint of a clue, beset by mystery and contradiction, I saw nothing that might help me, and began to wonder whether, after all, I had not escaped from the white mist of the suburb at too dear a rate. I hinted something of my thought to the professor; I said enough to let him know that I was in the most acute perplexity, but the moment after regretted what I had done when I saw his face contort with a spasm of pain.

"My dear Miss Lally," he said, "you surely do not wish to leave us? No, no, you would not do it. You do not know how I rely on you, how confidently I go forward, assured that you are here to watch over my children. You, Miss Lally, are my rearguard; for let me tell you the business in which I am engaged is not wholly devoid of peril. You have not forgotten what I said the first morning here; my lips are shut by an old and firm resolve till they can open to utter no ingenious hypothesis or vague surmise but irrefragable fact, as certain as a demonstration in mathematics. Think over it, Miss Lally: not for a moment would I endeavour to keep you here against your own instincts, and yet I tell you frankly that I am persuaded it is here, here amidst the woods, that your duty lies."

I was touched by the eloquence of his tone, and by the remembrance that the man, after all, had been my salvation, and I gave him my hand on a promise to serve him loyally and without question. A few days later the rector of our church—a little church, grey and severe and quaint, that hovered on the very banks of the river and watched the tides swim and return—came to see us, and Professor Gregg easily persuaded him to stay and share our dinner. Mr. Meyrick was a member of an antique family of squires, whose old manor-house stood amongst the hills some seven miles away, and thus rooted in the soil, the rector was a living store of all the old fading customs and lore of the country. His manner, genial, with a deal of retired oddity, won on Professor Gregg; and towards the cheese, when a curious Burgundy had begun its incantations, the two men glowed like the wine, and talked of philology with the enthusiasm of a burgess over the peerage. The parson was expounding the pronunciation of the Welsh *ll*, and producing sounds like the gurgle of his native brooks, when Professor Gregg struck in.

"By the way," he said, "that was a very odd word I met with the other day. You know my boy, poor Jervase Cradock? Well, he has got the bad habit of talking to himself, and the day before yesterday I was walking in the garden here and heard him; he was evidently quite unconscious of my presence. A lot of what he said I couldn't make out, but one word struck me distinctly. It was such an odd sound, half sibilant, half guttural, and as quaint as those double *l's* you have been demonstrating. I do not know whether I can give you an idea of the sound; 'Ishakshar' is perhaps as near as I can get. But the *k* ought to be a Greek *chi* or a Spanish *j*. Now what does it mean in Welsh?"

"In Welsh?" said the parson. "There is no such word in Welsh, nor any word remotely resembling it. I know the book-Welsh, as they call it, and the colloquial dialects as well as any man, but there's no word like that from Anglesea to Usk. Besides, none of the Cradocks speaks a word of Welsh; it's dying out about here."

"Really. You interest me extremely, Mr. Meyrick. I confess the word didn't strike me as having the Welsh ring. But I thought it might be some local corruption."

"No, I never heard such a word, or anything like it. Indeed," he added, smiling whimsically, "if it belongs to any language, I should say it must be that of the fairies—the Tylwydd Teg, as we call them."

The talk went on to the discovery of a Roman villa in the neighbourhood; and soon after I left the room, and sat down apart to wonder at the drawing together of such strange clues of evidence. As the professor had spoken of the curious word, I had caught the glint of his eye upon me; and though the pronunciation he gave was grotesque in the extreme, I recognized the name of the stone of sixty characters mentioned by Solinus, the black seal shut up in some secret drawer of the study, stamped for ever by a vanished race with signs that no man could read, signs that might, for all I knew, be the veils of awful things done long ago, and forgotten before the hills were moulded into form.

When the next morning I came down, I found Professor Gregg pacing the terrace in his eternal walk.

"Look at that bridge," he said, when he saw me; "observe the quaint and Gothic design, the angles between the arches, and the silvery grey of the stone in the awe of the morning light. I confess it seems to me symbolic; it should illustrate a mystical allegory of the passage from one world to another."

"Professor Gregg," I said quietly, "it is time that I knew something of what has happened, and of what is to happen."

For the moment he put me off, but I returned again with the same question in the evening, and then Professor Gregg flamed with excitement. "Don't you understand yet?" he cried. "But I have told you a good deal; yes, and shown you a good deal; you have heard pretty nearly all that I have heard, and seen what I have seen; or at least," and his voice chilled as he spoke, "enough to make a good deal clear as noonday. The servants told you, I have no doubt, that the wretched boy Cradock had another seizure the night before last; he awoke me with cries in that voice you heard in the garden, and I went to him, and God forbid you should see what I saw that night. But all this is useless; my time here is drawing to a close; I must be back in town in three weeks, as I have a course of lectures to prepare, and need all my books about me. In a very few days it will be all over, and I shall no longer hint, and no longer be liable to ridicule as a madman and a quack. No, I shall speak plainly, and I shall be heard with such emotions as perhaps no other man has ever drawn from the breasts of his fellows."

He paused, and seemed to grow radiant with the joy of great and wonderful discovery.

"But all that is for the future, the near future certainly, but still the future," he went on at length. "There is something to be done yet; you will remember my telling you that my researches were not altogether devoid of peril? Yes, there is a certain amount of danger to be faced; I did not know how much when I spoke on the subject before, and to a certain extent I am still in the dark. But it will be a strange adventure, the last of all, the last demonstration in the chain."

He was walking up and down the room as he spoke, and I could hear in his voice the contending tones of exultation and despondence, or perhaps I should say awe, the awe of a man who goes forth on unknown waters, and I thought of his allusion to Columbus on the night he had laid his book before me. The evening was a little chilly, and a fire of logs had been lighted in the study where we were; the remittent flame and the glow on the walls reminded me of the old days. I was sitting silent in an arm-chair by the fire, wondering over all I had heard, and still vainly speculating as to the secret springs concealed from me under all the phantasmagoria I had witnessed, when I became suddenly aware of a sensation that change of some sort had been at work in the room, and that there was something unfamiliar in its aspect. For some time I looked about me, trying in vain to localize the alteration that I knew had been made; the table by the window, the chairs, the faded settee were all as I had known them. Suddenly, as a sought-for recollection flashes into the mind, I knew what was amiss. I was facing the professor's desk, which stood on the other side of the fire, and above the desk was a grimy-looking bust of Pitt, that I had never seen there before. And then I remembered the true position of this work of art; in the furthest corner by the door was an old cupboard, projecting into the room, and on the top of the cupboard, fifteen feet from the floor, the bust had been, and there, no doubt, it had delayed, accumulating dirt, since the early years of the century.

I was utterly amazed, and sat silent still, in a confusion of thought. There was, so far as I knew, no such thing as a step-ladder in the house, for I had asked for one to make some alterations in the curtains of my room, and a tall man standing on a chair would have found it impossible to take down the bust. It had been placed, not on the edge of the cupboard, but far back against the wall; and Professor Gregg was, if anything, under the average height.

"How on earth did you manage to get down Pitt?" I said at last.

The professor looked curiously at me, and seemed to hesitate a little.

"They must have found you a step-ladder, or perhaps the gardener brought in a short ladder from outside?"

"No, I have had no ladder of any kind. Now, Miss Lally," he went on with an awkward simulation of jest, "there is a little puzzle for you; a problem in the manner of the inimitable Holmes; there are the facts, plain and patent; summon your acuteness to the solution of the puzzle. For Heaven's sake," he cried with a breaking voice, "say no more .about it! I tell you, I never touched the thing," and he went out of the room with horror manifest on his face, and his hand shook and jarred the door behind him.

I looked round the room in vague surprise, not at all realizing what had happened, making vain and idle surmises by way of explanation, and wondering at the stirring of black waters by an idle word and the trivial change of an ornament. "This is some petty business, some whim on which I have jarred," I reflected; "the professor is perhaps scrupulous and superstitious over trifles, and my question may have outraged unacknowledged fears, as though one killed a spider or spilled the salt before the very eyes of a practical Scotchwoman." I was immersed in these fond suspicions, and began to plume myself a little on my immunity from such empty fears, when the truth fell heavily as lead upon my heart, and I recognized with cold terror that some awful influence had been at work. The bust was simply inaccessible; without a ladder no one could have touched it.

I went out to the kitchen and spoke quietly as I could to the housemaid.

"Who moved that bust from the top of the cupboard, Anne?" I said to her. "Professor Gregg says he has not touched it. Did you find an old step-ladder in one of the outhouses?"

The girl looked at me blankly.

"I never touched it," she said. "I found it where it is now the other morning when I dusted the room. I remember now, it was Wednesday morning, because it was the morning after Cradock was taken bad in the night. My room is next to his, you know, miss," the girl went on piteously, "and it was awful to hear how he cried and called out names that I couldn't understand. It made me feel all afraid; and the master came and I heard him speak, and he took down Cradock to the study and gave him something."

"And you found that bust moved the next morning?"

"Yes, miss. There was a queer sort of smell in the study when I came down and opened the windows; a bad smell it was, and I wondered what it could be. Do you know miss, I went a long time ago to the Zoo in London with my cousin Thomas Barker, one afternoon that I had off, when I was at Mrs. Prince's in Stanhope Gate, and we went into the snake-house to see the snakes, and it was just the same sort of smell; very sick it made me feel, I remember, and I got Barker to take me out. And it was just the same kind of a smell in the study, as I was saying, and I was wondering what it could be from, when I see that bust with Pitt cut in it, standing on the master's desk, and I thought to myself, Now who has done that, and how have they done it? And when I came to dust the things, I looked at the bust, and I saw a great mark on it where the dust was gone, for I don't think it can have been touched with a duster for years and years, and it wasn't like finger-marks, but a large patch like, broad and spread out. So I passed my hand over it, without thinking what I was doing, and where that patch was it was all sticky and slimy, as if a snail had crawled over it. Very strange, isn't it, miss? and I wonder who can have done it, and how that mess was made."

The well-meant gabble of the servant touched me to the quick; I lay down upon my bed, and bit my lip that I should not cry out loud in the sharp anguish of my terror and bewilderment. Indeed, I was almost mad with dread; I believe that if it had been daylight I should have fled hot foot, forgetting all courage and all the debt of gratitude that was due to Professor Gregg, not caring whether my fate were that I must starve slowly, so long as I might escape from the net of blind and panic fear that every day seemed to draw a little closer round me. If I knew, I thought, if I knew what there were to dread, I could guard against it; but here, in this lonely house, shut in on all sides by the olden woods and the vaulted hills, terror seems to spring inconsequent from every covert, and the flesh is aghast at the half-heard murmurs of horrible things. All in vain I strove to summon scepticism to my aid, and endeavoured by cool common sense to buttress my belief in a world of natural order, for the air that blew in at the open window was a mystic breath, and in the darkness I felt the silence go heavy and sorrowful as a mass of requiem, and I conjured images of strange shapes gathering fast amidst the reeds, beside the wash of the river.

In the morning, from the moment that I set foot in the breakfast-room, I felt that the unknown plot was drawing to a crisis; the professor's face was firm and set, and he seemed hardly to hear our voices when we spoke.

"I am going out for a rather long walk," he said, when the meal was over. "You mustn't be expecting me, now, or thinking anything has happened if I don't turn up to dinner. I have been getting stupid lately, and I dare say a miniature walking tour will do me good. Perhaps I may even spend the night in some little inn, if I find any place that looks clean and comfortable."

I heard this, and knew by my experience of Professor Gregg's manner that it was no ordinary business or pleasure that impelled him. I knew not, nor even remotely guessed, where he was bound, nor had I the vaguest notion of his errand, but all the fear of the night before returned; and as he stood, smiling, on the terrace, ready to set out, I implored him to stay, and to forget all his dreams of the undiscovered continent.

"No, no, Miss Lally," he replied, still smiling, "it's too late now. *Vestigia nulla retrorsum*, you know, is the device of all true explorers, though I hope it won't be literally true in my case. But, indeed, you are wrong to alarm yourself so; I look upon my little expedition as quite commonplace; no more exciting than a day with the geological hammers. There is a risk, of course, but so there is on the commonest excursion. I can afford to be jaunty; I am doing nothing so hazardous as 'Arry does a hundred times over in the course of every Bank Holiday. Well, then, you must look more cheerfully; and so goodbye till tomorrow at latest."

He walked briskly up the road, and I saw him open the gate that marks the entrance of the wood, and then he vanished in the gloom of the trees.

All the day passed heavily with a strange darkness in the air, and again I felt as if imprisoned amidst the ancient woods, shut in an olden land of mystery and dread, and as if all was long ago and forgotten by the living outside. I hoped and dreaded; and when the dinner-hour came I waited, expecting to hear the professor's step in the hall, and his voice exulting at I knew not what triumph. I composed my face to welcome him gladly, but the night descended dark, and he did not come.

In the morning, when the maid knocked at my door, I called out to her, and asked if her master had returned; and when she replied that his bedroom stood open and empty, I felt the cold clasp of despair.

U

Still, I fancied he might have discovered genial company, and would return for luncheon, or perhaps in the afternoon, and I took the children for a walk in the forest, and tried my best to play and laugh with them, and to shut out the thoughts of mystery and veiled terror. Hour after hour I waited, and my thoughts grew darker; again the night came and found me watching, and at last, as I was making much ado to finish my dinner, I heard steps outside and the sound of a man's voice.

The maid came in and looked oddly at me. "Please, miss," she began, "Mr. Morgan the gardener wants to speak to you for a minute, if you didn't mind."

"Show him in, please," I answered, and I set my lips tight.

The old man came slowly into the room, and the servant shut the door behind him.

"Sit down, Mr. Morgan," I said; "what is it that you want to say to me?"

"Well, miss, Mr. Gregg he gave me something for you yesterday morning, just before he went off; and he told me particular not to hand it up before eight o'clock this evening exactly, if so be as he wasn't back again home before, and if he should come home before I was just to return it to him in his own hands. So, you see, as Mr. Gregg isn't here yet, I suppose I'd better give you the parcel directly."

He pulled out something from his pocket, and gave it to me, half rising. I took it silently, and seeing that Morgan seemed doubtful as to what he was to do next, I thanked him and bade him good-night, and he went out. I was left alone in the room with the parcel in my hand— a paper parcel neatly sealed and directed to me, with the instructions Morgan had quoted all written in the professor's large loose hand. I broke the seals with a choking at my heart, and found an envelope inside, addressed also, but open, and I took the letter out.

"MY DEAR MISS LALLY," it began, "To quote the old logic manual, the case of your reading this note is a case of my having made a blunder of some sort, and, I am afraid, a blunder that turns these lines into a farewell. It is practically certain that neither you nor anyone else will ever see me again. I have made my will with provision for this eventuality, and I hope you will consent to accept the small remembrance addressed to you, and my sincere thanks for the way in which you joined your fortunes to mine. The fate which has come upon me is desperate and terrible beyond the remotest dreams of man; but this fate you have a right to know—if you please. If you look in the left-hand drawer of my dressing-table, you will find the key of the escritoire, properly labelled. In the well of the escritoire is a large envelope sealed and addressed to your name. I advise you to throw it forthwith into the fire; you will sleep better of nights if you do so. But if you must know the history of what has happened, it is all written down for you to read."

The signature was firmly written below, and again I turned the page and read out the words one by one, aghast and white to the lips, my hands cold as ice, and sickness choking me. The dead silence of the room, and the thought of the dark woods and hills closing me in on every side, oppressed me, helpless and without capacity, and not knowing where to turn for counsel. At last I resolved that though knowledge should haunt my whole life and all the days to come, I must know the meaning of the strange terrors that had so long tormented me, rising grey, dim, and awful, like the shadows in the wood at dusk. I carefully carried out Professor Gregg's directions, and not without reluctance broke the seal of the envelope, and spread out his manuscript before me. That manuscript I always carry with me, and I see that I cannot deny your unspoken request to read it. This, then, was what I read that night, sitting at the desk, with a shaded lamp beside me.

The young lady who called herself Miss Lally then proceeded to recite

The Statement of William Gregg, F.R.S., etc.

It is many years since the first glimmer of the theory which is now almost, if not quite, reduced to fact dawned on my mind. A somewhat extensive course of miscellaneous and obsolete reading had done a good deal to prepare the way, and, later, when I became somewhat of a specialist, and immersed myself in the studies known as ethnological, I was now and then startled by facts that would not square with orthodox scientific opinion, and by discoveries that seemed to hint at something still hidden for all our research. More particularly I became convinced that much of the folk-lore of the world is but an exaggerated account of events that really happened, and I was especially drawn to consider the stories of the fairies, the good folk of the Celtic races.

Here I thought I could detect the fringe of embroidery and exagger-ation, the fantastic guise, the little people dressed in green and gold sporting in the flowers, and I thought I saw a distinct analogy between the name given to this race (supposed to be imaginary) and the descrip-tion of their appearance and manners. Just as our remote ancestors called the dreaded beings "fair" and "good" precisely because they dreaded them, so they had dressed them up in charming forms, knowing the truth to be the very reverse. Literature, too, had gone early to work, and had lent a powerful hand in the transformation, so that the playful elves of Shakespeare are already far removed from the true original, and the real horror is disguised in a form of prankish mischief. But in the older tales, the stories that used to make men cross themselves as they sat round the burning logs, we tread a different stage; I saw a widely opposed spirit in certain histories of children and of men and women who vanished strangely from the earth. They would be seen by a peasant in the fields walking towards some green and rounded hillock, and seen no more on earth; and there are stories of mothers who have left a child quietly sleeping, with the cottage door rudely barred with a piece of wood, and have returned, not to find the plump and rosy little Saxon, but a thin and wizened creature, with sallow skin and black, piercing eyes, the child of another race. Then, again, there were myths darker still; the dread of witch and wizard, the lurid evil of the Sabbath, and the hint of demons who mingled with the daughters of men. And just as we have turned the terrible "fair folk" into a company of benignant, if freakish, elves, so we have hidden from us the black foulness of the witch and her companions under a popular *diablerie* of old women and broomsticks and a comic cat with tail on end. So the Greeks called the hideous furies benevolent ladies, and thus the northern nations have followed their example. I pursued my investigations, stealing odd hours from other and more imperative labours, and I asked myself the question: Supposing these traditions to be true, who were the demons who are reported to have attended the Sabbaths? I need not say that I laid aside what I may call the super-natural hypothesis of the Middle Ages, and came to the conclusion that fairies and devils were of one and the same race and origin; inven-tion, no doubt, and the Gothic fancy of old days, had done much in the way of exaggeration and distortion; yet I firmly believe that beneath all this imagery there was a black background of truth. As for some of the alleged wonders, I hesitated. While I should be very loath to receive any one specific instance of modern spiritualism as containing even a grain of the genuine, yet I was not wholly prepared to deny that human flesh may now and then, once perhaps in ten million cases, be the veil of powers which seem magical to us—powers which, so far from proceeding from the heights and leading men thither, are in reality survivals from the depths of being. The amœba and the snail have powers which we do not possess; and I thought it possible that the theory of reversion might explain many things which seem wholly inexplicable. Thus stood my position; I saw good reason to believe that much of the tradition, a vast deal of the earliest and uncorrupted tradition of the so-called fairies, represented solid fact, and I thought that the purely supernatural element in these traditions was to be accounted for on the hypothesis that a race which had fallen out of the grand march of evolution might have retained, as a survival, cer ain powers which would be to us wholly miraculous. Such was my theory as it stood conceived in my mind; and working with this in view, I seemed to gather confirmation from every side, from the spoils of a tumulus or a barrow, from a local paper reporting an antiquarian meeting in the country, and from general literature of all kinds. Amongst other instances, I remember being struck by the phrase "articulate-speaking men" in Homer, as if the writer knew or had heard of men whose speech was so rude that it could hardly be termed articulate; and on my hypothesis of a race who had lagged far behind the rest, I could easily conceive that such a folk would speak a jargon but little removed from the inar iculate noises of brute beasts.

Thus I stood, satisfied that my conjecture was at all events not far removed from fact, when a chance paragraph in a small country print one day arrested my attention. It was a short account of what was to all appearance the usual sordid tragedy of the village—a young girl unaccountably missing, and evil rumour blatant and busy with her reputation. Yet I could read between the lines that all this scandal was purely hypothetical, and in all probability invented to account for what was in any other manner unaccountable. A flight to London or Liverpool, or an undiscovered body lying with a weight about its neck in the foul depths of a woodland pool, or perhaps murder—such were the theories of the wretched girl's neighbours. But as I idly scanned the paragraph, a flash of thought passed through me with the violence of an electric shock: what if the obscure and horrible race of the hills still survived, still remained haunting wild places and barren hills, and now and then repeating the evil of Gothic legend, unchanged and unchangeable as the Turanian Shelta, or the Basques of Spain? I have said that the thought came with violence; and indeed I drew in my breath sharply, and clung with both hands to my elbow-chair, in a strange confusion of horror and elation. It was as if one of my *confrères* of physical science, roaming in a quiet English wood, had been suddenly stricken aghast by the presence of the slimy and loathsome terror of the ichthyosaurus, the original of the stories of the awful worms killed by valorous knights, or had seen the sun darkened by the pterodactyl, the dragon of tradition. Yet as a resolute explorer of knowledge, the thought of such a discovery threw me into a passion of joy, and I cut out the slip from the paper and put it in a drawer in my old bureau, resolved that it should be but the first piece in a collection of the strangest significance. I sat long that evening dreaming of the conclusions I should establish, nor did cooler reflection at first dash my confidence. Yet as I began to put the case fairly, I saw that I might be building on an unstable foundation; the facts might possibly be in accordance with local opinion, and I regarded the affair with a mood of some reserve. Yet I resolved to remain perched on the look-out, and I hugged to myself the thought that I alone was watching and wakeful, while the great crowd of thinkers and searchers stood heedless and indifferent, perhaps letting the most prerogative facts pass by unnoticed.

Several years elapsed before I was enabled to add to the contents of the drawer; and the second find was in reality not a valuable one, for it was a mere repetition of the first, with only the variation of another and distant locality. Yet I gained something; for in the second case, as in the first, the tragedy took place in a desolate and lonely country, and so far my theory seemed justified. But the third piece was to me far more decisive. Again, amongst outland hills, far even from a main road of traffic, an old man was found done to death, and the instrument of execution was left beside him. Here, indeed, there were rumour and conjecture, for the deadly tool was a primitive stone axe, bound by gut to the wooden handle, and surmises the most extravagant and improbable were indulged in. Yet, as I thought with a kind of glee, the wildest conjectures went far astray; and I took the pains to enter into correspondence with the local doctor, who was called at the inquest. He, a man of some acuteness, was dumbfounded. "It will not do to speak of these things in country places," he wrote to me; "but frankly, there is some hideous mystery here. I have obtained possession of the stone axe, and have been so curious as to test its powers. I took it into the back-garden of my house one Sunday afternoon when my family and the servants were all out, and there, sheltered by the poplar hedges, I made my experiments. I found the thing utterly unmanageable; whether there is some peculiar balance, some nice adjustment of weights, which require incessant practice, or whether an effectual blow can be struck only by a certain trick of the muscles, I do not know; but I assure you that I went into the house with but a sorry opinion of my athletic capacities. It was like an inexperienced man trying 'putting the hammer'; the force exerted seemed to return on oneself, and I found myself hurled backwards with violence, while the axe fell harmless to the ground. On another occasion I tried the experiment with a clever woodman of the place; but this man, who had handled his axe for forty years, could do nothing with the stone implement, and missed every stroke most ludicrously. In short, if it were not so supremely absurd, I should say that for four thousand years no one on earth could have struck an effective blow with the tool that undoubtedly was used to murder the old man." This, as may be imagined, was to me rare news; and afterwards, when I heard the whole story, and learned that the unfortunate old man had babbled tales of what might be seen at night on a certain wild hillside, hinting at unheard-of wonders, and that he had been found cold one morning on the very hill in question, my exultation was extreme, for I felt I was leaving conjecture far behind me. But the next step was of still greater importance. I had possessed for many years an extraordinary stone seal—a piece of dull black stone, two inches long from the handle to the stamp, and the stamping end a rough hexagon an inch and a quarter in diameter. Altogether, it presented the appearance of an enlarged tobacco stopper of an old-fashioned make. It had been sent to me by an agent in the East, who informed me that it had been found near the site of the ancient Babylon. But the characters engraved on the seal were to me an intolerable puzzle. Somewhat of the cuneiform pattern, there were yet striking differences, which I detected at the first glance, and all efforts to read the inscription on the hypothesis that the rules for deciphering the arrow-headed writing would apply proved futile. A riddle such as this stung my pride, and at odd moments I would take the Black Seal out of the cabinet, and scrutinize it with so much idle perseverance that every letter was familiar to my mind, and I could have drawn the inscription from memory without the slightest error. Judge, then, of my surprise when I one day received from a correspondent in the west of England a letter and an enclosure that positively left me thunderstruck. I saw carefully traced on a large piece of paper the very characters of the Black Seal, without alteration of any kind, and above the inscription my friend had written: *Inscription found on a limestone rock on the Grey Hills, Monmouthshire. Done in some red earth, and quite recent.* I turned to the letter. My friend wrote: "I send you the enclosed inscription with all due reserve. A shepherd who passed by the stone a week ago swears that there was then no mark of any kind. The characters, as I have noted, are formed by drawing some red earth over the stone, and are of an average height of one inch. They look to me like a kind of cuneiform character, a good deal altered, but this, of course, is impossible. It may be either a hoax, or more probably some scribble of the gipsies, who are plentiful enough in this wild country. They have, as you are aware, many hieroglyphics which they use in communicating with one another. I happened to visit the stone in question two days ago in connection with a rather painful incident which has occurred here."

As may be supposed, I wrote immediately to my friend, thanking him for the copy of the inscription, and asking him in a casual manner the history of the incident he mentioned. To be brief, I heard that a woman named Cradock, who had lost her husband a day before, had set out to communicate the sad news to a cousin who lived some five miles away. She took a short cut which led by the Grey Hills. Mrs. Cradock, who was then quite a young woman, never arrived at her relative's house. Late that night a farmer who had lost a couple of sheep, supposed to have wandered from the flock, was walking over the Grey Hills, with a lantern and his dog. His attention was attracted by a noise, which he described as a kind of wailing, mournful and pitiable to hear; and, guided by the sound, he found the unfortunate Mrs. Cradock crouched on the ground by the limestone rock, swaying her body to and fro, and lamenting and crying in so heart-rending a manner that the farmer was, as he says, at first obliged to stop his ears, or he would have run away. The woman allowed herself to be taken home, and a neighbour came to see to her necessities. All the night she never ceased her crying, mixing her lament with words of some unintelligible jargon, and when the doctor arrived he pronounced her insane. She lay on her bed for a week, now wailing, as people said, like one lost and damned for eternity, and now sunk in a heavy coma; it was thought that grief at the loss of her husband had unsettled her mind, and the medical man did not at one time expect her to live. I need not say that I was deeply interested in this story, and I made my friend write to me at intervals with all the particulars of the case. I heard then that in the course of six weeks the woman gradually recovered the use of her faculties, and some months later she gave birth to a son, christened Jervase, who unhappily proved to be of weak intellect. Such were the facts known to the village; but to me, while I whitened at the suggested thought of the hideous enormities that had doubtless been committed, all this was nothing short of conviction, and I incautiously hazarded a hint of something like the truth to some scientific friends. The moment the words had left my lips I bitterly regretted having spoken, and thus given away the great secret of my life, but with a good deal of relief mixed with indignation I found my fears altogether misplaced, for my friends ridiculed me to my face, and I was regarded as a madman; and beneath a natural anger I chuckled to myself, feeling as secure amidst these blockheads as if I had confided what I knew to the desert sands.

But now, knowing so much, I resolved I would know all, and I concentrated my efforts on the task of deciphering the inscription on the Black Seal. For many years I made this puzzle the sole object of my leisure moments, for the greater portion of my time was, of course, devoted to other duties, and it was only now and then that I could snatch a week of clear research. If I were to tell the full history of this curious investigation, this statement would be wearisome in the extreme, for it would contain simply the account of long and tedious failure. By what I knew already of ancient scripts I was well equipped for the chase, as I always termed it to myself. I had correspondents amongst all the scientific men in Europe, and, indeed, in the world, and I could not believe that in these days any character, however ancient and however perplexed, could long resist the search-light I should bring to bear upon it. Yet, in point of fact, it was fully fourteen years before I succeeded. With every year my professional duties increased, and my leisure became smaller. This no doubt retarded me a good deal; and yet, when I look back on those years, I am astonished at the vast scope of my investigations of the Black Seal. I made my bureau a centre, and from all the world and from all the ages I gathered transcripts of ancient writing. Nothing, I resolved, should pass me unawares, and the faintest hint should be welcomed and followed up. But as one covert after another was tried and proved empty of result, I began in the course of years to despair, and to wonder whether the Black Seal were the sole relic of some race that had vanished from the world and left no other trace of its existence—had perished, in fine, as Atlantis is said to have done, in some great cataclysm, its secrets perhaps drowned beneath the ocean or moulded into the heart of the hills. The thought chilled my warmth a little, and though I still persevered, it was no longer with the same certainty of faith. A chance came to the rescue. I was staying in a considerable town in the north of England, and took the opportunity of going over the very creditable museum that had for some time been established in the place. The curator was one of my correspondents; and, as we were looking through one of the mineral cases, my attention was struck by a specimen, a piece of black stone some four inches square, the appearance of which reminded me in a measure of the Black Seal. I took it up carelessly, and was turning it over in my hand, when I saw, to my astonishment, that the under side was inscribed. I said, quietly enough, to my friend the curator that the specimen interested me, and that I should be much obliged if he would allow me to take it with me to my hotel for a couple of days. He, of course, made no objection, and I hurried to my rooms and found that my first glance had not deceived me. There were two inscriptions; one in the regular cuneiform character, another in the character of the Black Seal, and I realized that my task was accomplished. I made an exact copy of the two inscriptions; and when I got to my London study, and had the Seal before me, I was able seriously to grapple with the great problem. The interpreting inscription on the museum specimen, though in itself curious enough, did not bear on my quest, but the transliteration made me master of the secret of the Black Seal. Conjecture, of course, had to enter into my calculations; there was here and there uncertainty about a particular ideograph, and one sign recurring again and again on the seal baffled me for many successive nights. But at last the secret stood open before me in plain English, and I read the key of the awful transmutation of the hills. The last word was hardly written, when with fingers all trembling and unsteady I tore the scrap of paper into the minutest fragments, and saw them flame and blacken in the red hollow of the fire, and then I crushed the grey films that remained into finest powder. Never since then have I written those words; never will I write the phrases which tell how man can be reduced to the slime from which he came, and be forced to put on the flesh of the reptile and the snake. There was now but one thing remaining. I knew, but I desired to see, and I was after some time able to take a house in the neighbourhood of the Grey Hills, and not far from the cottage where Mrs. Cradock and her son Jervase resided. I need not go into a full and detailed account of the apparently inexplicable events which have occurred here, where I am writing this. I knew that I should find in Jervase Cradock·something of the blood of the "Little People", and I found later that he had more than once encountered his kinsmen in lonely places in that lonely land. When I was summoned one day to the garden, and found him in a seizure speaking or hissing the ghastly jargon of the Black Seal, I am afraid that exultation prevailed over pity. I heard bursting from his lips the secrets of the underworld, and the word of dread, "Ishakshar", the signification of which I must be excused from giving.

But there is one incident I cannot pass over unnoticed. In the waste hollow of the night I awoke at the sound of those hissing syllables I knew so well; and on going to the wretched boy's room, I found him convulsed and foaming at the mouth, struggling on the bed as if he strove to escape the grasp of writhing demons. I took him down to my room and li the lamp, while he lay twisting on the floor, calling on the power within his flesh to leave him. I saw his body swell and become distended as a bladder, while the face blackened before my eyes; and then at the crisis I did what was necessary according to the directions on the Seal, and putting all scruple on one side, I became a man of science, observant of what was passing. Yet the sight I had to witness was horrible, almost beyond the power of human conception and the most fearful fantasy. Something pushed out from the body there on the floor, and stretched forth, a slimy, wavering tentacle, across the room, grasped the bust upon the cupboard, and laid it down on my desk.

When it was over, and I was left to walk up and down all the rest of the night, white and shuddering, with sweat pouring from my flesh, I

vainly tried to reason with myself: I said, truly enough, that I had seen
nothing really supernatural, that a snail pushing out his horns and
drawing them in was but an instance on a smaller scale of what I had
witnessed; and yet horror broke through all such reasonings and left me
shattered and loathing myself for the share I had taken in the night's
work.

There is little more to be said. I am going now to the final trial and
encounter; for I have determined that there shall be nothing wanting,
and I shall meet the "Little People" face to face. I shall have the Black
Seal and the knowledge of its secrets to help me, and if I unhappily
do not return from my journey, there is no need to conjure up here a
picture of the awfulness of my fate.

Pausing a little at the end of Professor Gregg's statement, Miss
Lally continued her tale in the following words:

Such was the almost incredible story that the professor had left
behind him. When I had finished reading it, it was late at night, but
the next morning I took Morgan with me, and we proceeded to search
the Grey Hills for some trace of the lost professor. I will not weary
you with a description of the savage desolation of that tract of country,
a tract of utterest loneliness, of bare green hills dotted over with grey
limestone boulders, worn by the ravages of time into fantastic sem-
blances of men and beasts. Finally, after many hours of weary searching,
we found what I told you—the watch and chain, the purse, and the
ring—wrapped in a piece of coarse parchment. When Morgan cut the
gut that bound the parcel together, and I saw the professor's property,
I burst into tears, but the sight of the dreaded characters of the Black
Seal repeated on the parchment froze me to silent horror, and I think
I understood for the first time the awful fate that had come upon my
late employer.

I have only to add that Professor Gregg's lawyer treated my account
of what had happened as a fairy tale, and refused even to glance at the
documents I laid before him. It was he who was responsible for the
statement that appeared in the public press, to the effect that Professor
Gregg had been drowned, and that his body must have been swept into
the open sea.

Miss Lally stopped speaking, and looked at Mr. Phillipps, with a glance of some inquiry. He, for his part, was sunken in a deep reverie of thought; and when he looked up and saw the bustle of the evening gathering in the square, men and women hurrying to partake of dinner, and crowds already besetting the music-halls, all the hum and press of actual life seemed unreal and visionary, a dream in the morning after an awakening.

"I thank you," he said at last, "for your most interesting story; interesting to me, because I feel fully convinced of its exact truth."

"Sir," said the lady, with some energy of indignation, "you grieve and offend me. Do you think I should waste my time and yours by concocting fictions on a bench in Leicester Square?"

"Pardon me, Miss Lally, you have a little misunderstood me. Before you began I knew that whatever you told would be told in good faith, but your experiences have a far higher value than that of *bona fides*. The most extraordinary circumstances in your account are in perfect harmony with the very latest scientific theories. Professor Lodge would, I am sure, value a communication from you extremely; I was charmed from the first by his daring hypothesis in explanation of the wonders of spiritualism (so called), but your narrative puts the whole matter out of the range of mere hypothesis."

"Alas! sir, all this will not help me. You forget, I have lost my brother under the most startling and dreadful circumstances. Again, I ask you, did you not see him as you came here? His black whiskers, his spectacles, his timid glance to right and left; think, do not these particulars recall his face to your memory?"

"I am sorry to say I have never seen anyone of the kind," said Phillipps, who had forgotten all about the missing brother. "But let me ask you a few questions. Did you notice whether Professor Gregg——"

"Pardon me, sir, I have stayed too long. My employers will be expecting me. I thank you for your sympathy. Goodbye."

Before Mr. Phillipps had recovered from his amazement at this abrupt departure Miss Lally had disappeared from his gaze, passing into the crowd that now thronged the approaches to the Empire. He walked home in a pensive frame of mind, and drank too much tea. At ten o'clock he had made his third brew, and had sketched out the outlines of a little work to be called "Protoplasmic Reversion".

INCIDENT OF THE PRIVATE BAR

MR. DYSON often meditated at odd moments over the singular tale he had listened to at the Café de la Touraine. In the first place, he cherished a profound conviction that the words of truth were scattered with a too niggardly and sparing hand over the agreeable history of Mr. Smith and the Black Gulf Canyon; and secondly, there was the undeniable fact of the profound agitation of the narrator, and his gestures on the pavement, too violent to be simulated. The idea of a man going about London haunted by the fear of meeting a young man with spectacles struck Dyson as supremely ridiculous; he searched his memory for some precedent in romance, but without success; he paid visits at odd times to the little café, hoping to find Mr. Wilkins there; and he kept a sharp watch on the great generation of the spectacled men, without much doubt that he would remember the face of the individual whom he had seen dart out of the aerated bread shop. All his peregrinations and researches, however, seemed to lead to nothing of value, and Dyson needed all his warm conviction of his innate detective powers and his strong scent for mystery to sustain him in his endeavours. In fact, he had two affairs on hand; and every day, as he passed through streets crowded or deserted, lurked in the obscure districts and watched at corners, he was more than surprised to find that the affair of the gold coin persistently avoided him, while the ingenious Wilkins, and the young man with spectacles whom he dreaded, seemed to have vanished from the pavements.

He was pondering these problems one evening in a house of call in the Strand, and the obstinacy with which the persons he so ardently desired to meet hung back gave the modest tankard before him an additional touch of bitter. As it happened, he was alone in his compartment, and, without thinking, he uttered aloud the burden of his meditations. "How bizarre it all is!" he said, "a man walking the pavement with the dread of a timid-looking young man with spectacles continually hovering before his eyes. And there was some tremendous feeling at work, I could swear to that." Quick as thought, before he had finished the sentence, a head popped round the barrier, and was withdrawn again; and while Dyson was wondering what this could mean, the door of the compartment was swung open, and a smooth, clean-shaven, and smiling gentleman entered.

"You will excuse me, sir," he said politely, "for intruding on your thoughts, but you made a remark a minute ago."

"I did," said Dyson; "I have been puzzling over a foolish matter, and I thought aloud. As you heard what I said, and seem interested, perhaps you may be able to relieve my perplexity?"

"Indeed, I scarcely know; it is an odd coincidence. One has to be cautious. I suppose, sir, that you would be glad to assist the ends of justice."

"Justice," replied Dyson, "is a term of such wide meaning, that I too feel doubtful about giving an answer. But this place is not altogether fit for such a discussion; perhaps you would come to my rooms?"

"You are very kind; my name is Burton, but I am sorry to say I have not a card with me. Do you live near here?"

"Within ten minutes' walk."

Mr. Burton took out his watch, and seemed to be making a rapid calculation.

"I have a train to catch," he said; "but after all, it is a late one. So if you don't mind, I think I will come with you. I am sure we should have a little talk together. We turn up here?"

The theatres were filling as they crossed the Strand; the street seemed alive with voices, and Dyson looked fondly about him. The glittering lines of gas-lamps, with here and there the blinding radiance of an electric light, the hansoms that flashed to and fro with ringing bells, the laden 'buses, and the eager hurrying east and west of the foot-passengers, made his most enchanting picture; and the graceful spire of St. Mary-le-Strand on the one hand, and the last flush of sunset on the other, were to him a cause of thanksgiving, as the gorse blossom to Linnæus. Mr. Burton caught his look of fondness as they crossed the street.

"I see you can find the picturesque in London," he said. "To me this great town is as I see it is to you—the study and the love of life. Yet how few there are that can pierce the veils of apparent monotony and meanness! I have read in a paper, which is said to have the largest circulation in the world, a comparison between the aspects of London and Paris, a comparison which should be positively laureate as the great masterpiece of fatuous stupidity. Conceive if you can a human being of ordinary intelligence preferring the Boulevards to our London streets; imagine a man calling for the wholesale destruction of our most charming city, in order that the dull uniformity of that whited sepulchre called Paris should be reproduced here in London. Is it not positively incredible?"

"My dear sir," said Dyson, regarding Burton with a good deal of interest, "I agree most heartily with your opinions, but I really can't share your wonder. Have you heard how much George Eliot received for 'Romola'? Do you know what the circulation of 'Robert Elsmere' was? Do you read *Tit-Bits* regularly? To me, on the contrary, it is constant matter both for wonder and thanksgiving that London was not boulevardized twenty years ago. I praise that exquisite jagged skyline that stands up against the pale greens and fading blues and flushing clouds of sunset, but I wonder even more than I praise. As for St. Mary-le-Strand, its preservation is a miracle, nothing more or less. A thing of exquisite beauty versus four 'buses abreast! Really, the conclusion is too obvious. Didn't you read the letter of the man who proposed that the whole mysterious system, the immemorial plan of computing Easter, should be abolished off-hand, because he doesn't like his son having his holidays as early as March 25th? But shall we be going on?"

They had lingered at the corner of a street on the north side of the Strand, enjoying the contrasts and the glamour of the scene. Dyson pointed the way with a gesture, and they strolled up the comparatively deserted streets, slanting a little to the right, and thus arriving at Dyson's lodging on the verge of Bloomsbury. Mr. Burton took a comfortable arm-chair by the open window, while Dyson lit the candles and produced the whisky and soda and cigarettes.

"They tell me these cigarettes are very good," he said; "but I know nothing about it myself. I hold at last that there is only one tobacco, and that is shag. I suppose I could not tempt you to try a pipeful?"

Mr. Burton smilingly refused the offer, and picked out a cigarette from the box. When he had smoked it half through, he said with some hesitation—

"It is really kind of you to have me here, Mr. Dyson; the fact is that the interests at issue are far too serious to be discussed in a bar, where, as you found for yourself, there may be listeners, voluntary or involuntary, on each side. I think the remark I heard you make was something about the oddity of an individual going about London in deadly fear of a young man with spectacles?"

"Yes; that was it."

"Well, would you mind confiding to me the circumstances that gave rise to the reflection?"

"Not in the least. It was like this." And he ran over in brief outline the adventure in Oxford Street, dwelling on the violence of Mr. Wilkins's gestures, but wholly suppressing the tale told in the café. "He told me he lived in constant terror of meeting this man; and I left him when I thought he was cool enough to look after himself," said Dyson, ending his narrative.

"Really," said Mr. Burton. "And you actually saw this mysterious person?"

"Yes."

"And could you describe him?"

"Well, he looked to me a youngish man, pale and nervous. He had small black side-whiskers, and wore rather large spectacles."

"But this is simply marvellous! You astonish me. For I must tell you that my interest in the matter is this. I'm not in the least in terror of meeting a dark young man with spectacles, but I shrewdly suspect a person of that description would much rather not meet me. And yet the account you give of the man tallies exactly. A nervous glance to right and left—is it not so? And, as you observed, he wears prominent spectacles, and has small black whiskers. There cannot be, surely, two people exactly identical—one a cause of terror, and the other, I should imagine, extremely anxious to get out of the way. But have you seen this man since?"

"No, I have not; and I have been looking out for him pretty keenly. But of course he may have left London, and England too, for the matter of that."

"Hardly, I think. Well, Mr. Dyson, it is only fair that I should explain my story, now that I have listened to yours. I must tell you, then, that I am an agent for curiosities and precious things of all kinds. An odd employment, isn't it? Of course, I wasn't brought up to the business; I gradually fell into it. I have always been fond of things queer and rare, and by the time I was twenty I had made half a dozen collections. It is not generally known how often farm-labourers come

X

upon rarities; you would be astonished if I told you what I have seen turned up by the plough. I lived in the country in those days, and I used to buy anything the men on the farms brought me; and I had the queerest set of rubbish, as my friends called my collection. But that's how I got the scent of the business, which means everything; and, later on, it struck me that I might very well turn my knowledge to account and add to my income. Since those early days I have been in most quarters of the world, and some very valuable things have passed through my hands, and I have had to engage in difficult and delicate negotiations. You have possibly heard of the Khan opal—called in the East 'The Stone of a Thousand and One Colours'? Well, perhaps the conquest of that stone was my greatest achievement. I call it myself the stone of the thousand and one lies, for I assure you that I had to invent a cycle of folk-lore before the Rajah who owned it would consent to sell the thing. I subsidized wandering story-tellers, who told tales in which the opal played a frightful part; I hired a holy man—a great ascetic— to prophesy against the thing in the language of Eastern symbolism; in short, I frightened the Rajah out of his wits. So, you see, there is room for diplomacy in the traffic I am engaged in. I have to be ever on my guard, and I have often been sensible that unless I watched every step and weighed every word, my life would not last me much longer. Last April I became aware of the existence of a highly valuable antique gem; it was in southern Italy, and in the possession of persons who were ignorant of its real value. It has always been my experience that it is precisely the ignorant who are most difficult to deal with. I have met farmers who were under the impression that a shilling of George the First was a find of almost incalculable value; and all the defeats I have sustained have been at the hands of people of this description. Reflecting on these facts, I saw that the acquisition of the gem I have mentioned would be an affair demanding the nicest diplomacy; I might possibly have got it by offering a sum approaching its real value, but I need not point out to you that such a proceeding would be most unbusinesslike. Indeed, I doubt whether it would have been successful; for the cupidity of such persons is aroused by a sum which seems enormous, and the low cunning which serves them in place of intelligence immediately suggests that the object for which such an amount is offered must be worth at least double. Of course, when it is a matter of an ordinary curiosity—an old jug, a carved chest, or a queer brass lantern—one does not much care; the cupidity of the owner defeats its object; the collector laughs and goes away, for he is aware that such things are by no means unique. But this gem I fervently desired to possess; and as I did not see my way to giving more than a hundredth part of its value, I was conscious that all my, let us say, imaginative and diplomatic powers would have to be exerted. I am sorry to say that I came to the conclusion that I could not undertake to carry the matter through single-handed, and I determined to confide in my assistant, a young man named William Robbins, whom I judged to be by no means devoid of capacity. My idea was that Robbins should get himself up as a low-class dealer in precious stones; he could patter a little Italian, and would go to the town in question and manage to see the gem we were after, possibly by offering some trifling article of jewellery for sale, but that I left to be decided. Then my work was to begin, but I will no† trouble you with a tale told twice over. In due course, then, Robbins went off to Italy with an assortment of uncut stones and a few rings, and some jewellery I bought in Birmingham on purpose for his expedition. A week later I followed him, travelling leisurely, so that I was a fortnight later in arriving at our common destination. There was a decent hotel in the town, and on my inquiring of the landlord whether there were many strangers in the place, he told me very few; he had heard there was an Englishman staying in a small tavern, a pedlar, he said, who sold beautiful trinkets very cheaply, and wanted to buy old rubbish. For five or six days I took life leisurely, and I must say I enjoyed myself. It was part of my plan to make the people think I was an enormously rich man; and I knew that such items as the extravagance of my meals, and the price of every bottle of wine I drank, would not be suffered, as Sancho Panza puts it, to rot in the landlord's breast. At the end of the week I was fortunate enough to make the acquaintance of Signore Melini, the owner of the gem I coveted, at the café, and with his ready hospitality, and my geniality, I was soon established as a friend of the house. On my third or fourth visit I managed to make the Italians talk about the English pedlar, who, they said, spoke a most detestable Italian. 'But that does not matter,' said the Signora Melini, 'for he has beautiful things, which he sells very, very cheap.' 'I hope you may not find he has cheated you,' I said, 'for I must tell you that English people give these fellows a very wide berth. They usually make a great parade of the cheapness of their goods, which often turn out to be double the price of better articles in the shops.' They would not hear of this, and Signora Melini insisted on showing me the three rings and the bracelet she had bought of the pedlar. She told me the price she had paid; and after scrutinizing the articles carefully, I had to confess that she had made a bargain, and indeed Robbins had sold her the things at about fifty per cent below market value. I admired the trinkets as I gave them back to the lady, and I hinted that the pedlar must be a somewhat foolish specimen of his class. Two days later, as I was taking my vermouth at the café with Signore Melini, he led the conversation back to the pedlar, and mentioned casually that he had shown the man a little curiosity, for which he had made rather a handsome offer. 'My dear sir,' I said, 'I hope you will be careful. I told you that the travelling tradesman does not bear a very high reputation in England; and notwithstanding his apparent simplicity, this fellow may turn out to be an arrant cheat. May I ask you what is the nature of the curiosity you have shown him?' He told me it was a little thing, a pretty little stone with some figures cut on it: people said it was old. 'I should like to examine it,' I replied, 'as it happens I have seen a good deal of these gems. We have a fine collection of them in our Museum at London.' In due course I was shown the article, and I held the gem I so coveted between my fingers. I looked at it coolly, and put it down carelessly on the table. 'Would you mind telling me, Signore,' I said, 'how much my fellow-countryman offered you for this?' 'Well,' he said, 'my wife says the man must be mad; he said he would give me twenty lire for it.'

"I looked at him quietly, and took up the gem and pretended to examine it in the light more carefully; I turned it over and over, and finally pulled out a magnifying glass from my pocket, and seemed to search every line in the cutting with minutest scrutiny. 'My dear sir,' I said at last, 'I am inclined to agree with Signora Melini. If this gem were genuine, it would be worth some money; but as it happens to be a rather bad forgery, it is not worth twenty centesimi. It was sophisticated, I should imagine, some time in the last century, and by a very unskilful hand.' 'Then we had better get rid of it,' said Melini. 'I never thought it was worth anything myself. Of course, I am sorry for the pedlar, but one must let a man know his own trade. I shall tell him we will take the twenty lire.' 'Excuse me,' I said, 'the man wants a lesson. It would be a charity to give him one. Tell him that you will not take anything under eighty lire, and I shall be much surprised if he does not close with you at once.'

"A day or two later I heard that the English pedlar had gone away, after debasing the minds of the country people with Birmingham art jewellery; for I admit that the gold sleeve-links like kidney beans, the silver chains made apparently after the pattern of a dog-chain, and the initial brooches, have always been heavy on my conscience. I cannot acquit myself of having indirectly contributed to debauch the taste of a simple folk; but I hope that the end I had in view may finally out-balance this heavy charge. Soon afterwards I paid a farewell visit at the Melinis, and the signore informed me with an oily chuckle that the plan I had suggested had been completely successful. I congratulated him on his bargain, and went away after expressing a wish that Heaven might send many such pedlars in his path.

"Nothing of interest occurred on my return journey. I had arranged that Robbins was to meet me at a certain place on a certain day, and I went to the appointment full of the coolest confidence; the gem had been conquered, and I had only to reap the fruits of victory. I am sorry to shake that trust in our common human nature which I am sure you possess, but I am compelled to tell you that up to the present date I have never set eyes on my man Robbins, or on the antique gem in his custody. I have found out that he actually arrived in London, for he was seen three days before my arrival in England by a pawnbroker of my acquaintance, consuming his favourite beverage—four ale—in the tavern where we met to-night. Since then he has not been heard of. I hope you will now pardon my curiosity as to the history and adven-tures of dark young men with spectacles. You will, I am sure, feel for me in my position; the savour of life has disappeared for me; it is a bitter thought that I have rescued one of the most perfect and exquisite specimens of antique art from the hands of ignorant, and indeed un-scrupulous persons, only to deliver it into the keeping of a man who is evidently utterly devoid of the very elements of commercial morality."

"My dear sir," said Dyson, "you will allow me to compliment you on your style; your adventures have interested me exceedingly. But, forgive me, you just now used the word morality; would not some persons take exception to your own methods of business? I can con-ceive, myself, flaws of a moral kind being found in the very original conception you have described to me; I can imagine the Puritan shrinking in dismay from your scheme, pronouncing it unscrupulous —nay, dishonest."

Mr. Burton helped himself very frankly to some more whisky.

"Your scruples entertain me," he said. "Perhaps you have not gone very deeply into these questions of ethics. I have been compelled to do so myself, just as I was forced to master a simple system of book-keeping. Without book-keeping, and still more without a system of ethics, it is impossible to conduct a business such as mine. But I assure you that I am often profoundly saddened, as I pass through the crowded streets and watch the world at work, by the thought of how few amongst all these hurrying individuals, black-hatted, well-dressed, educated we may presume sufficiently—how few amongst them have any reasoned system of morality. Even you have not weighed the question; although you study life and affairs, and to a certain extent penetrate the veils and masks of the comedy of man, even you judge by empty conventions, and the false money which is allowed to pass current as sterling coin. Allow me to play the part of Socrates; I shall teach you nothing that you do not know. I shall merely lay aside the wrappings of prejudice and bad logic, and show you the real image which you possess in your soul. Come then. Do you allow that happiness is anything?"

"Certainly," said Dyson.

"And happiness is desirable or undesirable?"

"Desirable, of course."

"And what shall we call the man who gives happiness? Is he not a philanthropist?"

"I think so."

"And such a person is praiseworthy, and the more praiseworthy in the proportion of the persons whom he makes happy?"

"By all means."

"So that he who makes a whole nation happy is praiseworthy in the extreme, and the action by which he gives happiness is the highest virtue?"

"It appears so, O Burton," said Dyson, who found something very exquisite in the character of his visitor.

"Quite so; you find the several conclusions inevitable. Well, apply them to the story I have told you. I conferred happiness on myself by obtaining (as I thought) possession of the gem; I conferred happiness on the Melinis by getting them eighty lire instead of an object for which they had not the slightest value, and I intended to confer happiness on the whole British nation by selling the thing to the British Museum, to say nothing of the happiness a profit of about nine thousand per cent would have conferred on me. I assure you, I regard Robbins as an interferer with the cosmos and fair order of things. But that is nothing; you perceive that I am an apostle of the very highest morality; you have been forced to yield to argument."

"There certainly seems a great deal in what you advance," said Dyson. "I admit that I am a mere amateur of ethics, while you, as you say, have brought the most acute scrutiny to bear on these perplexed and doubtful questions. I can well understand your anxiety to meet the fallacious Robbins, and I congratulate myself on the chance which has made us acquainted. But you will pardon my seeming inhospitality; I see it is half-past eleven, and I think you mentioned a train."

"A thousand thanks, Mr. Dyson. I have just time, I see. I will look you up some evening, if I may. Good-night."

THE RECLUSE OF BAYSWATER

AMONGST the many friends who were favoured with the occasional pleasure of Mr. Dyson's society was Mr. Edgar Russell, realist and obscure struggler, who occupied a small back room on the second floor of a house in Abingdon Grove, Notting Hill. Turning off from the main street, and walking a few paces onward, one was conscious of a certain calm, a drowsy peace, which made the feet inclined to loiter, and this was ever the atmosphere of Abingdon Grove. The houses stood a little back, with gardens where the lilac, and laburnum, and blood-red may blossomed gaily in their seasons, and there was a corner where an older house in another street had managed to keep a back garden of real extent, a walled-in garden, whence there came a pleasant scent of greenness after the rains of early summer, where old elms held memories of the open fields, where there was yet sweet grass to walk on. The houses in Abingdon Grove belonged chiefly to the nondescript stucco period of thirty-five years ago, tolerably built, with passable accommodation for moderate incomes; they had largely passed into the state of lodgings, and cards bearing the inscription "Furnished Apartments" were not infrequent over the doors. Here, then, in a house of sufficiently good appearance, Mr. Russell had established himself; for he looked upon the traditional dirt and squalor of Grub Street as a false and obsolete convention, and preferred, as he said, to live within sight of green leaves. Indeed, from his room one had a magnificent view of a long line of gardens, and a screen of poplars shut out the melancholy back premises of Wilton Street during the summer months. Mr. Russell lived chiefly on bread and tea, for his means were of the smallest; but when Dyson came to see him, he would send out the slavey for six-ale, and Dyson was always at liberty to smoke as much of his own tobacco as he pleased. The landlady had been so unfortunate as to have her drawing-room floor vacant for many months; a card had long proclaimed the void within; and Dyson, when he walked up the steps one evening in early autumn, had a sense that something was missing, and, looking at the fanlight, saw the appealing card had disappeared.

"You have let your first floor, have you?" he said, as he greeted Mr. Russell.

"Yes; it was taken about a fortnight ago by a lady."

"Indeed," said Dyson, always curious; "a young lady?"

"Yes; I believe so. She is a widow, and wears a thick crape veil. I have met her once or twice on the stairs and in the street; but I should not know her face."

"Well," said Dyson, when the beer had arrived, and the pipes were in full blast, "and what have you been doing? Do you find the work getting any easier?"

"Alas!" said the young man, with an expression of great gloom, "the life is a purgatory, and all but a hell. I write, picking out my words, weighing and balancing the force of every syllable, calculating the minutest effects that language can produce, erasing and rewriting, and spending a whole evening over a page of manuscript. And then, in the morning, when I read what I have written—— Well, there is nothing to be done but to throw it in the waste-paper basket, if the verso has been already written on, or to put it in the drawer if the other side happens to be clean. When I have written a phrase which undoubtedly embodies a happy turn of thought, I find it dressed up in feeble commonplace; and when the style is good, it serves only to conceal the baldness of superannuated fancies. I sweat over my work, Dyson—every finished line means so much agony. I envy the lot of the carpenter in the side street who has a craft which he understands. When he gets an order for a table he does not writhe with anguish; but if I were so unlucky as to get an order for a book, I think I should go mad."

"My dear fellow, you take it all too seriously. You should let the ink flow more readily. Above all, firmly believe, when you sit down to write, that you are an artist, and that whatever you are about is a masterpiece. Suppose ideas fail you, say, as I heard one of our most exquisite artists say, "It's of no consequence; the ideas are all there, at the bottom of that box of cigarettes!' You, indeed, smoke a pipe, but the application is the same. Besides, you must have some happy moments; and these should be ample consolation."

"Perhaps you are right. But such moments are so few; and then there is the torture of a glorious conception matched with execution beneath the standard of the 'Family Story Paper'. For instance, I was happy for two hours a night or two ago; I lay awake and saw visions. But then the morning!"

"What was your idea?"

"It seemed to me a splendid one: I thought of Balzac and the 'Comédie Humaine', of Zola and the Rougon-Macquart family. It dawned upon me that I would write the history of a street. Every house should form a volume. I fixed upon the street, I saw each house, and read as clearly as in letters the physiology and psychology of each; the little byway stretched before me in its actual shape—a street that I know and have passed down a hundred times, with some twenty houses, prosperous and mean, and lilac bushes in purple blossom. And yet it was, at the same time, a symbol, a *via dolorosa* of hopes cherished and disappointed, of years of monotonous existence without content or discontent, of tragedies and obscure sorrows; and on the door of one of those houses I saw the red stain of blood, and behind a window two shadows, blackened and faded on the blind, as they swayed on tightened cords—the shadows of a man and a woman hanging in a vulgar gaslit parlour. These were my fancies; but when pen touched paper they shrivelled and vanished away."

"Yes," said Dyson, "there is a lot in that. I envy you the pains of transmuting vision into reality, and, still more, I envy you the day when you will look at your bookshelf and see twenty goodly books upon the shelves—the series complete and done for ever. Let me entreat you to have them bound in solid parchment, with gold lettering. It is the only real cover for a valiant book. When I look in at the windows of some choice shop, and see the bindings of levant morocco, with pretty tools and panellings, and your sweet contrasts of red and green, I say to myself, 'These are not books, but *bibelots*.' A book bound so—a true book, mind you—is like a Gothic statue draped in brocade of Lyons."

"Alas!" said Russell, "we need not discuss the binding—the books are not begun."

The talk went on as usual till eleven o'clock, when Dyson bade his friend good-night. He knew the way downstairs, and walked down by himself; but, greatly to his surprise, as he crossed the first-floor landing the door opened slightly, and a hand was stretched out, beckoning.

Dyson was not the man to hesitate under such circumstances. In a moment he saw himself involved in adventure; and, as he told himself, the Dysons had never disobeyed a lady's summons. Softly, then, with due regard for the lady's honour, he would have entered the room, when a low but clear voice spoke to him—

"Go downstairs and open the door and shut it again rather loudly. Then come up to me; and for Heaven's sake, walk softly."

Dyson obeyed her commands, not without some hesitation, for he was afraid of meeting the landlady or the maid on his return journey. But, walking like a cat, and making each step he trod on crack loudly, he flattered himself that he had escaped observation; and as he gained the top of the stairs the door opened wide before him, and he found himself in the lady's drawing-room, bowing awkwardly.

"Pray be seated, sir. Perhaps this chair will be the best; it was the favoured chair of my landlady's deceased husband. I would ask you to smoke, but the odour would betray me. I know my proceedings must seem to you unconventional; but I saw you arrive this evening, and I do not think you would refuse to help a woman who is so unfortunate as I am."

Mr. Dyson looked shyly at the young lady before him. She was dressed in deep mourning, but the piquant smiling face and charming hazel eyes ill accorded with the heavy garments and the mouldering surface of the crape.

"Madam," he said gallantly, "your instinct has served you well. We will not trouble, if you please, about the question of social con-

ventions; the chivalrous gentleman knows nothing of such matters.
I hope I may be privileged to serve you."

"You are very kind to me, but I knew it would be so. Alas! sir, I
have had experience of life, and I am rarely mistaken. Yet man is too
often so vile and so misjudging that I trembled even as I resolved to
take this step, which, for all I knew, might prove to be both desperate
and ruinous."

"With me you have nothing to fear," said Dyson. "I was nurtured
in the faith of chivalry, and I have always endeavoured to remember
the proud traditions of my race. Confide in me, then, and count upon
my secrecy, and if it prove possible, you may rely on my help."

"Sir, I will not waste your time, which I am sure is valuable, by
idle parleyings. Learn, then, that I am a fugitive, and in hiding here;
I place myself in your power; you have but to describe my features,
and I fall into the hands of my relentless enemy."

Mr. Dyson wondered for a passing instant how this could be, but he
only renewed his promise of silence, repeating that he would be the
embodied spirit of dark concealment.

"Good," said the lady, "the Oriental fervour of your style is delightful. In the first place, I must disabuse your mind of the conviction
that I am a widow. These gloomy vestments have been forced on me
by strange circumstance; in plain language, I have deemed it expedient
to go disguised. You have a friend, I think, in the house, Mr. Russell?
He seems of a coy and retiring nature."

"Excuse me, madam," said Dyson, "he is not coy, but he is a realist;
and perhaps you are aware that no Carthusian monk can emulate the
cloistral seclusion in which a realistic novelist loves to shroud himself.
It is his way of observing human nature."

"Well, well," said the lady; "all this, though deeply interesting,
is not germane to our affair. I must tell you my history."

With these words the young lady proceeded to relate

THE NOVEL OF THE WHITE POWDER

My name is Leicester; my father, Major-General Wyn Leicester, a
distinguished officer of artillery, succumbed five years ago to a complicated liver complaint acquired in the deadly climate of India. A
year later my only brother, Francis, came home after an exceptionally
brilliant career at the University, and settled down with the resolution
of a hermit to master what has been well called the great legend of the

law. He was a man who seemed to live in utter indifference to every-thing that is called pleasure; and though he was handsomer than most men, and could talk as merrily and wittily as if he were a mere vagabond, he avoided society, and shut himself up in a large room at the top of the house to make himself a lawyer. Ten hours à day of hard reading was at first his allotted portion; from the first light in the east to the late afternoon he remained shut up with his books, taking a hasty half-hour's lunch with me as if he grudged the wasting of the moments, and going out for a short walk when it began to grow dusk. I thought that such relentless application must be injurious, and tried to cajole him from the crabbed textbooks, but his ardour seemed to grow rather than diminish, and his daily tale of hours increased. I spoke to him seriously, suggesting some occasional relaxation, if it were but an idle afternoon with a harmless novel; but he laughed, and said that he read about feudal tenures when he felt in need of amusement, and scoffed at the notion of theatres, or a month's fresh air. I confessed that he looked well, and seemed not to suffer from his labours, but I knew that such unnatural toil would take revenge at last, and I was not mistaken. A look of anxiety began to lurk about his eyes, and he seemed languid, and at last he avowed that he was no longer in perfect health; he was troubled, he said, with a sensation of dizziness, and awoke now and then of nights from fearful dreams, terrified and cold with icy sweats. "I am taking care of myself," he said, "so you must not trouble; I passed the whole of yesterday afternoon in idleness, leaning back in that comfortable chair you gave me, and scribbling nonsense on a sheet of paper. No, no; I will not overdo my work; I shall be well enough in a week or two, depend upon it."

Yet in spite of his assurances I could see that he grew no better, but rather worse; he would enter the drawing-room with a face all miser-ably wrinkled and despondent, and endeavour to look gaily when my eyes fell on him, and I thought such symptoms of evil omen, and was frightened sometimes at the nervous irritation of his movements, and at glances which I could not decipher. Much against his will, I prevailed on him to have medical advice, and with an ill grace he called in our old doctor.

Dr. Haberden cheered me after examination of his patient.

"There is nothing really much amiss," he said to me. "No doubt he reads too hard, and eats hastily, and then goes back again to his books in too great a hurry, and the natural consequence is some digestive trouble and a little mischief in the nervous system. But I think—I do indeed, Miss Leicester—that we shall be able to set this all right. I have written him a prescription which ought to do great things. So you have no cause for anxiety."

My brother insisted on having the prescription made up by a chemist in the neighbourhood. It was an odd, old-fashioned shop, devoid of the studied coquetry and calculated glitter that make so gay a show on the counters and shelves of the modern apothecary; but Francis liked the old chemist, and believed in the scrupulous purity of his drugs. The medicine was sent in due course, and I saw that my brother took it regularly after lunch and dinner. It was an innocent-looking white powder, of which a little was dissolved in a glass of cold water; I stirred it in, and it seemed to disappear, leaving the water clear and colourless. At first Francis seemed to benefit greatly; the weariness vanished from his face, and he became more cheerful than he had ever been since the time when he left school; he talked gaily of reforming himself, and avowed to me that he had wasted his time.

"I have given too many hours to law," he said, laughing; "I think you have saved me in the nick of time. Come, I shall be Lord Chancellor yet, but I must not forget life. You and I will have a holiday together before long; we will go to Paris and enjoy ourselves, and keep away from the Bibliothèque Nationale."

I confessed myself delighted with the prospect.

"When shall we go?" I said. "I can start the day after to-morrow if you like."

"Ah! that is perhaps a little too soon; after all, I do not know London yet, and I suppose a man ought to give the pleasures of his own country the first choice. But we will go off together in a week or two, so try and furbish up your French. I only know law French myself, and I am afraid that wouldn't do."

We were just finishing dinner, and he quaffed off his medicine with a parade of carousal as if it had been wine from some choicest bin.

"Has it any particular taste?" I said.

"No; I should not know I was not drinking water," and he got up from his chair and began to pace up and down the room as if he were undecided as to what he should do next.

"Shall we have coffee in the drawing-room?" I said; "or would you like to smoke?"

"No, I think I will take a turn; it seems a pleasant evening. Look at the afterglow; why, it is as if a great city were burning in flames, and down there between the dark houses it is raining blood fast, fast. Yes, I will go out; I may be in soon, but I shall take my key; so good-night, dear, if I don't see you again."

The door slammed behind him, and I saw him walk lightly down the street, swinging his malacca cane, and I felt grateful to Dr. Haberden for such an improvement.

I believe my brother came home very late that night, but he was in a merry mood the next morning.

"I walked on without thinking where I was going," he said, "enjoying the freshness of the air, and livened by the crowds as I reached more frequented quarters. And then I met an old college friend, Orford, in the press of the pavement, and then—well, we enjoyed ourselves. I have felt what it is to be young and a man; I find I have blood in my veins, as other men have. I made an appointment with Orford for to-night; there will be a little party of us at the restaurant. Yes; I shall enjoy myself for a week or two, and hear the chimes at midnight, and then we will go for our little trip together."

Such was the transmutation of my brother's character that in a few days he became a lover of pleasure, a careless and merry idler of western pavements, a hunter out of snug restaurants, and a fine critic of fantastic dancing; he grew fat before my eyes, and said no more of Paris, for he had clearly found his paradise in London. I rejoiced, and yet wondered a little; for there was, I thought, something in his gaiety that indefinitely displeased me, though I could not have defined my feeling. But by degrees there came a change; he returned still in the cold hours of the morning, but I heard no more about his pleasures, and one morning as we sat at breakfast together I looked suddenly into his eyes and saw a stranger before me.

"Oh, Francis!" I cried. "Oh, Francis, Francis, what have you done?" and rending sobs cut the words short. I went weeping out of the room; for though I knew nothing, yet I knew all, and by some odd play of thought I remembered the evening when he first went abroad, and the picture of the sunset sky glowed before me; the clouds like a city in burning flames, and the rain of blood. Yet I did battle with such thoughts, resolving that perhaps, after all, no great harm had been done, and in the evening at dinner I resolved to press him to fix a day for our holiday in Paris. We had talked easily enough, and my brother had just taken his medicine, which he had continued all the while. I was about to begin my topic when the words forming in my mind vanished, and I wondered for a second what icy and intolerable weight oppressed my heart and suffocated me as with the unutterable horror of the coffin-lid nailed down on the living.

We had dined without candles; the room had slowly grown from twilight to gloom, and the walls and corners were indistinct in the shadow. But from where I sat I looked out into the street; and as I thought of what I would say to Francis, the sky began to flush and shine, as it had done on a well-remembered evening, and in the gap between two dark masses that were houses an awful pageantry of flame appeared—lurid whorls of writhed cloud, and utter depths burning, grey masses like the fume blown from a smoking city, and an evil glory blazing far above shot with tongues of more ardent fire, and below as if there were a deep pool of blood. I looked down to where my brother sat facing me, and the words were shaped on my lips, when I saw his hand resting on the table. Between the thumb and forefinger of the closed hand there was a mark, a small patch about the size of a six-pence, and somewhat of the colour of a bad bruise. Yet, by some sense I cannot define, I knew that what I saw was no bruise at all; oh! if human flesh could burn with flame, and if flame could be black as pitch, such was that before me. Without thought or fashioning of words grey horror shaped within me at the sight, and in an inner cell it was known to be a brand. For a moment the stained sky became dark as midnight, and when the light returned to me I was alone in the silent room, and soon after I heard my brother go out.

Late as it was, I put on my hat and went to Dr. Haberden, and in his great consulting room, ill lighted by a candle which the doctor brought in with him, with stammering lips, and a voice that would break in spite of my resolve, I told him all, from the day on which my brother began to take the medicine down to the dreadful thing I had seen scarcely half an hour before.

When I had done, the doctor looked at me for a minute with an expression of great pity on his face.

"My dear Miss Leicester," he said, "you have evidently been

anxious about your brother; you have been worrying over him, I am sure. Come, now, is it not so?"

"I have certainly been anxious," I said. "For the last week or two I have not felt at ease."

"Quite so; you know, of course, what a queer thing the brain is?"

"I understand what you mean; but I was not deceived. I saw what I have told you with my own eyes."

"Yes, yes, of course. But your eyes had been staring at that very curious sunset we had to-night. That is the only explanation. You will see it in the proper light to-morrow, I am sure. But, remember, I am always ready to give any help that it in my power; do not scruple to come to me, or to send for me if you are in any distress."

I went away but little comforted, all confusion and terror and sorrow, not knowing where to turn. When my brother and I met the next day, I looked quickly at him, and noticed, with a sickening at heart, that the right hand, the hand on which I had clearly seen the patch as of a black fire, was wrapped up with a handkerchief.

"What is the matter with your hand, Francis?" I said in a steady voice.

"Nothing of consequence. I cut a finger last night, and it bled rather awkwardly. So I did it up roughly to the best of my ability."

"I will do it neatly for you, if you like."

"No, thank you, dear; this will answer very well. Suppose we have breakfast; I am quite hungry."

We sat down, and I watched him. He scarcely ate or drank at all, but tossed his meat to the dog when he thought my eyes were turned away; there was a look in his eyes that I had never yet seen, and the thought flashed across my mind that it was a look that was scarcely human. I was firmly convinced that awful and incredible as was the thing I had seen the night before, yet it was no illusion, no glamour of bewildered sense, and in the course of the morning I went again to the doctor's house.

He shook his head with an air puzzled and incredulous, and seemed to reflect for a few minutes.

"And you say he still keeps up the medicine? But why? As I understand, all the symptoms he complained of have disappeared long ago; why should be go on taking the stuff when he is quite well? And by the by, where did he get it made up? At Sayce's? I never send anyone there;

the old man is getting careless. Suppose you come with me to the chemist's; I should like to have some talk with him."

We walked together to the shop; old Sayce knew Dr. Haberden, and was quite ready to give any information.

"You have been sending that in to Mr. Leicester for some weeks, I think, on my prescription," said the doctor, giving the old man a pencilled scrap of paper.

The chemist put on his great spectacles with trembling uncertainty, and held up the paper with a shaking hand.

"Oh, yes," he said, "I have very little of it left; it is rather an uncommon drug, and I have had it in stock some time. I must get in some more, if Mr. Leicester goes on with it."

"Kindly let me have a look at the stuff," said Haberden, and the chemist gave him a glass bottle. He took out the stopper and smelt the contents, and looked strangely at the old man.

"Where did you get this?" he said, "and what is it? For one thing, Mr. Sayce, it is not what I prescribed. Yes, yes, I see the label is right enough, but I tell you this is not the drug."

"I have had it a long time," said the old man in feeble terror; "I got it from Burbage's in the usual way. It is not prescribed often, and I have had it on the shelf for some years. You see there is very little left."

"You had better give it to me," said Haberden. "I am afraid something wrong has happened."

We went out of the shop in silence, the doctor carrying the bottle neatly wrapped in paper under his arm.

"Dr. Haberden," I said, when we had walked a little way—"Dr. Haberden."

"Yes," he said, looking at me gloomily enough.

"I should like you to tell me what my brother has been taking twice a day for the last month or so."

"Frankly, Miss Leicester, I don't know. We will speak of this when we get to my house."

We walked on quickly without another word till we reached Dr. Haberden's. He asked me to sit down, and began pacing up and down the room, his face clouded over, as I could see, with no common fears.

"Well," he said at length, "this is all very strange; it is only natural that you should feel alarmed, and I must confess that my mind is far from easy. We will put aside, if you please, what you told me last night

Y

and this morning, but the fact remains that for the last few weeks Mr. Leicester has been impregnating his system with a drug which is completely unknown to me. I tell you, it is not what I ordered; and what that stuff in the bottle really is remains to be seen."

He undid the wrapper, and cautiously tilted a few grains of the white powder on to a piece of paper, and peered curiously at it.

"Yes," he said, "it is like the sulphate of quinine, as you say; it is flaky. But smell it."

He held the bottle to me, and I bent over it. It was a strange, sickly smell, vaporous and overpowering, like some strong anæsthetic.

"I shall have it analysed," said Haberden; "I have a friend who has devoted his whole life to chemistry as a science. Then we shall have something to go upon. No, no; say no more about that other matter; I cannot listen to that; and take my advice and think no more about it yourself."

That evening my brother did not go out as usual after dinner.

"I have had my fling," he said with a queer laugh, "and I must go back to my old ways. A little law will be quite a relaxation after so sharp a dose of pleasure," and he grinned to himself, and soon after went up to his room. His hand was still all bandaged.

Dr. Haberden called a few days later.

"I have no special news to give you," he said. "Chambers is out of town, so I know no more about that stuff than you do. But I should like to see Mr. Leicester, if he is in."

"He is in his room," I said; "I will tell him you are here."

"No, no, I will go up to him; we will have a little quiet talk together. I daresay that we have made a good deal of fuss about very little; for, after all, whatever the white powder may be, it seems to have done him good."

The doctor went upstairs, and standing in the hall I heard his knock, and the opening and shutting of the door; and then I waited in the silent house for an hour, and the stillness grew more and more intense as the hands of the clock crept round. Then there sounded from above the noise of a door shut sharply, and the doctor was coming down the stairs. His footsteps crossed the hall, and there was a pause at the door; I drew a long, sick breath with difficulty, and saw my face white in a little mirror, and he came in and stood at the door. There was an unutterable horror shining in his eyes; he steadied himself by holding the back of a chair with one hand, his lower lip trembled like a horse's, and he gulped and stammered unintelligible sounds before he spoke.

"I have seen that man," he began in a dry whisper. "I have been sitting in his presence for the last hour. My God! And I am alive and in my senses! I, who have dealt with death all my life, and have dabbled with the melting ruins of the earthly tabernacle. But not this, oh! not this," and he covered his face with his hands as if to shut out the sight of something before him.

"Do not send for me again, Miss Leicester," he said with more composure. "I can do nothing in this house. Good-bye."

As I watched him totter down the steps, and along the pavement towards his house, it seemed to me that he had aged by ten years since the morning.

My brother remained in his room. He called out to me in a voice I hardly recognized that he was very busy, and would like his meals brought to his door and left there, and I gave the order to the servants. From that day it seemed as if the arbitrary conception we call time had been annihilated for me; I lived in an ever-present sense of horror, going through the routine of the house mechanically, and only speaking a few necessary words to the servants. Now and then I went out and paced the streets for an hour or two and came home again; but whether I were without or within, my spirit delayed before the closed door of the upper room, and, shuddering, waited for it to open. I have said that I scarcely reckoned time; but I suppose it must have been a fortnight after Dr. Haberden's visit that I came home from my stroll a little refreshed and lightened. The air was sweet and pleasant, and the hazy form of green leaves, floating cloud-like in the square, and the smell of blossoms, had charmed my senses, and I felt happier and walked more briskly. As I delayed a moment at the verge of the pavement, waiting for a van to pass by before crossing over to the house, I happened to look up at the windows, and instantly there was the rush and swirl of deep cold waters in my ears, my heart leapt up, and fell down, down as into a deep hollow, and I was amazed with a dread and terror without form or shape. I stretched out a hand blindly through folds of thick darkness, from the black and shadowy valley, and held myself from falling, while the stones beneath my feet rocked and swayed and tilted, and the sense of solid things seemed to sink away from under me. I had glanced up at the window of my brother's study, and at that moment the blind was drawn aside, and something that had life stared out into the world. Nay, I cannot say I saw a face or any human likeness; a living thing, two eyes of burning flame glared at me, and they were in the midst of something as formless as my fear, the symbol and presence of all evil and all hideous corruption. I stood shuddering and quaking as with the grip of ague, sick with unspeakable agonies of fear and loathing, and for five minutes I could not summon force or motion to my limbs. When I was within the door, I ran up the stairs to my brother's room and knocked.

"Francis, Francis," I cried, "for Heaven's sake, answer me. What is the horrible thing in your room? Cast it out, Francis; cast it from you."

I heard a noise as of feet shuffling slowly and awkwardly, and a choking, gurgling sound, as if someone was struggling to find utterance, and then the noise of a voice, broken and stifled, and words that I could scarcely understand.

"There is nothing here," the voice said. "Pray do not disturb me. I am not very well to-day."

I turned away, horrified, and yet helpless. I could do nothing, and I wondered why Francis had lied to me, for I had seen the appearance beyond the glass too plainly to be deceived, though it was but the sight of a moment. And I sat still, conscious that there had been something else, something I had seen in the first flash of terror, before those burning eyes had looked at me. Suddenly I remembered; as I lifted my face the blind was being drawn back, and I had had an instant's glance of the thing that was moving it, and in my recollection I knew that a hideous image was engraved for ever on my brain. It was not a hand; there were no fingers that held the blind, but a black stump pushed it aside, the mouldering outline and the clumsy movement as of a beast's paw had glowed into my senses before the darkling waves of terror had overwhelmed me as I went down quick into the pit. My mind was aghast at the thought of this, and of the awful presence that dwelt with my brother in his room; I went to his door and cried to him again, but no answer came. That night one of the servants came up to me and told me in a whisper that for three days food had been regularly placed at the door and left untouched; the maid had knocked but had received no answer; she had heard the noise of shuffling feet that I had noticed. Day after day went by, and still my brother's meals were brought to his door and left untouched; and though I knocked and called again and again, I could get no answer. The servants began to talk to me; it appeared they were as alarmed as I; the cook said that when my brother first shut himself up in his room she used to hear him come out at night and go about the house; and once, she said, the hall door had opened and closed again, but for several nights she had heard no sound. The climax came at last; it was in the dusk of the evening, and I was sitting in the darkening dreary room when a terrible shriek jarred and rang harshly out of the silence, and I heard a frightened scurry of feet dashing down the stairs. I waited, and the servant-maid staggered into the room and faced me, white and trembling.

"Oh, Miss Helen!" she whispered; "oh! for the Lord's sake, Miss Helen, what has happened? Look at my hand, miss; look at that hand!"

I drew her to the window, and saw there was a black wet stain upon her hand.

"I do not understand you," I said. "Will you explain to me?"

"I was doing your room just now," she began. "I was turning down the bed-clothes, and all of a sudden there was something fell upon my hand, wet, and I looked up, and the ceiling was black and dripping on me."

I looked hard at her and bit my lip.

"Come with me," I said. "Bring your candle with you."

The room I slept in was beneath my brother's, and as I went in I felt I was trembling. I looked up at the ceiling, and saw a patch, all black and wet, and a dew of black drops upon it, and a pool of horrible liquor soaking into the white bed-clothes.

I ran upstairs, and knocked loudly.

"Oh, Francis, Francis, my dear brother," I cried, "what has happened to you?"

And I listened. There was a sound of choking, and a noise like water bubbling and regurgitating, but nothing else, and I called louder, but no answer came.

In spite of what Dr. Haberden had said, I went to him; with tears streaming down my cheeks I told him of all that had happened, and he listened to me with a face set hard and grim.

"For your father's sake," he said at last, "I will go with you, though I can do nothing."

We went out together; the streets were dark and silent, and heavy with heat and a drought of many weeks. I saw the doctor's face white under the gas-lamps, and when we reached the house his hand was shaking.

We did not hesitate, but went upstairs directly. I held the lamp, and he called out in a loud, determined voice—

"Mr. Leicester, do you hear me? I insist on seeing you. Answer me at once."

There was no answer, but we both heard that choking noise I have mentioned.

"Mr. Leicester, I am waiting for you. Open the door this instant, or I shall break it down." And he called a third time in a voice that rang and echoed from the walls—

"Mr. Leicester! For the last time I order you to open the door."

"Ah!" he said, after a pause of heavy silence, "we are wasting time here. Will you be so kind as to get me a poker or something of the kind?"

I ran into a little room at the back where odd articles were kept, and found a heavy adze-like tool that I thought might serve the doctor's purpose.

"Very good," he said, "that will do, I daresay. I give you notice, Mr. Leicester," he cried loudly at the keyhole, "that I am now about to break into your room."

Then I heard the wrench of the adze, and the woodwork split and cracked under it; with a loud crash the door suddenly burst open, and for a moment we started back aghast at a fearful screaming cry, no human voice, but as the roar of a monster, that burst forth inarticulate and struck at us out of the darkness.

"Hold the lamp," said the doctor, and we went in and glanced quickly round the room.

"There it is," said Dr. Haberden, drawing a quick breath; "look, in that corner."

I looked, and a pang of horror seized my heart as with a white-hot iron. There upon the floor was a dark and putrid mass, seething with corruption and hideous rottenness, neither liquid nor solid, but melting and changing before our eyes, and bubbling with unctuous oily bubbles like boiling pitch. And out of the midst of it shone two burning points like eyes, and I saw a writhing and stirring as of limbs, and something moved and lifted up what might have been an arm. The doctor took a step forward, raised the iron bar and struck at the burning points; he drove in the weapon, and struck again and again in a fury of loathing. At last the thing was quiet.

. . . .

A week or two later, when I had recovered to some extent from the terrible shock, Dr. Haberden came to see me.

"I have sold my practice," he began, "and to-morrow I am sailing on a long voyage. I do not know whether I shall ever return to England; in all probability I shall buy a little land in California, and settle there for the remainder of my life. I have brought you this packet, which you may open and read when you feel able to do so. It contains the report of Dr. Chambers on what I submitted to him. Goodbye, Miss Leicester, goodbye."

When he was gone I opened the envelope; I could not wait, and proceeded to read the papers within. Here is the manuscript, and if you will allow me, I will read you the astounding story it contains.

"My dear Haberden," the letter began, "I have delayed inexcusably in answering your questions as to the white substance you sent me. To tell you the truth, I have hesitated for some time as to what course I should adopt, for there is a bigotry and an orthodox standard in physical science as in theology, and I knew that if I told you the truth I should offend rooted prejudices which I once held dear myself. However, I have determined to be plain with you, and first I must enter into a short personal explanation.

"You have known me, Haberden, for many years as a scientific man; you and I have often talked of our profession together, and discussed the hopeless gulf that opens before the feet of those who think to attain to truth by any means whatsoever except the beaten way of experiment and observation in the sphere of material things. I remember the scorn with which you have spoken to me of men of science who have dabbled a little in the unseen, and have timidly hinted that perhaps the senses are not, after all, the eternal, impenetrable bounds of all knowledge, the everlasting walls beyond which no human being has ever passed. We have laughed together heartily, and I think justly, at the 'occult' follies of the day, disguised under various names—the mesmerisms, spiritualisms, materializations, theosophies, all the rabble rout of imposture, with their machinery of poor tricks and feeble conjuring, the true back-parlour magic of shabby London streets. Yet, in spite of what I have said, I must confess to you that I am no materialist, taking the word of course in its usual signification. It is now many years since I have convinced myself—convinced myself, a sceptic, remember—that the old ironbound theory is utterly and entirely false. Perhaps this confession will not wound you so sharply as it would have done twenty years ago; for I think you cannot have failed to notice that for some time hypotheses have been advanced by men of pure science which are nothing less than transcendental, and I suspect that most modern chemists and biologists of repute would not hesitate to subscribe the *dictum* of the old Schoolman, *Omnia exeunt in mysterium*, which means, I take it, that every branch of human knowledge if traced up to its source and final principles vanishes into mystery. I need not trouble you now with a detailed account of the painful steps which led me to my conclusions; a few simple experiments suggested a doubt as to my then standpoint, and a train of thought that rose from circumstances comparatively trifling brought me far; my old conception of the universe has been swept away, and I stand in a world that seems as strange and awful to me as the endless waves of the ocean seen for the first time, shining, from a peak in Darien. Now I know that the walls of sense that seemed so impenetrable, that seemed to loom up above the heavens and to be founded below the depths, and to shut us in for evermore, are no such everlasting impassable barriers as we fancied, but thinnest and most airy veils that melt away before the seeker, and dissolve as the early mist of the morning about the brooks. I know that you never adopted the extreme materialistic position; you did not go about trying to prove a universal negative, for your logical sense withheld you from that crowning absurdity; but I am sure that you will find all that I am saying strange and repellent to your habits of thought. Yet, Haberden, what I tell you is the truth, nay, to adopt our common language, the sole and scientific truth, verified by experience; and the universe is verily more splendid and more awful than we used to dream. The whole universe, my friend, is a tremendous sacrament; a mystic, ineffable force and energy, veiled by an outward form of matter; and man, and the sun and the other stars, and the flower of the grass, and the crystal in the test-tube, are each and every one as spiritual, as material, and subject to an inner working.

"You will perhaps wonder, Haberden, whence all this tends; but I think a little thought will make it clear. You will understand that from such a standpoint the whole view of things is changed, and what we thought incredible and absurd may be possible enough. In short, we must look at legend and belief with other eyes, and be prepared to accept tales that had become mere fables. Indeed, this is no such great demand. After all, modern science will concede as much, in a hypocritical manner; you must not, it is true, believe in witchcraft, but you may credit hypnotism; ghosts are out of date, but there is a good deal to be said for the theory of telepathy. Give a superstition a Greek name, and believe in it, should almost be a proverb.

"So much for my personal explanation. You sent me, Haberden, a phial, stoppered and sealed, containing a small quantity of a flaky white powder, obtained from a chemist who has been dispensing it, to one of your patients. I am not surprised to hear that this powder refused to yield any results to your analysis. It is a substance which was known to a few many hundred years ago, but which I never expected to have submitted to me from the shop of a modern apothecary. There seems no reason to doubt the truth of the man's tale; he no doubt got, as he says, the rather uncommon salt you prescribed from the wholesale chemist's; and it has probably remained on his shelf for twenty years, or perhaps longer. Here what we call chance and coincidence begin to work; during all these years the salt in the bottle was exposed to certain recurring variations of temperature, variations probably ranging from 40 degrees to 80 degrees. And, as it happens, such changes, recurring year after year at irregular intervals, and with varying degrees of intensity and duration, have constituted a process, and a process so complicated and so delicate, that I question whether modern scientific apparatus directed with the utmost precision could produce the same result. The white powder you sent me is something very different from the drug you prescribed; it is the powder from which the wine of the Sabbath, the *Vinum Sabbati*, was prepared. No doubt you have read of the Witches' Sabbath, and have laughed at the tales which terrified our ancestors; the black cats, and the broomsticks, and dooms pronounced against some old woman's cow. Since I have known the truth I have often reflected that it is on the whole a happy thing that such burlesque as this is believed, for it serves to conceal much that it is better should not be known generally. However, if you care to read the appendix to Payne Knight's monograph, you will find that the true Sabbath was something very different, though the writer has very nicely refrained from printing all he knew. The secrets of the true Sabbath were the secrets of remote times surviving into the Middle Ages, secrets of an evil science which existed long before Aryan man entered Europe. Men and women, seduced from their homes on specious pretences, were met by beings well qualified to assume, as they did assume, the part of devils, and taken by their guides to some desolate and lonely place, known to the initiate by long tradition, and unknown to all else. Perhaps it was a cave in some bare and wind-swept hill, perhaps some inmost recess of a great forest, and there the Sabbath was held. There, in the blackest hour of night, the *Vinum Sabbati* was prepared, and this evil graal was poured forth and offered to the neophytes, and they partook of an infernal sacrament; *sumentes calicem principis inferorum,* as an old author well expresses it. And suddenly, each one that had drunk found himself attended by a companion, a shape of glamour and unearthly allurement, beckoning him apart, to share in joys more exquisite, more piercing than the thrill of any dream, to the consummation of the marriage of the Sabbath. It is hard to write of such things as these, and chiefly because that shape that allured with loveliness was no hallucination, but awful as it is to express, the man himself. By the power of that Sabbath wine, a few grains of white powder thrown into a glass of water, the house of life was riven asunder and the human trinity dissolved, and the worm which never dies, that which lies sleeping within us all, was made tangible and an external thing, and clothed with a garment of flesh. And then, in the hour of midnight, the primal fall was repeated and re-presented, and the awful thing veiled in the mythos of the Tree in the Garden was done anew. Such was the *nuptiæ Sabbati.*

"I prefer to say no more; you, Haberden, known as well as I do that the most trivial laws of life are not to be broken with impunity; and for so terrible an act as this, in which the very inmost place of the temple was broken open and defiled, a terrible vengeance followed. What began with corruption ended also with corruption."

Underneath is the following in Dr. Haberden's writing:

"The whole of the above is unfortunately strictly and entirely true. Your brother confessed all to me on that morning when I saw him in his room. My attention was first attracted to the bandaged hand, and I forced him to show it me. What I saw made me, a medical man of many years' standing, grow sick with loathing, and the story I was forced to listen to was infinitely more frightful than I could have believed possible. It has tempted me to doubt the Eternal Goodness which can permit nature to offer such hideous possibilities; and if you had not with your own eyes seen the end, I should have said to you—disbelieve it all. I have not, I think, many more weeks to live, but you are young, and may forget all this.   "JOSEPH HABERDEN, M.D."

In the course of two or three months I heard that Dr. Haberden had died at sea shortly after the ship left England.

Miss Leicester ceased speaking, and looked pathetically at Dyson, who could not refrain from exhibiting some symptoms of uneasiness.

He stuttered out some broken phrases expressive of his deep interest in her extraordinary history, and then said with a better grace—

"But pardon me, Miss Leicester, I understood you were in some difficulty. You were kind enough to ask me to assist you in some way."

"Ah," she said, "I had forgotten that; my own present trouble seems of such little consequence in comparison with what I have told you. But as you are so good to me, I will go on. You will scarcely believe it, but I found that certain persons suspected, or rather pretended to suspect, that I had murdered my brother. These persons were relatives of mine, and their motives were extremely sordid ones; but I actually found myself subject to the shameful indignity of being watched. Yes, sir, my steps were dogged when I went abroad, and at home I found myself exposed to constant if artful observation. With my high spirit this was more than I could brook, and I resolved to set my wits to work and elude the persons who were shadowing me. I was so fortunate as to succeed; I assumed this disguise, and for some time have lain snug and unsuspected. But of late I have reason to believe that the pursuer is on my track; unless I am greatly deceived, I saw yesterday the detective who is charged with the odious duty of observing my movements. You, sir, are watchful and keen-sighted; tell me, did you see anyone lurking about this evening?"

"I hardly think so," said Dyson, "but perhaps you would give me some description of the detective in question."

"Certainly; he is a youngish man, dark, with dark whiskers. He had adopted spectacles of large size in the hope of disguising himself effectually, but he cannot disguise his uneasy manner, and the quick, nervous glances he casts to right and left."

This piece of description was the last straw for the unhappy Dyson, who was foaming with impatience to get out of the house, and would gladly have sworn eighteenth-century oaths, if propriety had not frowned on such a course.

"Excuse me, Miss Leicester," he said with cool politeness, "I cannot assist you."

"Ah," she said sadly, "I have offended you in some way. Tell me what I have done, and I will ask you to forgive me."

"You are mistaken," said Dyson, grabbing his hat, but speaking with some difficulty; "you have done nothing. But, as I say, I cannot help you, Perhaps," he added, with some tinge of sarcasm, "my friend Russell might be of service."

"Thank you," she replied; "I will try him," and the lady went off into a shriek of laughter, which filled up Mr. Dyson's cup of scandal and confusion.

He left the house shortly afterwards, and had the peculiar delight of a five-mile walk, through streets which slowly changed from black to grey, and from grey to shining passages of glory for the sun to brighten. Here and there he met or overtook strayed revellers, but he reflected that no one could have spent the night in a more futile fashion than himself; and when he reached his home he had made resolves for reformation. He decided that he would abjure all Milesian and Arabian methods of entertainment, and subscribe to Mudie's for a regular supply of mild and innocuous romance.

STRANGE OCCURRENCE IN CLERKENWELL

MR. DYSON had inhabited for some years a couple of rooms in a moderately quiet street in Bloomsbury, where, as he somewhat pompously expressed it, he held his finger on the pulse of life without being deafened with the thousand rumours of the main arteries of London. It was to him a source of peculiar, if esoteric, gratification that from the adjacent corner of Tottenham Court Road a hundred lines of omnibuses went to the four quarters of the town; he would dilate on the facilities for visiting Dalston, and dwell on the admirable line that knew extremest Ealing and the streets beyond Whitechapel. His rooms, which had been originally "furnished apartments", he had gradually purged of their more peccant parts; and though one would not find here the glowing splendours of his old chambers in the street off the Strand, there was something of severe grace about the appointments which did credit to his taste. The rugs were old, and of the true faded beauty; the etchings, nearly all of them proofs printed by the artist, made a good show with broad white margins and black frames, and there was no spurious black oak. Indeed, there was but little furniture of any kind: a plain and honest table, square and sturdy, stood in one corner; a seventeenth-century settle fronted the hearth; and two wooden elbow-chairs and a bookshelf of the Empire made up the equipment, with an exception worthy of note. For Dyson cared for none of these things: his place was at his own bureau, a quaint old piece of lacquered-work, at which he would sit for hour after hour, with his back to the room, engaged in the desperate pursuit of literature, or, as he termed his profession, the chase of the phrase. The neat array of pigeon-holes and drawers teemed and overflowed with manuscript and notebooks, the experiments and efforts of many years; and the inner well, a vast and cavernous receptacle, was stuffed with accumulated ideas. Dyson was a craftsman who loved all the detail and the technique of his work intensely; and if, as has been hinted, he deluded himself a little with the name of artist, yet his amusements were eminently harmless, and, so far as can be ascertained, he (or the publishers) had chosen the good part of not tiring the world with printed matter.

Here, then, Dyson would shut himself up with his fancies, experimenting with words, and striving, as his friend the recluse of Bayswater strove, with the almost invincible problem of style, but always with a fine confidence, extremely different from the chronic depression of the realist. He had been almost continuously at work on some scheme that struck him as well-nigh magical in its possibilities since the night of his adventure with the ingenious tenant of the first floor in Abingdon Grove; and as he laid down the pen with a glow of triumph, he reflected that he had not viewed the streets for five days in succession. With all the enthusiasm of his accomplished labour still working in his brain, he put away his papers and went out, pacing the pavement at first in that rare mood of exultation which finds in every stone upon the way the possibilities of a masterpiece. It was growing late, and the autumn evening was drawing to a close amidst veils of haze and mist, and in the stilled air the voices, and the roaring traffic, and incessant feet seemed to Dyson like the noise upon the stage when all the house is silent. In the square the leaves rippled down as quick as summer rain, and the street beyond was beginning to flare with the lights in the butchers' shops and the vivid illumination of the greengrocer. It was a Saturday night, and the swarming populations of the slums were turning out in force; the battered women in rusty black had begun to paw the lumps of cagmag, and others gloated over unwholesome cabbages, and there was a brisk demand for four-ale. Dyson passed through these night-fires with some relief; he loved to meditate, but his thoughts were not as De Quincey's after his dose; he cared not two straws whether onions were dear or cheap, and would not have exulted if meat had fallen to twopence a pound. Absorbed in the wilderness of the tale he had been writing, weighing nicely the points of plot and construction, relishing the recollection of this and that happy phrase, and dreading failure here and there, he left the rush and whistle of the gas-flares behind him, and began to touch upon pavements more deserted.

He had turned, without taking note, to the northward, and was passing through an ancient fallen street, where now notices of floors and offices to let hung out, but still about it lingered the grace and the stiffness of the Age of Wigs—a broad roadway, a broad pavement, and on each side a grave line of houses with long and narrow windows flush with the walls, all of mellowed brickwork. Dyson walked with quick steps, as he resolved that short work must be made of a certain episode; but he was in that happy humour of invention, and another chapter rose in the inner chamber of his brain, and he dwelt on the circumstances he was to write down with curious pleasure. It was charming to have the quiet streets to walk in, and in his thought he made a whole district the cabinet of his studies, and vowed he would come again. Heedless of his course, he struck off to the east again, and soon found himself involved in a squalid network of grey two-storied houses, and then in the waste void and elements of brickwork, the passages and unmade roads behind great factory walls, encumbered with the refuse of the neighbourhood, forlorn, ill-lighted, and desperate. A brief turn, and there rose before him the unexpected, a hill suddenly lifted from the level ground, its steep ascent marked by the lighted lamps, and eager as an explorer, Dyson found his way to the place, wondering where his crooked paths had brought him. Here all was again decorous, but hideous in the extreme. The builder, someone lost in the deep gloom of the early 'twenties, had conceived the idea of twin villas in grey brick, shaped in a manner to recall the outlines of the Parthenon, each with its classic form broadly marked with raised bands of stucco. The name of the street was all strange, and for a further surprise the top of the hill was crowned with an irregular plot of grass and fading trees, called a square, and here again the Parthenon-motive had persisted. Beyond, the streets were curious, wild in their irregularities, here a row of sordid, dingy dwellings, dirty and disreputable in appearance, and there, without warning, stood a house, genteel and prim, with wire blinds and brazen knocker, as clean and trim as if it had been the doctor's house in some benighted little country town. These surprises and discoveries began to exhaust Dyson, and he hailed with delight the blazing windows of a public-house, and went in with the intention of testing the beverage provided for the dwellers in this region, as remote as Libya and Pamphylia and the parts about Mesopotamia. The babble of voices from within warned him that he was about to assist at the true parliament of the London workman, and he looked about him for that more retired entrance called private. When he had settled himself on an exiguous bench, and had ordered some beer, he began to listen to the jangling talk in the public bar beyond; it was a senseless argument, alternately furious and maudlin, with appeals to Bill and Tom, and mediæval survivals of speech, words that Chaucer wrote belched out with zeal and relish, and the din of pots jerked down and coppers rapped smartly on the zinc counter made a thorough bass for it all. Dyson was calmly smoking his pipe between the sips of beer, when an indefinite-looking figure slid rather than walked into the compartment. The man started violently when he saw Dyson placidly sitting in the corner, and glanced keenly about him. He seemed to be on wires, controlled by some electric machine, for he almost bolted out of the door when the barman asked with what he could serve him, and his hand shivered as he took the glass. Dyson inspected him with a little curiosity. He was muffled up almost to the lips, and a soft felt hat was drawn down over his eyes; he looked as if he shrank from every glance, and a more raucous voice suddenly uplifted in the public bar seemed to find in him a sympathy that made him shake and quiver like a jelly. It was pitiable to see anyone so thrilled with nervousness, and Dyson was about to address some trivial remark of casual inquiry to the man, when another person came into the compartment, and laying a hand on his arm, muttered something in an undertone, and vanished as he came. But Dyson had recognized him as the smooth-tongued and smooth-shaven Burton; and yet he thought little of it, for his whole faculty of observation was absorbed in the lamentable and yet grotesque spectacle before him. At the first touch of the hand on his arm the unfortunate man had wheeled round as if spun on a pivot, and shrank back with a low, piteous cry, as if some dumb beast were caught in the toils. The blood fled away from the wretch's face, and the skin became grey as if a shadow of death had passed in the air and fallen on it, and Dyson caught a choking whisper—

"Mr. Davies! For God's sake, have pity on me, Mr. Davies! On my oath, I say——" and his voice sank to silence as he heard the message, and strove in vain to bite his lips, and summon up to his aid some tinge of manhood. He stood there a moment, wavering as the leaves of an aspen, and then he was gone out into the street, as Dyson thought silently, with his doom upon his head. He had not been gone a minute when it suddenly flashed into Dyson's mind that he knew the man; it was undoubtedly the young man with spectacles for whom so many ingenious persons were searching; the spectacles indeed were missing, but the pale face, the dark whiskers, and the timid glances were enough to identify him. Dyson saw at once that by a succession of hazards he had unawares hit upon the scent of some desperate conspiracy, wavering as the track of a loathsome snake in and out of the highways and byways of the London cosmos; the truth was instantly pictured before him, and he divined that all unconscious and unheeding he had been privileged to see the shadows of hidden forms, chasing and hurrying, and grasping and vanishing across the bright curtain of common life, soundless and silent, or only babbling fables and pretences. For him in an instant the jargoning of voices, the garish splendour, and all the vulgar tumult of the public-house became part of magic; for here before his eyes a scene in this grim mystery play had been enacted, and he had seen human flesh grow grey with a palsy of fear; the very hell of cowardice and terror had gaped wide within an arm's-breadth. In the midst of these reflections the barman came up and stared at him as if to hint that he had exhausted his right to take his ease, and Dyson bought another lease of the seat by an order for more beer. As he pondered the brief glimpse of tragedy, he recollected that with his first start of haunted fear the young man with whiskers had drawn his hand swiftly from his greatcoat pocket, and that he had heard something fall to the ground; and pretending to have dropped his pipe, Dyson began to grope in the corner, searching with his fingers. He touched something and drew it gently to him, and with one brief glance, as he put it quietly in his pocket, he saw it was a little old-fashioned notebook, bound in faded green morocco.

He drank down his beer at a gulp, and left the place, overjoyed at his fortunate discovery, and busy with conjecture as to the possible import-ance of the find. By turns he dreaded to find perhaps mere blank leaves, or the laboured follies of a betting-book, but the faded morocco cover seemed to promise better things, and to hint at mysteries. He piloted himself with no little difficulty out of the sour and squalid quarter he had entered with a light heart, and emerging at Gray's Inn Road, struck off down Guilford Street and hastened home, only anxious for a lighted candle and solitude.

Dyson sat down at his bureau, and placed the little book before him; it was an effort to open the leaves and dare disappointment. But in desperation at last he laid his finger between the pages at haphazard, and rejoiced to see a compact range of writing with a margin, and as it chanced, three words caught his glance and stood out apart from the mass. Dyson read—

"The Gold Tiberius,"

and his face flushed with fortune and the lust of the hunter.

He turned at once to the first leaf of the pocket-book, and pro-ceeded to read with rapt interest

THE HISTORY OF THE YOUNG MAN WITH SPECTACLES

From the filthy and obscure lodging, situated, I verily believe, in one of the foulest slums of Clerkenwell, I indite this history of a life which, daily threatened, cannot last for very much longer. Every day —nay, every hour, I know too well my enemies are drawing their nets closer about me; even now I am condemned to be a close prisoner in my squalid room, and I know that when I go out I shall go to my destruc-tion. This history, if it chance to fall into good hands, may, perhaps, be

z

of service in warning young men of the dangers and pitfalls that most surely must accompany any deviation from the ways of rectitude.

My name is Joseph Walters. When I came of age I found myself in possession of a small but sufficient income, and I determined that I would devote my life to scholarship. I do not mean the scholarship of these days; I had no intention of associating myself with men whose lives are spent in the unspeakably degrading occupation of "editing" classics, befouling the fair margins of the fairest books with idle and superfluous annotation, and doing their utmost to give a lasting disgust of all that is beautiful. An abbey church turned to the base use of a stable or bakehouse is a sorry sight; but more pitiable still is a masterpiece spluttered over with the commentator's pen, and his hideous mark "cf".

For my part, I chose the glorious career of scholar in its ancient sense; I longed to possess encyclopædic learning, to grow old amongst books, to distil day by day, and year after year, the inmost sweetness of all worthy writings. I was not rich enough to collect a library, and I was therefore forced to betake myself to the reading-room of the British Museum.

O dim, far-lifted and mighty dome, Mecca of many minds, mausoleum of many hopes, sad house where all desires fail! For there men enter in with hearts uplifted, and dreaming minds, seeing in those exalted stairs a ladder to fame, in that pompous portico the gate of knowledge, and going in, find but vain vanity, and all but in vain. There, when the long streets are ringing, is silence, there eternal twilight, and the odour of heaviness. But there the blood flows thin and cold, and the brain burns adust; there is the hunt of shadows, and the chase of embattled phantoms; a striving against ghosts, and a war that has no victory. O dome, tomb of the quick! surely in thy galleries, where no reverberant voice can call, sighs whisper ever, and mutterings of dead hopes; and there men's souls mount like moths towards the flame, and fall scorched and blackened beneath thee, O dim, far-lifted, and mighty dome!

Bitterly do I now regret the day when I took my place at a desk for the first time, and began my studies. I had not been an habitué of the place for many months, when I became acquainted with a serene and benevolent gentleman, a man somewhat past middle age, who nearly always occupied a desk next to mine. In the reading-room it takes little to make an acquaintance—a casual offer of assistance, a hint as to the search in the catalogue, and the ordinary politeness of men who constantly sit near each other; it was thus I came to know the man calling himself Dr. Lipsius. By degrees I grew to look for his presence, and to miss him when he was away, as was sometimes the case, and so a friendship sprang up between us. His immense range of learning was placed freely at my service; he would often astonish me by the way in which he would sketch out in a few minutes the bibliography of a given subject, and before long I had confided to him my ambitions.

"Ah," he said, "you should have been a German. I was like that myself when I was a boy. It is a wonderful resolve, an infinite career. I will know all things; yes, it is a device indeed. But it means this—a life of labour without end, and a desire unsatisfied at last. The scholar has to die, and die saying, 'I know very little!' "

Gradually, by speeches such as these, Lipsius seduced me: he would praise the career, and at the same time hint that it was as hopeless as the search for the philosopher's stone, and so by artful suggestions, insinuated with infinite address, he by degrees succeeded in undermining all my principles. "After all," he used to say, "the greatest of all sciences, the key to all knowledge, is the science and art of pleasure. Rabelais was perhaps the greatest of all the encyclopædic scholars; and he, as you know, wrote the most remarkable book that has ever been written. And what does he teach men in this book? Surely the joy of living. I need not remind you of the words, suppressed in most of the editions, the key of all the Rabelaisian mythology, of all the enigmas of his grand philosophy, *Vivez joyeux*. There you have all his learning; his work is the institutes of pleasure as the fine art; the finest art there is; the art of all arts. Rabelais had all science, but he had all life too. And we have gone a long way since his time. You are enlightened, I think; you do not consider all the petty rules and by-laws that a corrupt society has made for its own selfish convenience as the immutable decrees of the Eternal."

Such were the doctrines that he preached; and it was by such insidious arguments, line upon line, here a little and there a little, that he at last succeeded in making me a man at war with the whole social system. I used to long for some opportunity to break the chains and to live a free life, to be my own rule and measure. I viewed existence with the eyes of a pagan, and Lipsius understood to perfection the art of stimulating the natural inclinations of a young man hitherto a hermit. As I gazed up at the great dome I saw it flushed with the flames and colours of a world of enticement unknown to me, my imagination played me a thousand wanton tricks, and the forbidden drew me as surely as a loadstone draws on iron. At last my resolution was taken, and I boldly asked Lipsius to be my guide.

He told me to leave the Museum at my usual hour, half-past four, to walk slowly along the northern pavement of Great Russell Street, and to wait at the corner of the street till I was addressed, and then to obey in all things the instructions of the person who came up to me. I carried out these directions, and stood at the corner looking about me anxiously, my heart beating fast, and my breath coming in gasps. I waited there for some time, and had begun to fear I had been made the object of a joke, when I suddenly became conscious of a gentleman who was looking at me with evident amusement from the opposite pavement of Tottenham Court Road. He came over, and raising his hat, politely begged me to follow him, and I did so without a word, wondering where we were going, and what was to happen. I was taken to a house of quiet and respectable aspect in a street lying to the north of Oxford Street, and my guide rang the bell. A servant showed us into a large room, quietly furnished, on the ground floor. We sat there in silence for some time, and I noticed that the furniture, though unpretending, was extremely valuable. There were large oak presses, two book-cases of extreme elegance, and in one corner a carved chest which must have been mediæval. Presently Dr. Lipsius came in and welcomed me with his usual manner, and after some desultory conversation my guide left the room. Then an elderly man dropped in and began talking to Lipsius, and from their conversation I understood that my friend was a dealer in antiques; they spoke of the Hittite seal, and of the prospects of further discoveries, and later, when two or three more persons joined us, there was an argument as to the possibility of a systematic exploration of the pre-Celtic monuments in England. I was, in fact, present at an archæological reception of an informal kind; and at nine o'clock, when the antiquaries were gone, I stared at Lipsius in a manner that showed I was puzzled, and sought an explanation.

"Now," he said, "we will go upstairs."

As we passed up the stairs, Lipsius lighting the way with a hand-lamp, I heard the sound of a jarring lock and bolts and bars shot on at the front door. My guide drew back a baize door and we went down a passage, and I began to hear odd sounds, a noise of curious mirth; then he pushed me through a second door, and my initiation began. I cannot write down what I witnessed that night; I cannot bear to recall what went on in those secret rooms fast shuttered and curtained so that no light should escape into the quiet street; they gave me red wine to drink, and a woman told me as I sipped it that it was wine of the Red Jar that Avallaunius had made. Another asked me how I liked the wine of the Fauns, and I heard a dozen fantastic names, while the stuff boiled in my veins, and stirred, I think, something that had slept within me from the moment I was born. It seemed as if my self-consciousness deserted me; I was no longer a thinking agent, but at once subject and object; I mingled in the horrible sport, and watched the mystery of the Greek groves and fountains enacted before me, saw the reeling dance and heard the music calling as I sat beside my mate, and yet I was outside it all, and viewed my own part an idle spectator. Thus with strange rites they made me drink the cup, and when I woke up in the morning I was one of them, and had sworn to be faithful. At first I was shown the enticing side of things; I was bidden to enjoy myself and care for nothing but pleasure, and Lipsius himself indicated to me as the acutest enjoyment the spectacle of the terrors of the unfortunate persons who were from time to time decoyed into the evil house. But after a time it was pointed out to me that I must take my share in the work, and so I found myself compelled to be in my turn a seducer; and thus it is on my conscience that I have led many to the depths of the pit.

One day Lipsius summoned me to his private room, and told me that he had a difficult task to give me. He unlocked a drawer and gave me a sheet of type-written paper, and bade me read it.

It was without place, or date, or signature, and ran as follows:

Mr. James Headley, F.S.A., will receive from his agent in Armenia, on the 12th inst., a unique coin, the gold Tiberius. It bears on the reverse a faun with the legend VICTORIA. It is believed that this coin is of immense value. Mr. Headley will come up to town to show the coin to his friend, Professor Memys, of Chenies Street, Oxford Street, on some date between the 13th and the 18th.

Dr. Lipsius chuckled at my face of blank surprise when I laid down this singular communication.

"You will have a good chance of showing your discretion," he said. "This is not a common case; it requires great management and infinite tact. I am sure I wish I had a Panurge in my service, but we will see what you can do."

"But is it not a joke?" I asked him. "How can you know—or rather, how can this correspondent of yours know—that a coin has been despatched from Armenia to Mr. Headley? And how is it possible to fix the period in which Mr. Headley will take it into his head to come up to town? It seems to me a lot of guesswork."

"My dear Mr. Walters," he replied, "we do not deal in guesswork here. It would bore you if I went into all these little details, the cogs and wheels, if I may say so, which move the machine. Don't you think it is much more amusing to sit in front of the house and be astonished than to be behind the scenes and see the mechanism? Better tremble at the thunder, believe me, than see the man rolling the cannon-ball. But, after all, you needn't bother about the how and why; you have your share to do. Of course I shall give you full instructions, but a great deal depends on the way the thing is carried out. I have often heard very young men maintain that style is everything in literature, and I can assure you that the same maxim holds good in our far more delicate profession. With us style is absolutely everything, and that is why we have friends like yourself."

I went away in some perturbation: he had no doubt designedly left everything in mystery, and I did not know what part I should have to play. Though I had assisted at scenes of hideous revelry, I was not yet dead to all echo of human feeling, and I trembled lest I should receive the order to be Mr. Headley's executioner.

A week later, it was on the sixteenth of the month, Dr. Lipsius made me a sign to come into his room.

"It is for to-night," he began. "Please to attend carefully to what I am going to say, Mr. Walters, and on peril of your life, for it is a dangerous matter—on peril of your life, I say, follow these instructions to the letter. You understand? Well, to-night at about half-past seven, you will stroll quietly up the Hampstead Road till you come to Vincent Street. Turn down here and walk along, taking the third turning to your right, which is Lambert Terrace. Then follow the terrace, cross the road, and go along Hertford Street, and so into Lillington Square. The second turning you will come to in the square is called Sheen Street; but in reality it is more a passage between blank walls than a street. Whatever you do, take care to be at the corner of this street at eight o'clock precisely. You will walk along it, and just at the bend where you lose sight of the square you will find an old gentleman with white beard and whiskers. He will in all probability be abusing a cabman for having brought him to Sheen Street instead of Chenies Street. You will go up to him quietly and offer your services; he will tell you where he wants to go, and you will be so courteous as to offer to show him the way. I may say that Professor Memys moved into Chenies Street a month ago; thus Mr. Headley has never been to see him there, and, moreover, he is very short-sighted, and knows little of the topography of London. Indeed, he has quite lived the life of a learned hermit at Audley Hall.

"Well, need I say more to a man of your intelligence? You will bring him to this house, he will ring the bell, and a servant in quiet livery will let him in. Then your work will be done, and I am sure done well. You will leave Mr. Headley at the door, and simply continue your walk, and I shall hope to see you the next day. I really don't think there is anything more I can tell you."

These minute instructions I took care to carry out to the letter. I confess that I walked up the Tottenham Court Road by no means blindly, but with an uneasy sense that I was coming to a decisive point in my life. The noise and rumour of the crowded pavements were to me but dumb show; I revolved again and again in ceaseless iteration the task that had been laid on me, and I questioned myself as to the possible results. As I got near the point of turning, I asked myself whether danger were not about my steps; the cold thought struck me that I was suspected and observed, and every chance foot-passenger who gave me a second glance seemed to me an officer of police. My time was running out, the sky had darkened, and I hesitated, half resolved to go no farther, but to abandon Lipsius and his friends for ever. I had almost determined to take this course, when the conviction suddenly came to me that the whole thing was a gigantic joke, a fabrication of rank improbability. Who could have procured the information about the Armenian agent? I asked myself. By what means could Lipsius have known the particular day and the very train that Mr.

Headley was to take? how engage him to enter one special cab amongst the dozens waiting at Paddington? I vowed it a mere Milesian tale, and went forward merrily, turned down Vincent Street, and threaded out the route that Lipsius had so carefully impressed upon me. The various streets he had named were all places of silence and an oppressive cheap gentility; it was dark, and I felt alone in the musty squares and crescents, where people pattered by at intervals, and the shadows were growing blacker. I entered Sheen Street, and found it as Lipsius had said, more a passage than a street; it was a by-way, on one side a low wall and neglected gardens, and grim backs of a line of houses, and on the other a timber-yard. I turned the corner, and lost sight of the square, and then, to my astonishment, I saw the scene of which I had been told. A hansom cab had come to a stop beside the pavement, and an old man, carrying a handbag, was fiercely abusing the cabman, who sat on his perch the image of bewilderment.

"Yes, but I'm sure you said Sheen Street, and that's where I brought you," I heard him saying as I came up, and the old gentleman boiled in a fury, and threatened police and suits at law.

The sight gave me a shock, and in an instant I resolved to go through with it. I strolled on, and without noticing the cabman, lifted my hat politely to old Mr. Headley.

"Pardon me, sir," I said, "but is there any difficulty? I see you are a traveller; perhaps the cabman has made a mistake. Can I direct you?"

The old fellow turned to me, and I noticed that he snarled and showed his teeth like an ill-tempered cur as he spoke.

"This drunken fool has brought me here," he said. "I told him to drive to Chenies Street, and he brings me to this infernal place. I won't pay him a farthing, and I meant to have given him a handsome sum. I am going to call for the police and give him in charge."

At this threat the cabman seemed to take alarm; he glanced round, as if to make sure that no policeman was in sight, and drove off grumbling loudly, and Mr. Headley grinned savagely with satisfaction at having saved his fare, and put back one and sixpence into his pocket, the "handsome sum" the cabman had lost.

"My dear sir," I said, "I am afraid this piece of stupidity has annoyed you a great deal. It is a long way to Chenies Street, and you will have some difficulty in finding the place unless you know London pretty well."

"I know it very little," he replied. "I never come up except on important business, and I've never been to Chenies Street in my life."

"Really? I should be happy to show you the way. I have been for a stroll, and it will not at all inconvenience me to take you to your destination."

"I want to go to Professor Memys, at Number 15. It's most annoying to me; I'm short-sighted, and I can never make out the numbers on the doors."

"This way, if you please," I said, and we set out.

I did not find Mr. Headley an agreeable man; indeed, he grumbled the whole way. He informed me of his name, and I took care to say, "The well-known antiquary?" and thenceforth I was compelled to listen to the history of his complicated squabbles with publishers, who had treated him, as he said, disgracefully; the man was a chapter in the Irritability of Authors. He told me that he had been on the point of making the fortune of several firms, but had been compelled to abandon the design owing to their rank ingratitude. Besides these ancient histories of wrong, and the more recent misadventure of the cabman, he had another grievous complaint to make. As he came along in the train, he had been sharpening a pencil, and the sudden jolt of the engine as it drew up at a station had driven the penknife against his face, inflicting a small triangular wound just on the cheek-bone, which he showed me. He denounced the railway company, heaped imprecations on the head of the driver, and talked of claiming damages. Thus he grumbled all the way, not noticing in the least where he was going; and so unamiable did his conduct appear to me, that I began to enjoy the trick I was playing on him.

Nevertheless, my heart beat a little faster as we turned into the street where Lipsius was waiting. A thousand accidents, I thought, might happen; some chance might bring one of Headley's friends to meet us; perhaps, though he knew not Chenies Street, he might know the street where I was taking him; in spite of his short sight, he might possibly make out the number; or, in a sudden fit of suspicion, he might make an inquiry of the policeman at the corner. Thus every step upon the pavement, as we drew nearer to the goal, was to me a pang and a terror, and every approaching passenger carried a certain threat of danger. I gulped down my excitement with an effort, and made shift to say pretty quietly—

"Number 15, I think you said? That is the third house from this. If you will allow me, I will leave you now; I have been delayed a little, and my way lies on the other side of Tottenham Court Road."

He snarled out some kind of thanks, and I turned my back and walked swiftly in the opposite direction. A minute or two later I looked round, and saw Mr. Headley standing on the doorstep, and then the door opened and he went in. For my part, I gave a sigh of relief; I hastened to get away from the neighbourhood, and endeavoured to enjoy myself in merry company.

The whole of the next day I kept away from Lipsius. I felt anxious, but I did not know what had happened, or what was happening, and a reasonable regard for my own safety told me that I should do well to remain quietly at home. My curiosity, however, to learn the end of the odd drama in which I had played a part stung me to the quick, and late in the evening I made up my mind to see how events had turned out. Lipsius nodded when I came in, and asked me if I could give him five minutes' talk. We went into his room, and he began to walk up and down, while I sat waiting for him to speak.

"My dear Mr. Walters," he said at length, "I congratulate you warmly; your work was done in the most thorough and artistic manner. You will go far. Look."

He went to his escritoire and pressed a secret spring; a drawer flew out, and he laid something on the table. It was a gold coin; I took it up and examined it eagerly, and read the legend about the figure of the faun.

"Victoria," I said, smiling.

"Yes; it was a great capture, which we owe to you. I had great difficulty in persuading Mr. Headley that a little mistake had been made; that was how I put it. He was very disagreeable, and indeed ungentlemanly, about it; didn't he strike you as a very cross old man?"

I held the coin, admiring the choice and rare design, clear cut as if from the mint; and I thought the fine gold glowed and burnt like a lamp.

"And what finally became of Mr. Headley?" I said at last.

Lipsius smiled, and shrugged his shoulders.

"What on earth does it matter?" he said. "He might be here, or there, or anywhere; but what possible consequence could it be? Besides, your question rather surprises me; you are an intelligent man, Mr.

Walters. Just think it over, and I'm sure you won't repeat the question."

"My dear sir," I said, "I hardly think you are treating me fairly. You have paid me some handsome compliments on my share in the capture, and I naturally wish to know how the matter ended. From what I saw of Mr. Headley, I should think you must have had some difficulty with him."

He gave me no answer for the moment, but began again to walk up and down the room, apparently absorbed in thought.

"Well," he said at last, "I suppose there is something in what you say. We are certainly indebted to you. I have said that I have a high opinion of your intelligence, Mr. Walters. Just look here, will you?"

He opened a door communicating with another room, and pointed. There was a great box lying on the floor, a queer, coffin-shaped thing. I looked at it, and saw it was a mummy case, like those in the British Museum, vividly painted in the brilliant Egyptian colours, with I knew not what proclamation of dignity or hopes of life immortal. The mummy swathed about in the robes of death was lying within, and the face had been uncovered.

"You are going to send this away?" I said, forgetting the question I had put.

"Yes; I have an order from a local museum. Look a little more closely, Mr. Walters."

Puzzled by his manner, I peered into the face, while he held up the lamp. The flesh was black with the passing of the centuries; but as I looked I saw upon the right cheek bone a small triangular scar, and the secret of the mummy flashed upon me: I was looking at the dead body of the man whom I had decoyed into that house.

There was no thought or design of action in my mind. I held the accursed coin in my hand, burning me with a foretaste of hell, and I fled as I would have fled from pestilence and death, and dashed into the street in blind horror, not knowing where I went. I felt the gold coin grasped in my clenched fist, and throwing it away, I knew not where, I ran on and on through by-streets and dark ways, till at last I issued out into a crowded thoroughfare and checked myself. Then as consciousness returned I realized my instant peril, and understood what would happen if I fell into the hands of Lipsius. I knew that I had put forth my finger to thwart a relentless mechanism rather than a man. My recent adventure with the unfortunate Mr. Headley had taught me that Lipsius had agents in all quarters; and I foresaw that if I fell into his hands, he would remain true to his doctrine of style, and cause me to die a death of some horrible and ingenious torture. I bent my whole mind to the task of outwitting him and his emissaries, three of whom I knew to have proved their ability for tracking down persons who for various reasons preferred to remain obscure. These servants of Lipsius were two men and a woman, and the woman was incomparably the most subtle and the most deadly. Yet I considered that I too had some portion of craft, and I took my resolve. Since then I have matched myself day by day and hour by hour against the ingenuity of Lipsius and his myrmidons. For a time I was successful; though they beat furiously after me in the covert of London, I remained *perdu*, and watched with some amusement their frantic efforts to recover the scent lost in two or three minutes. Every lure and wile was put forth to entice me from my hiding-place; I was informed by the medium of the public prints that what I had taken had been recovered, and meetings were proposed in which I might hope to gain a great deal without the slightest risk. I laughed at their endeavours, and began a little to despise the organization I had so dreaded, and ventured more abroad. Not once or twice, but several times, I recognized the two men who were charged with my capture, and I succeeded in eluding them easily at close quarters; and a little hastily I decided that I had nothing to dread, and that my craft was greater than theirs. But in the meanwhile, while I congratulated myself on my cunning, the third of Lipsius's emissaries was weaving her nets; and in an evil hour I paid a visit to an old friend, a literary man named Russell, who lived in a quiet street in Bayswater. The woman, as I found out too late, a day or two ago, occupied rooms in the same house, and I was followed and tracked down. Too late, as I have said, I recognized that I had made a fatal mistake, and that I was besieged. Sooner or later I shall find myself in the power of an enemy without pity; and so surely as I leave this house I shall go to receive doom. I hardly dare to guess how it will at last fall upon me; my imagination, always a vivid one, paints to me appalling pictures of the unspeakable torture which I shall probably endure; and I know that I shall die with Lipsius standing near and gloating over the refinements of my suffering and my shame.

Hours, nay minutes, have become very precious to me. I sometimes pause in the midst of anticipating my tortures, to wonder whether even now I cannot hit upon some supreme stroke, some design of infinite subtlety, to free myself from the toils. But I find that the faculty of combination has left me; I am as the scholar in the old myth, deserted by the power which has helped me hitherto. I do not know when the supreme moment will come, but sooner or later it is inevitable; before long I shall receive sentence, and from the sentence to execution will not be long.

. . . .

I cannot remain here a prisoner any longer. I shall go out to-night when the streets are full of crowds and clamours, and make a last effort to escape.

. . . .

It was with profound astonishment that Dyson closed the little book, and thought of the strange series of incidents which had brought him into touch with the plots and counterplots connected with the Gold Tiberius. He had bestowed the coin carefully away, and he shuddered at the bare possibility of its place of deposit becoming known to the evil band who seemed to possess such extraordinary sources of information.

It had grown late while he read, and he put the pocket-book away, hoping with all his heart that the unhappy Walters might even at the eleventh hour escape the doom he dreaded.

ADVENTURE OF THE DESERTED RESIDENCE

"A WONDERFUL story, as you say, an extraordinary sequence and play of coincidence. I confess that your expressions when you first showed me the Gold Tiberius were not exaggerated. But do you think that Walters has really some fearful fate to dread?"

"I cannot say. Who can presume to predict events when life itself puts on the robe of coincidence and plays at drama? Perhaps we have not yet reached the last chapter in the queer story. But, look, we are drawing near to the verge of London; there are gaps, you see, in the serried ranks of brick, and a vision of green fields beyond."

Dyson had persuaded the ingenious Mr. Phillipps to accompany him on one of those aimless walks to which he was himself so addicted. Starting from the very heart of London, they had made their way westward through the stony avenues, and were now just emerging from the red lines of an extreme suburb, and presently the half-finished road ended, a quiet lane began, and they were beneath the shade of elm trees. The yellow autumn sunlight that had lit up the bare distance of the suburban street now filtered down through the boughs of the trees and shone on the glowing carpet of fallen leaves, and the pools of rain glittered and shot back the gleam of light. Over all the broad pastures there was peace and the happy rest of autumn before the great winds begin, and afar off London lay all vague and immense amidst the veiling mist; here and there a distant window catching the sun and kindling with fire, and a spire gleaming high, and below the streets in shadow, and the turmoil of life. Dyson and Phillipps walked on in silence beneath the high hedges, till at a turn of the lane they saw a mouldering and ancient gate standing open, and the prospect of a house at the end of a moss-grown carriage drive.

"There is a survival for you," said Dyson; "it has come to its last days, I imagine. Look how the laurels have grown gaunt and weedy, and black and bare beneath; look at the house, covered with yellow wash, and patched with green damp. Why, the very notice-board, which informs all and singular that the place is to be let, has cracked and half fallen."

"Suppose we go in and see it," said Phillipps; "I don't think there is anybody about."

They turned up the drive, and walked slowly towards this remnant of old days. It was a large, straggling house, with curved wings at either end, and behind a series of irregular roofs and projections, showing that the place had been added to at divers dates; the two wings were roofed in cupola fashion, and at one side, as they came nearer, they could see a stableyard, and a clock turret with a bell, and the dark masses of gloomy cedars. Amidst all the lineaments of dissolution there was but one note of contrast: the sun was setting beyond the elm trees; and all the west and south were in flames; on the upper windows of the house the glow shone reflected, and it seemed as if blood and fire were mingled. Before the yellow front of the mansion, stained, as Dyson had remarked, with gangrenous patches, green and blackening, stretched what once had been, no doubt, a well-kept lawn, but it was now rough and ragged, and nettles and great docks, and all manner of coarse weeds, struggled in the places of the flower-beds. The urns had fallen from their pillars beside the walk, and lay broken in shards upon the ground, and everywhere from grass-plot and path a fungoid growth had sprung up and multiplied, and lay dank and slimy like a festering sore upon the earth. In the middle of the rank grass of the lawn was a desolate fountain; the rim of the basin was crumbling and pulverized with decay, and within the water stood stagnant, with green scum for the lilies that had once bloomed there; rust had eaten into the bronze flesh of the Triton that stood in the middle, and the conch-shell he held was broken.

"Here," said Dyson, "one might moralize over decay and death. Here all the stage is decked out with the symbols of dissolution; the cedarn gloom and twilight hang heavy around us, and everywhere within the pale dankness has found a harbour, and the very air is changed and brought to accord with the scene. To me, I confess, this deserted house is as moral as a graveyard, and I find something sublime in that lonely Triton, deserted in the midst of his water-pool. He is the last of the gods; they have left him, and he remembers the sound of water falling on water, and the days that were sweet."

"I like your reflections extremely," said Phillipps; "but I may mention that the door of the house is open."

"Let us go in, then."

The door was just ajar, and they passed into the mouldy hall and looked in at a room on one side. It was a large room, going far back, and the rich, old, red flock paper was peeling from the walls in long strips, and blackened with vague patches of rising damp; the ancient clay, the dank reeking earth rising up again, and subduing all the work of men's hands after the conquest of many years. The floor was thick with the dust of decay, and the painted ceiling fading from all gay colours and light fancies of cupids in a career, and disfigured with sores of dampness, seemed transmuted into other work. No longer the amorini chased one another pleasantly, with limbs that sought not to advance, and hands that merely simulated the act of grasping at the wreathed flowers; but it appeared some savage burlesque of the old careless world and of its cherished conventions, and the dance of the Loves had become a Dance of Death; black pustules and festering sores swelled and clustered on fair limbs and smiling faces showed corruption, and the fairy blood had boiled with the germs of foul disease; it was a parable of the leaven working, and worms devouring for a banquet the heart of the rose.

Strangely, under the painted ceiling, against the decaying walls, two old chairs still stood alone, the sole furniture of the empty place. High-backed, with curving arms and twisted legs, covered with faded gold leaf, and upholstered in tattered damask, they too were a part of the symbolism, and struck Dyson with surprise. "What have we here?" he said. "Who has sat in these chairs? Who, clad in peach-bloom satin, with lace ruffles and diamond buckles, all golden, *a conté fleurettes* to his companion? Phillips, we are in another age. I wish I had some snuff to offer you, but failing that, I beg to offer you a seat, and we will sit and smoke tobacco. A horrid practice, but I am no pedant."

They sat down on the queer old chairs, and looked out of the dim and grimy panes to the ruined lawn, and the fallen urns, and the deserted Triton.

Presently Dyson ceased his imitation of eighteenth-century airs; he no longer pulled forward imaginary ruffles, or tapped a ghostly snuff-box.

"It's a foolish fancy," he said at last; "but I keep thinking I hear a noise like someone groaning. Listen; no, I can't hear it now. There it is again! Did you notice it, Phillipps?"

"No, I can't say I heard anything. But I believe that old places like this are like shells from the shore, ever echoing with noises. The old beams, mouldering piecemeal, yield a little and groan; and such a house as this I can fancy all resonant at night with voices, the voices of matter so slowly and so surely transformed into other shapes, the voice of the worm that gnaws at last the very heart of the oak, the voice of stone grinding on stone, and the voice of the conquest of Time."

They sat still in the old arm-chairs, and grew graver in the musty ancient air, the air of a hundred years ago.

"I don't like the place," said Phillipps, after a long pause. "To me it seems as if there were a sickly, unwholesome smell about it, a smell of something burning."

"You are right; there is an evil odour here. I wonder what it is. Hark! Did you hear that?"

A hollow sound, a noise of infinite sadness and infinite pain, broke in upon the silence, and the two men looked fearfully at one another, horror, and the sense of unknown things, glimmering in their eyes.

"Come," said Dyson, "we must see into this," and they went into the hall and listened in the silence.

"Do you know," said Phillipps, "it seems absurd, but I could almost fancy that the smell is that of burning flesh."

They went up the hollow-sounding stairs, and the odour became thick and noisome, stifling the breath, and a vapour, sickening as the smell of the chamber of death, choked them. A door was open, and they entered the large upper room, and clung hard to one another, shuddering at the sight they saw.

A naked man was lying on the floor, his arms and legs stretched wide apart, and bound to pegs that had been hammered into the boards. The body was torn and mutilated in the most hideous fashion, scarred with the marks of red-hot irons, a shameful ruin of the human shape. But upon the middle of the body a fire of coals was smouldering; the flesh had been burnt through. The man was dead, but the smoke of his torment mounted still, a black vapour.

"The young man with spectacles," said Mr. Dyson.

THEO MARZIALS[1]

Tragedy

In the warm wax-light one lounged at the spinet,
    And high in the window came peeping the moon;
At his side was a bowl of blue china, and in it
    Were large blush-roses, and cream and maroon.

They crowded, and strain'd, and swoon'd to the music,
    And some to the gilt board languor'd and lay;
They open'd and breathed, and trembled with pleasure,
    And all the sweet while they were fading away.

[1]He was well-known as the composer, both as to their words and music, of many popular songs, of which mention may be made of "Twickenham Ferry" and "The River of Years."

AA

Châtelard

A LONG day spent at Châtelard for sketching;
　A glowing sky above; another sky
As clear the lake beneath; towards it stretching
　The vines and long white walls where melons lie.

We set our easels in a small oasis
　Of orchard-shade, and wearied with the glare
Of noon, our eyes sought on each other's faces
　A rest in reading love, no secret there.

And in that love was nothing to remind us
　How we were leaving other things undone,
And Châtelard rose gloomily behind us,
　And cast a broad black shadow from the sun.

The chatty magpies whirl'd into the thickets,
　The deep datura's breath grew over-sweet,
The finches left their trilling to the crickets,
　The glow-worms glimmered faintly at our feet.

The yellowing tendrils quiver'd on the trestle,
　The night-wind found a word still to be said,
And made her heedless hands but closer nestle
　In mine—and yet the love was but half-read.

*

A long day spent for sketching!—Who'd discover
　A sketch in those unfinished shades and lines?
For now my heart alone can there recover
　The sense of glowing slopes and torrid vines.

O Châtelard! she left me when your orchard
　Grew cold and bare with Summer and the sun,
And death has left my heart all cleft and tortured,
　And stopp'd the loving ere the sketch was done.

The Love-Token

She has griffins twain to guard her gate,
    A mastiff-hound to watch her in the hall,
A page for her train when she walks in state,
And minstrels and maidens around her to wait,
    And lovers and gallants at beck and call;
But ah! she left her shutter a-jar
For the cool to climb over the window-bar!

The griffins grinned in the moonlight green,
    The hound by the grim red embers slept;
I scraped a chord on my mandoline,
A chord, pardie, that might ruin a queen!
    And softly a-down the garden I crept;
And ah! the song slid thro' the shutter a-jar,
And the lady leaned over the window-bar!

ALICE MEYNELL

To a Daisy

Slight as thou art, thou art enough to hide
    Like all created things, secrets from me,
    And stand a barrier to eternity.
And I, how can I praise thee well and wide
From where I dwell—upon the hither side?
    Thou little veil for so great mystery,
    When shall I penetrate all things and thee,

And then look back? For this I must abide,
Till thou shalt grow and fold and be unfurled
Literally between me and the world.
    Then I shall drink from in beneath a spring,
And from a poet's side shall read his book.
    O daisy mine, what will it be to look
    From God's side even of such a simple thing?

A Letter from a Girl to her own Old Age

LISTEN, and when thy hand this paper presses,
O time-worn woman, think of her who blesses
What thy thin fingers touch, with her caresses.

O mother, for the weight of years that break thee!
O daughter, for slow Time must yet awake thee,
And from the changes of my heart must make thee.

O fainting traveller, morn is grey in heaven.
Dost thou remember how the clouds were driven?
And are they calm about the fall of even?

Pause near the ending of thy long migration,
For this one sudden hour of desolation
Appeals to one hour of thy meditation.

Suffer, O silent one, that I remind thee
Of the great hills that stormed the sky behind thee,
Of the wild winds of power that have resigned thee.

Know that the mournful plain where thou must wander
Is but a grey and silent world, but ponder
The misty mountains of the morning yonder.

Listen:—the mountain winds with rain were fretting,
And sudden gleams the mountain-tops besetting.
I cannot let thee fade to death, forgetting.

What part of this wild heart of mine I know not
Will follow with thee where the great winds blow not,
And where the young flowers of the mountain grow not.

Yet let my letter with my lost thoughts in it
Tell what the way was when thou didst begin it,
And win with thee the goal when thou shalt win it.

Oh, in some hour of thine my thoughts shall guide thee.
Suddenly, though time, darkness, silence, hide thee,
This wind from thy lost country flits beside thee,—

Telling thee: all thy memories moved the maiden,
With thy regrets was morning over-shaden,
With sorrow, thou hast left, her life was laden.

But whither shall my thoughts turn to pursue thee?
Life changes, and the years and days renew thee.
Oh, Nature brings my straying heart unto thee.

Her winds will join us, with their constant kisses
Upon the evening as the morning tresses,
Her summers breathe the same unchanging blisses.

And we, so altered in our shifting phases,
Track one another 'mid the many mazes
By the eternal child-breath of the daisies.

I have not writ this letter of divining
To make a glory of thy silent pining,
A triumph of thy mute and strange declining.

Only one youth, and the bright life was shrouded.
Only one morning, and the day was clouded.
And one old age with all regrets is crowded.

O hush, O hush! Thy tears my words are steeping.
O, hush, hush, hush! So full, the fount of weeping?
Poor eyes, so quickly moved, so near to sleeping?

Pardon the girl; such strange desires beset her.
Poor woman, lay aside the mournful letter
That breaks thy heart; the one who wrote, forget her:

The one who now thy faded features guesses,
With filial fingers thy grey hair caresses,
With morning tears thy mournful twilight blesses.

Your Own Fair Youth

YOUR own fair youth, you care so little for it,
    Smiling towards Heaven, you would not stay the
      advances
  Of time and change upon your happiest fancies.
I keep your golden hour, and will restore it.

If ever, in time to come, you would explore it—
    Your old self, whose thoughts went like last year's
      pansies,
  Look unto me; no mirror keeps its glances;
In my unfailing praises now I store it.

To guard all joys of yours from Time's estranging,
    I shall be then a treasury where your gay,
      Happy, and pensive past for ever is.

I shall be then a garden charmed from changing,
    In which your June has never passed away.
      Walk there awhile among my memories.

GEORGE MOORE

The Lovers of Orelay

I HAD come a thousand miles—rather more, nearly fifteen hundred—
in the hope of picking up the thread of a love-story that had got entangled some years before and had been broken off abruptly. A strange
misadventure our love-story had been; for Doris had given a great

deal of herself while denying me much, so much that at last, in despair, I fled from a one-sided love-affair; too one-sided to be borne any longer, at least by me. And it was difficult to fly from her pretty, inveigling face, delightful and winsome as the faces one finds on the panels of the early German masters. One may look for her face and find it on an oak panel in the Frankfort Gallery, painted in pale tints, the cheeks faintly touched with carmine. In the background of these pictures there are all sorts of curious things; very often a gold bower with roses clambering up everywhere. Who was that master who painted cunning virgins in rose bowers? The master of Cologne, was it not? I have forgotten. No matter. Doris's hair was darker than the hair of those virgins, a rich gold hair, a mane of hair growing as luxuriously as the meadows in June. And the golden note was continued everywhere, in the eyebrows, in the pupils of the eyes, in the freckles along her little nose so firmly and beautifully modelled about the nostrils; never was there a more lovely or affectionate mouth, weak and beautiful as a flower; and the long hands were curved like lilies. There is her portrait, dear reader, prettily and truthfully painted by me, the portrait of a girl I left one afternoon in London more than seventeen years ago, and that I had lost sight of, I feared for ever. Thought of her? Yes, I thought of her occasionally. Time went by, and I wondered if she were married. What her husband was like, and why I never wrote. It were surely unkind not to write. . . . Reader, you know those little regrets. Perhaps life would be all on the flat without regret. Regret is like a mountain-top from which we survey our dead life, a mountain-top on which we pause and ponder, and very often looking into the twilight we ask ourselves whether it would be well to send a letter or some token. Now we had agreed upon one which should be used in case of an estrangement—a few bars of Schumann's melody, "The Walnut Tree", should be sent, and the one who received it should at once hurry to the side of the other and all difference be healed. But this token was never sent by me, perhaps because I did not know how to scribble the musical phrase: pride perhaps kept her from sending it; in any case five years are a long while, and she seemed to have died out of my life altogether; but one day the sight of a woman who had known her brought her before my eyes, and I asked if Doris were married. The woman could not tell me; she had not seen her for many years; they, too, were estranged, and I went home saying to myself, "Doris must be married. What sort of husband has she chosen? Is she happy? Has she a baby? O shameful thought!" Do you remember, dear reader, how Balzac, when he had come to the last page of *Massimilla Doni*, declares that he dare not tell you the end of this adventure? One word, he says, will suffice for the worshippers of the ideal: "Massimilla Doni was expecting.' Then in a passage that is pleasanter to think about than to read—for Balzac when he spoke about art was something of a sciolist, and I am not sure that the passage is altogether grammatical—he tells how the ideas of all the great artists, painters and sculptors—the ideas they have wrought on panels and in stone—escaped from their niches and their frames—all these disembodied maidens gathered round Massimilla's bed and wept. It would be as disgraceful for Doris to be "expecting" as it was for Massimilla Doni, and I like to think of all the peris, the nymphs, the sylphs, the fairies of ancient legend, all her kinsfolk gathering about her bed, deploring her condition, regarding her as lost to them—were such a thing to happen I should certainly kneel there in spirit with them. And feeling just as Balzac did about Massimilla Doni, that it was a sacrilege that Doris should be "expecting" or even married, I wrote, omitting, however, to tell her why I had suddenly resolved to break silence; I sent her a little note, only a few words, that I was sorry not to have heard of her for so long a time; but though we had been estranged she had not been forgotten; a little commonplace note, relieved perhaps by a touch of wistfulness, of regret. And this note was sent by a messenger duly instructed to ask for an answer. The news the messenger brought back was somewhat disappointing. The lady was away, but the letter would be forwarded to her. "She is not married," I thought, "were she married her name would be sent to me. . . . Perhaps not." Other thoughts came into my mind, and I did not think of her again for the next two days, not till a long telegram was put into my hands. Doris! It had come from her. It had come more than a thousand miles, "regardless of expense". I said, "This telegram must have cost her ten or twelve shillings at the least." She was delighted to hear from me; she had been ill, but was better now, and the telegram concluded with the usual "Am writing." The letter that arrived, two days afterwards was like herself, full of impulse and affection; but it contained one phrase which put black misgiving into my heart. In her description of her illness and her health, which was returning, and how she had come to be staying in this far-away Southern town, she alluded to its dulness, saying that if I came there virtue must be its own reward. "Stupid of her to speak to me of virtue," I muttered, "for she must know well enough that it was her partial virtue that had separated us and caused this long estrangement." And I sat pondering, trying to discover if she applied the phrase to herself or to the place where she was staying. How could it apply to the place? All places would be a paradise if——

At the close of a long December evening I wrote a letter, the answer to which would decide whether I should go to her, whether I should undertake the long journey. "The journey back will be detestable," I muttered, and taking up the pen again I wrote, "Your letter contains a phrase which fills me with dismay: you say, 'Virtue must be its own reward,' and this would seem that you are determined to be more aggressively Platonic than ever. Doris, this is ill news indeed; you would not have me consider it good news, would you?"

Other letters followed, but I doubt if I knew more of Doris's intentions when I got into the train than I did when I sat pondering by my fireside, trying to discover her meaning when she wrote that vile phrase, "Virtue must be its own reward." But somehow I seemed to have come to a decision, and that was the main thing. We act obeying a law deep down in our being, a law which in normal circumstances we are not aware of. If the stone rolling down the hill were to become conscious, it would think it was rolling itself. As I drove to the station, so did Doris's pretty face remind me of Spinoza. Doris's pretty face might be pretty no longer; yet she could not have changed much. She had said she was sure that in ten minutes we should be talking just as in old times. Even so, none but madmen travel a thousand miles in search of a pretty face. And the madman that is in us all was propelling me, or it was the primitive man who crouches in some jungle of our being. Of one thing I was sure, that I was no longer a conventional citizen of the nineteenth century; I had gone back two or three thousand years, for all characteristic traits, everything whereby I knew myself, had disappeared! Yet I seemed to have met myself somewhere, in some book or poem or opera. . . . I could not remember at first, but after some time I began to perceive a shadowy similarity between myself and—dare I mention the names?—the heroes of ancient legend —Menelaus or Jason—which? Both had gone a thousand miles on

Beauty's quest. The colour of Helen's hair isn't mentioned in either the *Iliad* or the *Odyssey*. Jason's quest was a golden fleece, and so was mine. And it was the primitive hero that I had discovered in myself that helped me to face the idea of the journey, for there is nothing that wearies me so much as a long journey in the train.

Twenty-five years ago I started with the intention of long travel, but the train journey from Calais to Paris wearied me so much that I rested in Paris for eight years, to return home then on account of some financial embarrassments. During those eight years I had thought often of Italy and the south of France, but the train journey of sixteen or seventeen or eighteen hours to the Italian frontier had always seemed so much like what purgatory must be that the heaven of Italy on the other side never tempted me sufficiently to undertake it. A companion would be of no use; for who can talk for fifteen or sixteen hours? and while debating whether the journey to Plessy should be undertaken, every hour seemed drawing out into an endless perspective. But everything, pleasure and pain alike, is greater in imagination than in reality—there is always a reaction, and having anticipated more than mortal weariness, it was surprising to find that the first two hours in the train had passed very pleasantly. It seemed that I had only been in the train quite a little while when it stopped, yet Laroche is more than an hour from Paris, quite a countryside station, and it seems strange that the *Côte d' Azur* should stop there. That was the grand name of the train that I was travelling by. Think of any English company running a train and calling it "The Azure Shore"! Think of going to Euston or to Charing Cross, saying you are going by "The Azure Shore"! So long as the name of this train endures, it is impossible to doubt that the French mind is more picturesque than the English, and one no longer wonders why the French school of painting, etc.

A fruit-seller was crying his wares along the platform, and just before we started from Laroche breakfast was preparing on board the train; I thought a basket of French grapes—the grapes that grow in the open air, not the leathery hot-house grapes filled with lumps of glue that we eat in England—would pass the time. I got out and bought a basket from him. On journeys like these one has to resort to many various little expedients. Alas! The grapes were decaying; only the bunch on the top was eatable; nor was that one worth eating, and I began to think that the railway company's attention should be directed to the fraud, for in my case a deliberate fraud had been effected. The directors of the railway would probably think that passengers should exercise some discrimination; it were surely easy for the passenger to examine the quality of a basket of grapes before purchasing—that would be the company's answer to my letter. The question of a letter to the newspaper did not arise, for French papers are not like ours— they do not print all the letters that are sent to them. The French public has no means of ventilating its grievances; a misfortune no doubt, but not such a misfortune as it seems, when one reflects on how little good a letter addressed to the public press does in the way of remedying abuses.

I don't think we stopped again till we got to Lyons, and all the way there I sat at the window looking at the landscape—the long, long plain that the French peasant cultivates unceasingly. Out of that long plain came all the money that was lost in Panama, and all the money invested in Russian bonds—five milliards came out of the French peasant's stockings. We passed through La Beauce. I believe it was there that Zola went to study the French peasant before he wrote *La Terre*. Huysmans, with that benevolent malice so characteristic of him, used to say that Zola's investigation was limited to going out once for a drive in a carriage with Madame Zola. The primitive man that had risen out of some jungle of my being did not view this immense and highly cultivated plain sympathetically. It seemed to him to differ little from the town, so utterly was nature dominated by man and portioned out. On a subject like this one can meditate for a long time, and I meditated till my meditation was broken by the stopping of the train. We were at Lyons. The tall white-painted houses reminded me of Paris—Lyons, as seen from the windows of *La Côte d'Azur* at the end of a grey December day might be Paris. The climate seemed the same; the sky was as sloppy and as grey. At last the train stopped at a place from which I could look down a side street, and I decided that Lyons wore a more provincial look than Paris, and I thought of the great silk trade and the dull minds of the merchants . . . their dinner-parties, etc. I noticed everything there was to notice in order to pass the time; but there was so little of interest that I wrote out a telegram and ran with it to the office, for Doris did not know what train I was coming by, and it is pleasant to be met at a station, to meet one familiar face, not to find oneself amid a crowd of strangers. Very nearly did I miss the train; my foot was on the footboard when the guard blew his whistle. "Just fancy if I had missed the train," I said, and settling myself in my seat I added, "now, let us study the landscape; such an opportunity as this may never occur again."

The long plain cultivated with tedious regularity that we had been passing through before we came to Lyons flowed on field after field; it seemed as if we should never reach the end of it, and looking on those same fields, for they were the same, I said to myself, "If I were an economist that plain would interest me, but since I got Doris's letter I am primitive man, and he abhors the brown and the waving field, and 'the spirit in his feet' leads him to some grassy glen where he follows his flocks, listening to the song of the wilding bee that sings as it labours amid the gorse. What a soulless race that plain must breed," I thought; "what soulless days are lived there; peasants going forth at dusk to plough, and turning home at dusk to eat, procreate and sleep." At last a river appeared flowing amid sparse and stunted trees and reeds, a great wide sluggish river with low banks, flowing so slowly that it hardly seemed to flow at all. Rooks flew past, but they are hardly wilding birds; a crow—yes, we saw one; and I thought of a heron rising slowly out of one of the reedy islands; maybe an otter or two survives the persecution of the peasant, and I liked to think of a poacher picking up a rabbit here and there; hares must have almost disappeared, even the flock and the shepherd. France is not as picturesque a country as England; only Normandy seems to have pasturage, there alone the shepherd survives along the banks of the Seine. Picardy, though a swamp, never conveys an idea of the wild; and the middle of France, which I looked at then for the first time, shocked me, for primitive man, as I have said, was uppermost in me, and I turned away from the long plain, "dreary", I said, "uneventful as a boarding-house."

But it is a long plain that has no hill in it, and when I looked out again a whole range showed so picturesquely that I could not refrain, but turned to a travelling companion to ask its name. It was the Esterelles; and never shall I forget the picturesqueness of one moment —the jagged end of the Esterelles projecting over the valley, showing against what remained of the sunset, one or two bars of dusky red, disappearing rapidly amid heavy clouds massing themselves as if for a storm, and soon after night closed over the landscape.

"Henceforth," I said, "I shall have to look to my own thoughts for amusement, and in my circumstances there was nothing reasonable for me to think of but Doris. Some time before midnight I should catch sight of her on the platform. It seemed to me wonderful that it should be so, and I must have been dreaming, for the voice of the guard, crying out that dinner was served awoke me with a start.

It is said to be the habit of my countrymen never to get into conversation with strangers in the train, but I doubt if that be so. Everything depends on the tact of him who first breaks silence; if his manner inspires confidence in his fellow-traveller he will receive such answers as will carry the conversation on for a minute or two, and in that time both will have come to a conclusion whether the conversation should be continued or dropped. A pleasant little book might be written about train acquaintances. If I were writing such a book I would tell of the Americans I met once at Nuremberg, and with whom I travelled to Paris; for it was such a pleasant journey. I should have liked to keep up their acquaintance, but it is not the etiquette of the road to do so. But I am writing no such book; I am writing the quest of a golden fleece, and may allow myself no further deflection in the narrative; I may tell, however, of the two very interesting people I met at dinner on board *La Côte d'Azur*, though some readers will doubt if it be any integral part of my story. The woman was a typical French woman, pleasant and agreeable, a woman of the upper middle classes, so she seemed to me, but as I knew all her ideas the moment I looked at her, conversation with her did not flourish; or would it be more true to say that her husband interested me more, being less familiar? His accent told me he was French; but when he took off his hat I could see that he had come from the tropics—Algeria, I thought; not unlikely a soldier. His talk was less stilted than a soldier's, and I began to notice that he did not look like a Frenchman, and when he told me that he lived in an oasis in the desert, and was on his way home, his Oriental appearance I explained by his long residence among the Arabs. He had lived in the desert since he was fourteen. "Almost a Saharian," I said to him. And during dinner and long after dinner, we sat talking of the difference between the Oriental races and the European; of the various Arab *patois*. He spoke the Tunisian *patois* and wrote the language of the Koran, which is understood all over the Sahara and the Soudan, as well as in Mecca. What interested me, perhaps even more than the language question, was the wilding's enterprise in attempting to cultivate the desert. He had already enlarged his estate by the discovery of two ancient Roman wells, and he had no doubt that all that part of the desert lying between the three oases could be brought into cultivation. In ancient times there were not three oases but one; the wells had been destroyed, and hundreds of thousands of acres had been laid waste by the Numidians in order, I think he told me, to save themselves from the Saracens who were following them. He spent eight months of every year in his oasis, and begged of me, as soon as I had wearied of Plessy, to take the boat from Marseilles—I suppose it was from Marseilles—and spend some time with him in the wild.

"Visitors," he said, "are rare. You'll be very welcome. The railway will take you within a hundred miles; the last hundred miles will be accomplished on the back of a dromedary; I shall send you a fleet one and an escort."

"Splendid," I answered. "I see myself arriving sitting high up on the hump gathering dates—I suppose there are date palms where you are? Yes?—and wearing a turban and a bournous."

"Would you like to see my bournous?" he said, and opening his valise he showed me a splendid one which filled me with admiration, and only shame forbade me to ask him to allow me to try it on. Ideas haunt one. When I was a little child I insisted on wearing a turban and going out for a ride on the pony, flourishing a Damascus blade which my father had brought home from the East. Nothing else would have satisfied me; my father led the pony, and I have always thought this fantasy exceedingly characteristic; it must be so, for it awoke in me twenty years afterwards; and fanciful and absurd as it may appear, I certainly should have liked to have worn my travelling companion's bournous in the train if only for a few minutes. All this is twelve years ago, and I have not yet gone to visit him in his oasis, but how many times have I done so in my imagination, seeing myself arriving on the back of a dromedary crying out, "Allah! Allah! And Mahommad is his prophet!" But though one can go on thinking year after year about a bournous, one cannot talk for more than two or three hours about one; and though I looked forward to spending at least a fortnight with my friends, and making excursions in the desert, finding summer, as Fromentin says, *chez lui*, I was glad to say good-bye to my friends at Marseilles. I was still far from the end of my journey, and so weary of talk that at first I was doubtful whether it would be worth while to engage again in conversation, but a pleasant gentleman had got into my carriage, and he required little encouragement to tell me his story. His beginnings were very humble, but he was now a rich merchant. It is always interesting to hear how the office-boy gets his first chance; the first steps are the interesting onces, and I should be able to tell his story here if we had not been interrupted in the middle of it by his little girl. She had wearied of her mother, who was in the next carriage, and had come in to sit on her father's knee. Her hair hung about her shoulders just as Doris's had done five years ago, taking the date from the day that I journeyed in quest of the golden fleece. She was a winsome child, with a little fluttering smile about her lips and a curious intelligence in her eyes. She admitted that she was tired, but had not been ill, and her father told me that long train journeys produced the same effect on her as a sea journey. She spoke with a pretty abruptness, and went away suddenly, I thought for good, but she returned half an hour afterwards looking a little faint, I thought, green about the mouth, and smiling less frequently. One cannot remember everything, and I have forgotten at what station these people got out; they bade me a kindly farewell, telling me that in about two hours and a half I should be at Plessy, and that I should have to change at the next station, and this lag end of my journey dragged itself out very wearily. Plessy is a difficult place to get at; one has to change, and while waiting for the train I seemed to lose heart; nothing seemed to matter, not even Doris. But these are momentary capitulations of the intellect and the senses, and when I saw her pretty face on the platform I congratulated myself again on my wisdom in having sent her the telegram. How much pleasanter it was to walk with her to the hotel than to walk there alone! "She is," I said to myself, "still the same pretty girl whom I so bitterly reproached for selfishness in Cumberland Place five years ago." To compliment her on her looks, to tell her that she did not look a day older, a little thinner, a little paler, that was all, but the same enchanting Doris, was the facile inspiration of the returned lover. And we walked down the platform talking, my talk full of gentle reproof—why had she waited up? There was a reason. . . . My hopes, till now buoyant as corks, began to sink. "She is going to tell me that I cannot come to her hotel. Why did I send that telegram from Lyons?" Had it not been for that telegram I could have gone straight to her hotel. It was just the telegram that had brought her to the station, and she had come to tell me that it was impossible for me to stay at her hotel. After thirty hours of travel which hotel I stayed at mattered little, but to-morrow and the next day, the long week we were to spend together passed before my eyes, the tedium of the afternoons, the irritation and emptiness of Platonic evenings—'Heavens! what have I let myself in for,' I thought, and my mind went back over the long journey and the prospect of returning *bredouille*, as the sportsmen say. But to argue about details with a woman, to get angry, is a thing that no one versed in the arts of love ever does. We are in the hands of women always; it is they who decide, and our best plan is to accept the different hotel without betraying disappointment, or as little as possible. But we had not seen each other for so long that we could not part at once. Doris said that I must come to her hotel and eat some supper. No; I had dined on board the train, and all she could persuade me to have was a cup of chocolate. Over that cup of chocolate we talked for an hour, and then I had to bid her good-night. The moon looked down the street coldly; I crossed from shadow to light, feeling very weary in all my body, and there was a little melancholy in my heart, for after all I might not win Doris. There was sleep, however, and sleep is at times a good thing, and that night it must have come quickly, so great was the refreshment I experienced in the morning when my eyes opened and, looking through mosquito curtains (themselves symbols of the South), were delighted by the play of the sunlight flickering along the flower-papered wall. The impulse in me was to jump out of bed at once and to throw open *les croisées*. And what did I see? Tall palm-trees in the garden, and above them a dim, alluring sky, and beyond them a blue sea in almost the same tone as the sky. And what did I feel? Soft perfumed airs moving everywhere. And what was the image that rose up in my mind? The sensuous gratification of a vision of a woman bathing at the edge of a summer wood, the intoxica-tion of the odour of her breasts. . . . Why should I think of a woman bathing at the edge of a summer wood? Because the morning seemed the very one that Venus should choose to rise from the sea and come into one's bedroom. Forgive my sensuousness, dear reader; remember that it was the first time I breathed the soft Southern air, the first time I saw orange-trees; remember that I am a poet, a modern Jason in search of a golden fleece. 'Is this the garden of the Hesperides?' I

asked myself, for nothing seemed more unreal than the golden fruit
hanging like balls of yellow worsted among dark and sleek leaves; it
reminded me of the fruit I used to see, when I was a child, under glass
shades in lodging-houses; but I knew, nevertheless, that I was looking
upon orange-trees, and that the golden fruit growing amid the green
leaves was the fruit I used to pick from the barrows when I was a boy;
the fruit of which I ate so much in boyhood that I cannot eat it any
longer; the fruit whose smell we associate with the pit of a theatre;
the fruit that women never weary of, high and low. It seemed to me
a wonderful thing that at last I should see oranges growing on trees;
and I felt so happy that morning that I could not but wonder at my
happiness, and seeking for a cause for it I stumbled on the reflection
that perhaps after all happiness is no more than a faculty for being
surprised. The *valet de chambre* brought in my bath, and while I
bathed and dressed I reflected on the luck of him who in middle age
can be astonished by a blue sky, and still find the sunlight a bewitch-
ment. But who would not be bewitched by the pretty sunlight that
finds its way into the gardens of Plessy? Moreover, I knew I was
going to walk with Doris by a sea blue as any drop-curtain, and as
she came towards me, her parasol aslant, she seemed to be but a figure
on a drop-curtain. Are we not all figures on drop-curtains, and is not
all drop-curtain, and La Belle Helène perhaps the only true reality?
Amused by the idea of Jason or Paris or Menelaus in Plessy, I asked
Doris what music was played by the local orchestra, and she told me it
played "The March of Aida" every evening. "On the cornet," I said,
understanding at once that the mission of Plessy was to redeem one from
the coil of one's daily existence, from Hebrew literature and its con-
comitants, bishops, vicars and curates—all these, especially bishops,
are regarded as being serious; whereas French novels and their con-
comitants, pretty girls, are supposed to represent the trivial side of
life. A girl becomes serious only when she is engaged to be married;
the hiring of the house in which the family is reared is regarded as
serious; in fact all prejudices are serious; every deflection from the
normal, from the herd, is looked upon as trivial; and I suppose that
this is right: the world could not do without the herd nor could the herd
do without us—the eccentrics who go to Plessy in quest of a golden
fleece instead of putting stoves in the parish churches (stoves and organs
are always regarded as too devilishly serious for words). Once I had a

BB

conversation with my archbishop about the Book of Daniel, and were
I to write out his lordship's erudition I might even be deemed sufficiently serious for a review in the *Church Gazette*. But looking back
on this interview, and judging it with all the impartiality of which
my nature is capable, it is impossible for me to say that it should be
regarded as more serious than pretty Doris's fluent conversation, or
the melancholy aspect of his Lordship's cathedral as more serious than
the pretty Southern sunlight glancing along the seashore, lighting up
the painted houses, and causing Doris to shift her parasol. What a
splendid article I might write on the trivial side of seriousness, but discussion is always trivial; I shall be much more serious in trying to recall
the graceful movement of her waist, and how prettily her parasol
enframed her face. True that almost every face is pretty against the
distended silk full of sunlight and shadow, but Doris's, I swear to you,
was as pretty as any mediæval virgin despite its modernness. Memling
himself never designed a more appealing little face. Think of the
enchantment of such a face after a long journey, by the sea that the
Romans and the Greeks used to cross in galleys, that I used to read
about when I was a boy. There it was, and on the other side the shore
on which Carthage used to stand; there it was, a blue bay with long
red hills reaching out, reminding me of hills I had seen somewhere, I
think in a battle piece by Salvator Rosa. It seemed to me that I had
seen those hills before—no, not in a picture; had I dreamed them, or
was there some remembrance of a previous existence struggling in my
brain? There was a memory somewhere, a broken memory, and I
sought for the lost thread as well as I could, for Doris rarely ceased
talking.

"And there is the restaurant," she said, flinging up her parasol,
"built at the end of those rocks."

We were the first swallows to arrive; the flocks would not be here
for about three weeks. So we had the restaurant to ourselves, the waiter
and doubtless the cook; and they gave us all their attention. Would we
have breakfast in the glass pavilion? How shall I otherwise describe it,
for it seemed to be all glass. The scent of the sea came through the
window, and the air was like a cordial—it intoxicated; and looking
across the bay one seemed to be looking on the very thing that Whistler
had sought for in his Nocturnes, and that Steer had nearly caught in
that picture of children paddling, that dim, optimistic blue that allures

and puts the world behind one, the dream of the opium-eater, the phrase of the syrens in *Tannhäuser*, the phrase which begins like a barcarole; but the accompaniment tears underneath until we thrill with expectation.

As I looked across the bay Doris seemed but a little thing, almost insignificant, and the thought came that I had not come for nothing even if I did not succeed in winning her.

"Doris, dear, forgive me if I am looking at this bay instead of you, but I've never seen anything like this before," and feeling I was doing very poor justice to the emotions I was experiencing, I said, "Is it not strange that all this is at once to me new and old? I seem, as it were, to have come into my inheritance."

"Your inheritance! Am I not——"

"Dearest, you are. Say that you are my inheritance, my beautiful inheritance; how many years have I waited for it?" As I took her in my arms she caught sight of the waiter, and turning from her I looked across the bay, and my desire nearly died in the infinite sweetness blowing across the bay.

"Azure hills, not blue; hitherto I have only seen blue."

"They're blue to-day because there is a slight mist, but they are in reality red."

"A red-hilled bay," I said, "and all the slopes flecked with the white sides of villas."

"Peeping through olive-trees."

"Olive-trees, of course. I have never yet seen the olive; the olive begins at Avignon or thereabouts, doesn't it? It was dark night when we passed through Avignon."

"You'll see very few trees here; only olives and ilex."

"The ilex I know, and there is no more beautiful tree than the ilex.

> Were not the crocuses that grew
> Under that ilex tree,
> As beautiful in scent and hue
> As ever fed the bee?"

"Whose verses are those?"

"Shelley's. I know no others. Are the lines very wonderful? They seem no more than a statement, yet they hang about my memory. I am glad I shall see the ilex tree."

"And the eucalyptus—plenty of eucalyptus trees."

"That was the scent that followed us this morning as we came through the gardens?"

"Yes, as we passed from our hotel one hung over the garden wall, and the wind carried its scent after us."

The arrival of the waiter with *hors d'œuvres* distracted our attention from the olive-tree to its fruit. I rarely touch olives, but that morning I ate many. Should we have mutton cutlets or lamb? Doris said the Southern mutton was detestable. "Then we'll have lamb." An idea came into my head, and it was this, that I had been mistaken about Doris's beauty. Hers was not like any face that one may find in a panel by Memlinc. She was like something, but I could not lay my thoughts on what she was like.

"A sail would spoil the beauty of the bay," I said when the waiter brought in the coffee, and left us —we hoped for the last time. Taking hands and going to the window we sat looking across the sailless bay. "How is it that no ships come here? Is the bay looked upon as a mere ornament, and reserved exclusively for the appreciation of visitors? Those hills, too, look as if they had been designed in a like intent. . . . How much more beautiful the bay is without a sail—why I cannot tell, but——"

"But what?"

"A great galley rowed by fifty men would look well under the curl of the headland. . . . The bay is antiquity, and those hills; all the morning while talking to you a memory or a shadow of a memory has fretted in my mind like a fly on a pane. Now I know why I have been expecting a nymph to rise out of those waves during breakfast. For a thousand years men believed that nymphs came up on those rocks, and that satyrs and their progeny might be met in the woods and on the hillsides. Only a thin varnish has been passed over these beliefs. One has only to come here to look down into that blue sea-water to believe that nymphs swim about those rocks; and when we go for a drive among those hillsides we'll keep a sharp look-out for satyrs. Now I know why I like this country. It is heathen. Those mountains —how different from the shambling Irish hills from whence I have come! And you, Doris, you might have been dug up yesterday, though you are but two-and-twenty. You are a thing of yester age, not a bit like the little Memlinc head which I imagined you to be like when I was coming here in the train, nor like anything done by the Nuremberg painters. You are a Tanagra figure, and one of the finest. In you I read all the winsomeness of antiquity. But I must look at the bay now, for I may never see anything like it again; never have I seen anything like it before. Forgive me, remember that three days ago I was in Ireland, the day before yesterday I was in England, yesterday I was in Paris. I have come out of the greyness of the North. When I left Paris all was grey, and when the train passed through Lyons a grey night was gathering; now I see no cloud at all: the change is so wonderful. You cannot appreciate my admiration. You have been looking at the bay for the last three weeks, and *la côte d'azur* has become nothing to you now but palms and promenades. To me it is still quite different. I shall always see you beautiful, whereas Plessy may lose her beauty in a few days. Let me enjoy it while I may."

"Perhaps I shall not outlast Plessy?"

"Yes, you will. Do you know, Doris, that you don't look a day older since the first time I saw you walking across the room to the piano in your white dress, your gold hair hanging down over your shoulders. It has darkened a little, that is all."

"It is provoking you should see me when I am thin. I wish you had seen me last year when I came from the rest cure. I went up more than a stone in weight. Everyone said that I didn't look more than sixteen. I know I didn't, for all the women were jealous of me."

As I sat watching the dissolving line of the horizon, lost in a dream, I heard my companion say—

"Of what are you thinking?"

"I'm thinking of something that happened long ago in that very bay."

"Tell me about it;" and her hand sought mine for a moment.

"Would you like to hear it? I'd like to tell it, but it's a long, long story, and to remember it would be an effort. The colour of the sea and the sky is enough; the warmth of the sunlight penetrates me; I feel like a plant; the only difference between me and one of those palm-trees——"

"I am sure those poor palms are shivering. There is not enough heat here for them; they come from the south, and you come from the north."

"I suppose that is so. They grow, but they don't flourish here. However, my mood is not philanthropic; I cannot pity even a palm-tree at the present moment. See how my cigar smoke curls and goes out! It is strange, Doris, that I should meet you here, for some years ago it was arranged that I should come here——"

"With a woman?"

"Yes, of course. How can it be otherwise? Our lives are woven along and across with women. Some men find the reality of their lives in women, others, as we were saying just now, in bishops."

"Tell me about the woman who asked you to come here. Did you love her? And what prevented you from coming here with her?"

"It is one of the oddest stories—odd only because it is like myself. Every character creates its own stories; we are like spools, and each spool fills itself up with a different-coloured thread. The story, such as it is, began one evening in Victoria Street at the end of a long day's work. A letter began it. She wrote asking me to dine with her, and her letter was most welcome, for I had no plans for that evening. I do not know if you know that curious dread of life which steals through the twilight; it had just laid its finger on my shoulder when the bell rang, and I said, 'My visitor is welcome, whoever she or he may be.' The visitor would have only spent a few minutes perhaps with me, but Gertrude's letter—that was her name—was a promise of a long and pleasant evening, for it was more than a mere invitation to dinner. She wrote: 'I have not asked anyone to meet you, but you will not mind dining alone with me. I hope you will be able to come, for I want to consult you on a matter about which I think you will be able to advise me.' As I dressed I wondered what she could have to propose, and with my curiosity enkindled I walked to her house. The evening was fine—I remember it—and she did not live far from me; we were neighbours. You see I knew Gertrude pretty well, and I liked her. There had been some love passages between us, but I had never been her lover; our story had got entangled, and as I went to her I hoped that this vexatious knot was to be picked at last. To be Gertrude's lover would be a pleasure indeed, for though a woman of forty, a natural desire to please, a witty mind and pretty manners, still kept her young; she had all the appearance of youth; and French gowns and underwear that cost a little fortune made her a woman that one would still take a pleasure in making love to. It would be pleasant to be her lover for many reasons. There were disadvantages, however, for Gertrude, though never vulgar herself, liked vulgar things. Her friends were vulgar; her flat, for she had just left her husband, was opulent, over-decorated; the windows were too heavily curtained, the electric light seemed to be always turned on, and as for the pictures —well, we won't talk of them; Gertrude was the only one worth looking at. And she was rather like a Salon picture, a Gervex, a Boldini—I will not be unjust to Gertrude, she was not as vulgar as a Boldini. She had a pretty cooing manner, and her white dress fell gracefully from her slender flanks. You can see her, can't you, coming forward to meet me, rustling a little, breathing an odour of orris root, taking my hand and very nearly pressing it against her bosom? Gertrude knew how to suggest, and no sooner had the thought that she wished to inspire passed through my mind than she let go my hand, saying, 'Come, sit down by me, tell me what you have been doing'; and her charm was that it was impossible to say whether what I have described, dress, manner, and voice, was unconscious or intentional."

"Probably a little of both," Doris said.

"I see you understand. You always understand."

"And to make amends for the familiarity of pressing your hand to her bosom she would say, 'I hope you will not mind dining alone with me,' and immediately you would propound a little theory that two is company, and three is a county council, unless indeed the three consist of two men and one woman. A woman is never really happy unless she is talking to two men, woman being at heart a polyandrist."

"Doris, you know me so well that you can invent my conversations."

"Yes, I think I can. You have not changed; I have not forgotten you though we have not seen each other for five years; and now go on, tell me about Gertrude."

"Well, sitting beside her on the sofa—"

"Under the shaded electric light," interrupted Doris.

"—I tried to discover—not the reason of this invitation to dinner; of course it was natural that old friends should dine together, but she had said in her letter that she wished to talk to me about some matter on which she thought I could advise her. The servant would come in a moment to announce that dinner was ready, and if Gertrude did not tell me at once I might, if the story were a long one, have to wait till dinner was over; her reluctance to confide in me seemed to point to pecuniary help. Was it possible that Gertrude was going to ask me to lend her money? If so, the loan would be a heavy one, more than I could afford to lend. That is the advantage of knowing rich people; when they ask for money they ask for more than one can afford to lend, and one can say with truth, 'Were I to lend you five hundred pounds, I should not be able to make ends meet at the end of the year.' Her reluctance to confide in me seemed incomprehensible, unless indeed she wanted to borrow money. But Gertrude was not that kind, and she was a rich woman. At last, just before the servant came into the room, she turned round saying that she had sent for me because she wished to speak to me about a yacht. Imagine my surprise. To speak to me about a yacht! If it had been about a picture.

"The door opened, the servant announced that dinner was ready, and we had to talk in French during dinner, for her news was that she had hired a yacht for the winter in order that she might visit Greece and the Greek Islands. But she did not dare to travel in Greece alone for six months, and it was difficult to find a man who was free and whom one could trust. She thought she could trust me, and remembering that I had once liked her, it had occurred to her to ask me if I would like to go with her. I shall never forget how Gertrude confided her plan to me, the charming modesty with which she murmured, 'Perhaps you do still, and you will not bore me by claiming rights over me. I don't mind your making love to me, but I don't like rights. You know what I mean. When we return to England you will not pursue me. You know what I have suffered from such pursuits; you know all about it.' Is it not curious how a woman will sometimes paint her portrait in a single phrase; not paint, but indicate in half-a-dozen lines her whole moral nature? Gertrude exists in the words I have quoted just as God made her. And now I have to tell you about the pursuit. When Gertrude mentioned it I had forgotten it; a blankness came into my face, and she said, 'Don't you remember?' 'Of course, of course,' I said, and this is the story within the story.

"One day after lunch Gertrude, getting up, walked unconsciously towards me, and quite naturally I took her in my arms, and when I had told her how much I liked her, and the pleasure I took in her company, she promised to meet me at a hotel in Lincoln. We were to meet there in a fortnight's time; but two days before she sent for me, and told me that she would have to send me away. I really did like Gertrude, and I was quite overcome, and a long hour was spent begging of her to tell why she had come to this determination. One of course says unjust things, one accuses a woman of cruelty; what could be the meaning of it? Did she like to play with a man as a cat plays with a mouse? But Gertrude, though she seemed distressed at my accusations, refused to give me any explanation of her conduct; tears came into her eyes—they seemed like genuine tears—and it was difficult to believe that she had taken all this trouble merely to arrive at this inexplicable and most disagreeable end. Months passed without my hearing anything of Gertrude, till one day she sent me a little present, and in response to a letter she invited me to come to see her in the country. And, walking through some beautiful woods, she told me the reason why she had not gone to Lincoln. A Pole whom she had met at the gambling tables at Monte Carlo, was pursuing her, threatening her that if he saw her with any other man, he would murder her and her lover. This at first seemed an incredible tale, but when she entered into details, there could be no doubt that she was telling the truth, for had she not on one occasion very nearly lost her life through this man? They were in Germany together, she and the Pole, and he had locked her up in her room without food for many hours, and coming in suddenly he had pressed the muzzle of a pistol against her temple, and pulled the trigger. Fortunately, it did not go off. 'It was a very near thing,' she said; 'the cartridge was indented, and I made up my mind that if things went any further, I should have to tell my husband.' 'But things can't go further than an indented cartridge,' I answered. 'What you tell me is terrible'; and we talked for a long time, walking about the woods, fearing that the Pole might spring from behind every bush, the pistol in his hand. But he did not appear; she evidently knew where he was, or had made some compact with him. Nevertheless, at the close of the day, I drove through the summer evening not having got anything from Gertrude except a promise that if she should find herself free, she would send for me. Weeks and months went by during which I saw Gertrude occasionally; you see love-stories, once they get entangled, remain entangled; that is what makes me fear that we shall never be able to pick the knot that you have tied our love-story into. Misadventure followed misadventure. It seemed to me that I behaved very stupidly on many occasions; it would take too long to tell you how—when I met her at the theatre I did not do exactly what I should have done; and on another occasion when I met her driving in a suburb, I did not stop her cab, and so on and so on until, resolved to bring matters to a crisis, Gertrude had sent me an invitation to dinner, and her plan was the charming one which I have told you, that we should spend six months sailing about the Greek Islands in a yacht. We left the dining-room and returned to the drawing-room, she telling me that the yacht had been paid for—the schooner, the captain, the crew, everything for six months; but I not unnaturally pointed out to her that I could not accept her hospitality for so long a time, and the greater part of the evening was spent in trying to persuade her to allow me to pay—Gertrude was the richer— at least a third of the upkeep of the yacht must come out of my pocket.

"The prospect of a six months' cruise among the Greek Islands kindled my imagination, and while listening to Gertrude I was often in spirit far away, landing perchance at Cyprus, exalted at the prospect of visiting the Cyprians' temple; or perchance standing with Gertrude on the deck of the yacht watching the stars growing dim in the east; the sailors would be singing at the time, and out of the ashen stillness a wind would come, and again we would hear the ripple of the water parting as the jib filled and drew the schooner eastward. I imagined how half an hour later an island would appear against the golden sky, a lofty island lined with white buildings, perchance ancient fanes. 'What a delicious book my six months with Gertrude will be!' I said as I walked home, and the title of the book was an inspiration, 'An Unsentimental Journey'. It was Gertrude's own words that had suggested it. Had she not said that she did not mind my making love to her, but she did not like rights? She couldn't complain if I wrote a book, and I imagined how every evening when the lover left her the chronicler would sit for an hour recording his impressions. Very often he would continue writing until the pencil dropped from his hand, till he fell asleep in the chair. An immediate note-taking would be necessary, so fugitive are impressions, and an analysis of his feelings, their waxing and their waning; he would observe himself as an astronomer observes the course of a somewhat erratic star, and his descriptions of himself and of her would be interwoven with descriptions of the seas across which Menelaus had gone after Helen's beauty—beauty, the noblest of men's quests.

"For once Nature seemed to me to put into the hands of the artist a subject perfect in its every part; the end especially delighted me, and I imagined our good-byes at Plymouth or Portsmouth or Hull, wherever we might land. 'Well, Gertrude, good-bye. We have spent a very pleasant six months together; I shall never forget our excursion. But this is not a rupture; I may hope to see you sometime during the season? You will allow me to call about tea-time?' And she would answer, 'Yes, you may call. You have been very nice.' Each would turn away sighing, conscious of a little melancholy in the heart, for all partings are sad; but at the bottom of the heart there would be a sense of relief, of gladness—that gladness which the bird feels when it leaves its roost: there is nothing more delicious perhaps than the first beat of the wings. I forget now whether I looked forward most to the lady or to the book. . . . If the winds had been more propitious, I might have written a book that would have compared favourably with the eighteenth-century literature, for the eighteenth century was cynical in love; while making love to a woman, a gallant would often consider a plan for her subsequent humiliation. Goncourt——"

"But, dear one, finish about the yacht."

"Well, it seemed quite decided that Gertrude and I were to go to Marseilles to meet the schooner; but the voyage from the Bay of Biscay is a stormy and a tedious one; the weather was rough all the way, and she took a long time to get to Gibraltar. She passed the strait signalling to Lloyd's; we got a telegram; everything was ready; I had ordered yachting clothes, shoes, and quantities of things; but after that telegram no news came, and one evening Gertrude told me she was beginning to feel anxious; the yacht ought to have arrived at Marseilles. Three or four days passed, and then we read in the paper—the *Evening Standard*, I think it was—the *Ring-Dove*, a large schooner, had sunk off the coast while making for the Bay of Plessy. Had she passed that point over yonder, no doubt she would have been saved; all hands were lost, the captain, seven men, and my book."

"Good heavens, how extraordinary! And what became of Gertrude? Were you never her lover?"

"Never. We abstained while waiting for the yacht. Then she fell in love with somebody else; she married her lover; and now he deplores her; she found an excellent husband, and she died in his arms."

At every moment I expected Doris to ask me how it was that, for the sake of writing a book, I had consented to go away for a six months' cruise with a woman whom I didn't love. But there was a moment when I loved her—the week before Lincoln. Whether Doris agreed tacitly that my admiration of Gertrude's slender flanks and charm of manner and taste in dress justified me in agreeing to go away with her, I don't know; she did not trouble me with the embarrassing question I had anticipated. Isn't it strange that people never ask the embarrassing questions one foresees? She asked me instead with whom I had been in love during the past five years, and this too embarrassed me, though not to the extent the other question would have done. To say that since I had seen Doris I had led a chaste life, would be at once incredible and ridiculous. Sighing a little, I spoke of a *liaison* that had lasted many years and had come to an end at last. Fearing that Doris would ask if it had come to an end through weariness, it seemed well to add that the lady had a daughter growing up, and it was for the girl's sake we had agreed to bring our love-story to a close. We had, however, promised to remain friends. Doris's silence embarrassed me a little, for she didn't ask any questions about the lady and her daughter; and it was impossible to tell from her manner whether she believed that this lady comprised the whole of my love life for the last five years, and if she thought I had really broken with her. For a moment or two I did not dare to look at Doris, and then I felt that her disbelief mattered little, so long as it did not enter as an influencing factor into the present situation. Under a sky as blue and amid nature poetical as a drop-curtain one's moral nature dozes. No doubt that was it. There is an English church at Plessy, but really! Dear little town, town of my heart, where the local orchestra plays "The March of Aida" and "La Belle Helène"! If I could innoculate you, reader, with the sentiment of the delicious pastoral you would understand why, all the time I was at Plessy, I looked upon myself as a hero of legend, whether of the Argonauts or the siege of Troy matters little. Returning from Mount Ida after a long absence, after presenting in imagination the fairest of women with the apple, I said—

"You asked me whom I had been in love with; now tell me with whom have you been in love?"

"For the last three years I have been engaged to be married."

"And you are still engaged?"

She nodded, her eyes fixed on the blue sea, and I said laughing that it was not of a marriage or an engagement to be married that I spoke, but of the beautiful irrepressible caprice.

"You wouldn't have me believe that no passion has caught you and dragged you about for the last five years, just as a cat drags a little mouse about?"

"It is strange that you should ask me that, for that is exactly what happened."

"Really?"

"Only that I suffered much more than any mouse ever suffered."

"Doris, tell me. You know how sympathetic I am; you know I shall understand. All things human interest me. If you have loved as much as you say, your story will . . . I must hear it."

"Why should I tell it?" and her eyes filled with tears. "I suffered horribly. Don't speak to me about it. What is the good of going over it all again?"

"Yes, there is good; very much good comes of speaking, if this love-story is over, if there is no possibility of reviving it. Tell it, and in telling, the bitterness will pass from you. Who was this man? How did you meet him?"

"He was a friend of Albert's. Albert introduced him."

"Albert is the man you are engaged to? The old story, the very oldest. Why should it always be the friend? There are so many other men, but it is always the friend who attracts." And I told Doris the story of a friend who had once robbed me, and my story had the effect of drying her tears. But they began again as soon as she tried to tell her own story. There could be no doubt that she had suffered. Things are interesting in proportion to the amount of ourselves we put into them; Doris had clearly put all her life into this story; a sordid one it may seem to some, a story of deception and lies, for of course Albert was deceived as cruelly as many another good man. But Doris must have suffered deeply, for at the memory of her sufferings her face streamed with tears. As I looked at her tears I said, "It is strange that she should weep so, for her story differs nowise from the many stories happening daily in the lives of men and women. She will tell me the old and beautiful story of lovers forced asunder by cruel fate, and this spot is no doubt a choice one to hear her story. And raising my eyes I admired once again the drooping shore, the serrated line of mountains sweeping round the bay. And the colour was so intense that it over-powered the senses like a perfume, 'like musk', I thought. When I turned to Doris, I could see she was wholly immersed in her own sorrow, and it took all my art to persuade her to tell it, or it seemed as if all my art of persuasion were necessary.

"As soon as you knew you loved him, you resolved to see him no more?"

Doris nodded.

"You sent him away before you yielded to him?"

She nodded, and looking at me, her eyes filled with tears, but which only seemed to make them still more beautiful, she told me that they had both felt that it was impossible to deceiveAlbert.

"We resisted till flesh and blood could bear it no longer."

All love-stories are alike in this; they all contain what the reviewers call "sordid details". But if Tristan had not taken advantage of King Mark's absence on a hunting expedition, the world would have been the poorer of a great love-story; and what, after all, does King Mark's happiness matter to us—a poor passing thing, whose life was only useful in this, that it gave us an immortal love-story? And if Wagner had not loved Madame Wasendonck, and if Madame Wasendonck had not been unfaithful to her husband, we should not have had *Tristan*. Who then would, for the sake of Wasendonck's honour, destroy the score of *Tristan*? Nor is the story of *Tristan* the only one, nor the most famous. There is also the story of Helen. If Menelaus' wife had not been unfaithful to him, the world would have been the poorer of the greatest of all poems, the *Iliad* and the *Odyssey*. Dear me, when one thinks of it, one must admit that art owes a good deal to adultery. Children are born of the marriage, stories of the adulterous bed, and the world needs both—stories as well as children. Even my little tale would not exist if Doris had been a prudent maiden, nor would it have interested me to listen to her that day by the sea, if she had nought to tell me but her unswerving love for Albert. Her story is not what the world calls a great story, and it would be absurd to pretend that if a shorthand writer had taken it down, his report would compare with the stories of Isolde and Helen, but I heard it from her lips, and her tears and her beauty replaced the language of Wagner and of Homer; and so well did they do this, that I am not sure that the emotion I experienced in listening to her was less than that which I have experienced before a work of art.

"Do you know," she began, "perhaps you don't, perhaps you've never loved enough to know the anxiety one may feel for the absent.

We had been together all day once, and when we bade each other good-bye we agreed that we should not see each other for two days, till Thursday; but that night in bed an extraordinary desire took hold of me to know what had become of him. I felt I must hear from him; one word would be enough. But we had promised. It was stupid, it was madness, yet I had to take down the telephone, and when I got into communication what do you think the answer was?—'Thank God you telephoned. I've been walking about the room nearly out of my mind, feeling that I should go mad if the miracle did not happen.'"

"If you loved Ralph better than Albert——"

"Why didn't I give up Albert? Albert's life would have been broken and ruined if I had done that. You see he has loved me so many years that his life has become centred in me. He is not one of those men who like many women. Outside of his work nothing exists but me. He doesn't care much for reading, but he reads the books I like. I don't know that he cares much about music for its own sake, but he likes to hear me sing just because it is me. He never notices other women; I don't think that he knows what they wear, but he likes my dresses, not because they are in good taste, but because I wear them. One can't sacrifice a man like that. What would one think of oneself? One would die of remorse. So there was nothing to be done but for Ralph to go away. It nearly killed me."

"I'm afraid I can give you no such love; my affection for you will prove very tepid after such violent emotions."

"I don't want such emotions again: I could not bear them, they would kill me; even a part would kill me. Two months after Ralph left I was but a little shadow. I was thinner than I am now, I was worn to a thread, I could hardly keep body and skirt together."

We laughed at Doris's little joke; and we watched it curling and going out like a wreath of cigarette smoke.

"But did you get no happiness at all out of this great love?"

"We were happy only a very little while."

"How long?"

Doris reflected.

"We had about six weeks of what I should call real happiness, the time while Albert was away. When he came back the misery and remorse began again. I had to see him—not Albert, the other— every day; and Albert began to notice that I was different. We used to go out together, we three, and at last the sham became too great and Albert said he could not stand it any longer. 'I prefer you should go out with him alone, and if it be for your happiness I'll give you up." '

"So you nearly died of love! Well, now you must live for love, liking things as they go by. Life is beautiful at the moment, sad when we look back, fearful when we look forward; but I suppose it's hopeless to expect a little Christian like you to, live without drawing conclusions, liking things as they go by as the nymphs do. Dry those tears; forget that man. You tell me it is over and done. Remember nothing except that the sky and the sea are blue, that it is a luxury to feel alive here by the sea-shore. My happiness would be to make you happy, to see you put the past out of your mind, to close your eyes to the future. That will be easy to do by this beautiful sea-shore, under those blue skies with flowers everywhere and drives among the mountains awaiting us. We create our own worlds. Chance has left you here and sent me to you. I want you to eat a great deal and to sleep and to get fatter and to dream and to read Theocritus, so that when we go to the mountains we shall be transported into antiquity. You must forget Albert and him who made you unhappy—he allowed you to look back and forwards."

"I think I deserve some happiness; you see I have sacrificed so much."

At these words my hopes rose—shall I say like a balloon out of which a great weight of ballast has been thrown?—and so high did they go that failure seemed like a little feather swimming in the gulf below. "She deserved some happiness," and intends to make me her happiness. Her words could bear no other interpretation; she had spoken without thought, and instinctively. Albert was away; why should she not take this happiness which I offered her? Would she understand that distance made a difference, that it was one thing to deceive Albert if he were with her, and another, when she was a thousand miles away? It was as if we were in a foreign country; we were under palm-trees, we were by the Mediterranean. With Albert a thousand miles away it would be so easy for her to love me. She had said there was no question of her marrying anyone but Albert—and to be unfaithful is not to be inconstant. These were the arguments which I would use if I found that I had misunderstood her; but for the moment I did not dare to inquire; it would be too painful to hear I had misunderstood her; but at last, feeling she might guess the cause of my silence, I said, not being able to think of anything more plausible—

"You spoke, didn't you, of going for a drive?"

"We were speaking of happiness—but if you'd like to go for a drive. There's no happiness like driving."

"Isn't there?"

She pinched my arm, and with a choking sensation in the throat I asked her if I should send for a carriage.

"There will be time for a short drive before the sun setting. You said you admired the hills—one day we will go to a hill town. There is a beautiful one—Florac is the name of it—but we must start early in the morning. To-day there will be only time to drive as far as the point you have been admiring all the morning. The road winds through the rocks, and you want to see the ilex trees."

"My dear, I want to see you."

"Well, you're looking at me. Come, don't be disagreeable."

"Disagreeable, Doris! I never felt more kindly in my life. I'm still absorbed in the strange piece of luck which has brought us together, and in such a well-chosen spot; no other would have pleased me as much."

"Now why do you like the landscape? Tell me."

"I cannot think of the landscape now, Doris: I'm thinking of you, of what you said just now."

"What did I say?"

"You said—I tried to remember the words at the time, but I have forgotten them, so many thoughts have passed through my mind since —you said—how did you word it?—after having suffered as much as you did, some share of happiness——"

"No, I didn't say that; I said, having sacrificed so much, I thought I deserved a little happiness."

'So she knew what she was saying,' I said to myself. 'Her words were not casual,' but not daring to ask her if she intended to make me her happiness, I spoke about the landscape. "You ask me why I like the landscape? Because it carries me back into past times when men believed in nymphs and in satyrs. I have always thought it must be a wonderful thing to believe in the dryad. Do you know that men wandering in the woods sometimes used to catch sight of a white breast between the leaves, and henceforth they could love no mortal woman.

cc

The beautiful name of their malady was nympholepsy. A disease that everyone would like to catch."

"But if you were to catch it you wouldn't be able to love me, so I'll not bring you to the mountains. Some peasant girl——"

"Fie! Doris, I have never liked peasant girls."

"Your antiquity is eighteenth-century antiquity. There are many alcoves in it."

"I don't know that the alcove was an invention of the eighteenth century. There were alcoves at all times. But Doris, good heavens! what are those trees? Never did I see anything so ghastly; they are like ghosts. Not only have they no leaves, but they have no bark nor any twigs; nothing but great white trunks and branches."

"I think they are called plantains."

"That won't do, you are only guessing; I must ask the coachman."

"I think, sir, they are called plantains."

"You only think. Stop and I'll ask those people."

"*Sont des plantains, Monsieur.*"

"Well, I told you so," Doris said, laughing.

Beyond this spectral avenue, on either side of us there were fields, and Doris murmured—

"See how flat the country is, to the very feet of the hills, and the folk working in the fields are pleasant to watch."

I declared that I could not watch them, nor could you, reader, if you had been sitting by Doris. I had risen and come away from long months of toil; and I remember how I told Doris as we drove across those fields towards the hills, that it was not her beauty alone that interested me; her beauty would not be itself were it not illumed by her wit and her love of art. What would she be, for instance, if she were not a musician? Or would her face be the same face if it were robbed of its mirth? But mirth is enchanting only when the source of it is the intelligence. Vacuous laughter is the most tiresome of things; a face of stone is more inveigling. But Doris prided herself on her beauty more than on her wit, and she was disinclined to admit the contention that beauty is dependent upon the intelligence. Our talk rambled on, now in one direction, now in another.

Lovers are divided into two kinds, the babbling and the silent. We meet specimens of the silent kind on a Thames back-water—the punt drawn up under the shady bank with the twain lying side by side, their arms about each other all the afternoon. When evening comes, and it is time to return home, her fellow gets out the sculls, and they part saying, "Well, dear, next Sunday, at the same time." "Yes, at the same time next Sunday." We were of the babbling kind, as the small part of our conversation that appears in this story shows.

"My dear, my dear, remember that we are in an open carriage."

"What do those folks matter to us?"

"My dear, if I don't like it?"

To justify my desire of her lips I began to compare her beauty with that of a Greek head on a vase, saying that hers was a cameo-like beauty, as dainty as any Tanagra figure. Her body that I had hardly seen was certainly as perfect; her breasts I remembered.

"And to see you and not possess you, not to hold your face in my hands just as one holds a vase, is——"

"Is what?"

"A kind of misery. I long to possess you. Fancy my disappointment if, on digging among these mountains, I were to find a beautiful vase, and some one were to say, 'You can look at it but not touch it.'"

"Do you love me as well as that?" she answered, somewhat moved, for my words expressed a genuine emotion.

"I do indeed, Doris."

"We might get out here. I want you to see the view from the hill-top."

And, telling the driver that he need not follow us, to stay there and rest his panting horse, we walked on. Whether Doris was thinking of the view I know not; I only know that I thought only of kissing Doris. To do so would be pleasant—in a way—even on this cold hillside, and I noticed that the road bent round the shoulder of the mount. We soon reached the hill-top, and we could see the road enter the village in the dip between the hills, a double line of houses—not much more—facing the sea, a village where we might go to have breakfast; we might never go there; however that might be, we certainly should remember that village and the road streaming out of it on the other side towards the hills. Now and then we lost sight of the road; it doubled round some rock or was hidden behind a group of trees; and then we caught sight of it a little further on, ascending the hills in front of us, and no doubt on the other side it entered another village, and so on around the coast of Italy. Even with the thought of Doris's kisses in my mind, I could admire the road and the curves of the bay. I felt in my pocket for a piece of paper and a pencil. The colour was as beautiful as a Barbizon; there were many tints of blue, no doubt, but the twilight had gathered the sea and sky into one tone, or what seemed to be one tone.

"You wanted to see olive-trees—those are olives."

"So those are olives! Do I at last look upon olives?"

"Are you disappointed?"

"Yes and no. The white gnarled trunk makes even the young trees seem old. The olive is like an old man with skimpy legs. It seems to me a pathetic tree. One does not like to say it is ugly, it is not ugly, but it would be puzzling to say wherein lies its charm, for it throws no shade, and is so grey—nothing is so grey as the olive. I like the ilex better."

Where the road dipped there was a group of ilex trees, and it was in their shade that I kissed Doris, and the beauty of the trees helps me to appreciate the sentiment of those kisses. And I remember that road and those ilex trees as I might remember a passage in Theocritus. Doris—her very name suggests antiquity, and it was well that she was kissed by me for the first time under ilex trees; true that I had kissed her before, but that earlier love-story has not found a chronicler, and probably it never will. I like to think that the beauty of the ilex is answerable, perhaps, for Doris's kisses—in a measure. Her dainty grace, her Tanagra beauty, seemed to harmonise with that of the ilex, for there is an antique beauty in this tree that we find in none other. Theocritus must have composed many a poem beneath it. It is the only tree that the ancient world could have cared to notice; and if it were possible to carve statues of trees, I am sure that the ilex is the tree sculptors would choose. The beech and the birch, all the other trees, only began to be beautiful when men invented painting. No other tree shapes itself out so beautifully as the ilex, lifting itself up to the sky so abundantly and with such dignity—a very queen in a velvet gown is the ilex tree; and we stood looking at the group, admiring its glossy thickness, till suddenly the ilex tree went out of my mind, and I thought of the lonely night that awaited me.

"Doris, dear, it is more than flesh and blood can bear. My folly lay in sending the telegram. Had I not sent it you wouldn't have known by what train I was coming; you would have been fast asleep in your bed, and I should have gone straight to your hotel."

"But, darling, you wouldn't compromise me. Everyone would know that we stayed at the same hotel."

"Dearest, it might happen by accident, and were it to happen by accident what could you do?"

"All I can say is that it would be a most unfortunate accident."

"Then I have come a thousand miles for nothing. This is worse than the time in London when I left you for your strictness. Can nothing be done?"

"Am I not devoted to you? We have spent the whole day together. Now I don't think it's at all nice of you to reproach me with having brought you on a fool's errand."

"I didn't say that," and we quarrelled a little until we reached the carriage. Doris was angry, and when she spoke again it was to say, "If you are not satisfied, you can go back. I'm sorry. I think it's most unreasonable that you should ask me to compromise myself."

"And I think it's unkind of you to suggest that I should go back, for how can I go back?"

She did not ask me why—she was too angry at the moment—and it was well she did not, for I should have been embarrassed to tell her that I was fairly caught. I had come a thousand miles to see her, and I could not say I was going to take the *Côte d'Azur* back again, because she would not let me stay at her hotel; to do so would be too childish, too futile. The misery of the journey back would be unendurable. There was nothing to do but to wait, and hope that life, which is always full of accidents, would favour us; for Doris was clearly as anxious that an opportunity should occur as I was, only she did not wish to compromise herself. Better think no more about it. For it is thinking that makes one miserable.

There were many little things which helped to pass the time away. Doris went every evening to a certain shop to fetch two eggs that had been laid that morning. It was necessary for her health that she should eat eggs beaten up with milk, between the first and second breakfast. We went there, and it was amusing to pick my way through the streets, carrying her eggs back to the hotel for her. She knew a few people—strange folk, I thought them—elderly spinsters living *en pension* at different hotels. We dined with her friends, and after dinner Doris sang, and when she had played many things that she used to play to me in the old days, it was time for her to go to bed, for she rarely slept after six o'clock, so she said.

"Good-night. Ah, no, the hour is ill," I murmured to myself as I wended my lonely way, and I lay awake thinking if I had said anything that would prejudice my chances of winning her, if I had omitted to say anything that might have inclined her to yield. One lies awake at night thinking of the mistakes one has made; thoughts clatter in one's head. Good heavens! how stupid it was of me not to have used a certain argument. Perhaps if I had spoken more tenderly, displayed a more Christian spirit—all that paganism, that talk about nymphs and dryads and satyrs and fauns frightened her. In the heat of the moment one says more than one intends, though it is quite true that, as a rule, it is well to insist that there is no such thing as our lower nature, that everything about us is divine. So constituted are we that the mind accepts the convention, and what we have to do is to keep to the convention, just as in opera. Singing appears natural so long as the characters do not speak. Once they speak they cannot go back to music; the convention has been broken. As in Art so it is in life. Tell a woman that she is a nymph, and she must not expect any more from you than she would from a faun, that all you know is the joy of the sunlight, that you have no dreams beyond the worship of the perfect circle of her breast, and the desire to gather grapes for her, and she will give herself to you unconscious of sin. I must have fallen asleep thinking of these things, and I must have slept soundly, for I remembered nothing until the servant came in with my bath, and I saw again the pretty sunlight flickering along the wall-paper. Before parting the previous night, Doris and I had arranged that I was to call an hour earlier than usual at the hotel; I was to be there at half-past ten. She had promised to be ready. We were going to drive to Florac, to one of the hill towns, and it would take two hours to get there. We were going to breakfast there, and while I dressed, and in the carriage going there, I cherished the hope that perhaps I might be able to persuade Doris to breakfast in a private room, though feeling all the while that it would be difficult to do so, for the public room would be empty, and crowds of waiters would gather about us like rooks, each trying to entice us towards his table.

The village of Florac is high up among the hills, built along certain ledges of rock overlooking the valley, and going south in the train one catches sight of many towns, like it built among mountain declivities, hanging out like nests over the edge of precipices, showing against a red background, crowning the rocky hill. No doubt these mediæval towns were built in these strange places because of the security that summit gives against raiders. One can think of no other reason, for it is hard to believe that in the fifteenth century men were so captivated with the picturesque that for the sake of it they would drag every necessary of life up these hills, several hundred feet above the plain, probably by difficult paths—the excellent road that wound along the edge of the hills, now to the right, now to the left, looping itself round every sudden ascent like a grey ribbon round a hat, did not exist when Florac was built. On the left the ground shelves away into the valley, down towards the sea, and olives were growing down all these hillsides. Above us were olive-trees, with here and there an orange orchard, and the golden fruit shining among the dark leaves continued to interest me. Every now and again some sudden aspect interrupted our conversation; the bay as it swept round the carved mountains, looking in the distance more than ever like an old Italian picture of a time before painters began to think about values and truth of effect, when the minds of men were concerned with beauty; as mine was, for every time I looked at Doris it occurred to me that I had never seen anything prettier, and not only her face but her talk still continued to enchant me. She was always so eager to tell me things, that she must interrupt, and these interruptions were pleasant. I identified them with her, and so closely that I can remember how our talk began when we got out of the suburbs. By the last villa there was a eucalyptus tree growing; the sun was shining, and Doris had asked me to hold her parasol for her; but the road zig-zagged so constantly that I never shifted the parasol in time, and a ray would catch her just in the face, adding perhaps to the freckles—there were just a few down that little nose which was always pleasant to look upon. I was saying that I still remember our talk as we passed that eucalyptus tree. Doris had begun one of those little confessions which are so interesting, and which one hears only from a woman one is making love to, which probably would not interest us were we to hear them from anyone else. It delighted me to hear Doris say, "This is the first time I have ever lived alone, that I have ever been free from questions. It was a pleasure to remember suddenly as I was dressing that no one would ask me where I was going, that I was just like a bird by myself, free to spring off the branch and to fly. At home there are always people round one; somebody is in the dining-room, somebody is in the drawing-room; and if one goes down the passage with one's hat on there is always somebody to ask where one is going, and if you say you don't know they say, 'Are you going to the right or to the left, because if you are going to the left I should like you to stop at the apothecary's and to ask——' " How I agreed with her! Family life I said degrades the individual, and is only less harmful than socialism, because one can escape from it. . . .

"But, Doris, you're not ill! You are looking better."

"I weighed this morning, and I have gone up two pounds. You see I am amused, and a woman's health is mainly a question whether she is amused, whether somebody is making love to her."

"Making love! Doris, dear, there is no chance of making love to anybody here. That is the only fault I find with the place; the sea, the bay, the hill towns, everything I see is perfect in every detail, only the essential is lacking. I was thinking, Doris, that for the sake of your health we might go and spend a few days at Florac."

"My dear, it would be impossible. Everybody would know that I had been there."

"Maybe, but I don't agree. However, I am glad that you have gone up two pounds. . . . I am sure that what you need is mountain air. The seaside is no good at all for nerves. I have a friend in Paris who suffers from nerves and has to go every year to Switzerland to climb the Matterhorn."

"The Matterhorn!"

"Well, the Matterhorn or Mont Blanc; he has to climb mountains, glaciers, something of that kind. I remember last year I wrote to him saying that I did not understand the three past tenses in French, and would he explain why—something, I have forgotten what—and he answered, '*Avec mes pieds sur des glaciers je ne puis m'arrêter pour vous expliquer les trois passés.*' "

Doris laughed and was interested, for I had introduced her some years ago to the man who had written this letter; and then we discussed the *fussent* and the *eussent*, *été*, and when our language of the French Grammar was exhausted we returned to the point whence we had come, whether it was possible to persuade Doris to pass three days in the hotel at Florac—in the interests of her health, of course.

"I'm not sure at all that mountain air would not do me good. Plessy lies very low and is very relaxing."

"Very."

But though I convinced her that it would have been better if she had gone at once to stop at Florac, I could do nothing to persuade her to pass three days with me in the inn there. As we drove up through the town the only hope that remained in my mind was that I might induce her to take breakfast in a private room. But the *salle du restaurant* was fifty feet long by thirty feet wide, it contained a hundred tables, maybe more, the floor was polished oak, and the ceilings were painted and gilded, and there were fifty waiters waiting for the swallows that would soon arrive from the north. We were the van birds.

"Shall we breakfast in a private room?" I whispered humbly.

"Good heavens, no! I wouldn't dare to go into a private room before all these waiters."

My heart sank again, and when Doris said, "Where shall we sit?" I answered, "Anywhere, anywhere, it doesn't matter."

It had taken two hours for the horses to crawl up to the mountain town, and as I had no early breakfast I was ravenously hungry. A box of sardines and a plate of butter, and the prospect of an omelette and a steak, put all thoughts of Doris for the moment out of my head, and that was a good thing. We babbled on, and it was impossible to say which was the more interested, which enjoyed talking most; and the pleasure which each took in talking and hearing the other talk became noticeable.

"I didn't interrupt you just now, I thought it would be cruel, for you were enjoying yourself so much," said Doris, laughing.

"Well, I promise not to interrupt the next time—you were in the midst of one of your stories."

It was not long before she was telling me another story, for Doris was full of stories. She observed life as it went by, and could recall what she had seen. Our talk had gone back to years before, to the evening when I first saw her cross the drawing-room in a white dress, her gold hair hanging over her shoulders; and in that moment, as she crossed the room, I had noticed a look of recognition in her eyes; the look was purely instinctive; she was not aware of it herself, but I could not help understanding it as a look whereby she recognised me as one of her kin. I had often spoken to her of that look, and we liked speaking about it, and about the time when we became friends in Paris. She had written asking me to go to see her and her mother. I had found them in a strange little hotel, just starting for some distant suburb, going there to buy presents from an old couple, dealers in china and glass, from whom, Doris's mother explained, she would be able to buy her presents fifty per cent. cheaper than elsewhere. She was one of those women who would spend three shillings on a cab in order to save twopence on a vase.

"It took us hours to get to that old, forgotten quarter, to the old quaint street where they lived. They were old-world Jews who read the Talmud, and seemed to be quite isolated, out of touch with the modern world. It was like going back to the Middle Ages; this queer old couple moving like goblins among the china and glass. Do you ever see them now? Are they dead?"

"Let me tell you," cried Doris, "what happened. The old man died two years ago, and his wife, who had lived with him for forty years, could not bear to live alone, so what do you think she did? She sent for her brother-in-law——"

"To marry him?"

"No, not to marry him, but to talk to him about her husband. You see this couple had lived together for so many years that she had become ingrained, as it were, in the personality of her late husband, her habits had become his habits, his thoughts had become hers. The story really is very funny," and Doris burst out laughing, and for some time she could not speak for laughing. "I am sorry for the poor man," she said at last.

"For whom? For the brother-in-law?"

"Yes; you see he is dyspeptic, and he can't eat the dishes at all that his brother used to like, but the wife can't and won't cook anything else."

"In other words," I said, "the souvenir of brother Esau is poisoning brother Jacob."

"That is it."

"What a strange place this world is!" And then my mind drifted back suddenly. "Oh, Doris, I'm so unhappy—this place—I wish I had never come."

"Now, now, have a little patience. Everything comes right in the end."

"We shall never be alone."

"Yes, we shall. Why do you think that?"

"Because I can't think of anything else."

"Well, you must think of something else. We're going to the factory where they make perfume, and I'm going to buy a great many bottles of scent for myself, and presents for friends. We shall be able to buy the perfume twenty-five per cent. or fifty per cent. cheaper."

"Don't you think we might go to see the pictures? There are some in a church here."

On inquiry we heard that they had been taken away, and I followed Doris through the perfume factory. Very little work was doing; the superintendent told us that they were waiting for the violets. A few old women were stirring caldrons, and I listened wearily, for it did not interest me in the least, particularly at that moment, to hear that the flowers were laid upon layers of grease, that the grease absorbed the perfume, and then the grease was got rid of by means of alcohol. The workrooms were cold and draughty, and the choice of what perfumes we were to buy took a long time. However, at last, Doris decided that she would prefer three bottles of this, three bottles of that, four of these, and two of those. Her perfume was heliotrope; she always used it.

"And you like it, don't you, dear?"

"Yes, but what does it matter what I like?"

"Now, don't be cross. Don't look so sad."

"I don't mind the purchase you made for your friends, but the purchase of heliotrope is really too cynical."

"Cynical! Why is it cynical?"

"Because, dear, it is evocative of you, of that slender body moving among fragrances of scented cambrics, and breathing its own dear odour as I come forward to greet you. Why do you seek to torment me?"

"But, dear one——"

I was not to be appeased, and sat gloomily in the corner of the carriage away from her. But she put out her hand, and the silken palm calmed my nervous irritation, and we descended the steep roads, the driver putting on and taking off the brake. The evening was growing chilly, so I asked Doris if I might tell the coachman to stop his horses and to put up the hood of the carriage. In a close carriage one is nearly alone. But every moment I was reminded that people were passing, and between her kisses the thought passed that I must go back to Paris, however unkind it might be. It would be unkind to leave her, for she was not very strong; she would require somebody to look after her. As I was debating the question in my mind, Doris said—

"You don't mind, dear, but before we go back to the hotel, I have a visit to pay."

In the three weeks' time she had spent at Plessy before I came there, Doris had made the acquaintance of all kinds of elderly spinsters, who lived in the different hotels *en pension*, and who would go away as soon as the visitors arrived, to seek another "resort" where the season had not yet commenced, and where they could be boarded and bedded for ten francs a day. I had made the acquaintance of Miss Tubbs and Miss Whitworth, and we were dining with them that night. Doris had explained that we could not refuse to dine with them at least once.

"But as we're going to spend the evening with them, I don't see the necessity——"

"Of course not, dear, but don't you remember you promised to go to see the Formans with me?"

Miss Forman had dined with us last night, but her mother had not been able to come, and that was a relief to me whatever it may have been to Doris; I had heard that Mrs. Forman was a very old woman, and as her daughter struck me as an ineffectual person, I said as I sat down to dinner, "One of the family is enough." What her mother's age could be I could not guess, for Miss Forman herself might pass for seventy. But after speaking to her for a little while one saw that she was not so old as she looked at first sight. Nothing saddens me more than those who have aged prematurely, for the cause of premature ageing is generally a declension of the mind. As soon as the mind begins to narrow and wither the body follows suit; prejudices and conventions age us more than years do. Before speaking a word it was easy to see from Miss Forman's appearance that no new idea had entered into her life for a long while, and I imagined her at once to be one of those daughters that one finds abroad in different provincial towns, living with their mothers on small incomes. "The daughter's tragedy is written all over her face," I said, and while speaking to her I scrutinised her, reading in her everything that goes to make up that tragedy. She had the face of those heroines, for they are heroines—

the broad low brow, the high nose, the sympathetic eyes, grey and expressive of duty and sacrifice of self. Her dress and her manners were as significant as her face, and seemed to hint at the life she had lived. She wore a black silk gown which looked old-fashioned—why I cannot say. Was it the gown or the piece of black lace that she wore on her head, or the Victorian ear-rings that hung from her ears down her dust-coloured neck, that gave her a sort of bygone appearance, the look of an old photograph? Her manners took me further back in the century even than the photograph did; she seemed to have come out of the pages of some trite and uninteresting novel, a rather listless book written at the end of the eighteenth century, before the art of novel-writing had been found out. She listened, and her listening was in itself a politeness, and she never lost her politeness, though she seldom understood what I said. When I finished speaking she answered what I had said indirectly, like one whose mind was not quite capable of following any conversation except the most trite. She laughed if she thought I had said anything humorous, and sometimes looked a little embarrassed; she only seemed to be at her ease when speaking of her mother. If, for instance, we were speaking of books, she would break in with her mother's opinions, thinking it wonderful that her mother had read—shall we say, *The Three Musketeers*? three times. She was interested in all her mother's characteristics, and her habit was to speak of her mother as her mamma. She seemed to delight in the word, and every time she pronounced it a light came into her old face, and I began to understand her and to feel that I could place her, to use a colloquialism which is so expressive that perhaps its use may be forgiven. "The daughter's tragedy," I muttered, and considering it, philosophising according to my wont I tried to reconcile myself to this visit. "After all," I said, "I am on my own business, therefore I have no right to grumble."

I wished to see what Miss Forman was like in her own house; above all, I wished to see if her mother were as typical of the mother who accepts her daughter's sacrifice, as Miss Forman was of the daughter that has been sacrificed. From the daughter's appearance I had imagined Mrs. Forman to be a tall, good-looking, distinguished woman, lying upon a sofa, wearing a cap upon her white hair, her feet covered with a shawl, and Miss Forman arranging it from time to time. Nature is always surprising; she follows a rhythm of her own; we beat one, two, three, four, but the invisible leader of the orchestra sets a more subtle rhythm. But though Nature's rhythm is irregular, its irregularity is more apparent than real, for when we listen we hear that everything goes to a beat, and in looking at Mrs. Forman I recognised that she was the inevitable mother of such a daughter, and that Nature's combination was more harmonious than mine. The first thing that struck me was that the personal energy I had missed in the daughter survived in the mother, notwithstanding her seventy-five years. The daughter reminded me now of a tree that had been overshadowed. Miss Forman had remained a child, nor could she have grown to womanhood unless somebody had taken her away; no doubt somebody had wanted to marry her; there is nobody that has not had her love affair, very few at least, and I imagined Miss Forman giving up hers for the sake of her mamma, and I could hear her mamma—that short, thick woman, looking more like a ball of lard than anything else in the world, alert notwithstanding her sciatica, with two small beady eyes in the glaring whiteness of her face—forgetful of her daughter's sacrifice, saying to her some evening as they warmed their shins over the fire—

"Well, Caroline, I never understood how it was that you didn't marry Mr. So-and-so; I think he would have suited you very well."

My interest in these two women who had lived side by side all their lives was slight; it was just animated by a slight curiosity to see if Miss Forman would be as much interested in her mother in her own house by her mother's side as she had been in the hotel among strangers. I waited to hear her call her mother mamma; nor had I to wait long, for as soon as the conversation turned on the house which the Formans had lately purchased, and the land which Mrs. Forman was buying up and planting with orange-trees, Miss Forman broke in, and in her high-pitched voice she told us enthusiastically that mamma was so energetic; she never could be induced to sit down and be quiet; even her sciatica could not keep her in her chair. A few moments after Miss Forman told us that they did not leave Plessy even during the summer heat. Mamma could not be induced to go away. The last time they had gone to a hill village intending to spend some three or four weeks there, but the food did not suit mamma at all, and Miss Forman explained how the critical moment came and she had said to her mamma, "Well, mamma, this place does not suit you; I think we had better go home again"; and they had come home after six days in the hill village, probably never to leave Plessy again; and turning to her mother with a look of admiration on her face, Miss Forman said, "I always tell mamma that she will never be able to get away from here until balloon travelling comes into fashion. If a balloon were to come down to mamma's balcony, mamma might get into it and be induced to go away for a little while for a change of air. She would not be afraid. I don't think mamma was ever afraid of anything." Her voice seemed to me to attain a certain ecstasy in the words, "I don't think mamma was ever afraid of anything," and I said, "She is proud of her ideal, and it is well that she should be, for there is no other in the world, not for her at least," and noticing that the three women were talking together, that I was no longer observed, I got up with a view to studying the surroundings in which Mrs. Forman and her daughter lived.

On the wall facing the fireplace there were two portraits—two engravings—and I did not need to look at the date to know that they had been done in 1840; one was her Majesty Queen Victoria, the other her Royal Consort, Prince Albert. Shall I be believed if I say that in my little excursions round the room and the next room I discovered a small rosewood table on which stood some wax fruit, a small sofa covered with rep and antimacassars, just as in old days. More characteristic still was the harmonium, with a hymn-book on the music rest, and every Sunday, no doubt, Miss Forman played hymns with her stiff, crooked fingers, and they said prayers together, the same old-fashioned English prayers for which I always hanker. A grain of faith would make me an excellent Protestant.

Fearing that it might be regarded as an impertinence if I stayed away any longer, I returned to the back drawing-room, only to accompany the Formans and Doris back again to the front drawing-room, for there was a piano there and the Formans had persuaded Doris to sing. She was going to do so to please them. "They don't know anything about singing," she whispered to me; "but what does that matter? You see, poor things, they have so little to distract them in their lives; it will be quite a little event for them to hear me sing," and she went to the piano and sang song after song.

"It is kind indeed of you to sing to us, to an old woman and a middle-aged woman," Mrs. Forman said, "and I hope you will come to see us again, both of you."

'What should bring me to see them again?' I asked myself as I tried to get Doris away, for she lingered about the doorway with them, making impossible plans, asking them to come to see her when they came to England, telling them that if her health required it and she came to Plessy again she would rush to see them. 'Why should she go on like that, knowing well that we shall never see them again, never in this world?' I thought. Mrs. Forman insisted that her daughter should accompany us to the gate, and all the way there Doris begged of Miss Forman to come to dine with us; we were dining with Miss Tubbs and Miss Whitworth, friends of hers; it would be so nice if she would come. The carriage would be sent back for her; it would be so easy to send it back. I offered up a prayer that Miss Forman might refuse, and she did refuse many times; but Doris was so pressing that she consented; but when we got into the carriage a thought struck her. "No," she said, "I cannot go, for the dressmaker is coming this evening to try on mamma's dress, and mamma is very particular about her gowns; she hates any fulness in the waist; the last time the gown had to go back—you must excuse me."

"Good-bye, dear, good-bye," I heard Doris crying, and I said to myself, 'How kind she is!'

"Now, my dear, aren't you glad that you came to see them? Aren't they nice? Isn't she good? And you like goodness."

"Dear Doris, I like goodness, and I like to discover your kind heart. Don't you remember my saying that your pretty face was dependent upon your intelligence; that without your music and without your wit your face would lose half its charm. Well, now, do you know that it seems to me that it would only lose a third of its charm, a third of my love for you is my admiration of your good heart. You remember how, years ago, I used to catch you doing acts of kindness. What has become of the two blind women you used to help?"

"So you haven't forgotten them. You used to say that it was wonderful that a blind woman should be able to get her living."

"Of course it is. It has always seemed to me extraordinary that anyone should be able to earn his living."

"You see, dear, you have not been forced to get yours, and you do not realize that ninety per cent. of men and women have to get theirs."

"But a blind woman! To get up in the morning and go out to earn enough money to pay for her dinner; think of it! Getting up in the dark, knowing that she must earn four, five, ten shillings a day, whatever it is. Every day the problem presents itself, and she always in the dark."

"Do you remember her story?"

"I think so. She was once rich, wasn't she? In fairly easy circumstances, and she lost her fortune. It all went away from her bit by bit. It is all coming back to me, how Fate in the story as you told it seemed like a black shadow stretching out a paw, grabbing some part of her income again and again, till the last farthing was taken. Even then Fate was not satisfied, and your friend must catch the smallpox and lose her eyes. But as soon as she was well she decided to come to England and learn to be a masseuse. I suppose she did not want to stop in Australia, where she was known. How attractive courage is! And where shall we find an example of courage equal to that of this blind woman coming to England to learn to be a masseuse? What I don't understand is bearing with her life in the dark, going out to her work every day to earn her dinner, and very often robbed by the girl who led her about."

"How well you remember, dear!"

"Of course I do. Now, how was it? Her next misfortune was a sentimental one. There was some sort of a love-story in this blind woman's life, not the conventional sentimental story which never happens, but a hint, a suggestion, of that passion which takes a hundred thousand shapes, finding its way even to a blind woman's life. Now don't tell me; it's all coming back to me. Something about a student who lived in the same house as she did; a very young man; and they made acquaintance on the stairs; they took to visiting each other; they became friends, but it was not with him she fell in love. This student had a pal who came to share his rooms, an older man with serious tastes, a great classical scholar, and he used to go down to read to the blind woman in the evening. It really was a very pretty story, and very true. He used to translate the Greek tragedies aloud to her. I wonder if she expected him to marry her?"

"No, she knew he could not marry her, but that made no difference."

"You're quite right. It was just the one interest in her life, and it was taken from her. He was a doctor, wasn't he?"

Doris nodded, and I remembered how he had gone out to Africa. "No sooner did he get there than he caught a fever, one of the worst kinds. The poor blind masseuse did not hear anything of her loss for a

DD

long time. The friend upstairs didn't dare to come down to tell her. But at last the truth could be hidden from her no longer. It's extraordinary how tragedy follows some."

"Isn't it?"

"And now she sits alone in the dark. No one comes to read to her. But she bears with her solitude rather than put up with the pious people who would interest themselves in her. You said there were no interesting books written for the blind, only pieties. The charitable are often no better than Shylocks, they want their money's worth. I only see her, of course, through your description, but if I see her truly she was one of those who loved life, and life took everything from her!"

"Do you remember the story of the other blind woman?"

"Yes and no, vaguely. She was a singer, wasn't she?" Doris nodded. "And I think she was born blind, or lost her sight when she was three or four years old. You described her to me as a tall, handsome woman with dark crinkly hair, and a mouth like red velvet."

"I don't think I said like red velvet, dear."

"Well, it doesn't sound like a woman's description of another woman, but I think you told me that she had had love-affairs, and it was that that made me give her a mouth like red velvet. Why should she not have love affairs? She was as much a woman as another; only one doesn't realize until one hears a story of this kind what the life of the blind must be, how differently they must think and feel about things from those who see. Her lover must have been a wonder to her, something strange, mysterious; the blind must be more capable of love than anybody else. She wouldn't know if he were a man of forty or one of twenty. And what difference could it make to her?"

"Ah, the blind are very sensitive, much more so than we are."

"Perhaps."

"I think Judith would have known the difference between a young man and a middle-aged. There was little she didn't know."

"I daresay you're quite right. But still everything must have been more intense and vague. When the blind woman's lover is not speaking to her he is away; she is unable to follow him, and sitting at home she imagines him in society surrounded by others who are not blind. She doesn't know what eyes are, but she imagines them like—what? anyhow she imagines them more beautiful than they are. No, Doris, no eyes are more beautiful than yours; she imagines everyone with eyes like yours. I have not thought of her much lately, but I used to think of her when you told me the story, as standing on a platform in front of the public calm as a Caryatid. She must have had a beautiful voice to have been able to get an engagement; and the great courage that these blind women have! Fancy the struggle to get an engagement, a difficult thing to do in any circumstances—but in hers! And when her voice began to fail her she must have suffered, for her voice was her one possession, the one thing that distinguished her from others, the one thing she knew herself by, her personality as it were. She didn't know her face as other women know theirs: she only knew herself when she sang, then she became an entity, as it were. Nor could teaching recompense her for what she had lost, however intelligent her pupils might be, or however well they paid her. How did she lose her pupils?"

"I don't think there was any reason. She lost her pupils in the ordinary way; she was unlucky. As you were just saying, it was more difficult for her to earn her living than for those who could see; and Judith is no longer as young as she was; she isn't old, she is still a handsome woman; but in a few years. . . . If old age pensions are to be granted to people, they surely ought to be granted to blind women."

"Yes, I remember; the sentiment of the whole story is in my mind; only I am a little confused about the facts. I remember you wrote a lot of letters—how was it?"

"Well, I just felt that the thing to do was to get an annuity for Judith; I could not afford to give her one myself, so after a great deal of trouble I got into communication with a rich woman who was interested in the blind and wanted to found one."

"You are quite right, that was it. You must have written dozens of letters."

"Yes, indeed, and all to no purpose. Judith knew the trouble I was taking, but she couldn't bear with her loneliness any longer; the dread of the long evenings by herself began to prey upon her nerves, and she went off to Peckham to marry a blind man—quite an elderly man; he was over sixty. They had known each other for some time, and he taught music like her; but though he only earned forty or fifty pounds a year, still she preferred to have somebody to live with than the annuity."

"But I don't see why she should lose her annuity."

"Don't you remember, dear? This to me is the point of the story.

The charitable woman drew back, not from any sordid motive, because she regretted her money, but for a fixed idea; she had learned from somebody that blind people shouldn't marry, and she did not feel herself justified in giving her money to encouraging such marriages."

"Was there ever anything so extraordinary as human nature? Its goodness, its stupidity, its cruelty! The woman meant well; one can't even hate her for it; it was just a lack of perception, a desire to live up to principles. That is what sets everyone agog, trying to live up to principles, abstract ideas. If they only think of what they are, and what others are! The folly of it! This puzzle-headed woman—I mean the charitable woman pondering over the fate of the race, as if she could do anything to advance or retard its destiny?"

"You always liked those stories, dear. You said that you would write them."

"Yes, but I'm afraid the pathos is a little deeper than I could reach; only Tourgenev could write them. But here we are at the Dog's Home."

"Don't talk like that—it's unkind."

"I don't mean to be unkind, but I have to try to realize things before I can appreciate them."

It seemed not a little incongruous that these two little spinsters should pay for our dinners, and I tried to induce Doris to agree to some modification in the present arrangements, but she said it was their wish to entertain us.

The evening I spent in that hotel hearing Doris sing, and myself talking literature to a company of about a dozen spinsters, all plain and elderly, all trying to live upon incomes varying from a hundred and fifty to two hundred pounds a year, comes up before my mind, every incident. Life is full of incidents, only our intelligence is not always sufficiently trained to perceive them; and the incident I am about to mention was important in the life I am describing. Miss Tubbs had asked me what wine I would drink. And in a moment of inadvertence I said 'Vin Ordinaire', forgetting that the two shillings the wine cost would probably mean that Miss Tubbs would very likely have to go without her cup of tea at five o'clock next day in order that her expenditure should not exceed her limit, and I thought how difficult life must be on these slippery rocks, incomes of one hundred and fifty a year. Poor little gentlefolk, roving about from one boarding-house to another, always in search of the cheapest, sometimes getting into boarding-houses where the cheapness of the food necessitates sending for the doctor, so the gain on one side is a loss on the other! Poor little gentlefolk, the odds-and-ends of existence, the pence and threepenny bits of human life!

That Doris's singing should have provoked remarks painfully inadequate mattered little. Inadequate remarks about singing and about the other arts are as common in London drawing-rooms as in hotels and boarding-houses (all hotels are boarding-houses; there is really no difference), and the company I found in these winter resorts would have interested me at any other time. I can be interested in the woman who collects stamps, in the gentle soul who keeps a botany book in which all kinds of quaint entries are found, in the lady who writes for the papers, and the one who is supposed to have a past. Wherever human beings collect there is always to be found somebody of interest, but when one's interest is centred in a lady everybody else becomes an enemy; and I looked upon all these harmless spinsters as my enemies, and their proposals for excursions, and luncheons, and dinners caused me much misgiving, not only because they separated me from Doris, but because I felt that any incident, the proposed picnic, might prove a shipwrecking reef. One cannot predict what will happen. Life is so full of incidents; a woman's jealous tongue or the arrival of some acquaintance might bring about a catastrophe. A love affair hangs upon a gossamer thread, you know, and that is why I tried to persuade Doris away from her friends.

She was very kind and good and didn't inflict the society of these people too much upon me. Perhaps she was conscious of the danger herself, and we only visited the boarding-houses in the evening. But these visits grew intolerable. The society of Miss Tubbs and Miss Whitworth jarred the impressions of a long day spent in the open air, in a landscape where once the temples of the Gods had been, where men had once lived who had seen, or at all events believed, in the fauns and the dryads, in the grotto where the siren swims.

One afternoon I said to Doris, "I'm afraid I can't go to see Miss Tubbs this evening. Can't we devise something else? Another dinner in a boarding-house would lead me to suicide, I think."

"You would like to drown yourself in that bay and join the nymphs? Do you think they would prove kinder than I?"

I did not answer Doris. I suddenly seemed to despair; the exquisite tenderness of the sky, and the inveigling curves of the bay seemed to become detestable to me, theatrical, absurd. 'Good God!' I thought, 'I shall never possess her. All my journey is in vain, and all this love-making.' The scene before me was the most beautiful in shape and colour I had ever seen; but I am in no mood to describe the Leonardo-like mountains enframing the azure bay. The reader must imagine us leaning over a low wall watching the sea-water gurgling among the rocks. We had come to see some gardens. The waiter at my hotel had told me of some, the property of a gentleman kind enough to throw them open to the public twice a week; and I had taken his advice, though gardens find little favour with me—now and again an old English garden, but the well-kept horticultural is my abhorrence. But one cannot tell a coachman to drive along the road, one must tell him to go somewhere, so we had come to see what was to be seen. And all was as I had imagined it, only worse: the tall wrought-iron gate was twenty feet high, there was a naked pavilion behind it, and a woman seated at a table with a cash-box in front of her. This woman took a franc apiece, and told us that the money was to be devoted to a charitable purpose; we were then free to wander down a gravel walk twenty feet wide branching to the right and the left, along a line of closely-clipped shrubs, with a bunch of tall grasses here and a foreign fir there; gardens that a painter would turn from in horror. I said to Doris—

"This is as tedious as a play at the Comédie, as tiresome as a tragedy by Racine, and very like one. Let us seek out one of the external walks overlooking the sea; even there I'm afraid the knowledge that these shrubs are behind us will spoil our pleasure."

Doris laughed; that was one of her charms, she could be amused; and it was in this mood that we sat down on a seat placed in a low wall overlooking the bay, looking at each other, basking in the rays of the afternoon sun, and there we sat for some little while indolent as lizards. Pointing to one at a little distance I said—

"It is delightful to be here with you, Doris, but the sunlight is not sufficient for me. Doris, dear, I am very unhappy. I have lain awake all night thinking of you, and now I must tell you that yesterday I was sorely tempted to go down to that bay and join the nymphs there. Don't ask me if I believe that I should find a nymph to love me; one doesn't know what one believes, I only know that I am unhappy."

"But why, dear, do you allow yourself to be unhappy? Look at that lizard. Isn't he nice? Isn't he satisfied? He desires nothing but what he has got, light and warmth."

"And, Doris, would you like me to be as content as that lizard—to desire nothing more than light and warmth?"

Doris looked at me, and thinking her eyes more beautiful even than the sunlight, I said—

> "And the sunlight clasps the earth,
> And the moonbeams kiss the sea,
> What are all these kissings worth,
> If thou kiss not me?

That is the eternal song of the spheres and of the flowers. If I don't become part of the great harmony, I must die."

"But you do kiss me," Doris answered wilfully, "when the evening turns cold and the coachman puts up the hood of the carriage."

"Wilful Doris! Pretty puss cat!"

"I'm not a puss cat; I'm not playing with you, dear. I do assure you I feel the strain of these days; but what am I do do? You wouldn't have me tell you to stay at my hotel and to compromise myself before all these people?"

"These people! Those boarding-houses are driving me mad! That Miss Forman!"

"I thought you liked her. You said she is good, 'a simple, kind person, without pretensions.' And that is enough, according to yesterday's creed. You were never nicer than you were yesterday speaking of her (I remember your words): you said the flesh fades, the intellect withers, only the heart remembers. Do you recant all this?"

"No, I recant nothing; only yesterday's truth is not to-day's. One day we are attracted by goodness, another day by beauty; and beauty has been calling me day after day: at first the call was heard far away like a horn in the woods, but now the call has become more imperative, and all the landscape is musical. Yesterday standing by those ancient ruins, it seemed to me as if I had been transported out of my present nature back to my original nature of two thousand years ago. The sight of those ancient columns quickened a new soul within me; or should I say a soul that had been overlaid began to emerge? The dead are never wholly dead; their ideas live in us. I am sure that in England I never appreciated you as intensely as I do here. Doris, I have learned to appreciate you like a work of art. It is the spirit of antiquity that has taken hold of me, that has risen out of the earth and claimed me. That hat I would put away——"

"Don't you like my hat?"

"Yes, I like it, but I am thinking of the Doris that lived two thousand years ago; she did not wear a hat. It is not only the beauty of your face that I desire, but all your beauty, the pink breast flowers, the pretty fore-arms, the sides soft as wool, the flanks so daintily designed, the round thighs, the well-jointed knees, the long calves, the sloping ankles, the thin, white-skinned feet . . . and those hands! their long transparent fingers, their long red nails. In imagination I see the nymph, though I may never see her with mortal eyes."

"Why should you not see me, dear?"

"I have begun to despair. All these boarding-houses and their inhabitants jar the spirit that this landscape had kindled within me. I want to go away with you where I may love you. I am afraid what I am saying may seem exaggerated, but it is quite true that you remind me of antiquity, and in a way that I cannot explain though it is quite clear to me."

"But you do possess me, dear."

"No, Doris, not as I wish. You know very well what I mean by possession, the possession of sight and of touch and of scent. Dear Doris, if I do not go away with you where I can wholly possess you, this journey will be a bitter memory that will endure for ever; we must think not only of the day that we live, but of the days in front of us; we must store our memories as the squirrel stores nuts, we must have a winter hoard. If some way is not found out of this horrible dilemma, I shall remember you as a collector remembers a vase which a workman handed to him and which slipped and was broken, or like a vase that was stolen from him; I cannot find a perfect simile, at least not at this moment; my speech is imperfect, but you will understand."

"Yes I understand. I think I understand."

"If I do not get you, it will seem to me that I have lived in vain."

"But, dear one, things are not so bad as that. We need not be in Paris for some days yet, and though I cannot ask you to my hotel, there is no reason why——"

"Doris, do not raise up false hopes."

"I was only going to say, dear, that it does not seem to me necessary that we should go straight back to Paris."

"You mean that we might stop somewhere at some old Roman town, at Arles in an eighteenth-century house. Oh Doris, how enchanting this would be! I hardly dare to think lest——"

"Lest what, dear? Lest I should deceive you?"

There was a delicious coo in her voice, the very love coo; it cannot be imitated any more than the death-rattle, and exalted and inspired by her promise of herself, of all herself, I spoke in praise of the eighteenth century, saying that it had loved antiquity better than the nineteenth, and had reproduced its spirit.

"Is it not strange that, in the midst of reality, artistic conceptions always hang about me; but shall I ever possess you, Doris? Is it my delicious fate to spend three days with you in an old Roman town?"

"There is no reason why it shouldn't be. Where shall it be?"

"Any town would be sufficient with you, Doris; but let us think of some beautiful place;" and looking across the bay into the sunset, I recalled as many names as I could; many of those old Roman towns rose up before my eyes, classic remains mingling with mediæval towers, cathedral spires rising over walls on which Roman sentries had once paced. We could only spend our honeymoon in a town with a beautiful name—a beautiful name was essential—a name that it would be a delight to remember for ever after; the name would have to express by some harmonious combination of syllables the loves that would be expended there. Rocomadour imitated too obviously the sound of sucking doves, and was rejected for that reason. Cahor tempted us, but it was too stern a name; its Italian name, Devona, appealed to us; but, after all, we could not think of Cahor as Devona. And for many reasons were rejected Armance, Vezelay, Oloron, Correz, Valat, and Gedre. Among these, only Armance gave us any serious pause. Armance! That evening and the next we studied *L'Indicateur des Chemins de fer.* "Armance!" I said, interrupting Doris, who was telling me that we should lose our tickets by the *Côte d'Azur.* For in Doris's opinion it was necessary that we should leave Plessy by the *Côte d'Azur.* Her friends would certainly come to the station to see her off. "That is a matter of no moment," I said. "At Marseilles we can catch an express train, which will be nearly as good. There are

two excellent trains; either will do, if you have decided to spend the
three days at Armance."

She asked me if Armance were a village or a town, and I answered,
"What matter?"—for everywhere in France there are good beds and
good food and good wine—ay, and omelettes. We should do very well
in any village in the south of France for three days. But suddenly two
names caught my eye, Orelay and Verlancourt, and we agreed that we
preferred either of these names to Armance.

"Which name shall give shelter to two unfortunate lovers flying
in search of solitude?"

"Orelay is a beautiful name."

"Orelay it shall be," I said. "We shall be able to get there from
Marseilles in a few hours."

"You see, dear, it would be impossible for me to travel all the way to
Paris—a journey of at least twenty-four hours would kill me, and I'm
not strong; nothing tires me more than railway travelling. We must
stop somewhere. Why not at Orelay?"

As this history can have only one merit, that of absolute truth, I
must confess that the subterfuge whereby Doris sought to justify
herself to herself, delighted me. Perhaps no quality is more human
than that of subterfuge. She might unveil her body—I was living in
the hope of seeing her do so; but she could not unveil her soul. We
may only lift a corner of the veil; he who would strip human nature
naked and exhibit it displays a rattling skeleton, no more: where there
is no subterfuge there is no life.

This story will be read, no doubt, by the young and the old, the wise
and the foolish, by the temperate and the intemperate, but the subject-
matter is so common to all men that it will interest every one, even
ecclesiastics, everyone except certain gentlemen residing chiefly in
Constantinople, whose hostility to the lover on his errand is so well
known, and so easily understandable, that I must renounce all hope of
numbering them among the admirers of my own or Doris's frailty.
But happily these gentlemen are rare in England, though it is suspected
that one or two may be found among the reviewers on the staff of certain
newspapers; otherwise how shall we account for the solitary falsetto
voices in the choir of our daily and weekly press, shouting abstinence
from the house-tops? But with the exception of these few critics
everyone will find pleasure in this narrative; even in aged men and

women enough sex is left to allow them to take an interest in a love-story; in these modern days when the novel wanders even as far as the nuns in their cells (I have good authority for making this statement), perhaps I may be able to count upon an aged Mother Abbess to be, outwardly perhaps a disapproving, but at heart a sympathetic reader. Indeed, I count upon the ascetic more than upon any other class for appreciation, for the imagination of those who have had no experience in love adventures will enkindle, and they will appreciate perhaps more intensely than any other the mental trouble that a journey to Orelay with Doris would entail.

It would take nearly five hours according to the time-table to get from Marseilles to Orelay; and these five hours would wear themselves wearily away in conversation with Doris, in talking to her of every subject except the subject uppermost in my mind. I should have kept a notebook, just as I had arranged to do when I thought I was going on the yachting excursion among the Greek Islands with Gertrude; but, having no notes, I can only appeal to the reader's imagination. I must ask him to remember the week of cruel abstinence I had been through, and to take it into his consideration. My dear, dear reader, I am sure you can see me if you try (in your mind's eye, of course) walking about the corridors, seeking the guard, asking everyone I meet—

"How far away are we now from Orelay?"

"Orelay? Nearly two hours from Orelay."

Our heavy luggage had been sent on before, but we had a number of dressing-cases and bags with us, and there might not be time to remove all these. The guard, who had promised to take them out of the carriage for us, might not arrive in time. However this might be, he was not to be found anywhere, and I sought him how many times up and down the long length of the train. You can see me, reader, can you not? walking about the train, imagining all kinds of catas-trophes—that the train might break down, or that it might not stop at Orelay; or, a still more likely catastrophe, that the young lady might change her mind. What if that were to happen at the last moment! Ah, if that were to happen I should have perchance to throw myself out of the train, unless peradventure I refrained for the sake of writing the story of a lover's deception. The transitional stage is an intolerable one, and I wondered if Doris felt it as keenly, and every time I passed our carriage on my way up and down in search of the guard, I stopped a moment to study her face; she sat with her eyes closed, perhaps dozing. How prosaic of her to doze on the way to Orelay! Why was she not as agitated as I?

And the question presented itself suddenly, Do women attach the same interest to love adventures as we do? Do women ask themselves as often as we do if God, the Devil, or Calamitous Fate will intervene between us and our pleasure? Will it be snatched out of our arms and from our lips? Perhaps never before, only once in any case, did I experience an excitement so lancinating as I experienced that day. And as I write the sad thought floats past that such expectations will never be my lot again. The delights of the moment are perhaps behind me, but why should I feel sad for that? Life is always beautiful, in age as well as in youth; the old have a joy that the youths do not know—recollection. It is through memory we know ourselves; without memory it might be said we have hardly lived at all, or only like animals.

This is a point on which I would speak seriously to every reader, especially to my young readers; for it is of the utmost importance that everyone should select adventures that not only please them at the moment, but can be looked back upon with admiration, and for which one can offer up a mute thanksgiving. My life would not have been complete, a corner-stone would have been lacking, if Doris had not come to Orelay with me. Without her I should not have known the joy that perfect beauty gives; that beauty which haunted in antiquity would never have been known to me. But without more, as the lawyers say, we will return to Doris. I asked her if she had been asleep? No, she had not slept, only it rested her to keep her eyes closed, the sunlight fatigued her. I did not like to hear her talk of fatigue, and to hide from her what was passing in my mind I tried to invent some conversation. Orelay—what a lovely name it was! Did she think the town would vindicate or belie its name? She smiled faintly and said she would not feel fatigued as soon as she got out of the train, and there was some consolation in the thought that her health would not allow her to get further that day than Orelay.

We decided to stay at the Hôtel des Valois. One of the passengers had spoken to me of this hotel; he had never stayed there himself, but he believed it to be an excellent hotel. But it was not his recommendation that influenced me, it was the name—the Hôtel des Valois. How splendid! And when we got out at Orelay I asked the porters and the station-master if they could recommend a hotel. No, but they agreed that the Hôtel des Valois was as good as any other. We drove there wondering what it would be like. Everything had turned out well up to the present, but everything would go for nought if the Hôtel des Valois should prove unworthy of its name. And the first sight of it was certainly disappointing. Its courtyard was insignificant, only saved by a beautiful ilex tree growing in one corner. The next moment I noticed that the porch of the hotel was pretty and refined—a curious porch it was, giving the hotel for a moment the look of an eighteenth-century English country house. There were numerous windows with small panes, and one divined the hall beyond the porch. The hall delighted us, and I said to Doris as we passed through that the hotel must have been a nobleman's house some long while ago, when Orelay had a society of its own, perhaps a language, for in the seventeenth or the eighteenth centuries Provençal or some other dialect must have been written or spoken at Orelay. We admired the galleries overlooking the hall, and the staircase leading to them. We seemed to have been transported into the eighteenth century; the atmosphere was that of a Boucher, a provincial Boucher perhaps, but an eighteenth-century artist, for all that. The doves that crowd round Aphrodite seemed to have led us right; and we foresaw a large quiet bedroom with an Aubusson carpet in the middle of a parquet floor, writing-tables in the corners of the room or in the silken-curtained windows.

This was the kind of room I had imagined—one as large as a drawing-room, and furnished like a drawing-room, with sofas and arm-chairs that we could draw round the fire with myself and Doris sitting there talking; for part of my pleasure was to live her intimate life with her, the intimacy of her dressing and her undressing. Love is com-posed in a large measure of desire of intimacy, and if the affection that birds experience in making their nest be not imitated, love descends to the base satisfaction of animals which merely meet in obedience to an instinct, and separate as soon as the instinct has been served. Birds understand love better than all animals, except man. Who has not thought with admiration of the weaver-birds, and of our own native wren? But the rooms that were offered to us corresponded in nowise with those that we had imagined the doors of the beautiful galleries would lead us into. The French words *chambre meublée* will convey an idea of the rooms we were shown into; for do not the words evoke a high bed pushed into the corner, an eider-down on top, a tall dusty window facing the bed, with skimpy red curtains and a vacant fireplace? There were, no doubt, a few chairs—but what chairs! The voluptuous dream I cherished of sitting with Doris before a beautiful eighteenth-century chimney-piece, talking to her and watching her the while as she prepared herself for the night—looking on at the letting down of her hair and the brushing of it—a woman versed in the art of love prepares herself for bed so imperceptibly that any attempt to indicate a stage in her undressing breaks the harmony; for there is a harmony in the way she passes from the moment when she sits in her evening dress playing with her bracelets to the moment when she drops her nightgown over her head and draws her silk stockings off her legs white as milk, kicking her little slippers aside before she slips over the edge and curls herself into the middle of a bed broad as a battlefield—all the voluptuous dream that I cherished fell before the sight of those high beds; the entire fabric of my love, the nest in which we should enjoy it, the fluttering of pinions and the sensation of soft scents and delicate linen, were swept away.

The scene was at once tragic and comic. It was of vital importance to myself and Doris to find a bedroom in which we could love each other, and it was of equal indifference to the waiter whether we did or didn't. The appearance of each contributed to the character of the scene. Doris's appearance I have tried to make clear to the reader; mine must be imagined; it only remains for me to tell what the waiter was like; an old man, short and thick, slow on the feet from long service, enveloped in an enormous apron; one only saw the ends of his trousers and his head; and the head was one of the strangest ever seen, for there was not a hair upon it; he was bald as an egg, and his head was the shape of an egg, and the colour of an Easter egg, a pretty pink all over. The eyes were like a ferret's, small and restless and watery, a long nose and a straight drooping chin, and a thick provincial accent— that alone amused me.

"Have you no other rooms?"

"*Nous n'avons que cela.*"

I quote his words in the language in which they were spoken, for I remember how brutal they seemed, and how entirely in keeping with the character of the room. No doubt the words will seem flat and tame to the reader, but they never can seem that to me. *Nous n'avons que cela* will always be to me as pregnant with meaning as the famous *to be or not to be.* For it really amounted to that. I can see Doris standing by me, charming, graceful as a little Tanagra statuette, seemingly not aware of the degradation that the possession of her love would mean in such a room as that which we stood in; and I think I can honestly say that I wished we had never come to Orelay, that we had gone straight on to Paris. It were better even to sacrifice her love than that it should be degraded by vulgar circumstances; and instead of a holy rite my honeymoon had come to seem to me what the black mass must seem to the devout Christian.

"The rooms will look better," Doris said, "when fires have been lighted, and when our bags are unpacked. A skirt thrown over the arm of a chair furnishes a room."

Taking her hands in mine I kissed them, and was almost consoled; but at that moment my eyes fell upon the beds, and I said—

"Those beds! O Doris, those beds! yours is no better than mine."

Women are always satisfied, or they are kind, or they are wise, and accept the inevitable without a murmur.

"Dearest, ask the waiter to bring us some hot water."

I did so, and while he was away I paced the room, unable to think of anything but the high bed; it was impossible to put out of my sight the ridiculous spectacle of a couple in a nightgown and pyjama suit climbing into it. The vision of myself and Doris lying under that eider-down, facing that tall window, with nothing to shut out the light but those vulgar lace curtains, pursued me, and I paced the room till the pink waiter returned with two jugs; and then feeling very miserable, I began to unpack my bag without getting further than the removal of the brushes and comb; Doris unpacked a few things, and she washed her hands, and I thought I might wash mine; but before I had finished washing them I left the dreadful basin, and going to Doris with dripping hands I said—

"There is very little difference in the rooms. Perhaps you would like to sleep in mine?"

"I can see no difference. I think I'll remain where I am."

Which room she slept in may seem insignificant to the reader, but this is not so, for had we changed rooms this story would never have been written. I can see myself even now walking to and fro like a caged animal vainly seeking for a way of escape, till suddenly—my adventure reminds me very much of the beginning of many romantic novels—the tapestry that the wind had blown aside, the discovery of the secret door—suddenly I discovered a door in the wall-paper; it was unlatched, and pushing through it I descended two steps, and lo! I was in the room of my heart's desire; a large, richly-coloured saloon with beautifully proportioned windows and red silk damask curtains hanging from carved cornices, and all the old gilding still upon them. And the silk fell into such graceful folds that the proportions of the windows were enhanced. And the walls were stretched with silk of a fine romantic design, the dominant note of which was red to match the curtains. There were wall-lights, and a curious old clock on the marble chimney-piece amid branching candelabra. I stayed a moment to examine the clock, deciding very soon that it was not of much value. . . it was made in Marseilles a hundred years ago.

"A beautiful room in its proportions and in its colour," I said, and seeing another door ajar I went through it and discovered a bedroom likewise in red with two beds facing each other. The beds were high, it is true, and a phrase from a letter I had written to Doris, 'aggressively virtuous', rose up in my mind as I looked upon them. But the curtains hung well from *les ciels de lit* (one cannot say *cieux de lit*, I suppose)—the English word is, I think, tester. "This room is far from the bedroom of my dreams," I muttered, "but *à la rigueur ça peut marcher.*" But pursuing my quest a little further, I came upon a spacious bedroom with two windows looking out on the courtyard—a room which would have satisfied the most imaginative lover, a room worthy of the adorable Doris, and I can say this as I look back fondly on her many various perfections. A great bed wide and low, "like a battlefield as our bed should be," I said, for the lines of the old poet were running in my head:

Madame, shall we undress you for the fight?
The wars are naked that you make to-night.

And, looking upon it, I stood there like one transfigured, filled with a great joy; for the curtains hanging from a graceful tester like a crown would have satisfied the painter Boucher. . . . He rarely painted bedrooms. I do not remember any at this moment; but I remember many by Fragonard, and Fragonard would have said: 'I have no fault to find with that bed.' The carpet was not Aubusson, but it was nevertheless a finely-designed carpet, and its colour was harmonious; the sofa was shapely enough, and the Louis XVI arm-chairs were filled with deep cushions. I turned to the toilet-table fearing it might prove an incongruity, but it was in perfect keeping with the room, and I began at once to look forward to seeing it laid out with all the manifold ivories and silver of Doris's dressing-case.

Imagine my flight, dear reader, if you can, back to Doris, whom I had left trying to make the best of that miserable square room more like a prison cell than a bedroom.

"What is the matter, dearest?" she asked.

But without answering her I said, "Give me your hand," and led her as a prince leads his betrothed in a fairy tale, through the richly coloured saloon, lingering a moment for her to admire it, and then I took her through my room, the double-bedded room, saying, "All this is nothing; wait till you see your room." And Doris paused overcome by the beauty of the bed, of the curtains falling from the tester gracefully as laburnum or acacia branches in June.

"The rooms are beautiful, but a little cheerless."

"Doris, Doris, you don't deserve to lie there! The windows of course must be opened, fresh air must be let in, and fires must be lighted. But think of you and me sitting here side by side talking before our bedtime."

Fires were lighted quickly, servants came in bearing candelabra in their hands, and among them, and with Doris by my side, I imagined myself a prince, for who is a prince but he who possesses the most desirable thing in the world, who finds himself in the most delectable circumstances? And what circumstance is more delightful than sitting in a great shadowy bedroom, watching the logs burning, shedding their grateful heat through the room, for the logs that were brought to us, as we soon discovered, were not the soft wood grown for consumption in Parisian hotels; the logs that warmed our toes in Orelay were dense and hard as iron, and burned like coal, only more fragrantly, and very soon the bareness of the room disappeared. A petticoat, as Doris had said, thrown over a chair gives an inhabited look to a room at once; and the contents of her dressing-case, as I anticipated, took the room back to one hundred years ago, when some great lady sat there in a flowered silk gown before one of those inlaid dressing-tables, filled with pigments and powders and glasses.

EE

There was one of those tables in the room, and I drew it from the corner and raised its lid, the lid with the looking-glass in it. And I liked the unpacking of her dressing-case, the discovery of a multitude of things for bodily use, the various sponges; the flat sponge for the face, the round sponge for the body, and the little sponges; all the scissors and the powder for the nails, and the scents, the soft silks, the lace scarves, and the long silk nightgown soon to droop over her shoulders. My description by no means exhausts the many things she produced from her dressing-case and bags, nor would the most complete catalogue convey an impression of Doris's cleanliness of her little body! One would have to see her arranging her things, with her long curved hands and almond nails carefully cut—they were her immediate care, and many powders and ointments and polishers were called into requisition. Some reader will cry that all this is most unimportant, but he is either hypocritical or stupid, for it is only with scent and silk and artifices that we raise love from an instinct to a passion.

Not only must a mistress be careful of herself, and spend many hours upon herself when her maid is not with her, but a man must consider in what apparel he approaches his mistress. There are still, I believe, some married men in our far northern islands who go into their wives' bedrooms wearing flannel or jaeger nightshirts. Fie upon such things! And women I have always pitied a little, for they are obliged to take us—well, as a woman once said to me, and she was an artist in these matters, 'We have to take you as you are.'

This was five-and-twenty years ago, before pyjamas had been invented. Pyjamas redeem us from the shame of the nightshirt; no doubt they are the great redemption; and as the quality of the silk and its colour can be carefully chosen, and the silk cords and the tassels be tied to advantage, and a pocket be worn at the breast, a man may be said not to be wholly unfit now to enter a lady's room. I had not unnaturally looked over my things with great care before leaving London, seeing that many different suits of pyjamas and the most finely-coloured were among my luggage; many an evening at Plessy I had looked at these sighing, thinking that I might never wear them for Doris's pleasure and admiration, and my thoughts had gone back to my pyjamas at once, when Doris suggested that we might not go straight to Paris, but might stop at Orelay. I had told the *valet de chambre*, an excellent fellow, but somewhat stupid, who looked after me at my hotel, which suits he was to put into my suit-case; I remembered my very words, and I got up so suddenly that Doris asked me what was the matter, why I was going.

"I'm only going to unpack, dear. . . ."

In a few minutes I came back—how well I remember that moment!
—looking, she said, like one to whom a catastrophe had happened.
Perhaps the word catastrophe will seem an exaggeration, though a greater misfortune could hardly have fallen upon a lover, for not only did the *valet de chambre* forget to put in the special pyjamas that I had indicated—he had put no pyjamas in at all.

"How am I to go into your room to-night, dear?"

Doris did not answer, and I sat like one overwhelmed, not able yet fully to realize the misfortune that had befallen us. At last, getting up, I walked across the room, and stopping suddenly I said—

"Good God, Doris, I really believe that man Schopenhauer was right. For surely the sum of our pains exceeds the sum of our pleasures. The hawk that eats the sparrow does not get as much pleasure out of his meal as the sparrow gets pain from being devoured. Now think of it! That dear little body," I said, taking her in my arms, "that delicious face—who appreciates it more than I do?—but when I think of the week of agony that I suffered at Plessy, the torment that I endured in the railway train, the blank disappointment that fell upon me when we were shown into those bedrooms—never shall I forget the disappointment, for I foresaw it all as it would have been if we had remained there——"

"But, dearest, we didn't remain there."

"No, we didn't; by accident I discovered these rooms, but now the delight of finding these rooms, of being here, is spoilt by this accursed accident."

"It's very unlucky," Doris said. I looked at her kindly, for I knew she had substituted the word "unlucky" for "unfortunate". "Have you searched well in your suit-case?"

"Yes, I have turned it all out. There are no pyjamas. The only chance is that I might buy some in Orelay if we went out at once; the shops are not closed yet."

"I'm afraid," Doris answered, "that you will not find any pyjamas."

"Not like those I told that idiot to put into my dressing-case; I know that well enough. You think the rough things that the shops supply here would be worse than none? Perhaps."

We had ordered dinner for half-past seven, and Doris said as we walked through the hall, "You'd better leave word that we shall not be back till eight o'clock."

And away we went through the narrow dark streets of Orelay, through which the cold night wind was blowing. Doris was clad too lightly; she had only the summer things that she wore at Plessy, and I begged of her to draw her cloak tightly about her.

"Here is a shop," I said, and in we went. "Madame, have you got any pyjamas?"

"No, we have no pyjamas. We don't keep them," answered a matronly woman, and Doris said as we hurried away to another shop that she looked as if we had asked for something improper. The same answer befell us shop after shop, down the long street, each one advising us to try the next till at last there were no more to try.

"There is only one place," said a pretty young woman who seemed to have divined our misfortune and to sympathize with us, "where you can get pyjamas in Orelay. Turn down the street by the church and follow it till you come to the Place— (I've forgotten the name), and at the corner you will see a shop *Les Élégants*; if they have no pyjamas there you had better buy a nightshirt, sir."

"Thank you, thank you." Doris and I hurried away in quest of *Les Élégants*; we walked half a mile, stopping now and then at small shops. "Have you got pyjamas?" "No, we don't keep them, only nightshirts." At last the welcome letters appeared *Les Élégants*, and we addressed ourselves to the young man in attendance, who told us that the last he had he returned to the makers, there being no demand for pyjamas in Orelay.

"Alas! Doris, we have fallen upon a moral town!—high beds and nightshirts."

"But, sir, may I not offer you a silk nightshirt? We have some very pretty ones."

I looked at Doris.

"We might see them," she said; "this is a pretty stripe," and she examined the quality carefully with her long fingers, which I have already mentioned were slender and curved. While she was examining the nightshirts I tried to discover from the shopman how it was there was no demand for pyjamas. Were there no young men in Orelay who declined to enter a lady's room in a nightshirt? The shopman looked at me doubtfully, and answered that no doubt there were some, but those sent to Paris for their underwear.

"I think, dear, this nightshirt——"

"Yes, yes, Doris, let us have it."

And we raced home through the ill-paven streets of Orelay, the houses black about us, falling into rapid perspectives against the sky and the dome of the cathedral showing now and again, I carrying a parcel, a parcel containing a silk nightshirt with pink stripes, price ten francs. "I am sure that pyjamas are looked upon as immoral in Orelay," Doris said.

"No doubt you are right," and we ran on again tossing ideas from one to the other; at one moment I was telling Doris that everything unusual is considered immoral, nor should we be surprised that this is so, the original meaning of the word being unusual. The moralists are better grammarians than they think, for it would be correct to say that broken weather is immoral weather, though I doubt if one would be understood. At that moment the sight of a *marchant d'antiquité* interrupted our conversation, and going into the shop we spent some time hunting for a present for Doris. When we got out the ideas we had abandoned so hurriedly returned to us, and we remembered how in Western Europe it is considered moral for a woman to exhibit her bosom in the evening—the reason why women wear low dresses is apparent enough. "Doris dear, aren't we funny creatures?" Whereas in the East a woman would be considered a very frivolous person if she uncovered her bosom in the daytime, to say nothing of the evening; but she may uncover her feet, for it is customary to do so. "So you see, Doris dear, that grammar is an abiding rock standing in the midst of ethical quicksands."

"Do you think, then," said Doris, "that what we have agreed to look upon as a sin to-day was once regarded as meritorious?"

"Undoubtedly, and will again."

"Do you know," she said suddenly, "that I have often heard mother say that drawers were not worn by women in England until the sixties; they were brought into fashion by the Empress Eugenie, and were considered immoral."

"How amusing! How amusing!" I answered; "no humour is

comparable to unconscious humour. Stupidity is the great humorist. Where should we be, how should we get on without stupidity? I was only a little boy when the Empress sent her drawers to England, but I remember how ugly they were; they reached to the ankle, a grave error, no doubt," but before we had finished discussing the gravity of this mistake and how it has since been remedied, we had reached our hotel.

"I am longing," said Doris, "to see that beautiful red drawing-room with all the candelabra lighted and half a dozen logs blazing on the hearth. It is extraordinary how cold it is in the street."

To procure an impartial mind bodily ease is necessary, and we sat on either side of a splendid fire warming our toes; and when completely thawed I was prone to admit that the hostility which the Empress's drawers had met with in England was not so superficial as it seemed at first sight, for the English people are essentially Christian, and in declaring that drawers were immoral public feeling was only expressing —crudely if you will—but still expressing the belief that lies at the root of all Christianity, that refinement is in itself sinful, and all that conduces to refinement is dangerous. At the bottom of his heart every Christian feels, though he may not care to admit it in these modern days, that every attempt to make love a beautiful and pleasurable thing is a return to paganism. In his eyes the only excuse for man's love of woman is that without it the world would come to an end. Why he should consider the end of the world a misfortune I have never been able to find out, for if his creed be a true one the principal use of this world is to supply Hell with fuel. He is never weary of telling us that very few indeed may hope to get to Heaven.

"But France is not a Christian country, and yet you see the high bed has not become extinct," said Doris.

"Ideas die slowly. Pyjamas are still regarded as a capital luxury! The nightcap has disappeared, it is true, even in Orelay, but the night-shirt remains, alas! alas! " and I opened my parcel and produced the garment. "Love is dressed ridiculously, made to look like a zany. I would that I had bought a nightcap; it's a pity to wear the nightshirt without the cap."

"I am thankful you didn't," Doris murmured under her breath.

"I don't know; it is better to look awful than to look ugly."

"You would look awful, dear."

"Doris, I should like to see you in a nightcap and one of those long frilled nightgowns of our grandmothers that one sees in pictures."

"I wonder how I should look," Doris answered with a gravity which always comes into a woman's face when there is a question of what she is to wear.

"Of what are you thinking, dear?" she asked suddenly.

"Only of the nightcap, but it is late; I suppose we should find the shops closed; moreover, we might not be able to get one in Orelay. Besides, Doris, the nightcap would necessitate a return to the old custom of sleeping together. When the nightcap was in vogue love was cribbed, cabined, and confined, if I may quote Shakespeare, within the limits of a four-post bed, and the time for love was regulated—night was the time—and after the love-feast the married couple were expected to turn round to sleep, perchance to snore."

Doris's opinion on this point, whether lovers should sleep together, was not easily ascertained. Women are conservative, and old customs appeal to them.

"I have never slept with anyone in my life; *de cela au moins je suis vierge.*"

"Now you are quoting from *Les Confessions d'un Jeune Anglais.*"

"One never changes. Did I say that? I had forgotten. But since writing that confession I have been informed by the erudite in love that my abstinence has no doubt lost me a great deal; all my friends tell me so. I have been told, and by one who should know, that he who has not waked up in the morning with his beloved, seeing the sunlight in the window, hearing the birds in the branches, does not know the rapture of love, the enchantment of its intimacy."

As I confided my friend's opinion to Doris the firelight played over her face and hair, and I perceived for the first time what it must be to see the sleeping face beside one, lying in the disordered gold of long thick hair. And Doris, who was doubtless feeling a little tired, sat looking into the fire. Her attitude encouraged reverie; dream linked into dream till at last the chain of dreams was broken by the entrance of the pink waiter bringing in our dinner. In the afternoon I had called him an imbecile, which made him very angry, and he had explained that he was not an imbecile, but if I hurried him he lost his head altogether. Of course one is sorry for speaking rudely to a waiter; it is a shocking thing to do, and nothing but the appearance of the bedroom we were shown into would excuse me. His garrulousness, which was an irritation in the afternoon, was an amusement as he laid the cloth and told me the bill of fare; moreover, I had to consult him about the wine, and I liked to hear him telling me in his strong Southern accent of a certain wine of the country, as good as Pommard and as strong, and which would be known all over the world, only it did not bear transportation. Remembering how tired we were, and the verse—

> Quand on boit du Pommard on devient bon on aime,
> On devient aussi bon que le Pommard lui-même—

we drank, hoping that the wine would awaken us. But the effect of that strong Southern wine seemed to be more lethargic than exhilarating, and when dinner was over and we had returned to our seats by the fireside we were too weary to talk, and too nervous.

"The hour has come, Doris," I said with a choking sensation in my throat, and I seemed to be trembling in my very entrails; she, too, seemed nervous. "It is time to go to our room. We are both tired. Why should we sit up any longer?"

I have told how I looked forward to the intimacy of the fire in Doris's bedroom, to sitting by it with her, seeing her undo her hair, unloose her bodice, seeing her kick her velvet slippers aside, draw her silk stockings off her legs white as milk, and twist herself into the great bed wide as a battlefield. It is rarely that things happen exactly as we imagine them, but in this instance they did. I have told of the disappointment we experienced on seeing the rooms that were offered to us, and then of the loss of my pyjamas; but the fears of the lover were not ended yet. The great fear lest the eagerness of his desire should undermine his bodily strength was upon me; and it was only Doris's beauty—she had proved all that I had imagined her to be; she was not a Tanagra figure, a sketch in clay, but a finished marble; she was *une fille en marbre* but not at all *une fille de marbre*—that saved me from the misfortune dreaded by all lovers. Her beauty saved me, and it is with regret that I cannot tell her beauty in every intimate detail, for what is so well worth telling as beauty?—the beauty of a woman's arms when she opens them to you, the most beautiful movement in the world but one, and the pretty movement of the shapely hips when she rolls herself over like a little white ferret in its nest, and when she pokes her face up just as a ferret does? I think women are aware of their beauty just as cats are. Men are painfully aware of their ugliness; mine was a sore trouble to me. "It is beauty and the beast," I said. . . . But to speak of something else. One remembers everything better than the moment of ecstasy—the colour of the rooms, their shapes, the furniture, all is seen by me to-day as truly as if the reality were before me; the very wood we burned in the great fireplace, the shapes of one log, how it fell into ashes at one end leaving a great knotted stump at the other, the moving of the candles into shadowy places so that the light should not fall upon our eyes—all these details are remembered, only the moment of ecstasy is forgotten. It is a pity that this is so. But I remember how I stood at the foot of the bed bidding her good-night, for the moment comes when all lovers must part, unless indeed they are married folk 'who occupy the same room'. The occupation of the same room, one of the most important questions in love's economy, was being treated when the pink waiter brought in our dinner; and the reader will remember that I was telling Doris how those learned in love had told me that he who has not waked up in the morning with his beloved seeing the sunlight in the window, hearing the birds in the branches, does not know the rapture of love, the enchantment of its intimacy. The sympathetic reader will not have forgotten this avowal, and his instinct leaping forward he will have seen me standing triumphant on the summit of all earthly love; therefore the admission that, feeling myself falling asleep, I bade Doris goodnight at the foot of the bed will have cast him into the slough of despond from which my narrative, however lively it may prove, may fail to lift him. But though I did not realize the sacred moment at Orelay, and consequently will never realize it, in this world at least, that moment which, with the music of harps, Wagner depicts so completely, when Siegfried's kiss awakes Brunnhilde and she opens her eyes to the beauty of the world, I learned nevertheless at Orelay that my friend who said I was but a novice, a mere acolyte in Love's service, was not wholly wrong in his criticism of my life, for waking suddenly after sleeping for some hours, I heard Doris trying the handle of my door, and I called to ask her if she were seeking anything. She said she wished to know the time; there was no clock in her room, but there was one on my chimney-piece. It seemed so kind of her to come to my room that I could not refrain from taking her in my arms, and I told her that I had never seen a woman so early in the morning before. This pleased her, for she did not wish our love to be sullied with memories of other women. She shed such a delight about me that morning that I sought her the following morning in her room, and that visit, too, is remembered, though it is less distinct in my mind than her visit to my room. When I left her to dress myself she came running in to tell me something she had forgotten to tell me, and she sat watching me while I shaved, laughing at the absurdity, for it was absurd that she should always have something to say to me. No sooner had she gone than something awoke in my mind too something I had unfortunately forgotten to say and I had to rush back and to beg of her to let me open the door, though she was in her bath.

I know a statue of a woman leaning forward wiping her thighs, and that was the movement I discovered Doris in. The statue is a stupid thing, lacking in personal observation; all that the sculptor had omitted I perceived in Doris, but the comparison only floated across my mind; the delight of seeing her naked absorbed me, and I thought of other things, of Fragonard, for Fragonard realized what a little thing a woman is compared with a man, and this was just the idea that Doris conveyed; her great mass of hair made her look smaller than she really was, her head seemed too large for her body, yet this seeming, for it was no more than a seeming, did not detract from her beauty; she was as charming as if she had looked the regulation seven-and-a-half heads, for she was a Fragonard—an eighteenth-century bed-fellow, that is what she was. . . . She bid me away. No one had ever seen her in her bath before; she did not like it; no, she did not! And thinking how charming these subterfuges were, how little love would be without them, I heard her calling, saying that she would be with me in ten minutes, that I was to ring and tell the waiter to bring up our first breakfast.

The coffee and the rolls and butter were ready before Doris, and the vexation of seeing the breakfast growing cold was recompensed by the pleasure of teasing her, urging her to pass her arms into her dressing-gown, to come as she was, it did not matter what she had on underneath. The waiter did not count; he was not a man, he was a waiter, a pink creature, pinker than anything in the world, except a baby's bottom, and looking very like that.

"Hasten, dear, hasten!" and I went back to the salon and engaged in chatter with the old provincial, my English accent contrasting strangely with his. It was the first time I had heard the Southern accent. At Plessy I had heard all accents, Swiss, German, Italian; there was plenty of Parisian accent there, and I had told a Parisian flower-woman, whose husband was a Savoyard, that I declined to believe any more in the Southern accent, *C' est une blague qu'on m'a faite*; but at Orelay I had discovered the true accent, and I listened to the old man for the sake of hearing it. He was asking me for my appreciation of the wine we had drunk last night when Doris entered in a foamy white dressing-gown.

"You liked the wine, dear, didn't you? He wants to know if we will have the same wine for twelve o'clock breakfast."

"Dear me, it's eleven o'clock now," Doris answered, and she looked at the waiter.

"Monsieur and Madame will go for a little walk; perhaps you would like to breakfast at one?"

We agreed that we could not breakfast before one, and our waiter suggested a visit to the cathedral, it would fill up the time pleasantly and profitably; but Doris, when she had had her coffee, wanted to sit on my knee and to talk to me; and then there was a piano, and she wanted to play me some things, or rather I wanted to hear her. But the piano was a poor one; the notes did not come back, she said, and we talked for some hours without perceiving that the time was passing. After lunch the waiter again inquired if we intended to go for a little walk; there were vespers about four in the cathedral.

"It would do Monsieur and Madame good."

"The walk or the cathedral?" we inquired, and, a little embarrassed, the old fellow began to tell us that he had not been to the cathedral for some years, but the last time he was there he had been much impressed by the darkness. It was all he could do to find his way from pillar to pillar; he had nearly fallen over the few kneeling women who crouched there listening to the clergy intoning Latin verses. According to his account, there were no windows anywhere except high up in the dome. And leaning his hands on the table, looking like all the waiters that ever existed or that will ever exist, his *tablier* reaching nearly to his chin upheld by strings passed over the shoulders, he told us that it was impossible to see what was happening in the chancel; but there had seemed to be a great number of clergy seated in the darkness at the back, for one heard voices behind the tall pieces of furniture singing Latin verses; one only heard the terminations of the words, an "us" and a "noster", and words ending in "e", and the organ always coming in a little late.

"My good man," I said, "your description leaves nothing to be desired. Why should I go to the cathedral unless to verify your impressions? I am sure the service is exactly as you describe it, and I would not for the world destroy the picture you have evoked of those forgotten priests intoning their vespers in the middle of the granite church behind a three-branched candlestick."

The poor man left the room very much disconcerted, feeling, Doris said, as if he had lost one of the forks.

"Thank heaven that matter is done with—a great weight is off my mind."

"But there is the museum. You would like to see that?" said Doris, and a change came into my face.

"Well, Doris, the waiter has told us that there is a celebrated study by David in the museum, 'The Nymph of Orelay'."

"But, dear one, am I not your nymph of Orelay?" and Doris slipped on her knees and put her arms about me. "Will I not do as well as the painted creature in the museum?"

"Far better," I said, "far better. Now we are free, Doris, freed from the cathedral and from the museum. All the day belongs to us, and to-morrow we may pass it in bed if we like."

"And so we will," Doris said meditatively; and so we did, dear reader, and I consider the time was well spent, for by so doing we avoided catching cold, a thing easy to do when a mistral is blowing; and in Doris's bed I gathered many precious souvenirs of her beauty. And it was not until the following evening we remembered that time was always on the wing, that our little bags would have to be packed. Next morning we were going.

"Going away by the train," Doris said regretfully. "Would we were going away in a carriage! We shall leave Orelay knowing nothing of it but this suite of apartments."

"There is no reason why we should not drive," and I stopped packing my bag, and stood looking at her with a half-folded nightshirt in my hands. "Ah, that nightshirt!" and she laughed. "What shall I do with it?"

"You wouldn't part with it? You'll keep it in remembrance of Orelay."

"Yes; I would not have it fall on other backs," and looking at the cream silk faintly striped with pink, it seemed to me that it was not so ugly a garment after all. "It will always remind me of these rooms, where we shall never be again. Doris, is it not sad? We have spent three such days here and three such nights that one does not know which were the pleasanter, the days or the nights. Dear God, how thankful we ought to be that thou didst differentiate between man and woman! What a dismal place the world would have been without sex— all its romance and folly."

"I wonder if we should have stayed three days if we had not discovered these rooms? Dear one, I think I should not have meant so much to you in those humbler rooms: you attach much importance to these cornices and hangings."

"I should have loved you always, Doris, but I think I can love you better here," and with our bags in our hands we wandered from the bedroom into the drawing-room and stood admiring its bygone splendour. "Doris, dear, you must play me 'The Nut Bush'. I want to hear it on that old piano. Tinkle it, dear, tinkle it, and don't play 'The Nut Bush' too sentimentally, nor yet too gaily."

"Which way will you have it?" she said; " 'a true love's truth or a light love's art?' "

"I would have it dainty and fantastic as Schumann wrote it, 'only the song of a secret bird.' "

"With a pathos of loneliness in it?"

"That is it," I cried, "that is the right time to play it in, without stress on either side. . . . No, you mustn't leave the piano, Doris. Sing me some songs. Go on singing Schumann or Schubert; there are no other songs. Let me hear you sing 'The Moonlight' or 'The Lotusflower'. Schumann and Schubert were the singing-birds of the 'fifties; I love their romantic sentimentalities, orange gardens, south winds, a lake with a pinnace upon it, and a nightingale singing in a dark wood by a lonely shore; that is how they felt, how they dreamed."

And resigning herself to my humour she sang song after song, till at last, awaking from a long reverie of music and old association of memories, I said "Play me a waltz, Doris; I would hear an old-time waltz played in this room; its romantic flourishes will evoke the departed spirits," and very soon, sitting in my chair with half-closed eyes, it seemed to me that I saw crinolines faintly gliding over the floor, and white-stockinged feet, sloping shoulders and glistening necks with chignons—swan-like women, and long-whiskered cavaliers wearing peg-top trousers and braided coats dancing or talking with them. . . . The music suddenly stopped, and Doris said—

"If we are to catch our train we must go on with our packing."

"You mustn't talk to me of trains," and overcome with a Schumann-like longing and melancholy I took her in my arms overcome by her beauty. She was perfection. No Chelsea or Dresden figure was ever more dainty, gayer or brighter. She was Schumann and Dresden, but a Dresden of an earlier period than Schumann; but why compare her to anything? She was Doris, the very embodiment of her name.

"Ah, Doris, why are we leaving here? Why can't we remain here for ever?"

"It is strange," she said; "I feel the charm of these old stately rooms as much as you do. But dearest, we have missed the train."

The pink waiter came up, I promised to hasten, but my love of Doris delayed us unduly, and we arrived at the station only to hear that the train had gone away some ten minutes before. The train that had left was the only good train in the day, and missing it had given us another twenty-four hours in Orelay; but Doris was superstitious. "Our three days are done," she said; "if we don't go to-day we shall go to-morrow, and to go on the fourth day would be unlucky. What shall we do all day? The spell has been broken. We have left our hotel. Let us take a carriage," she pleaded, "and drive to the next station. The sun is shining, and the country is beautiful; we saw it from the railway, a strange red country grey with olives, olive orchards extending to the very foot of the mountains, and mingling with the pine trees descending the slopes."

"The slopes!" I said, "the precipitous sides of that high rock! Shall I ever forget it, beginning like the tail of a lion and rising up to the sky, towering above the level landscape like a sphinx."

"The drive would be delightful!"

"And it would be a continuation of the romance of the old Empire drawing-room. A postchaise would be the thing if we could discover one."

Sometimes Nature seems to conspire to carry out an idea, and though no veritable postchaise of old time was discovered in the coach-house behind the courtyard in which the ilex trees flourished, we happened to catch sight of a carriage some twenty-five or thirty years old, a cumbersome old thing hung upon C-springs, of the security of which the coachman seemed doubtful. He spoke disparagingly, telling us that the proprietor had been trying to sell it, but no one would buy it, so heavy was it on the horses' backs, so out of fashion, one was ashamed to go out in it. The coachman's notions of beauty did not concern us, but Doris dreaded lest one of the wheels should come off; however, on examination it was found to be roadworthy, and I said to Doris as I helped her into it—

"If it be no postchaise, at all events ladies wearing crinolines have sat inside it, that is certain, and gentlemen wearing peg-top trousers with braid upon them. Good God, Doris, if you were to wear a crinoline I should love you beyond hope of repentance. Don't I remember when I was a boy everyone wore white stockings; I had only heard of black ones, and I always hoped to meet a lady wearing black stockings . . . now my hope is to meet one wearing white."

"We might have searched the town for a crinoline and a pair of white stockings."

"Yes, and I might have discovered a black silk stock. I wonder how I should have looked in it."

"Doris," I said, "we have missed the best part of our adventure. We forgot to dress for the part we are playing, the lovers of Orelay,"

Who will disagree with me when I say that no adventure is complete unless it necessitates an amount of ceremonial, the wearing of wigs, high bodices, stockings and breeches? Everyone likes to dress himself up, whether for a masquerade ball or to be enrolled in some strange order. Have you, reader, ever seen anyone enrolled in any of these orders? If you have, you will excuse the little comedy and believe it to be natural—the comedy that Doris and I played in the old carriage driving from Orelay to Verlancourt, where we hoped to breakfast.

We could hardly speak for excitement. Doris thought of how she would look in a crinoline, and I remembered the illustrations in an early edition of Balzac of which I am the happy possessor. How nice the men looked in the tight trousers and the black stockings of the period; and crossing my legs I followed with interest the line of my calf. Somebody did that in *Les Illusions Perdues*. She and I lay back thinking which story in "The Human Comedy" was the most applicable to our case; and the only one we could think of was when Madame Bargeton, a provincial bluestocking, left Angoulême for Paris with Lucien de Rubempré. There were no railways in the 'forties; they must have travelled in a postchaise. Yes, I remember their journey; faintly, it is true, but I remember it. Madame Bargeton was a woman of five-and-thirty at least, and Doris was much younger. Lucien was only one-and-twenty, and even at that time I was more than that. The names of these people, and of the people they met at the theatre and in the Tuileries Gardens—Rastignac, Madame D'Espard, the Duchess of Chaulieu, Madame de Rochefide and Canalis—carried my mind back from crinolines and white stockings, from peg-top trousers and braided coats to the slim trousers that were almost breeches, and to the high-breasted gowns of the Restoration. Our mothers and fathers wore the crinolines and the peg-top trousers, and our grandfathers the tight trousers and the black silk stocks. The remembrance of these costumes filled me with a tenderness and a melancholy I could not subdue, and I could see that Doris was thinking of the same subject as myself.

We were thinking of that subject which interested men before history began, the mutability of human things, the vanishing of generations. Young as she was, Doris was thinking of death; nor is it the least extraordinary she should, for as soon as anyone has reached the age of reflection the thought of death may come upon him at any moment, though he be in the middle of a ballroom, or lying in the arms of his mistress. If the scene be a ballroom he has only to look outside, and the night will remind him that in a few years he will enter the eternal night; or if the scene be a bedroom the beautiful breast of his mistress may perchance remind him of another whose breast was equally beautiful and who is now under the earth; lesser things will suffice to recall his thoughts from life to death, a rose petal falling on a marble table, a dead bird in the path as he walks in his garden. And after the thought of death the most familiar thought is the decay of the bodily vesture. The first grey hair may seem to us an amusing accident, but very few years will pass before another and yet another appear, and if these do not succeed in reminding us that decay has begun, a black speck on a tooth cannot fail to do so; and when we go to the dentist to have it stopped we have begun to repair artificially the falling structure. The activity of youth soon passes, and its slenderness. I remember still the shock I felt on hearing an athlete say that he could no longer run races of a hundred yards; he was half a second or a quarter of a second slower than he was last year. I looked at him ,saying, "But you are only one-and-twenty," and he answered, "Yes, that is it." A football player, I believe, is out of date at eight-and-twenty. Out of date! What a pathos there is in the words—out of date! *Suranné*, as the French say. How are we to render it in English? By the beautiful but artificial word "yester-year"? Yester-year perhaps, for a sorrow clings about it; it conveys a sense of autumn, of "the long decline of roses." There is something ghostlike in the out-of-date. The landscape about Plessy had transported us back into antiquity, making us dream of nymphs and dryads, but the gilt cornices and damask hangings and the salon at Orelay had made us dream of a generation ago, of the youth of our parents. Ancient conveys no personal meaning, but the out-of-date transports us, as it were, to the stern of the vessel, throws us into a mournful attitude; we lean our heads upon our hands and, looking back, we see the white wake of the vessel with shores sinking in the horizon and the crests of the mountains passing away into the clouds.

While musing on these abstract questions raised by my remark that we had not managed our adventure properly, since we had forgotten to provide ourselves with proper costumes, the present suddenly thrust itself upon me.

"Good God," I said to Doris, "let us look back, for we shall never see Orelay again!" and she from one window, and I from the other, saw the spires of Orelay for the last time. We could not tear ourselves away, but fortunately the road turned; Orelay was blotted out from our sight for ever, and we sank back to remember that a certain portion of our lives was over and done, a beautiful part of our lives had been thrown into the void, into the great rubble-heap of emotions that had been lived through, that are no more.

"Of what are you thinking, dear? You have been far away. This is the first time we have been separated, and we are not yet five miles from Orelay."

"Five miles! Ah, if it were only five!"

We did not speak for a long time, and watching the midday sun, I thought that peradventure it was not further from us than yesterday.

FF

Were I to say so to Doris she would answer, 'It will be the same in Paris,' but if she did it would be the first falsehood she had told me, for we both knew that things are never the same, things change, for better or worse, but they change.

This last sentence seems to me somewhat trite, and if I were to continue this story any further, my pen would run into many other superficial and facile observations, for my mind is no longer engrossed with the story. I no longer remember it; I do not mean that I do not remember whether we got to Verlancourt, whether we had breakfast, or whether we drove all the way to Paris with relays of horses. I am of course quite certain about the facts: we breakfasted at Verlancourt, and after breakfast we asked the coachman whether he would care to go on to Paris with us; he raised his eyes, "The carriage is a very old one, surely, Monsieur——" Doris and I laughed, for, truth to tell, we had been so abominably shaken that we were glad to exchange the picturesque old coach of our father's generation for the train.

These stories are memories, not inventions, and an account of the days I spent in Paris would interest nobody; all the details are forgotten, and invention and remembrance do not agree any better than the goat and the cabbage. So, omitting all that does not interest me— and if it does not interest me how can it interest the reader?—I will tell merely that my adventure with Doris was barren of scandal or unpleasant consequences. Her mother, a dear unsuspicious woman— whether her credulity was the depth of folly or the depth of wisdom I know not; there are many such mothers, my blessing be upon them!— took charge of her daughter, and Doris and her mother returned to England. I am afraid that when I confess that I did not speak to Doris of marriage I shall forfeit the good opinion of my reader, who will, of course, think that a love-story with such an agreeable creature as Doris merited a lifetime of devotion; but I pray the reader to discover an excuse for me in the fact that Doris had told me when we were at Plessy that there was no question of her marrying anyone but Albert. Had she not sacrificed the great love of her life in order that she might remain constant to Albert? Is it to be expected, then, that having done that, she would put Albert aside and throw her lot in with mine? She might have done this; men and women act inconsequently. Having on one occasion refused to drop the mutton chop for the shadow, on the next occasion they would drop it for the shadow of the shadow;

but Doris was made of sterner stuff, and some months afterwards she wrote me a steady sensible little letter telling me that she was going to be married, and that it seemed to her quite natural that she should marry Albert. Years have passed away, and nothing has happened to lead me to believe that she has not proved a true and loving wife. Albert has always told me that he found all the qualities in her which he had foreseen from the first time he looked upon her pretty, sparkling face. Frown not, reader, accuse me not of superficial cynicism! Albert is part of the world's inheritance. You may be Albert yourself, every-one has been or will be Albert; Albert is in us all, just as I am in you all. Doris, too, is in you, dear lady, who sit reading my book—Doris my three-days mistress at Orelay, and Doris the faithful spouse of Albert for twenty years in a lonely London suburb.

Study and boudoir would like to know if Doris had any children. About two years afterwards I heard that she was "expecting". The word came up spontaneously in my mind, perhaps because I had written it in the beginning of the story. Reader, you will remember in *Massimilla Doni* how Balzac, when he came to the last pages, declares that he dare not tell you the end of the adventure; one word, he says, will suffice for the worshippres of the ideal—Massimilla Doni was "expecting". I have not read the story for many years, but the memory of it shines in my mind bright—well, as the morning star; and I looked up this last paragraph when I began to write this story, but had to excuse myself for not translating it, my pretext being that I was baffled by certain grammatical obscurities, or what seemed to me such. I seemed to understand and to admire it all till I came to the line that "*les peuplades de cent cathédrales gothiques* (which might be rendered as the figured company of a hundred Gothic cathedrals), *tout le peuple des figures qui brisent leur forme pour venir à vous, artistes compréhensifs, toutes ces angéliques filles incorporelles accoururent autour du lit de Massimilla, et y pleurèrent!*" What puzzles me is why statues should break their forms (*forme*, I suppose, should be translated by *mould*)—break their moulds—the expression seems very inadequate—break their moulds "in order to go to you, great imaginative artists." How could they break their moulds or their forms to go to the imaginative artists, the mould or the form being the gift of the imaginative artists? I should have understood Balzac better if he had said that the statues escape from their niches and the madonnas and the angels from their frames to gather round the bed of Massimilla to weep. Balzac's idea seems to have got a little tangled, or maybe, I am stupid to-day. However, here is the passage:

"*Lés peris, les ondines, les fées, les sylphides du vieux temps, les muses de la Grèce, les vierges de marbre de la Certosa di Pavia, le Jour et la Nuit de Michel Ange, les petits anges que Bellini le premier mit au bas des tableaux d'église, et que Raphaël a faits si divinement au bas de la vierge au donataire, et de la madone qui gèle a Dresde, les délicieuses filles d'Orcagna, dans l'église de San-Michèle à Florence, les chœurs célestes du tombeau de Saint Sébald à Nuremberg, quelques vierges du Duomo de Milan, les peuplades de cent cathédrales gothiques, tout le peuple des figures qui brisent leur forme pour venir à vous, artists compréhensifs, toutes ces angéliques filles incorporelles accoururent autour du lit de Massimilla, et y pleurèrent.*"

THOMAS STURGE MOORE

Beautiful Meals

How nice it is to eat!
All creatures love it so
That they who first did spread,
Ere breaking bread,
A cloth like level snow,
Were right, I know.

And they were wise and sweet
Who, glad that meats taste good,
Used speech in an arch style,
And oft would smile
To raise the cheerful mood,
While at their food.

And those who first, so neat,
Placed knife and fork quite straight,
The glass on the right hand;
And all, as planned,
Each day set round the plate,—
Be their praise great!

For then, their hearts being light,
They plucked hedge-posies bright—
Flowers who, their scent being sweet,
Give nose and eye a treat:
'Twas they, my heart can tell,
Not eating fast but well,
Who wove the spell
Which finds me every day,
And makes each meal-time gay;
I know 'twas they.

Water

"TELL me what hath water done?"
"From highest mountains it hath run
And found a way to distant seas,
And all the time flowed on with ease,
Welcome as those who love to please."

"Say, what else hath water done?"
"It hath soared up toward the sun
And piled cloud-ranges in the air,
Shaped city, ship or white steed there—
Forms that with happiest dreams compare."

"What hath water done beside?"
"Cleansed the hands we fain would hide,
Made soiled faces fit to kiss;
And water's crowning work it is
When tear-washed hearts recapture bliss."

Adaptation from Ronsard

TIME flits away, time flits away, lady;
Alas, not time, but we
Whose childish limbs once skipped so fairily,
And still to dance are free.

Things are forgot, things are forgot, lady;
Alas, not things alone,
But dames whose sweet, sweet names chimed airily,
Are no more loved or known.

How bright those stars! and think, each bright star stays,
Though all else fair be brief;
Leisure have they and peace and length of days,
And love, 'tis my belief.

For Love gives light, Love vows his light will last.
And Love instilleth peace . . .
As lake returns the star-rays downward cast,
Be thou the Love, Love sees.

Tempio di Venere

A MARBLE ruin nigh forgotten
Fronts sheer on Naples bay;
Its cornice stones are weather-rotten,
Stained by both rain and spray.

Its steps the mounting shore has buried,
All save the topmost three,
To which small waves run up like hurried
Sly kisses of the sea.

Its fluted columns crevice-jointed
Must totter every storm.
Bird-droppings have its eaves anointed,
Blunted each moulding's form.

With pavement chequer-rich sand-whitened,
Which tell-tales flaws of wind—
With walls, that once gay pictures brightened,
Blank as an old man's mind—

For fisher's painted boat 'tis stable,
Festooned with nets and cords,
Littered with dead-eyes, ends of cable,
Crab-baskets, boat-hooks, boards.

A wreckage mast, its only rafter,
Supports an old tanned sail.
Here Venus dwelt who so loved laughter;
Here now chinks flute and wail.

Here once the pirate-Pompey's seaman
Offered her shells and gold;
Here oft, flogged slave or pious leman
Complained that hearts are sold.

No more here marble limbs shall glisten,
Nor carved face smile here more,
And, bending forward half to listen,
Prompt those who mute adore.

Yet, though he call no goddess mother,
A child bathed here to-day
Who, naked, was as Cupid's brother,
So sturdy, arch, and gay.

VINCENT O'SULLIVAN

The Lady

Now, as he listens to the purring noise
Of words she soothes to guests who linger late
When the lights pale, that they may yet rejoice
In the dear sounds which their souls perturbate:
Alas! (he thinks), must this soft satin voice
       In the death-rattle grate?

And when he feels the glamour of her laugh,
Her red mouth, and her teeth—he tries to shun
Her mocking eyes, and heedless of her chaff,
Thinks how these teeth will rot out one by one,
Under a stone which bears her epitaph,
   Far from the silver sun.

The small white hands she nurses with such care,
While bracelets and old rings their charms confirm,
Ah! lover's kisses have but little share—
But little share and for a little term,
In the atrocious meal she doth prepare:
   Food for the slimy worm.

Great God! he knows that blighting day is near,
A day he often lives in monstrous dreams,
When, in a house where servants move in fear,
And dark men come, while some wretch sobs and screams,
'Mid stifling flowers he shall stand by her bier,
   And think how old she seems.

The Hour of Ghosts

WHEN the wind blows and stirs their earth-worn faces,
Sometimes they wake and rise up from their places,
Seeking each other's looks
In sad wise;
Sad, sad they gaze at the buffeted elms,
And shew the vague dismay that overwhelms
(Scaring the crazy rooks)
Their tired eyes.

Wistfully then they try to touch each other,
Yearning for life. One murmurs: "Lo my brother,
See you in yonder field
The red kine?
They and that small white farm-house with the gable
The garden, and the brown horse in the stable,
All that and all its yield—
All was mine!

"Now as I laboured on the brightling sward
I thought that life beneath the sun was hard,
That to lie here were peace,
Sleep, and death:
In yon square barn I took a rope one morn
And hanged myself amid the amber corn,
And swung till came full cease
To my breath.

"I had a red-haired woman for my wife;
A year past, when she saw me void of life,
Her weary strangling sobs
Bewildered me:
Now behind those lit windows she delights,
While I must lie here till the end of nights
Listing to the dull throbs
Of the sea."

Thus these old ghosts make converse in their woe,
While the day thickens and bats whir and go,
And in the twilight dream
Lad and lass:
Birds droop; the drowsy church-bell toils for bed;
'Tis bed-time too for the forgotten dead,
Who in the light's last gleam
Sigh "Alas!"

STEPHEN PHILLIPS

The Apparition

My dead Love came to me, and said:
  "God gives me one hour's rest
To spend upon the earth with thee:
  How shall we spend it best?"

"Why, as of old," I said; and so
  We quarrelled as of old.
But when I turned to make my peace
  That one short hour was told.

The Question

FATHER, beneath the moonless night,
This heavy stillness without light,
There comes a thought which I must speak:
Why is my body then so weak?
Why do I falter in the race,
And flag behind this mighty pace?
Why is my strength so quickly flown?
And hark! my mother sobs alone.

My son, when I was young and free,
When I was filled with sap and glee,
I squandered here and there my strength,
And to thy mother's arms at length
Weary I came and over tired;
With fever all my bones were fired:
Therefore so soon thy strength is flown,
Therefore thy mother sobs alone.

Father, since in your weaker thought,
And in your languor I was wrought,
Put me away as creature are;
I am infirm and filled with care.
Feebly you brought me to the light,
Ah, gently hide me out of sight!
Then sooner will my strength be flown,
Nor will my mother sob alone.

My son, stir up the fire, and pass
Quickly the comfortable glass!
The infirm and evil fly in vain
Is toiling up the window pane.
Fill up, for life is so, nor sigh;
We cannot run from Destiny.
Then cheer thy strength that's quickly flown,
Ah, how thy mother sobs alone!

To a Lost Love

I CANNOT look upon thy grave,
  Though there the rose is sweet:
Better to hear the long wave wash
  These wastes about my feet!

Shall I take comfort? Dost thou live
  A spirit, though afar,
With a deep hush about thee, like
  The stillness round a star?

Oh, thou art cold! In that high sphere
  Thou art a thing apart,
Losing in saner happiness
  This madness of the heart.

And yet, at times, thou still shalt feel
  A passing breath, a pain;
Disturb'd, as though a door in heaven
  Had oped and closed again.

And thou shalt shiver, while the hymns,
  The solemn hymns shall cease;
A moment half remember me:
  Then turn away to peace.

But oh, for evermore thy look,
  Thy laugh, thy charm, thy tone,
Thy sweet and wayward earthliness,
  Dear trivial things are gone!

Therefore I look not on thy grave,
  Though there the rose is sweet;
But rather hear the loud wave wash
  These wastes about my feet.

VICTOR PLARR

Ad Cinerarium

W HO in this small urn reposes,
   Celt or Roman, man or woman,
Steel of steel, or rose of roses?

Whose is the dust set rustling slightly,
   In its hiding-place abiding,
When this urn is lifted lightly?

Sure some mourner deemed immortal
   What thou holdest and enfoldest,
Little house without a portal!

When the artificers had slowly
   Formed thee, turned thee, scaled thee, burned thee,
Freighted with thy freightage holy,

Sure he thought there's no forgetting
   All the sweetness and completeness
Of his rising, of her setting,

And so bade them grave no token,
   Generation, age, or nation,
On thy round side still unbroken—

Let them score no cypress verses,
   Funeral glories, prayers, or stories,
Mourner's tears, or mourner's curses

Round thy brown rim time hath polished—
   Left thee dumbly cold and comely
As some shrine of gods abolished.

Ah, 'twas well! It scarcely matters
   What was sleeping in the keeping
Of this house of human tatters—

Steel of steel, or rose of roses,
Man, or woman, Celt or Roman,
If but soundly he reposes!

Epitaphium Citharistrae

STAND not uttering sedately
Trite oblivious praise about her!
Rather say you saw her lately
Lightly kissing her last lover.

Whisper not, "There is a reason
Why we bring her no white blossom:"
Since the snowy bloom's in season
Strow it on her sleeping bosom:

Oh, for it would be a pity
To o'erpraise her or to flout her:
She was wild, and sweet, and witty—
Let's not say dull things about her.

M. P. SHIEL

The Race of Orven

NEVER without grief and pain could I remember the fate of Prince Zaleski—victim of a too importunate, too unfortunate Love, which the fulgor of the throne itself could not abash; exile perforce from his native land, and voluntary exile from the rest of men! Having renounced the world over which, lurid and inscrutable as a falling star, he had passed, the world quickly ceased to wonder at him; and even I, to whom more than to another, the workings of that just and passionate mind had been revealed, half forgot him in the rush of things.

But during the time that what was called the "Pharanx labyrinth" was exercising many of the heaviest brains in the land, my thought turned repeatedly to him; and even when the affair had passed from the general attention, a bright day in Spring, combined perhaps with a latent mistrust of the *dénouement* of that dark plot, drew me to his place of hermitage.

I reached the gloomy abode of my friend as the sun set. It was a vast palace of the older world standing lonely in the midst of woodland, and approached by a sombre avenue of poplars and cypresses, through which the sunlight hardly pierced. Up this I passed, and seeking out the deserted stables (which I found all too dilapidated to afford shelter) finally put up my *calèche* in the ruined sacristy of an old Dominican chapel, and turned my mare loose to browse for the night on a paddock behind the domain.

As I pushed back the open front door and entered the mansion, I could not but wonder at the saturnine fancy that had led this wayward man to select a brooding-place so desolate for the passage of his days. I regarded it as a vast tomb of Mausolus in which lay deep sepulchred how much genius, culture, brilliancy, power! The hall was constructed in the manner of a Roman *atrium*, and from the oblong pool of turgid water in the centre a troop of fat and otiose rats fled weakly squealing at my approach. I mounted by broken marble steps to the corridors running round the open space, and thence pursued my way through a mazeland of apartments—suite upon suite—along many a length of passage, up and down many stairs. Dust-clouds rose from the uncarpeted floors and choked me; incontinent Echo coughed answering *ricochets* to my footsteps in the gathering darkness, and added emphasis to the funereal gloom of the dwelling. Nowhere was there a vestige of furniture—nowhere a trace of human life.

After a long interval I came, in a remote tower of the building and near its utmost summit, to a richly-carpeted passage, from the ceiling of which three mosaic lamps shed dim violet, scarlet and pale-rose lights around. At the end I perceived two figures standing as if in silent guard on each side of a door tapestried with the python's skin. One was a post-replica in Parian marble of the nude Aphrodite of Cnidus; in the other I recognized the gigantic form of the negro Ham, the prince's only attendant, whose fierce and glistening and ebon visage broadened into a grin of intelligence as I came nearer. Nodding to him, I pushed without ceremony into Zaleski's apartment.

The room was not a large one, but lofty. Even in the semi-darkness of the very faint greenish lustre radiated from an open censer-like *lampas* of fretted gold in the centre of the domed encausted roof, a certain incongruity of barbaric gorgeousness in the furnishing filled me with amazement. The air was heavy with the scented odour of this light, and the fumes of the narcotic *cannabis sativa*—the base of the *bhang* of the Mohammedans—in which I knew it to be the habit of my friend to assuage himself. The hangings were of wine-coloured velvet, heavy, golf-fringed and embroidered at Nurshedabad. All the world knew Prince Zaleski to be a consummate *cognoscente*—a profound amateur—as well as a savant and a thinker; but I was, nevertheless, astounded at the mere multitudinousness of the curios he had contrived to crowd into the space around him. Side by side rested a palæolithic implement, a Chinese "wise man", a Gnostic gem, an amphora of Græco-Etruscan work. The general effect was a *bizarrerie* of half-weird sheen and gloom. Flemish sepulchral brasses companied strangely with runic tablets, miniature paintings, a winged bull, Tamil scriptures on lacquered leaves of the talipot, mediæval reliquaries richly gemmed, Brahmin gods. One whole side of the room was occupied by an organ whose thunder in that circumscribed place must have set all these relics of dead epochs clashing and jingling in fantastic dances. As I entered, the vaporous atmosphere was palpitating to the low, liquid tinkling of an invisible musical box. The prince reclined on a couch from which a draping of cloth-of-silver rolled torrent over the floor. Beside him, stretched in its open sarcophagus which rested on three brazen trestles, lay the mummy of an ancient Memphian, from the upper part of which the brown cerements had rotted or been rent, leaving the hideousness of the naked, grinning countenance exposed to view.

Discarding his gemmed chibouque and an old vellum reprint of Anacreon, Zaleski rose hastily and greeted me with warmth, muttering at the same time some commonplace about his "pleasure" and the "unexpectedness" of my visit. He then gave orders to Ham to prepare me a bed in one of the adjoining chambers. We passed the greater part of the night in a delightful stream of that somnolent and half-mystic talk which Prince Zaleski alone could initiate and sustain, during which he repeatedly pressed on me a concoction of Indian hemp resembling *hashish*, prepared by his own hands, and quite innocuous. It was after a simple breakfast the next morning that I entered on the subject which was partly the occasion of my visit. He lay back on his couch, volumed in a Turkish *beneesh*, and listened to me, a little wearily perhaps at first, with woven fingers, and the pale inverted eyes of old anchorites and astrologers, the moony greenish light falling on his always wan features.

"You knew Lord Pharanx?" I asked.

"I have met him in 'the world'. His son Lord Randolph, too, I saw once at Court at Peterhof, and once again at the Winter Palace of the Tsar. I noticed in their great stature, shaggy heads of hair, ears of a very peculiar conformation, and a certain aggressiveness of demeanour—a strong likeness between father and son."

I had brought with me a bundle of old newspapers, and comparing these as I went on, I proceeded to lay the incidents before him.

"The father," I said, "held, as you know, high office in a late Administration, and was one of our big luminaries in politics; he has also been President of the Council of several learned societies, and author of a book on Modern Ethics. His son was rapidly rising to eminence in the *corps diplomatique*, and lately (though, strictly speaking, *unebenbürtig*) contracted an affiance with the Prinzessin Charlotte Mariana Natalia of Morgen-Ueppigen, a lady with a strain of indubitable Hohenzollern blood in her royal veins. The Orven family is a very old and distinguished one, though—especially in modern days— far from wealthy. However, some little time after Randolph had become engaged to this royal lady, the father insured his life for immense sums in various offices both in England and America, and the reproach of poverty is now swept from the race. Six months ago, almost simultaneously, both father and son resigned their various positions *en bloc*. But all this, of course, I am telling you on the assumption that you have not already read it in the papers."

"A modern newspaper," he said, "being what it mostly is, is the one thing insupportable to me at present. Believe me, I never see one."

"Well then, Lord Pharanx, as I said, threw up his posts in the fulness of his vigour, and retired to one of his country seats. A good many years ago, he and Randolph had a terrible row over some trifle, and with the implacability that distinguishes their race, had not since exchanged a word. But some little time after the retirement of the father, a message was despatched by him to the son, who was then in India. Considered as the first step in the *rapprochement* of this proud and selfish pair of beings, it was an altogether remarkable message, and was subsequently deposed to in evidence by a telegraph official; it ran: " '*Return. The beginning of the end is come.*' Whereupon Randolph did return, and in three months from the date of his landing in England, Lord Pharanx was dead."

"*Murdered?*"

A certain something in the tone in which this word was uttered by Zaleski puzzled me. It left me uncertain whether he had addressed to me an exclamation of conviction, or a simple question. I must have looked this feeling, for he said at once:

"I could easily, from your manner, surmise as much, you know. Perhaps I might even have foretold it, years ago."

"Foretold—what? Not the murder of Lord Pharanx?"

"Something of that kind," he answered with a smile; "but proceed—tell me all the facts you know."

Word-mysteries of this sort fell frequent from the lips of the prince. I continued the narrative.

"The two, then, met and were reconciled. But it was a reconciliation without cordiality, without affection—a shaking of hands across a barrier of brass; and even this hand-shaking was a strictly metaphorical one, for they do not seem ever to have got beyond the interchange of a frigid bow. The opportunities, however, for observation were few. Soon after Randolph's arrival at Orven Hall, his father entered on a life of the most absolute seclusion. The mansion is an old three-storied one, the top floor consisting for the most part of sleeping-rooms, the first of a library, drawing-room, and so on, and the ground-floor, in addition to the dining and other ordinary rooms, of another small library, looking out (at the side of the house) on a low balcony, which, in turn, looks on a lawn dotted with flower-beds. It was this smaller library on the ground-floor that was now divested of its books, and converted into a bedroom for the earl. Hither he migrated, and here he lived, scarcely ever leaving it. Randolph, on his part, moved to a room on the first floor immediately above his. Some of the retainers of the family were dismissed, and on the remaining few fell a hush of expectancy, a sense of wonder, as to what these things boded. A great enforced quiet pervaded the building, the least undue noise in any part being sure to be followed by the angry voice of the master demanding the cause. Once, as the servants were supping

GG

in the kitchen on the side of the house most remote from that which he occupied, Lord Pharanx, slippered and in dressing-gown, appeared at the doorway, purple with rage, threatening to pack the whole company of them out of doors if they did not moderate the clatter of their knives and forks. He had always been regarded with fear in his own household, and the very sound of his voice now became a terror. His food was taken to him in the room he had made his habitation, and it was remarked that, though simple before in his gustatory tastes, he now—possibly owing to the sedentary life he led—became fastidious, insisting on *recherché* bits. I mention all these details to you—as I shall mention others—not because they have the least connection with the tragedy as it subsequently occurred, but merely because I know them, and you have requested me to state all I know."

"Yes," he answered, with a suspicion of *ennui*, "you are right. I may as well hear the whole—if I must hear a part."

"Meanwhile, Randolph appears to have visited the earl at least once a day. In such retirement did he, too, live that many of his friends still supposed him to be in India. There was only one respect in which he broke through this privacy. You know, of course, that the Orvens are, and, I believe, always have been, noted as the most obstinate, the most crabbed of Conservatives in politics. Even among the past-enamoured families of England, they stand out conspicuously in this respect. Is it credible to you, then, that Randolph should offer himself to the Radical Association of the Borough of Orven as a candidate for the next election in opposition to the sitting member? It is on record, too, that he spoke at three public meetings—reported in local papers—at which he avowed his political conversion; afterwards laid the foundation-stone of a new Baptist chapel; presided at a Methodist tea-meeting; and taking an abnormal interest in the debased condition of the labourers in the villages round, fitted up as a class-room an apartment on the top floor at Orven Hall, and gathered round him on two evenings in every week a class of yokels, whom he proceeded to cram with demonstrations in elementary mechanics."

"Mechanics!" cried Zaleski, starting upright for a moment, "mechanics to agricultural labourers! Why not elementary chemistry? Why not elementary botany? *Why* mechanics?"

This was the first evidence of interest he had shown in the story. I was pleased, but answered:

"The point is unimportant; and there really is no accounting for the vagaries of such a man. He wished, I imagine, to give some idea to the young illiterates of the simple laws of motion and force. But now I come to a new character in the drama—the chief character of all. One day a woman presented herself at Orven Hall and demanded to see its owner. She spoke English with a strong French accent. Though approaching middle life she was still beautiful, having wild black eyes, and creamy-pale face. Her dress was tawdry, cheap, and loud, showing signs of wear; her hair was unkempt; her manners were not the manners of a lady. A certain vehemence, exasperation, unrepose, distinguished all she said and did. The footman refused her admission; Lord Pharanx, he said, was invisible. She persisted violently, pushed past him, and had to be forcibly ejected; during all which the voice of the master was heard roaring from the passage red-eyed remonstrance at the unusual noise. She went away gesticulating wildly, and vowing vengeance on Lord Pharanx and all the world. It was afterwards found that she had taken up her abode in one of the neighbouring hamlets, called Lee.

"This person, who gave the name of Maude Cibras, subsequently called at the Hall three times in succession, and was each time refused admittance. It was now, however, thought advisable to inform Randolph of her visits. He said she might be permitted to see him, if she returned. This she did on the next day, and had a long interview in private with him. Her voice was heard raised as if in angry protest by one Hester Dyett, a servant of the house, while Randolph in low tones seemed to try to soothe her. The conversation was in French, and no word could be made out. She passed out at length, tossing her head jauntily, and smiling a vulgar triumph at the footman who had before opposed her ingress. She was never known to seek admission to the house again.

"But her connection with its inmates did not cease. The same Hester asserts that one night, coming home late through the park, she saw two persons conversing on a bench beneath the trees, crept behind some bushes, and discovered that they were the strange woman and Randolph. The same servant bears evidence to tracking them to other meeting-places, and to finding in the letter-bag letters addressed to Maude Cibras in Randolph's hand-writing. One of these was actually unearthed later on. Indeed, so engrossing did the intercourse become, that it seems even to have interfered with the outburst of radical zeal in the new political convert. The *rendezvous*—always held under cover of darkness, but naked and open to the eye of the watchful Hester—sometimes clashed with the science lectures, when these latter would be put off, so that they became gradually fewer, and then almost ceased."

"Your narrative becomes unexpectedly interesting," said Zaleski; "but this unearthed letter of Randolph's—what was in it?"

I read as follows:

" 'Dear Mdlle. Cibras,—I am exerting my utmost influence for you with my father. But he shows no signs of coming round as yet. If I could only induce him to see you! But he is, as you know, a person of unrelenting will, and meanwhile you must confide in my loyal efforts on your behalf. At the same time, I admit that the situation is a precarious one: you are, I am sure, well provided for in the present will of Lord Pharanx, but he is on the point—within, say, three or four days—of making another; and exasperated as he is at your appearance in England, I know there is no chance of your receiving a *centime* under the new will. Before then, however, we must hope that something favourable to you may happen; and in the meantime, let me implore you not to let your only too just resentment pass beyond the bounds of reason.

" 'Sincerely yours,

" 'Randolph.' "

"I like the letter!" cried Zaleski. "You notice the tone of manly candour. But the *facts*—were they true? *Did* the earl make a new will in the time specified?"

"No—but that may have been because his death intervened."

"And in the old will, *was* Mdlle Cibras provided for?"

"Yes—that at least was correct."

A shadow of pain passed over his face.

"And now," I went on, "I come to the closing scene, in which one of England's foremost men perished by the act of an obscure assassin. The letter I have read was written to Maude Cibras on the 5th of January. The next thing that happens is on the 6th, when Lord Pharanx left his room for another during the whole day, and a skilled mechanic was introduced into it for the purpose of effecting some alterations. Asked by Hester Dyett, as he was leaving the house, what was the nature of his operations, the man replied that he had been applying a patent arrangement to the window looking out on the balcony, for the better protection of the room against burglars, several robberies having recently been committed in the neighbourhood. The sudden death of this man, however, before the occurrence of the tragedy, prevented his evidence being heard. On the next day—the 7th—Hester, entering the room with Lord Pharanx's dinner, fancies, though she cannot tell why (inasmuch as his back is towards her, he sitting in an arm-chair by the fire), that Lord Pharanx has been 'drinking heavily'.

"On the 8th a singular thing befell. The earl was at last induced to see Maude Cibras, and during the morning of that day, with his own hand, wrote a note informing her of his decision, Randolph handing the note to a messenger. That note also has been made public. It reads as follows:

"'MAUDE CIBRAS,—You may come here to-night after dark. Walk to the south side of the house, come up the steps to the balcony, and pass in through the open window to my room. Remember, however, that you have nothing to expect from me, and that from to-night I blot you eternally from my mind: but I will hear your story, which I know beforehand to be false. Destroy this note.

PHARANX.'"

As I progressed with my tale, I came to notice that over the countenance of Prince Zaleski there grew little by little a singular fixed aspect. His small, keen features distorted themselves into an expression of what I can only describe as an abnormal *inquisitiveness*—an inquisitiveness most impatient, arrogant, in its intensity. His pupils, contracted each to a dot, became the central *puncta* of two rings of fiery light; his little sharp teeth seemed to gnash. Once before I had seen him look thus greedily, when, grasping a Troglodyte tablet covered with half-effaced hieroglyphics—his fingers livid with the fixity of his grip—he bent on it that strenuous inquisition, that ardent questioning gaze, till, by a species of mesmeric dominancy, he seemed to wrench from it the arcanum it hid from other eyes; then he lay back, pale and faint from the too arduous victory.

When I had read Lord Pharanx's letter, he took the paper eagerly from my hand and ran his eyes over the passage.

"Tell me—the end," he said.

"Maude Cibras," I went on, "thus invited to a meeting with the earl failed to make her appearance at the appointed time. It happened that she had left her lodgings in the village early that very morning, and for some purpose or other had travelled to the town of Bath. Randolph, too, went away the same day in the opposite direction, to Plymouth. He returned on the following morning, the 9th; soon after walked over to Lee, and entered into conversation with the keeper of the inn where Cibras lodged; asked if she was at home, and on being told that she had gone away, asked further if she had taken her luggage with her; was informed that she had, and had also announced her intention of at once leaving England. He then walked away in the direction of the Hall. On this day Hester Dyett noticed that there were many articles of value scattered about the earl's room, notably a tiara of old Brazilian brilliants, sometimes worn by the late Lady Pharanx. Randolph—who was present at the time—further drew her attention to these by telling her that Lord Pharanx had chosen to bring together in his apartment many of the family jewels; and she was instructed to tell the other servants of this fact, in case they should notice any suspicious-looking loafers about the estate.

"On the 10th, both father and son remained in their rooms all day, except when the latter came down to meals; at which times he would lock his door behind him, and with his own hands take in the earl's food, giving as his reason that his father was writing a very important document, and did not wish to be disturbed by the presence of a servant. During the forenoon, Hester Dyett, hearing loud noises in Randolph's room, as if furniture was being removed from place to place, found some pretext for knocking at his door, when he ordered her on no account to interrupt him again, as he was busy packing his clothes in view of a journey to London on the next day. The subsequent conduct of the woman shows that her curiosity must have been excited to the utmost by the undoubtedly strange spectacle of Randolph packing his own clothes. During the afternoon a lad from the village was instructed to collect his companions for a science lecture the same evening at eight o'clock. And so the eventful day wore on.

"We arrive now at this hour of eight p.m. on this 10th day of

January. The night is dark and windy; some snow has been falling, but has now ceased. In an upper room is Randolph engaged in expounding the elements of dynamics; in the room under that is Hester Dyett—for Hester has somehow obtained a key that opens the door of Randolph's room, and takes advantage of his absence upstairs to explore it. Under her is Lord Pharanx, certainly in bed, probably asleep. Hester, trembling all over in a fever of fear and excitement, holds a lighted taper in one hand, which she religiously shades with the other; for the storm is gusty, and the gusts, tearing through the crevices of the rattling old casements, toss great flickering shadows on the hangings, which frighten her to death. She has just time to see that the whole room is in the wildest confusion, when suddenly a rougher puff blows out the flame, and she is left in what to her, standing as she was on that forbidden ground, must have been a horror of darkness. At the same moment, clear and sharp from right beneath her, a pistol-shot rings out on her ear. For an instant she stands in stone, incapable of motion. Then on her dazed senses there supervenes—so she swore—the consciousness that some object is moving in the room—moving apparently of its own accord—moving in direct opposition to all the laws of nature as she knows them. She imagines that she perceives a phantasm —a strange something—globular-white—looking, as she says, 'like a good-sized ball of cotton'—rise directly from the floor before her, ascending slowly upward, as if driven aloft by some invisible force. A sharp shock of the sense of the supernatural deprives her of ordered reason. Throwing forward her arms, and uttering a shrill scream, she rushes towards the door. But she never reaches it: midway she falls prostrate over some object, and knows no more; and when, an hour later, she is borne out of the room in the arms of Randolph himself, the blood is dripping from a fracture of her right tibia.

"Meanwhile, in the upper chamber the pistol-shot and the scream of the woman have been heard. All eyes turn to Randolph. He stands in the shadow of the mechanical contrivance on which he has been illustrating his points; leans for support on it. He essays to speak, the muscles of his face work, but no sound comes. Only after a time is he able to gasp: 'Did you hear something—from below?' They answer 'yes' in chorus; then one of the lads takes a lighted candle, and together they troop out, Randolph behind them. A terrified servant rushes up with the news that something dreadful has happened in the house.

They proceed for some distance, but there is an open window on the stairs, and the light is blown out. They have to wait some minutes till another is obtained, and then the procession moves forward once more. Arrived at Lord Pharanx's door, and finding it locked, a lantern is procured, and Randolph leads them through the house and out on the lawn. But having nearly reached the balcony, a lad observed a track of small woman's-feet in the snow; a halt is called, and then Randolph points out another track of feet, half obliterated by the snow, extending from a coppice close by up to the balcony, and forming an angle with the first track. These latter are great big feet, made by ponderous labourers' boots. He holds the lantern over the flower-beds, and shows how they have been trampled down. Someone finds a common scarf, such as workmen wear; and a ring and a locket, dropped by the burglars in their flight, are also found by Randolph half buried in the snow. And now the foremost reach the window. Randolph, from behind, calls to them to enter. They cry back that they cannot, the window being closed. At this reply he seems to be overcome by surprise, by terror. Someone hears him murmur the words, 'My God, what can have happened now?' His horror is increased when one of the lads bears to him a revolting trophy, which has been found just outside the window; it is the front phalanges of three fingers of a human hand. Again he utters the agonized moan, 'My God!' and then, mastering his agitation, makes for the window, he finds that the catch of the sash has been roughly wrenched off, and that the sash can be opened by merely pushing it up: does so, and enters. The room is in darkness: on the floor under the window is found the insensible body of the woman Cibras. She is alive, but has fainted. Her right fingers are closed round the handle of a large bowie-knife, which is covered with blood; parts of the left are missing. All the jewelry has been stolen from the room. Lord Pharanx lies on the bed, stabbed through the bedclothes to the heart. Later on a bullet is also found imbedded in his brain. I should explain that a trenchant edge, running along the bottom of the sash, was the obvious means by which the fingers of Cibras had been cut off. This had been placed there a few days before by the workman I spoke off. Several secret springs had been placed on the inner side of the lower horizontal piece of the window-frame, by pressing any one of which the sash was lowered; so that no one, ignorant of the secret, could pass out from within, without resting the hand on one of these springs, and so bringing down the armed sash suddenly on the underlying hand.

"There was, of course, a trial. The poor culprit, in mortal terror of death, shrieked out a confession of the murder just as the jury had returned from their brief consultation, and before they had time to pronounce their verdict of 'guilty'. But she denied shooting Lord Pharanx, and she denied stealing the jewels; and indeed no pistol and no jewels were found on her, or anywhere in the room. So that many points remain mysterious. What part did the burglars play in the tragedy? Were they in collusion with Cibras? Had the strange behaviour of at least one of the inmates of Orven Hall no hidden significance? The wildest guesses were made throughout the country; theories propounded. But no theory explained *all* the points. The ferment, however, has now subsided. To-morrow morning Maude Cibras ends her life on the gallows."

Thus I ended my narrative.

Without a word Zaleski rose from the couch, and walked to the organ. Assisted from behind by Ham, who foreknew his master's every whim, he proceeded to render with infinite feeling an air from the *Lakmé* of Delibes; long he sat, dreamily uttering the melody, his head sunken on his breast. When at last he rose, his great expanse of brow was clear, and a smile all but solemn in its serenity was on his lips. He walked up to an ivory *escritoire*, scribbled a few words on a sheet of paper, and handed it to the negro with the order to take my trap and drive with the message in all haste to the nearest telegraph office.

"That message," he said, resuming his place on the couch, "is a last word on the tragedy, and will, no doubt, produce some modification in the final stage of its history. And now, Shiel, let us sit together and confer on this matter. From the manner in which you have expressed yourself, it is evident that there are points which puzzle you—you do not get a clean *coup d'œil* of the whole regiments of facts, and their causes, and their consequences, as they occurred. Let us see if out of that confusion we cannot produce a coherence, a symmetry. A great wrong is done, and on the society in which it is done is imposed the task of making it translucent, of *seeing* it in all its relations, and of punishing it. But what happens? The society fails to rise to the occasion; on the whole, it contrives to make the opacity more opaque, does not see the crime in any human sense; is unable to punish it. Now this, you will admit, whenever it occurs, is a woeful failure: woeful I mean, not very in itself, but very in its significance: and there must be a precise cause for it. That cause is the lack of something not merely, or specially, in the investigators of the wrong, but in the world at large —shall we not boldly call it the lack of culture? Do not, however, misunderstand me: by the term I mean not so much attainment in general, as *mood* in particular. Whether or when such mood may become universal may be to you a matter of doubt. As for me, I often think that when the era of civilization begins—as assuredly it shall some day begin—when the races of the world cease to be credulous, ovine mobs and become critical, human nations, then will be the ushering in of the ten thousand years of a *clairvoyant* culture. But nowhere, and at no time during the very few hundreds of years that man has occupied the earth, has there been one single sign of its presence. In individuals, yes—in the Greek Plato, and I think in your English Milton and Bishop Berkeley—but in humanity, never, and hardly in any individual outside those two nations. The reason, I fancy, is not so much that man is a hopeless fool, as that Time, so far as he is concerned, has, as we know, only just begun: it being, of course, conceivable that the creation of a perfect society of men, as the first requisite to a *régime* of culture, must nick to itself a longer loop of time than the making of, say, a stratum of coal. A loquacious person—he is one of your cherished 'novel' writers, by the way, if that be indeed a Novel in which there is nowhere any pretence at novelty—once assured me that he could never reflect without swelling on the greatness of the age in which he lived, an age the mighty civilization of which he likened to the Augustan and Periclean. A certain stony gaze of anthropological interest with which I regarded his frontal bone seemed to strike the poor man dumb, and he took a hurried departure. Could he have been ignorant that ours is, in general, greater than the Periclean for the *very* reason that the Divinity is neither the devil nor a bungler; that three thousand years of human consciousness is not nothing; that a whole is greater than its part, and a butterfly than a chrysalis? But it was the assumption that it was therefore in any way great in the abstract that occasioned my profound astonishment, and indeed contempt. Civilization, if it means anything, can only mean the art by which men live musically together—to the lutings, as it were, of Pan-

pipes, or say perhaps, to triumphant organ-bursts of martial, marching
dithyrambs. Any formula defining it as 'the art of lying back and
getting elaborately tickled', should surely at this hour be *too* primitive—
too Opic—to bring anything but a smile to the lips of grown white-
skinned men; and the very fact that such a definition can still find
undoubting acceptance in all quarters may be an indication that the
true ἰδέα which this condition of being must finally assume is far
indeed—far, perhaps, by ages and æons—from becoming part of the
general conception. Nowhere since the beginning has the gross problem of living ever so much as approached solution, much less the
delicate and intricate one of living *together*: *à propos* of which your
body corporate not only still produces criminals (as the body-natural
fleas), but its very elementary organism cannot so much as catch a
really athletic one as yet. Meanwhile *you* and *I* are handicapped. The
individual travaileth in pain. In the struggle for quality, powers, air,
he spends his strength, and yet hardly escapes asphyxiation. He can no
more wriggle himself free of the psychic gravitations that invest him
than the earth can shake herself loose of the sun, or he of the omni-
potences that rivet him to the universe. If by chance one shoots a
downy hint of wings, an instant feeling of contrast puffs him with self-
consciousness: a tragedy at once: the unconscious being 'the alone
complete'. To attain to anything, he must needs screw the head up
into the atmosphere of the future, while feet and hands drip dark
ichors of despair from the crucifying cross of the crude present—*a
horrid strain!* Far up a nightly instigation of stars he sees: but he
may not strike them with the head. If earth were a boat, and mine, I
know well toward what wild azimuths I would compel her helm: but
gravity, gravity—chiefest curse of Eden's sin!—is hostile. When indeed
(as is ordained), the old mother swings herself into a sublimer orbit, we
on her back will follow: till then we make to ourselves Icarian 'organa'
in vain. I mean to say that it is the plane of station which is at fault:
move that upward, you move all. But meantime is it not Goethe who
assures us that 'further reacheth no man, make he what stretching he
will'? For Man, you perceive, is not many, but One. It is absurd
to suppose that England can be free while Poland is enslaved; Paris is
far from the beginnings of civilization whilst Toobooloo and Chicago
are barbaric. Probably no ill-fated, microcephalous son of Adam ever
tumbled into a mistake quite so huge, so infantile, as did Dives, if he

imagined himself rich while Lazarus sat pauper at the gate. Not many, I say, but one. Even Ham and I here in our retreat are not alone; we are embarrassed by the uninvited spirit of the present; the adamant root of the mountain on whose summit we stand is based ineradicably in the low world. Yet, thank Heaven, Goethe was not *quite* right— as, indeed, he proved in his proper person. I tell you, Shiel, I *know* whether Mary did or did not murder Darnley; I know—as clearly, as precisely, as a man can know—that Beatrice Cenci was not 'guilty' as certain recently-discovered documents 'prove' her, but that the Shelley version of the affair, though a guess, is the correct one. It *is* possible, by taking thought, to add one cubit—or say a hand, or a dactyl—to your stature; you *may* develop powers slightly—very slightly, but distinctly, both in kind and degree—in advance of those of the mass who live in or about the same cycle of time in which you live. But it is only when the powers to which I refer are shared by the mass—when what, for want of another term, I call the age of the Cultured Mood has at length arrived—that their exercise will become easy and familiar to the individual; and who shall say what presciences, prisms, *séances*, what introspective craft, Genie apocalypses, shall not *then* become possible to the few who stand spiritually in the van of men.

"All this, you will understand, I say as some sort of excuse for myself, and for you, for any hesitation we may have shown in loosening the very little puzzle you have placed before me—one which we certainly must not regard as difficult of solution. Of course, looking at all the facts, the first consideration that must inevitably rivet the attention is that arising from the circumstance that Viscount Randolph has strong reasons to wish his father dead. They are avowed enemies; he is the *fiancé* of a princess whose husband he is probably too poor to become, though he will very likely be rich enough when his father dies; and so on. All that appears on the surface. On the other hand, we— you and I—know the man: he is a person of gentle blood, as moral, we suppose, as ordinary people, occupying a high station in the world. It is impossible to imagine that such a person would commit an assassin- ation, or even countenance one, for any or all of the reasons that present themselves. In our hearts, with or without clear proof, we could hardly believe it of him. Earls' sons do not, in fact, go about murdering people. Unless, then, we can so reason as to discover other motives —strong, adequate, irresistible—and by 'irresistible' I mean a motive which must be *far* stronger than even the love of life itself—we should, I think, in fairness dismiss him from our mind.

"And yet it must be admitted that his conduct is not free of blame. He contracts a sudden intimacy with the acknowledged culprit, whom he does not seem to have known before. He meets her by night, corresponds with her. Who and what is this woman? I think we could not be far wrong in guessing some very old flame of Lord Pharanx's of *Théâtre des Variétés* type, whom he has supported for years, and from whom, hearing some story to her discredit, he threatens to withdraw his supplies. However that be, Randolph writes to Cibras—a violent woman, a woman of lawless passions—assuring her that in four or five days she will be excluded from the will of his father; and in four or five days Cibras plunges a knife into his father's bosom. It is a perfectly natural sequence—though, of course, the *intention* to produce by his words the actual effect produced might have been absent; indeed, the letter of Lord Pharanx himself, had it been received, would have tended to produce that very effect; for it not only gives an excellent opportunity for converting into action those evil thoughts which Randolph (thoughtlessly or guiltily) had instilled, but it further tends to rouse her passions by cutting off from her all hopes of favour. If we presume, then, as is only natural, that there was no such intention on the part of the earl, we *may* make the same presumption in the case of the son. Cibras, however, never receives the earl's letter: on the morning of the same day she goes away to Bath, with the double object, I suppose, of purchasing a weapon, and creating an impression that she has left the country. How then does she know the exact *locale* of Lord Pharanx's room? It is in an unusual part of the mansion, she is unacquainted with any of the servants, a stranger to the district. Can it be possible that Randolph *had told her*? And here again, even in that case, you must bear in mind that Lord Pharanx also told her in his note, and you must recognize the possibility of the absence of evil intention on the part of the son. Indeed, I may go further and show you that in all but every instance in which his actions are in themselves *outré*, suspicious, they are rendered, not less *outré*, but less suspicious, by the fact that Lord Pharanx himself knew of them, shared in them. There was the cruel barbing of that balcony window; about it the crudest thinker would argue thus to himself: 'Randolph practically incites Maude Cibras to murder his father on the 5th, and on the 6th he has that window so altered in order that, should she act on his suggestion, she will be caught on attempting to leave the room, while he himself, the actual culprit being discovered *en flagrant délit*, will escape every shadow of suspicion.' But on the other hand we know that the alteration was made with Lord Pharanx's consent most likely on his initiative—for he leaves his favoured room during a whole day for that very purpose. So with the letter to Cibras on the 8th—Randolph despatches it, but the earl writes it. So with the disposal of the jewels in the apartment on the 9th. There had been some burglaries in the neighbourhood, and the suspicion at once arises in the mind of the crude reasoner: Could Randolph—finding now that Cibras has 'left the country', that, in fact, the tool he had expected to serve his ends has failed him—could he have thus brought those jewels there, and thus warned the servants of their presence, in the hope that the intelligence might so get abroad and lead to a burglary, in the course of which his father might lose his life? There are evidences, you know, tending to show that the burglary did actually at last take place, and the suspicion, is, in view of that, by no means unreasonable. And yet, militating against it, is our knowledge that it was Lord Pharanx who '*chose*' to gather the jewels round him; that it was in his presence that Randolph drew the attention of the servant to them. In the matter, at least, of the little political comedy the son seems to have acted alone; but you surely cannot rid yourself of the impression that the radical speeches, the candidature, and the rest of it, formed all of them only a very elaborate, and withal clumsy, set of preliminaries to the *class*. Anything, to make the perspective, the sequence of *that* seem natural. But in the class, at any rate, we have the tacit acquiescence, or even the co-operation of Lord Pharanx. You have described the conspiracy of quiet which, for some reason or other, was imposed on the household; in that reign of silence the bang of a door, the fall of a plate, becomes a domestic tornado. But have you ever heard an agricultural labourer in clogs or heavy boots ascend a stair? The noise is terrible. The tramp of an army of them through the house and overhead, probably jabbering uncouthly together, would be insufferable. Yet Lord Pharanx seems to have made no objection; the novel institution is set up in his own mansion, in an unusual part of it, probably against his own principles; but we hear of no murmur from him. On the fatal day, too, the calm of the house is rudely broken by a considerable commotion in Randolph's room just overhead, caused by his preparation for 'a journey to London'. But the usual angry remonstrance is not forthcoming from the master. And do you not see how all this more than acquiescence of Lord Pharanx in the conduct of his son deprives that conduct of half its significance, its intrinsic suspiciousness?

"A hasty reasoner then would inevitably jump to the conclusion that Randolph was guilty of something—some evil intention—though of precisely what he would remain in doubt. But a more careful reasoner would pause: he would reflect that *as* the father was implicated in those acts, and *as* he was innocent of any such intention, so might possibly, even probably, be the son. This, I take it, has been the view of the officials, whose logic is probably far in advance of their imagination. But supposing we can adduce one act, undoubtedly actuated by evil intention on the part of Randolph—one act in which his father certainly did *not* participate—what follows next? Why, that we revert at once to the view of the hasty reasoner, and conclude that *all* the other acts in the same relation were actuated by the same evil motive; and having reached that point, we shall be unable longer to resist the conclusion that those of them in which his father had a share *might* have sprung from a like motive in *his* mind also; nor should the mere obvious impossibility of such a condition of things have even the very least influence on us, as thinkers, in causing us to close our mind against its logical possibility. I therefore make the inference, and pass on.

"Let us then see if we can by searching find out any absolutely certain deviation from right on the part of Randolph, in which we may be quite sure that his father was not an abettor. At eight on the night on the murder it is dark; there has been some snow, but the fall has ceased—how long before I know not, but so long that the interval becomes sufficiently appreciable to cause remark. Now the party going round the house come on two tracks of feet meeting at an angle. Of one track we are merely told that it was made by the small foot of a woman, and of it we know no more; of the other we learn that the feet were big and the boots clumsy, and, it is added, the marks were *half obliterated by the snow.* Two things then are clear: that the persons who made them came from different directions, and probably made them at different times. That, alone, by the way, may be a sufficient answer to your question as to whether Cibras was in collusion with the 'burglars'. But how does Randolph behave with reference to these tracks? Though he carries the lantern, he fails to perceive the first— the woman's—the discovery of which is made by a lad; but the second, half hidden in the snow, he notices readily enough, and at once points it out. He explains that burglars have been on the warpath. But examine his horror of surprise when he hears that the window is closed; when he sees the woman's bleeding fingers. He cannot help exclaiming, 'My God! what has happened *now*?' But why 'now'? The word cannot refer to his father's death, for that he knew, or guessed, before-hand, having heard the shot. Is it not rather the exclamation of a man whose schemes destiny has complicated? Besides, he should have *expected* to find the window closed: no one except himself, Lord Pharanx, and the workman, who was now dead, knew the secret of its construction; the burglars therefore, having entered and robbed the room, one of them, intending to go out, would press on the ledge, and the sash would fall on his hand with what result we know. The others would then either break the glass and so escape; or pass through the house; or remain prisoners. That immoderate surprise was therefore absurdly illogical, after seeing the burglar-track in the snow. But how, above all, do you account for Lord Pharanx's silence during and after the burglars' visit—if there was a visit? He was, you must remember, alive all that time; *they* did not kill him; certainly they did not shoot him, for the shot is heard after the snow has ceased to fall—that is, after, long after, they have left, since it was the falling snow that had half obliterated their tracks; nor did they stab him, for to this Cibras confesses. Why then, being alive, and not gagged, did he give no token of the presence of his visitors? There were in fact no burglars at Orven Hall that night."

"But the track!" I cried, "the jewels found in the snow—the neckerchief!"

Zaleski smiled.

"Burglars," he said, "are plain, honest folk who have a just notion of the value of jewelry when they see it. They very properly regard it as mere foolish waste to drop precious stones about in the snow, and would refuse to company with a man weak enough to let fall his necker-chief on a cold night. The whole business of the burglars was a particu-larly inartistic trick, unworthy of its author. The mere facility with which Randolph discovered the buried jewels by the aid of a dim lantern, should have served as a hint to an educated police not afraid of facing the improbable. The jewels had been *put* there with the object of throwing suspicion on the imaginary burglars; with the same design the catch of the window had been wrenched off, the sash purposely left open, the track made, the valuables taken from Lord Pharanx's room. All this was deliberately done by someone—would it be rash to say at once by whom?

"Our suspicions having now lost their whole character of vagueness, and begun to lead us in a perfectly definite direction, let us examine the statements of Hester Dyett. Now, it is immediately comprehensible to me that the evidence of this woman at the public examinations was looked at askance. There can be no doubt that she is a poor specimen of humanity, an undesirable servant, a peering, hysterical caricature of a woman. Her statements, if formally recorded, were not believed; or if believed, were believed with only half the mind. No attempt was made to deduce anything from them. But for my part, if I wanted specially reliable evidence as to any matter of fact, it is precisely from such a being that I would seek it. Let me draw you a picture of that class of intellect. They have a greed for information, but the information, to satisfy them, must relate to actualities; they have no sympathy with fiction; it is from their impatience of what seems to be that springs their curiosity of what *is*. Clio is their muse, and she alone. Their whole lust is to gather knowledge through a hole, their whole faculty is to *peep*. But they are destitute of imagination, and do not lie; in their passion for realities they would esteem it a sacrilege to distort history. They make straight for the substantial, the indubitable. For this reason the Peniculi and Ergasili of Plautus seem to me far more true to nature than the character of Paul Pry in Jerrold's comedy. In one instance, indeed, the evidence of Hester Dyett appears, on the surface of it, to be quite false. She declares that she sees a round white object moving upward in the room. But the night being gloomy, her taper having gone out, she must have been standing in a dense darkness. How then could she see this object? Her evidence, it was argued, must be designedly false, or else (as she was in an ecstatic condition) the result of an excited fancy. But I have stated that such persons, nervous, neurotic even as they may be, are not fanciful. I therefore accept her evidence as true. And now, mark the consequence of that acceptance. I am driven to admit that there

HH

must, from some source, have been light in the room—a light faint
enough, and diffused enough, to escape the notice of Hester herself.
This being so, it must have proceeded from around, from below, or
from above. There are no other alternatives. Around these was
nothing but the darkness of the night; the room beneath, we know, was
also in darkness. The light then came from the room above—from the
mechanic class-room. But there is only one possible means by which
the light from an upper can diffuse a lower room. It *must* be by a hole
in the intermediate boards. We are thus driven to the discovery of an
aperture of some sort in the flooring of that upper chamber. Given this,
the mystery of the round white object 'driven' upward disappears. We
at once ask, why not *drawn* upward through the newly-discovered
aperture by a string too small to be visible in the gloom? Assuredly it
was drawn upward. And now having established a hole in the ceiling
of the room in which Hester stands, is it unreasonable—even without
further evidence—to suspect another in the flooring? But we actually
have this further evidence. As she rushes to the door she falls, faints,
and fractures the lower part of her leg. Had she fallen *over* some object,
as you supposed, the result might have been a fracture also, but in a
different part of the body; being where it was, it could only have been
caused by placing the foot inadvertently in a hole while the rest of the
body was in rapid motion. But this gives us an approximate idea of the
size of the lower hole; it was at least big enough to admit the foot and
lower leg, big enough therefore to admit that 'good-sized ball of cotton'
of which the woman speaks: and from the lower we are able to conjecture the size of the upper. But how comes it that these holes are
nowhere mentioned in the evidence? It can only be because no one
ever saw them. Yet the rooms must have been examined by the police,
who, if they existed, must have seen them. They therefore did not
exist: that is to say, the pieces which had been removed from the floorings had by that time been neatly replaced, and, in the case of the lower
one, covered by the carpet, the removal of which had caused so much
commotion in Randolph's room on the fatal day. Hester Dyett would
have been able to notice and bring at least one of the apertures forward
in evidence, but she fainted before she had time to find out the cause of
her fall, and an hour later it was, you remember, Randolph himself
who bore her from the room. But should not the aperture in the top
floor have been observed by the class? Undoubtedly, if its position was

in the open space in the middle of the room. But it was not observed, and therefore its position was not there, but in the only other place left—behind the apparatus used in demonstration. That then was *one* useful object which the apparatus—and with it the elaborate hypocrisy of class, and speeches, and candidature—served: it was made to act as a curtain, a screen. But had it no other purpose? That question we may answer when we know its name and its nature. And it is not beyond our powers to conjecture this with something like certainty. For the only 'machines' possible to use in illustration of simple mechanics are the screw, the wedge, the scale, the lever, the wheel-and-axle, and Atwood's machine. The mathematical principles which any of these exemplify would, of course, be incomprehensible to such a class, but the first five most of all, and as there would naturally be some slight pretence of trying to make the learners understand, I therefore select the last; and this selection is justified when we remember that on the shot being heard, Randolph leans for support on the 'machine', and stands in its shadow; but any of the others would be too small to throw any appreciable shadow, except one—the wheel-and-axle—and that one would hardly afford support to a tall man in the erect position. The Atwood's machine is therefore forced on us; as to its construction, it is, as you are aware, composed of two upright posts, with a cross-bar fitted with pulleys and strings, and is intended to show the motion of bodies acting under a constant force—the force of gravity, to wit. But now consider all the really glorious uses to which those same pulleys may be turned in lowering and lifting unobserved that 'ball of cotton' through the two apertures, while the other strings with the weights attached are dangling before the dull eyes of the peasants. I need only point out that when the whole company trooped out of the room, Randolph was the last to leave it, and it is not not difficult to conjecture why.

"Of what, then, have we convicted Randolph? For one thing, we have shown that by marks of feet in the snow preparation was made beforehand for obscuring the cause of the earl's death. That death must therefore have been at least expected, foreknown. Thus we convict him of expecting it. And then, by an independent line of deduction, we can also discover the *means* by which he expected it to occur. It is clear that he did not expect it to occur when it did by the hand of Maude Cibras—for this is proved by his knowledge that she had left the neighbourhood, by his evidently genuine astonishment at the sight of the closed window, and, above all, by his truly morbid desire to establish a substantial, an irrefutable *alibi* for himself by going to Plymouth on the day when there was every reason to suppose she would do the deed—that is, on the 8th, the day of the earl's invitation. On the fatal night, indeed, the same morbid eagerness to build up a clear *alibi* is observable, for he surrounds himself with a cloud of witnesses in the upper chamber. But that, you will admit, is not nearly so perfect a one as a journey, say, to Plymouth would have been. Why then, expecting the death, did he not take some such journey? Obviously because on *this* occasion his personal presence was necessary. When, *in conjunction* with this, we recall the fact that during the intrigues with Cibras the lectures were discontinued, and again resumed immediately on her unlooked-for departure, we arrive at the conclusion that the means by which Lord Pharanx's death was expected to occur was the personal presence of Randolph *in conjunction* with the political speeches, the candidature, the class, the apparatus.

"But though he stands condemned of fore-knowing, and being in some sort connected with his father's death, I can nowhere find any indication of his having personally accomplished it, or even of his ever having had any such intention. The evidence is evidence of complicity —and nothing more. And yet—and yet—even of *this* we began by acquitting him unless we could discover, as I said, some strong, adequate, altogether irresistible motive for such complicity. Failing this, we ought to admit that at some point our argument has played us false, and led us into conclusions wholly at variance with our certain knowledge of the principles underlying human conduct in general. Let us therefore seek for such a motive—something deeper than personal enmity, stronger than personal ambition, *than the love of life itself!* And now, tell me, at the time of the occurrence of this mystery, was the whole past history of the House of Orven fully investigated?"

"Not to my knowledge," I answered; "in the papers there were, of course, sketches of the earl's career, but that I think was all."

"Yet it cannot be that their past was unknown, but only that it was ignored. Long, I tell you, long and often, have I pondered on that history, and sought to trace with what ghastly secret has been pregnant the destiny, gloomful as Erebus and the murk of black-peplosed Nux, which for centuries has hung its pall over the men of this ill-fated house.

Now at last I know. Dark, dark, and red with gore and horror is that history; down the silent corridors of the ages have these blood-soaked sons of Atreus fled shrieking before the pursuing talons of the dread Eumenides. The first earl received his patent in 1535 from the eighth Henry. Two years later, though noted as a rabid 'king's man', he joined the Pilgrimage of Grace against his master, and was soon after executed, with Darcy and some other lords. His age was then fifty. His son, meantime, had served in the king's army under Norfolk. It is remarkable, by the way, that females have all along been rare in the family, and that in no instance has there been more than one son. The second earl, under the sixth Edward, suddenly threw up a civil post, hastened to the army, and fell at the age of forty at the battle of Pinkie in 1547. He was accompanied by his son. The third in 1557, under Mary, renounced the Catholic faith, to which, both before and since, the family have passionately clung, and suffered (at the age of forty) the last penalty. The fourth earl died naturally, but suddenly, in his bed at the age of fifty during the winter of 1566. At midnight *of the same day* he was laid in the grave by his son. This son was later on, in 1591, seen by *his* son to fall from a lofty balcony at Orven Hall, while walking in his sleep at high noonday. Then for some time nothing happens; but the eighth earl dies mysteriously in 1651 at the age of forty-five. A fire occurring in his room, he leapt from a window to escape the flames. Some of his limbs were thereby fractured, but he was in a fair way to recovery when there was a sudden relapse, soon ending in death. He was found to have been poisoned by *radix aconiti indica*, a rare Arabian poison not known in Europe at that time except to *savants*, and first mentioned by Acosta some months before. An attendant was accused and tried, but acquitted. The then son of the House was a Fellow of the newly-founded Royal Society, and author of a now-forgotten work on Toxicology, which, however, I have read. No suspicion, of course, fell on *him*."

As Zaleski proceed with this retrospect, I could not but ask myself with stirrings of the most genuine wonder, whether he could possess this intimate knowledge of *all* the great families of Europe! It was as if he had spent a part of his life in making special study of the history of the Orvens.

"In the same manner," he went on, "I could detail the annals of the family from that time to the present. But all through they have been marked by the same latent tragic elements; and I have said enough to show you that in each of the tragedies there was invariably something large, leering, something of which the mind demands explanation, but seeks in vain to find it. Now we need no longer seek. Destiny did not design that the last Lord of Orven should any more hide from the world the guilty secret of his race. It was the will of the gods—and he betrayed himself. 'Return,' he writes, 'the beginning of the end is come.' What end? *The* end—perfectly well known to Randolph, needing no explanation for *him*. The old, old end, which in the ancient dim time led the first lord, loyal still at heart, to forsake his king; and another, still devout, to renounce his cherished faith, and yet another to set fire to the home of his ancestors. You have called the two last scions of the family 'a proud and selfish pair of beings'; proud they were, and selfish too, but you are in error if you think their selfishness a personal one: on the contrary, they were singularly oblivious of self in the ordinary sense of the word. Theirs was the pride and the selfishness of *race*. What consideration, think you, other than the weal of his house, could induce Lord Randolph to take on himself the shame—for as such he certainly regards it—of a conversion to radicalism? He would, I am convinced, have *died* rather than make this pretence for merely personal ends. But he does it—and the reason? It is because he has received that awful summons from home; because 'the end' is daily coming nearer, and it must not find him unprepared to meet it; it is because Lord Pharanx's senses are becoming *too* acute; because the clatter of the servants' knives at the other end of the house inflames him to madness; because his excited palate can no longer endure any food but the subtlest delicacies; because Hester Dyett is able from the posture in which he sits to conjecture that he is intoxicated; because, in fact, he is on the brink of the dreadful malady which physicians call '*General Paralysis of the Insane*'. You remember I took from your hands the newspaper containing the earl's letter to Cibras, in order to read it with my own eyes. I had my reasons, and I was justified. That letter contains three mistakes in spelling: 'here' is printed 'hear', 'pass' appears as 'pas', and 'room' as 'rume'. Printers' errors, you say? But not so—one might be, two in that short paragraph could hardly be, three would be impossible. Search the whole paper through, and I think you will not find another. Let us reverence the theory of probabilities: the errors were the writer's, not the printer's.

General Paralysis of the Insane is known to have this effect on the writing. It attacks its victims about the period of middle age—the age at which the deaths of all the Orvens who died mysteriously occurred. Finding then that the dire heritage of his race—the heritage of madness—is falling or fallen on him, he summons his son from India. On himself he passes sentence of death: it is the tradition of the family, the secret vow of self-destruction handed down through ages from father to son. But he must have aid: in these days it is difficult for a man to commit the suicidal act without detection—and if madness is a disgrace to the race, equally so is suicide. Besides, the family is to be enriched by the insurances on his life, and is thereby to be allied with royal blood; but the money will be lost if the suicide be detected. Randolph therefore returns and blossoms into a popular candidate.

"For a time he is led to abandon his original plans by the appearance of Maude Cibras; he hopes that *she* may be made to destroy the earl; but when she fails him, he recurs to it—recurs to it all suddenly, for Lord Pharanx's condition is rapidly becoming critical, patent to all eyes, could any eye see him—so much so that on the last day none of the servants are allowed to enter his room. We must therefore regard Cibras as a mere addendum to, an extraneous element in, the tragedy, not as an integral part of it. She did not shoot the noble lord, for she had no pistol; nor did Randolph, for he was at a distance from the bed of death, surrounded by witnesses; nor did the imaginary burglars. The earl therefore shot himself; and it was the small globular silver pistol, such as this"—here Zaleski drew a little embossed Venetian weapon from a drawer near him—"that appeared in the gloom to the excited Hester as a 'ball of cotton', while it was being drawn upward by the Atwood's machine. But if the earl shot himself he could not have done so *after* being stabbed to the heart. Maude Cibras, therefore, stabbed a dead man. She would, of course, have ample time for stealing into the room and doing so after the shot was fired, and before the party reached the balcony window, on account of the delay on the stairs in procuring a second light; in going to the earl's door; in examining the tracks, and so on. But having stabbed a dead man, she is not guilty of murder. The message I just now sent by Ham was one addressed to the Home Secretary, telling him on no account to let Cibras die to-morrow. He well knows my name, and will hardly be silly enough to suppose me capable of using words without meaning.

It will be perfectly easy to prove my conclusions, for the pieces removed from, and replaced in, the floorings can still be detected, if looked for; the pistol is still, no doubt, in Randolph's room, and its bore can be compared with the bullet found in Lord Pharanx's brain; above all, the jewels stolen by the 'burglars' are still safe in some cabinet of the new earl, and may readily be discovered. I therefore expect that the *dénouement* will now take a somewhat different turn."

That the *dénouement* did take a different turn, and pretty strictly in accordance with Zaleski's forecast, is now matter of history, and the incidents, therefore, need no further comment from me in this place.

JOHN ADDINGTON SYMONDS

In the Key of Blue

A SYMPHONY of black and blue—
Venice asleep, vast night, and you;
The skies were blurred with vapours dank:
The long canal stretched inky-blank,
With lights on heaving water shed
From lamps that trembled overhead.
Pitch-dark! You were the one thing blue;
Four tints of pure celestial hue:
The larkspur blouse by tones degraded
Through silken sash of sapphire faded,
The faintly floating violet tie,
The hose of lapis-lazuli.
How blue you were amid that black,
Lighting the wave, the ebon wrack!
The ivory pallor of your face
Gleamed from those glowing azures back
Against the golden gaslight; grapes
Of dusky curls your brows embrace,
And round you all the vast night gapes.

A symphony of blues and white—
You, the acacias, dewy-bright,
Transparent skies of chrysolite.
We wind along these leafy hills;
One chord of blue the landscape thrills,
Your three blent azures merged in those
Cerulean heavens above the blouse.
The highest tones flash forth in white:
Acacia branches bowed with snow
Of scented blossom; broken light;
The ivory of your brows, the glow
Of those large orbs that are your eyes:
Those starry orbs of lustrous jet
In clear enamelled turquoise set,
Pale as the marge of morning skies.

A symphony of blues and brown—
We were together in the town:
A grimy tavern with blurred walls,
Where dingy lamplight floats and falls
On working men and women, clad
In sober watchet, umber sad.
Two viols and one 'cello scream
Waltz music through the smoke and steam:
You rise, you clasp a comrade, who
Is clothed in triple blues like you:
Sunk in some dream voluptuously
Circle those azures richly blent,
Swim through the dusk, the melody;
Languidly breathing, you and he,
Uplifting the environment;
Ivory face and swart face laid
Cheek unto cheek, like man, like maid.

A symphony of pink and blue,
The lamp, the little maid, and you.
Your strong man's stature in those three
Blent azures clothed, so loved by me;

Your grave face framed in felt thrown back;
Your sad sweet lips, eyes glossy black,
Now laughing, while your wan cheeks flush
Like warm white roses with a blush.
Clasped to your breast, held by your hands,
Smothered in blues, the baby stands:
Her frock like some carnation gleams;
Her hair, a golden torrent, streams:
Blue as forget-me-not her eyes,
Or azure-wingèd butterflies:
Her cheeks and mouth so richly red,
One would not think her city-bred.
Your beautiful pale face of pain
Leaned to the child's cheeks breathing health;
Like feathers dropped from raven's wing,
The curls that round your forehead rain
Merged with her tresses' yellowy wealth;
Her mouth that was a rose in spring
Touched yours, her pouting nether lip
Clasped your fine upper lip, whose brink,
Wherefrom Love's self a bee might sip,
Is pencilled with faint Indian ink.
Such was the group I saw one night
Illumined by a flaring light,
In that dim tavern where we meet
Sometimes to smoke, and drink and eat;
Exquisite contrast, not of tone,
Or tint, or form, or face alone.

A symphony of blues and gold,
Among ravines of grey stones rolled
Adown the steep from mountains old.
Laburnum branches drop their dew
Of amber bloom on me, on you:
With cytisus and paler broom,
Electron glimmering through the gloom.
Around us all the field flames up,
Goldenrod, hawkweed, buttercup;

While curling through lush grass one spies
Tendrils of honeyed helichryse.
'Tis saffron, topaz, solar rays,
Dissolved in fervent chrysoprase.
Cool, yet how luminous, the blue,
Centred in triple tones by you,
Uniting all that yellow glare
With the blue circumambient air,
The violet shades, the hard cobalt
Of noon's inexorable vault.

A symphony of blues and green,
Swart indigo and eau-marine.
Stripped to the waist two dyers kneel
On grey steps strewn with orange peel;
The glaucous water to the brink
Welters with clouds of purplish pink:
The men wring cloth that drips and takes
Verditer hues of water-snakes,
While *pali* paled by sun and seas
Repeat the tint in verdigris.
Those brows, nude breasts, and arms of might,
The pride of youth and manhood white,
Now smirched with woad, proclaim the doom
Of labour and its life-long gloom.
Only the eyes emergent shine,
These black as coals, those opaline;
Lighten from storms of tangled hair,
Black curls and blonde curls debonnair,
Proving man's untamed spirit there.

A symphony of blues and red—
The broad lagoon, and overhead
Sunset, a sanguine banner, spread.
Fretty of azure and pure gules
Are sea, sky, city, stagnant pools:
You, by my side, within the boat,
Imperially purple float,

Beneath a burning sail, straight on
Into the west's vermilion.
The triple azures melt and glow
Like flaunting iris-flowers arow;
One amethystine gem of three
Fused by the heaven's effulgency.
Now fails the splendour, day dies down
Beyond the hills by Padua's town;
And all along the eastern sky
Blue reassumes ascendency.
Lapped in those tints of fluor-spar,
You shine intense, an azure star,
With roses flushed that slowly fade
Against the vast aërial shade.

At Castelfranco, with a blouse
Venetian, blent of triple blues,
I walked all through the sleepy town,
Worshipped Madonna gazing down
From that high throne Giorgione painted
Above the knight and friar sainted,
Drank in the landscape golden-green,
The dim primeval pastoral-scene.
The blouse beside me thrilled no less
Than I to that mute loveliness;
Spoke little, turned aside, and dwelt
Perchance on what he dumbly felt.
There throbbed a man's heart neath the shirt,
The sash, the hose, a life alert,
Veiled by that dominating hurt.
Then swept a storm-cloud from the hills;
Eddying dust the city fills,
The thunder crashes, and the rain
Hisses on roof and flooded plain.
Ere midnight, when the moon sailed low,
Peering through veils of indigo,
We went abroad, and heard the wail
Of many a darkling nightingale,

Pouring as birds will only pour
Their souls forth when heaven's strife is o'er.
Those red walls, and the mighty towers,
Which lustrous ivy over-flowers,
Loomed through the murk divinely warm,
As palpitating after storm.
Hushed was the night for friendly talk;
Under the dark arcades we walk,
Pace the wet pavement, where light steals
And swoons amid the huge abeles:
Then seek our chamber. All the blues
Dissolve, the symphony of hues
Fades out of sight, and leaves at length
A flawless form of simple strength,
Sleep-seeking, breathing, ivory-white,
Upon the couch in candle-light.

ARTHUR SYMONS

Stella Maris

WHY IS it I remember yet
You, of all women one has met
In random wayfare, as one meets
The chance romances of the streets,
The Juliet of a night? I know
Your heart holds many a Romeo.
And I, who call to mind your face
In so serene a pausing-place,
Where the bright pure expanse of sea,
The shadowy shore's austerity,
Seem a reproach to you and me,
I too have sought on many a breast
The ecstasy of love's unrest,
I too have had my dreams, and met
(Ah me!) how many a Juliet.
Why is it, then, that I recall
You, neither first nor last of all?

For, surely as I see to-night
The phantom of the lighthouse light,
Against the sky, across the bay,
Fade, and return, and fade away,
So surely do I see your eyes
Out of the empty night arise.
Child, you arise and smile to me
Out of the night, out of the sea,
The Nereid of a moment there,
And is it seaweed in your hair?

O lost and wrecked, how long ago,
Out of the drowning past, I know
You come to call me, come to claim
My share of your delicious shame.
Child, I remember, and can tell
One night we loved each other well,
And one night's love, at least or most,
Is not so small a thing to boast.
You were adorable, and I
Adored you to infinity,
That nuptial night too briefly borne
To the oblivion of morn.
Ah! no oblivion, for I feel
Your lips deliriously steal
Along my neck, and fasten there;
I feel the perfume of your hair,
I feel your breast that heaves and dips,
Desiring my desirous lips,
And that ineffable delight
When souls turn bodies, and unite
In the intolerable, the whole
Rapture of the embodied soul.

That joy was ours, we passed it by;
You have forgotten me, and I
Remember you thus strangely, won
An instant from oblivion.

And I, remembering, would declare
That joy, not shame, is ours to share,
Joy that we had the frank delight
To choose the chances of one night,
Out of vague nights, and days at strife,
So infinitely full of life.
What shall it profit me to know
Your heart holds many a Romeo?
Why should I grieve, though I forget
How many another Juliet?
Let us be glad to have forgot
That roses fade, and loves are not,
As dreams, immortal though they seem
Almost as real as a dream.
It is for this I see you rise,
A wraith, with starlight in your eyes,
Where calm hours weave, for such a mood
Solitude out of solitude;
For this, for this, you come to me
Out of the night, out of the sea.

In Bohemia

DRAWN blinds and flaring gas within,
And wine, and women, and cigars;
Without, the city's heedless din;
Above, the white unheeding stars.

And we, alike from each remote,
The world that works, the heaven that waits,
Con our brief pleasures o'er by rote,
The favourite pastime of the Fates.

We smoke, to fancy that we dream,
And drink, a moment's joy to prove,
And fain would love, and only seem
To live because we cannot love.

Draw back the blinds, put out the light!
'Tis morning, let the daylight come.
God, how the women's cheeks are white,
And how the sunlight strikes us dumb!

Love Song

O WOMAN of my love, I am walking with you on the sand,
And the moon's white on the sand and the foam's white in the sea;
And I am thinking my own thoughts, and your hand is on my hand,
And your heart thinks by my side, and it's not thinking of me.

O woman of my love, the world is narrow and wide,
And I wonder which is the lonelier of us two?
You are thinking of one who is near to your heart, and far from your
    side;
I am thinking my own thoughts, and they are all thoughts of you.

The Gardener

THE GARDENER in his old brown hands
Turns over the brown earth,
As if he loves and understands
The flowers before their birth,
The fragile childish little strands
He buries in the earth.

Like pious children one by one
He sets them head by head,
And draws the clothes when all is done,
Closely about each head,
And leaves his children to sleep on
In the one quiet bed.

Wanderer's Song

I HAVE had enough of women, and enough of love,
But the land waits, and the sea waits, and day and night is enough;
Give me a long white road, and the grey wide path of the sea,
And the wind's will and the bird's will, and the heartache still in me.

Why should I seek out sorrow, and give gold for strife?
I have loved much and wept much, but tears and love are not life;
The grass calls to my heart, and the foam to my blood cries up,
And the sun shines and the road shines, and the wine's in the cup.

I have had enough of wisdom, and enough of mirth,
For the way's one and the end's one, and it's soon to the ends of the
    earth;
And it's then good-night and to bed, and if heels or heart ache,
Well, it's a sound sleep and long sleep, and sleep too deep to wake.

FRANCIS THOMPSON

Messages

WHAT SHALL I your true-love tell,
    Earth-forsaking maid?
What shall I your true-love tell,
    When life's spectre's laid?

"Tell him that, our side the grave,
    Maid may not conceive
Life should be so sad to have,
    That's so sad to leave!"

What shall I your true-love tell,
    When I come to him?
What shall I your true-love tell—
    Eyes growing dim!

"Tell him this, when you shall part
    From a maiden pined;
That I see him with my heart,
    Now my eyes are blind."

What shall I your true-love tell?
    Speaking-while is scant.
What shall I your true-love tell,
    Death's white postulant?

"Tell him—love, with speech at strife,
    For last utterance saith:
I, who loved with all my life,
    Love with all my death."

Daisy

WHERE the thistle lifts a purple crown
    Six foot out of the turf,
And the harebell shakes on the windy hill—
O the breath of the distant surf!—

The hills look over the South,
    And southward dreams the sea;
And with the sea-breeze hand in hand
    Came innocence and she.

Where 'mid the gorse the raspberry
    Red for the gatherer springs,
Two children did we stray and talk
    Wise, idle, childish things.

She listened with big-lipped surprise,
    Breast-deep 'mid flower and spine:
Her skin was like a grape whose veins
    Run snow instead of wine.

She knew not those sweet words she spake,
    Nor knew her own sweet way;
But there's never a bird, so sweet a song
    Thronged in whose throat that day.

Oh, there were flowers in Storrington
    On the turf and on the spray;
But the sweetest flower on Sussex hills
    Was the Daisy-flower that day!

Her beauty smoothed earth's furrowed face;
    She gave me tokens three:
A look, a word of her winsome mouth,
    And a wild raspberry.

A berry red, a guileless look,
    A still word,—strings of sand!
And yet they made my wild, wild heart
    Fly down to her little hand.

For standing artless as the air,
    And candid as the skies,
She took the berries with her hand,
    And the love with her sweet eyes.

The fairest things have fleetest end,
    Their scent survives their close:
But the rose's scent is bitterness
    To him that loved the rose.

She looked a little wistfully,
    Then went her sunshine way:
The sea's eye had a mist on it,
    And the leaves fell from the day.

She went her unremembering way,
    She went and left in me
The pang of all the partings gone,
    And partings yet to be.

She left me marvelling why my soul
    Was sad that she was glad;
At all the sadness in the sweet,
    The sweetness in the sad.

Still, still I seemed to see her, still
    Look up with soft replies,
And take the berries with her hand,
    And the love with her lovely eyes.

Nothing begins, and nothing ends,
That is not paid with moan;
For we are born in other's pain,
And perish in our own.

Envoy

Go, SONGS, for ended is our brief, sweet play;
Go, children of swift joy and tardy sorrow:
And some are sung, and that was yesterday,
And some unsung, and that may be to-morrow.

Go forth; and if it be o'er stony way,
Old joy can lend what newer grief must borrow:
And it was sweet, and that was yesterday,
And sweet is sweet, though purchasèd with sorrow.

Go, songs, and come not back from your far way:
And if men ask you why ye smile and sorrow,
Tell them ye grieve, for your hearts know To-day,
Tell them ye smile, for your eyes know To-morrow.

WILLIAM WATSON

The Great Misgiving

"NOT OURS," say some, "the thought of death to dread;
Asking no heaven, we fear no fabled hell:
Life is a feast, and we have banqueted—
Shall not the worms as well?

"The after-silence, when the feast is o'er,
And void the places where the minstrels stood,
Differs in naught from what hath been before,
And is not ill nor good."

Ah, but the Apparition—the dumb sign—·
   The beckoning finger bidding me forgo
The fellowship, the converse, and the wine,
   The songs, the festal glow!

And ah, to know not, while with friends I sit,
   And while the purple joy is pass'd about,
Whether 'tis ampler day divinelier lit
   Or homeless night without;

And whether, stepping forth, my soul shall see
   New prospects, or fall sheer—a blinded thing!
There is, O grave, thy hourly victory,
   And there, O death, thy sting.

Ode in May

   Let me go forth, and share
      The overflowing Sun
      With one wise friend, or one
   Better than wise, being fair,
   Where the pewit wheels and dips
      On heights of bracken and ling,
   And Earth, unto her leaflet tips,
      Tingles with the Spring.

   What is so sweet and dear
      As a prosperous morn in May,
      The confident prime of the day,
   And the dauntless youth of the year,
   When nothing that asks for bliss,
      Asking aright, is denied,
   And half of the world a bridegroom is,
      And half of the world a bride?

   The Song of Mingling flows,
      Grave, ceremonial, pure,
      As once, from lips that endure,
   The cosmic descant rose,

When the temporal lord of life,
  Going his golden way,
Had taken a wondrous maid to wife
  That long had said him nay.

For of old the Sun, our sire,
  Came wooing the mother of men,
  Earth, that was virginal then,
Vestal fire to his fire.
Silent her bosom and coy,
  But the strong god sued and press'd;
And born of their starry nuptial joy
  Are all that drink of her breast.

And the triumph of him that begot,
  And the travail of her that bore,
  Behold they are evermore
As warp and weft in our lot.
We are children of splendour and flame,
  Of shuddering, also, and tears,
Magnificent out of the dust we came,
  And abject from the Spheres.

O bright irresistible lord!
  We are fruit of Earth's womb, each one,
  And fruit of thy loins, O Sun,
Whence first was the seed out pour'd.
To thee as our Father we bow,
  Forbidden thy Father to see,
Who is older and greater than thou, as thou
  Art greater and older than we.

Thou art but as a word of his speech;
  Thou art but as a wave of his hand;
  Thou art brief as a glitter of sand
'Twixt tide and tide on his beach;
Thou art less than a spark of his fire,
  Or a moment's mood of his soul:
Thou art lost in the notes on the lips of his choir
  That chant the chant of the Whole.

OSCAR WILDE

The Portrait of Mr. W. H.

I HAD been dining with Erskine in his pretty little house in Birdcage Walk, and we were sitting in the library over our coffee and cigarettes, when the question of literary forgeries happened to turn up in conversation. I cannot at present remember how it was that we struck upon this somewhat curious topic, as it was at that time, but I know that we had a long discussion about Macpherson, Ireland, and Chatterton, and that with regard to the last I insisted that his so-called forgeries were merely the result of an artistic desire for perfect representation; that we had no right to quarrel with an artist for the conditions under which he chooses to present his work; and that all Art being to a certain degree a mode of acting, an attempt to realize one's own personality on some imaginative plane out of reach of the trammelling accidents and limitations of real life, to censure an artist for a forgery was to confuse an ethical with an æsthetical problem.

Erskine, who was a good deal older than I was, and had been listening to me with the amused deference of a man of forty, suddenly put his hand upon my shoulder and said to me, "What would you say about a young man who had a strange theory about a certain work of art, believed in his theory, and committed a forgery in order to prove it?"

"Ah! that is quite a different matter," I answered.

Erskine remained silent for a few moments, looking at the thin grey threads of smoke that were rising from his cigarette. "Yes," he said, after a pause, "quite different."

There was something in the tone of his voice, a slight touch of bitterness perhaps, that excited my curiosity. "Did you ever know anybody who did that?" I cried.

"Yes," he answered, throwing his cigarette into the fire—"a great friend of mine, Cyril Graham. He was very fascinating, and very foolish, and very heartless. However, he left me the only legacy I ever received in my life."

"What was that?" I exclaimed. Erskine rose from his seat, and going over to a tall inlaid cabinet that stood between the two windows, unlocked it, and came back to where I was sitting, holding in his hand a small panel picture set in an old and somewhat tarnished Elizabethan frame.

It was a full-length portrait of a young man in late sixteenth-century costume, standing by a table, with his right hand resting on an open book. He seemed about seventeen years of age, and was of quite extraordinary personal beauty, though evidently somewhat effeminate. Indeed, had it not been for the dress and the closely cropped hair one would have said that the face with its dreamy wistful eyes, and its delicate scarlet lips, was the face of a girl. In manner, and especially in the treatment of the hands, the picture reminded one of François Clouet's later work. The black velvet doublet with its fantastically gilded points, and the peacock-blue background against which it showed up so pleasantly, and from which it gained such luminous value of colour, were quite in Clouet's style; and the two masks of Tragedy and Comedy that hung somewhat formally from the marble pedestal had that hard severity of touch—so different from the facile grace of the Italians—which even at the Court of France the great Flemish master never completely lost, and which in itself has always been a characteristic of the northern temper.

"It is a charming thing," I cried, "but who is this wonderful young man whose beauty Art has so happily preserved for us?"

"This is the portrait of Mr. W. H.," said Erskine, with a sad smile. It might have been a chance effect of light, but it seemed to me that his eyes were quite bright with tears.

"Mr. W. H.!" I exclaimed; "who was Mr. W. H.?"

"Don't you remember?" he answered; "look at the book on which his hand is resting."

"I see there is some writing there, but I cannot make it out," I replied.

"Take this magnifying-glass and try," said Erskine, with the same sad smile still playing about his mouth.

I took the glass, and moving the lamp a little nearer, I began to spell out the crabbed sixteenth-century handwriting. "To the onlie begetter of these insuing sonnets." . . . "Good heavens!" I cried, "is this Shakespeare's Mr. W. H.?"

"Cyril Graham used to say so," muttered Erskine.

"But it is not a bit like Lord Pembroke," I answered. "I know the Penshurst portraits very well. I was staying near there a few weeks ago."

"Do you really believe then that the sonnets are addressed to Lord Pembroke?" he asked.

"I am sure of it," I answered. "Pembroke, Shakespeare, and Mrs. Mary Fitton are the three personages of the Sonnets; there is no doubt at all about it."

"Well, I agree with you," said Erskine, "but I did not always think so. I used to believe—well, I suppose I used to believe in Cyril Graham and his theory."

"And what was that?" I asked, looking at the wonderful portrait, which had already begun to have a strange fascination for me.

"It is a long story," said Erskine, taking the picture away from me— rather abruptly I thought at the time—"a very long story; but if you care to hear it, I will tell it to you."

"I love theories about the Sonnets," I cried; "but I don't think I am likely to be converted to any new idea. The matter has ceased to be a mystery to anyone. Indeed, I wonder that it ever was a mystery."

"As I don't believe in the theory, I am not likely to convert you to it," said Erskine, laughing; "but it may interest you."

"Tell it to me, of course," I answered. "If it is half as delightful as the picture, I shall be more than satisfied."

"Well," said Erskine, lighting a cigarette, "I must begin by telling you about Cyril Graham himself. He and I were at the same house at Eton. I was a year or two older than he was, but we were immense friends, and did all our work and all our play together. There was, of course, a good deal more play than work, but I cannot say that I am sorry for that. It is always an advantage not to have received a sound commercial education, and what I learned in the playing fields at Eton has been quite as useful to me as anything I was taught at Cambridge. I should tell you that Cyril's father and mother were both dead. They had been drowned in a horrible yachting accident off the Isle of Wight. His father had been in the diplomatic service, and had married a daughter, the only daughter, in fact, of old Lord Crediton, who became Cyril's guardian after the death of his parents. I don't think that Lord Crediton cared very much for Cyril. He had never really forgiven his daughter for marrying a man who had not a title. He was an extraordinary old aristocrat, who swore like a costermonger, and had the manners of a farmer. I remember seeing him once on Speech-day. He growled at me, gave me a sovereign, and told me not to grow up 'a damned Radical' like my father. Cyril had very little affection for him, and was only too glad to spend most of his holidays with us in Scotland. They never really got on together at all. Cyril thought him a bear, and he thought Cyril effeminate. He was effeminate, I suppose, in some things, though he was a very good rider and a capital fencer. In fact he got the foils before he left Eton. But he was very languid in his manner, and not a little vain of his good looks, and had a strong objection to football. The two things that really gave him pleasure were poetry and acting. At Eton he was always dressing up and reciting Shakespeare, and when we went up to Trinity he became a member of the A.D.C. his first term. I remember I was always very jealous of his acting. I was absurdly devoted to him; I suppose because we were so different in some things. I was a rather awkward, weakly lad, with huge feet, and horribly freckled. Freckles run in Scotch families just as gout does in English families. Cyril used to say that of the two he preferred the gout; but he always set an absurdly high value on personal appearance, and once read a paper before our debating society to prove that it was better to be good-looking than to be good. He certainly was wonderfully handsome. People who did not like him, Philistines and college tutors, and young men reading for the Church, used to say that he was merely pretty; but there was a great deal more in his face than mere prettiness. I think he was the most splendid creature I ever saw, and nothing could exceed the grace of his movements, the charm of his manner. He fascinated everybody who was worth fascinating, and a great many people who were not. He was often wilful and petulant, and I used to think him dreadfully insincere. It was due, I think, chiefly to his inordinate desire to please. Poor Cyril! I told him once that he was contented with very cheap triumphs, but he only laughed. He was horribly spoiled. All charming people, I fancy, are spoiled. It is the secret of their attraction.

"However, I must tell you about Cyril's acting. You know that no actresses are allowed to play at the A.D.C. At least they were not in my time. I don't know how it is now. Well, of course, Cyril was always cast for the girls' parts, and when *As You Like It* was produced he played Rosalind. It was a marvellous performance. In fact, Cyril Graham was the only perfect Rosalind I have ever seen. It would be impossible to describe to you the beauty, the delicacy, the refinement of the whole thing. It made an immense sensation, and the horrid little theatre, as it was then, was crowded every night. Even when I read the play now I can't help thinking of Cyril. It might have been written for him. The next term he took his degree, and came to London to read for the diplomatic. But he never did any work. He spent his days in reading Shakespeare's Sonnets, and his evenings at the theatre. He was, of course, wild to go on the stage. It was all that I and Lord Crediton could do to prevent him. Perhaps if he had gone on the stage he would be alive now. It is always a silly thing to give advice, but to give good advice is absolutely fatal. I hope you will never fall into that error. If you do, you will be sorry for it.

"Well, to come to the real point of the story, one day I got a letter from Cyril asking me to come round to his rooms that evening. He had charming chambers in Piccadilly overlooking the Green Park, and as I used to go to see him every day, I was rather surprised at his taking the trouble to write. Of course I went, and when I arrived I found him in a state of great excitement. He told me that he had at last discovered the true secret of Shakespeare's Sonnets; that all the scholars and critics had been entirely on the wrong track; and that he was the first who, working purely by internal evidence, had found out who Mr. W. H. really was. He was perfectly wild with delight, and for a long time would not tell me his theory. Finally, he produced a bundle of notes, took his copy of the Sonnets off the mantelpiece, and sat down and gave me a long lecture on the whole subject.

"He began by pointing out that the young man to whom Shakespeare addressed these strangely passionate poems must have been somebody who was a really vital factor in the development of his dramatic art, and that this could not be said either of Lord Pembroke or Lord Southampton. Indeed, whoever he was, he could not have been anybody of high birth, as was shown very clearly by the 25th Sonnet, in which Shakespeare, contrasting himself with those who are 'great princes' favourites', says quite frankly—

> Let those who are in favour with their stars
> Of public honour and proud titles boast,
> Whilst I, whom fortune of such triumph bars,
> Unlook'd for joy in that I honour most.

And ends the sonnet by congratulating himself on the mean state of him he so adored:

> Then happy I, that love and am beloved
> Where I may not remove nor be removed.

This sonnet, Cyril declared, would be quite unintelligible if we fancied that it was addressed to either the Earl of Pembroke or the Earl of Southampton, both of whom were men of the highest position in England and fully entitled to be called 'great princes'; and he in corroboration of his view read me Sonnets 124 and 125, in which Shakespeare tells us that his love is not 'the child of state', that it 'suffers not in smiling pomp', but is 'builded far from accident'. I listened with a good deal of interest, for I don't think the point had ever been made before; but what followed was still more curious, and seemed to me at the time to dispose entirely of Pembroke's claim. We know from Meres that the Sonnets had been written before 1598, and Sonnet 104 informs us that Shakespeare's friendship for Mr. W. H. had been already in existence for three years. Now Lord Pembroke, who was born in 1580, did not come to London till he was eighteen years of age, that is to say till 1598, and Shakespeare's acquaintance with Mr. W. H. must have begun in 1594, or at the latest in 1595. Shakespeare, accordingly, could not have known Lord Pembroke till after the Sonnets had been written.

"Cyril pointed out also that Pembroke's father did not die till 1601; whereas it was evident from the line,

> You had a father; let your son say so,

that the father of Mr. W. H. was dead in 1598. Besides, it was absurd to imagine that any publisher of the time, and the preface is from the publisher's hand, would have ventured to address William Herbert, Earl of Pembroke, as Mr. W. H.; the case of Lord Buckhurst being spoken of as Mr. Sackville being not really a parallel instance, as Lord Buckhurst was not a peer, but merely the younger son of a peer, with a courtesy title, and the passage in *England's Parnassus*, where he is so spoken of, is not a formal and stately dedication, but simply a casual allusion. So far for Lord Pembroke, whose supposed claims Cyril easily demolished while I sat by in wonder. With Lord Southampton Cyril had even less difficulty. Southampton became at a very early age the lover of Elizabeth Vernon, so he needed no entreaties to marry;

he was not beautiful; he did not resemble his mother, as Mr. W. H. did—

> Thou art thy mother's glass, and she in thee
> Calls back the lovely April of her prime;

and, above all, his Christian name was Henry, whereas the punning sonnets (135 and 143) show that the Christian name of Shakespeare's friend was the same as his own— Will.

"As for the other suggestions of unfortunate commentators, that Mr. W. H. is a misprint for Mr. W. S., meaning Mr. William Shakespeare; that 'Mr. W. H. all' should be read 'Mr. W. Hall'; that Mr. W. H. is Mr. William Hathaway; and that a full stop should be placed after 'wisheth', making Mr. W. H. the writer and not the subject of the dedication—Cyril got rid of them in a very short time; and it is not worth while to mention his reasons, though I remember he sent me off into a fit of laughter by reading to me, I am glad to say not in the original, some extracts from a German commentator called Barnstorff, who insisted that Mr. W. H. was no less a person than 'Mr. William Himself'. Nor would he allow for a moment that the Sonnets are mere satires on the work of Drayton and John Davies of Hereford. To him, as indeed to me, they were poems of serious and tragic import, wrung out of the bitterness of Shakespeare's heart, and made sweet by the honey of his lips. Still less would he admit that they were merely a philosophical allegory, and that in them Shakespeare is addressing his Ideal Self, or Ideal Manhood, or the Spirit of Beauty, or the Reason, or the Divine Logos, or the Catholic Church. He felt, as indeed I think we all must feel, that the Sonnets are addressed to an individual— to a particular young man whose personality for some reason seems to have filled the soul of Shakespeare with terrible joy and no less terrible despair.

"Having in this manner cleared the way as it were, Cyril asked me to dismiss from my mind any preconceived ideas I might have formed on the subject, and to give a fair and unbiased hearing to his own theory. The problem he pointed out was this: Who was that young man of Shakespeare's day who, without being of noble birth or even of noble nature, was addressed by him in terms of such passionate adoration that we can but wonder at the strange worship, and are almost afraid to turn the key that unlocks the mystery of the poet's heart? Who was he

whose physical beauty was such that it became the very corner-stone of
Shakespeare's art; the very source of Shakespeare's inspiration; the
very incarnation of Shakespeare's dreams? To look upon him as simply
the object of certain love-poems is to miss the whole meaning of the
poems: for the art of which Shakespeare talks in the Sonnets is not the
art of the Sonnets themselves, which indeed were to him but slight
and secret things—it is the art of the dramatist to which he is always
alluding; and he to whom Shakespeare said—

> Thou art all my art, and dost advance
> As high as learning my rude ignorance,

he to whom he promised immortality,

> Where breath most breathes, even in the mouths of men,—

was surely none other than the boy-actor for whom he created Viola and
Imogen, Juliet and Rosalind, Portia and Desdemona, and Cleopatra
herself. This was Cyril Graham's theory, evolved as you see purely
from the Sonnets themselves, and depending for its acceptance not so
much on demonstrable proof or formal evidence, but on a kind of
spiritual and artistic sense, by which alone he claimed could the true
meaning of the poems be discerned. I remember his reading to me that
fine sonnet—

> How can my Muse want subject to invent,
> While thou dost breathe, that pour'st into my verse
> Thine own sweet argument, too excellent
> For every vulgar paper to rehearse?
> O, give thyself the thanks, if aught in me
> Worthy perusal stand against thy sight;
> For who's so dumb that cannot write to thee,
> When thou thyself dost give invention light?
> Be thou the tenth Muse, ten times more in worth
> Than those old nine which rhymers invocate;
> And he that calls on thee, let him bring forth
> Eternal numbers to outlive long date—

and pointing out how completely it corroborated his theory; and indeed he went through all the Sonnets carefully, and showed, or fancied that he showed, that according to his new explanation of their meaning, things that had seemed obscure, or evil, or exaggerated, became clear and rational, and of high artistic import, illustrating Shakespeare's conception of the true relations between the art of the actor and the art of the dramatist.

"It is of course evident that there must have been in Shakespeare's company some wonderful boy-actor of great beauty, to whom he intrusted the presentation of his noble heroines; for Shakespeare was a practical theatrical manager as well as an imaginative poet, and Cyril Graham had actually discovered the boy-actor's name. He was Will, or, as he preferred to call him, Willie Hughes. The Christian name he found of course in the punning sonnets, 135 and 143; the surname was, according to him, hidden in the seventh line of the 20th Sonnet, where Mr. W. H. is described as—

A man in hew, all *Hews* in his controwling.

"In the original edition of the Sonnets 'Hews' is printed with a capital letter and in italics, and this, he claimed, showed clearly that a play on words was intended, his view receiving a good deal of corroboration from those sonnets in which curious puns are made on the words 'use' and 'usury'. Of course I was converted at once, and Willie Hughes became to me as real a person as Shakespeare. The only objection I made to the theory was that the name of Willie Hughes does not occur in the list of the actors of Shakespeare's company as it is printed in the first folio. Cyril, however, pointed out that the absence of Willie Hughes's name from this list really corroborated the theory, as it was evident from Sonnet 86 that Willie Hughes had abandoned Shakespeare's company to play at a rival theatre, probably in some of Chapman's plays. It is in reference to this that in the great sonnet on Chapman, Shakespeare said to Willie Hughes—

But when your countenance fill'd up his line,
Then lack'd I matter; that enfeebled mine—

the expression 'when your countenance filled up his line' referring obviously to the beauty of the young actor giving life and reality and

added charm to Chapman's verse, the same idea being also put forward
in the 79th Sonnet—

> Whilst I alone did call upon thy aid,
> My verse alone had all thy gentle grace;
> But now my gracious numbers are decay'd,
> And my sick Muse doth give another place;

and in the immediately preceding sonnet, where Shakespeare says—

> Every alien pen has got my *use*
> And under thee their poesy disperse,

the play upon words (use—Hughes) being of course obvious, and the
phrase 'under thee their poesy disperse', meaning 'by your assistance as
an actor bring their plays before the people'.

"It was a wonderful evening, and we sat up almost till dawn reading
and re-reading the Sonnets. After some time, however, I began to
see that before the theory could be placed before the world in a really
perfected form, it was necessary to get some independent evidence about
the existence of this young actor, Willie Hughes. If this could be once
established, there could be no possible doubt about his identity with
Mr. W. H.; but otherwise the theory would fall to the ground. I
put this forward very strongly to Cyril, who was a good deal annoyed
at what he called my Philistine tone of mind, and indeed was rather
bitter upon the subject. However, I made him promise that in his own
interest he would not publish his discovery till he had put the whole
matter beyond the reach of doubt; and for weeks and weeks we searched
the registers of City churches, the Alleyn MSS. at Dulwich, the
Record Office, the papers of the Lord Chamberlain—everything, in
fact, that we thought might contain some allusion to Willie Hughes.
We discovered nothing, of course, and every day the existence of
Willie Hughes seemed to me to become more problematical. Cyril
was in a dreadful state, and used to go over the whole question day
after day, entreating me to believe; but I saw the one flaw in the
theory, and I refused to be convinced till the actual existence of Willie
Hughes, a boy-actor of Elizabethan days, had been placed beyond the
reach of doubt or cavil.

"One day Cyril left town, to stay with his grandfather, I thought at the time, but I afterwards heard from Lord Crediton that this was not the case; and about a fortnight afterwards I received a telegram from him, handed in at Warwick, asking me to be sure to come and dine with him that evening at eight o'clock. When I arrived, he said to me, 'The only apostle who did not deserve proof was St. Thomas, and St. Thomas was the only apostle who got it.' I asked him what he meant. He answered that he had not merely been able to establish the existence in the sixteenth century of a boy-actor of the name of Willie Hughes, but to prove by the most conclusive evidence that he was the Mr. W. H. of the Sonnets. He would not tell me anything more at the time; but after dinner he solemnly produced the picture I showed you, and told me that he had discovered it by the merest chance nailed to the side of an old chest that he had bought at a farmhouse in Warwickshire. The chest itself, which was a very fine example of Elizabethan work, he had, of course, brought with him, and in the centre of the front panel the initials W. H. were undoubtedly carved. It was this monogram that had attracted his attention, and he told me that it was not till he had had the chest in his possession for several days that he had thought of making any careful examination of the inside. One morning, however, he saw that one of the sides of the chest was much thicker than the other, and looking more closely, he discovered that a framed panel picture was clamped against it. On taking it out, he found it was the picture that is now lying on the sofa. It was very dirty, and covered with mould; but he managed to clean it, and, to his great joy, saw that he had fallen by mere chance on the one thing for which he had been looking. Here was an authentic portrait of Mr. W. H., with his hand resting on the dedicatory page of the Sonnets, and on the frame itself could be faintly seen the name of the young man written in black uncial letters on a faded gold ground, 'Master Will. Hews'.

"Well, what was I to say? It never occurred to me for a moment that Cyril Graham was playing a trick on me, or that he was trying to prove his theory by means of a forgery."

"But is it a forgery?" I asked.

"Of course it is," said Erskine. "It is a very good forgery; but it is a forgery none the less. I thought at the time that Cyril was rather calm about the whole matter; but I remember he more than once told me that he himself required no proof of the kind, and that he thought the

KK

theory complete without it. I laughed at him, and told him that without it the theory would fall to the ground, and I warmly congratulated him on the marvellous discovery. We then arranged that the picture should be etched or facsimiled, and placed as the frontispiece to Cyril's edition of the Sonnets; and for three months we did nothing but go over each poem line by line, till we had settled every difficulty of text or meaning. One unlucky day I was in a print-shop in Holborn, when I saw upon the counter some extremely beautiful drawings in silver-point. I was so attracted by them that I bought them; and the proprietor of the place, a man called Rawlings, told me that they were done by a young painter of the name of Edward Merton, who was very clever, but as poor as a church mouse. I went to see Merton some days afterwards, having got his address from the printseller, and found a pale, interesting young man, with a rather common-looking wife—his model, as I subsequently learned. I told him how much I admired his drawings, at which he seemed very pleased, and I asked him if he would show me some of his other work. As we were looking over a portfolio, full of really very lovely things—for Merton had a most delicate and delightful touch—I suddenly caught sight of a drawing of the picture of Mr. W. H. There was no doubt whatever about it. It was almost a facsimile—the only difference being that the two masks of Tragedy and Comedy were not suspended from the marble table as they are in the picture, but were lying on the floor at the young man's feet. 'Where on earth did you get that?' I said. He grew rather confused, and said— 'Oh, that is nothing. I did not know it was in this portfolio. It is not a thing of any value.' 'It is what you did for Mr. Cyril Graham,' exclaimed his wife; 'and if this gentleman wishes to buy it, let him have it.' 'For Mr. Cyril Graham?' I repeated. 'Did you paint the picture of Mr. W. H.?' 'I don't understand what you mean,' he answered, growing very red. Well, the whole thing was quite dreadful. The wife let it all out. I gave her five pounds when I was going away. I can't bear to think of it now; but of course I was furious. I went off at once to Cyril's chambers, waited there for three hours before he came in, with that horrid lie staring me in the face, and told him I had discovered his forgery. He grew very pale and said—'I did it purely for your sake. You would not be convinced in any other way. It does not affect the truth of the theory.' 'The truth of the theory!' I exclaimed; 'the less we talk about that the better. You never even believed it in yourself. If you had, you would not have committed a forgery to prove it.' High words passed between us; we had a fearful quarrel. I daresay I was unjust. The next morning he was dead."

"Dead!" I cried.

"Yes; he shot himself with a revolver. Some of the blood splashed upon the frame of the picture, just where the name had been painted. By the time I arrived—his servant had sent for me at once—the police were already there. He had left a letter for me, evidently written in the greatest agitation and distress of mind."

"What was in it?" I asked.

"Oh, that he believed absolutely in Willie Hughes; that the forgery of the picture had been done simply as a concession to me, and did not in the slightest degree invalidate the truth of the theory; and that in order to show me how firm and flawless his faith in the whole thing was, he was going to offer his life as a sacrifice to the secret of the Sonnets. It was a foolish, mad letter. I remember he ended by saying that he intrusted to me the Willie Hughes theory, and that it was for me to present it to the world, and to unlock the secret of Shakespeare's heart."

"It is a most tragic story," I cried; "but why have you not carried out his wishes?"

Erskine shrugged his shoulders. "Because it is a perfectly unsound theory from beginning to end," he answered.

"My dear Erskine," I said, getting up from my seat, "you are entirely wrong about the whole matter. It is the only perfect key to Shakespeare's Sonnets that has ever been made. It is complete in every detail. I believe in Willie Hughes."

"Don't say that," said Erskine gravely; "I believe there is something fatal about the idea, and intellectually there is nothing to be said for it. I have gone into the whole matter, and I assure you the theory is entirely fallacious. It is plausible up to a certain point. Then it stops. For heaven's sake, my dear boy, don't take up the subject of Willie Hughes. You will break your heart over it."

"Erskine," I answered, "it is your duty to give this theory to the world. If you will not do it, I will. By keeping it back you wrong the memory of Cyril Graham, the youngest and the most splendid of all the martyrs of literature. I entreat you to do him justice. He died for this thing—don't let his death be in vain."

Erskine looked at me in amazement. "You are carried away by the sentiment of the whole story," he said. "You forget that a thing is not necessarily true because a man dies for it. I was devoted to Cyril Graham. His death was a horrible blow to me. I did not recover from it for years. I don't think I have ever recovered from it. But Willie Hughes? There is nothing in the idea of Willie Hughes. No such person ever existed. As for bringing the whole thing before the world—the world thinks that Cyril Graham shot himself by accident. The only proof of his suicide was contained in the letter to me, and of this letter the public never heard anything. To the present day Lord Crediton thinks that the whole thing was accidental."

"Cyril Graham sacrificed his life to a great idea," I answered; "and if you will not tell of his martyrdom, tell at least of his faith."

"His faith," said Erskine, "was fixed in a thing that was false, in a thing that was unsound, in a thing that no Shakespearean scholar would accept for a moment. The theory would be laughed at. Don't make a fool of yourself, and don't follow a trail that leads nowhere. You start by assuming the existence of the very person whose existence is the thing to be proved. Besides, everybody knows that the Sonnets were addressed to Lord Pembroke. The matter is settled once for all."

"The matter is not settled!" I exclaimed. "I will take up the theory where Cyril Graham left it, and I will prove to the world that he was right."

"Silly boy!" said Erskine. "Go home: it is after two, and don't think about Willie Hughes any more. I am sorry I told you anything about it, and very sorry indeed that I should have converted you to a thing in which I don't believe."

"You have given me the key to the greatest mystery of modern literature," I answered; "and I shall not rest till I have made you recognize, till I have made everybody recognize, that Cyril Graham was the most subtle Shakespearean critic of our day."

As I walked home through St. James's Park the dawn was just breaking over London. The white swans were lying asleep on the polished lake, and the gaunt Palace looked purple against the pale-green sky. I thought of Cyril Graham, and my eyes filled with tears.

II

It was past twelve o'clock when I awoke, and the sun was streaming in through the curtains of my room in long slanting beams of dusty gold. I told my servant that I would be at home to no one; and after I had had a cup of chocolate and a *petit-pain*, I took down from the book-shelf my copy of Shakespeare's Sonnets, and began to go carefully through them. Every poem seemed to me to corroborate Cyril Graham's theory. I felt as if I had my hand upon Shakespeare's heart, and was counting each separate throb and pulse of passion. I thought of the wonderful boy-actor, and saw his face in every line.

Two sonnets, I remember, struck me particularly: they were the 53rd and the 67th. In the first of these, Shakespeare, complimenting Willie Hughes on the versatility of his acting, on his wide rang of parts, a range extending from Rosalind to Juliet, and from Beatrice to Ophelia, says to him—

> What is your substance, whereof are you made,
> That millions of strange shadows on you tend?
> Since every one hath, every one, one shade,
> And you, but one, can every shadow lend—

lines that would be unintelligible if they were not addressed to an actor, for the word "shadow" had in Shakespeare's day a technical meaning connected with the stage. "The best in this kind are but shadows," says Theseus of the actors in the *Midsummer Night's Dream*, and there are many similar allusions in the literature of the day. These sonnets evidently belonged to the series in which Shakespeare discusses the nature of the actor's art, and of the strange and rare temperament that is essential to the perfect stage-player. "How is it," says Shakespeare to Willie Hughes, "that you have so many personalities?" and then he goes on to point out that his beauty is such that it seems to realize every form and phase of fancy, to embody each dream of the creative imagination—an idea that is still further expanded in the sonnet that immediately follows, where, beginning with the fine thought,

> O, how much more doth beauty beauteous seem
> By that sweet ornament which *truth* doth give!

Shakespeare invites us to notice how the truth of acting, the truth of visible presentation on the stage, adds to the wonder of poetry, giving life to its loveliness, and actual reality to its ideal form. And yet, in the 67th Sonnet, Shakespeare calls upon Willie Hughes to abandon the stage with its artificiality, its false mimic life of painted face and unreal costume, its immoral influences and suggestions, its remoteness from the true world of noble action and sincere utterance:

> Ah, wherefore with infection should he live
> And with his presence grace impiety,
> That sin by him advantage should achieve
> And lace itself with his society?
> Why should false painting imitate his cheek,
> And steal dead seeming of his living hue?
> Why should poor beauty indirectly seek
> Roses of shadow, since his rose is true?

It may seem strange that so great a dramatist as Shakespeare, who realized his own perfection as an artist and his humanity as a man on the ideal plane of stage-writing and stage-playing, should have written in these terms about the theatre; but we must remember that in Sonnets 110 and 111 Shakespeare shows us that he too was wearied of the world of puppets, and full of shame at having made himself "a motley to the view". The 111th Sonnet is especially bitter:

> O, for my sake do you with Fortune chide,
> The guilty goddess of my harmful deeds,
> That did not better for my life provide
> Than public means which public manners breeds.
> Thence comes it that my name receives a brand,
> And almost thence my nature is subdued
> To what it works in, like the dyer's hand:
> Pity me then and wish I were renew'd—

and there are many signs elsewhere of the same feeling, signs familiar to all real students of Shakespeare.

One point puzzled me immensely as I read the Sonnets, and it was days before I struck on the true interpretation, which indeed Cyril

Graham himself seems to have missed. I could not understand how it was that Shakespeare set so high a value on his young friend marrying. He himself had married young, and the result had been unhappiness, and it was not likely that he would have asked Willie Hughes to commit the same error. The boy-player of Rosalind had nothing to gain from marriage, or from the passions of real life. The early sonnets, with their strange entreaties to have children, seemed to me a jarring note. The explanation of the mystery came on me quite suddenly, and I found it in the curious dedication. It will be remembered that the dedication runs as follows:

TO · THE · ONLIE · BEGETTER · OF ·
THESE · INSUING · SONNETS ·
MR. W. H. ALL · HAPPINESSE
AND · THAT · ETERNITIE ·
PROMISED ·
BY ·
OUR · EVER-LIVING · POET
WISHETH ·
THE · WELL-WISHING ·
ADVENTURER · IN ·
SETTING ·
FORTH.

T. T.

Some scholars have supposed that the word "begetter" in this dedication means simply the procurer of the Sonnets for Thomas Thorpe the publisher; but this view is now generally abandoned, and the highest authorities are quite agreed that it is to be taken in the sense of inspirer, the metaphor being drawn from the analogy of physical life. Now I saw that the same metaphor was used by Shakespeare himself all through the poems, and this set me on the right track. Finally I made my great discovery. The marriage that Shakespeare proposed for Willie Hughes is the marriage with his Muse, an expression which is definitely put forward in the 82nd Sonnet, where, in the bitterness of his heart at the defection of the boy-actor for whom he had written his greatest parts, and whose beauty had indeed suggested them, he opens his complaint by saying—

I grant thou wert not married to my Muse.

The children he begs him to beget are no children of flesh and blood, but more immortal children of undying fame. The whole cycle of the early sonnets is simply Shakespeare's invitation to Willie Hughes to go upon the stage and become a player. How barren and profitless a thing, he says, is this beauty of yours if it be not used:

> When forty winters shall besiege thy brow
> And dig deep trenches in thy beauty's field,
> Thy youth's proud livery, so gazed on now,
> Will be a tatter'd weed, of small worth held:
> Then being ask'd where all thy beauty lies,
> Where all the treasure of thy lusty days,
> To say, within thine own deep-sunken eyes,
> Were an all-eating shame and thriftless praise.

You must create something in art: my verse "is thine, and *born* of thee"; only listen to me, and I will "*bring forth* eternal numbers to outlive long date", and you shall people with forms of your own image the imaginary world of the stage. These children that you beget, he continues, will not wither away, as mortal children do, but you shall live in them and in my plays: do but—

> Make thee another self, for love of me,
> That beauty still may live in thine or thee.

I collected all the passages that seemed to me to corroborate this view, and they produced a strong impression on me, and showed me how complete Cyril Graham's theory really was. I also saw that it was quite easy to separate those lines in which he speaks of the Sonnets themselves from those in which he speaks of his great dramatic work. This was a point that had been entirely overlooked by all critics up to Cyril Graham's day. And yet it was one of the most important points in the whole series of poems. To the Sonnets Shakespeare was more or less indifferent. He did not wish to rest his fame on them. They were to him his "slight Muse", as he calls them, and intended, as Meres tells us, for private circulation only among a few, a very few friends. Upon the other hand he was extremely conscious of the high artistic value of his plays, and shows a noble self-reliance upon his dramatic genius. When he says to Willie Hughes:

> But thy eternal summer shall not fade,
> Nor lose possession of that fair thou owest;
> Nor shall Death brag thou wander'st in his shade,
> When in *eternal lines* to time thou grow'st:
>   So long as men can breathe, or eyes can see,
>   So long lives this, and this gives life to thee—

the expression "eternal lines" clearly alludes to one of his plays that he was sending him at the time, just as the concluding couplet points to his confidence in the probability of his plays being always acted. In his address to the Dramatic Muse (Sonnets 100 and 101), we find the same feeling.

> Where art thou, Muse, that thou forget'st so long
> To speak of that which gives thee all thy might?
> Spend'st thou thy fury on some worthless song,
> Darkening thy power to lend base subjects light?

he cries, and he then proceeds to reproach the Mistress of Tragedy and Comedy for her "neglect of Truth in Beauty dyed", and says—

> Because he needs no praise, wilt thou be dumb?
> Excuse not silence so, for 't lies in thee
> To make him much outlive a gilded tomb
> And to be praised of ages yet to be.
>   Then do thy office, Muse; I teach thee how
>   To make him seem long hence as he shows now.

It is, however, perhaps in the 55th Sonnet that Shakespeare gives to this idea its fullest expression. To imagine that the "powerful rhyme" of the second line refers to the sonnet itself, is to mistake Shakespeare's meaning entirely. It seemed to me that it was extremely likely, from the general character of the sonnet, that a particular play was meant, and that the play was none other but *Romeo and Juliet*.

Not marble, nor the gilded monuments
Of princes, shall outlive this powerful rhyme;
But you shall shine more bright in these contents
Than unswept stone besmear'd with sluttish time.
When wasteful wars shall statues overturn,
And broils root out the work of masonry,
Nor Mars his sword nor war's quick fire shall burn
The living record of your memory.
'Gainst death and all-oblivious enmity
Shall you pace forth; your praise shall still find room
Even in the eyes of all posterity
That wear this world out to the ending doom.
So, till the judgement that yourself arise,
You live in this, and dwell in lovers' eyes.

It was also extremely suggestive to note how here as elsewhere Shakespeare promised Willie Hughes immortality in a form that appealed to men's eyes—that is to say, in a spectacular form, in a play that is to be looked at.

For two weeks I worked hard at the Sonnets, hardly ever going out, and refusing all invitations. Every day I seemed to be discovering something new, and Willie Hughes became to me a kind of spiritual presence, an ever-dominant personality. I could almost fancy that I saw him standing in the shadow of my room, so well had Shakespeare drawn him, with his golden hair, his tender flower-like grace, his dreamy deep-sunken eyes, his delicate mobile limbs, and his white lily hands. His very name fascinated me. Willie Hughes! Willie Hughes! How musically it sounded! Yes; who else but he could have been "the master-mistress" of Shakespeare's passion, the lord of his love to whom he was bound in vassalage, "the delicate minion of pleasure," "the rose of the whole world," "the herald of the spring" "decked in the proud livery of youth," the lovely boy whom it was "sweet music to hear," and whose beauty was the very raiment of Shakespeare's heart, as it was the keystone of his dramatic power? How bitter now seemed the whole tragedy of his desertion and his shame!—shame that he made sweet and lovely by the mere magic of his personality, but that was none the less shame. Yet as Shakespeare forgave him, should not we forgive him also? I did not care to pry into the mystery of his sin.

His abandonment of Shakespeare's theatre was a different matter, and I investigated it at great length. Finally I came to the conclusion that Cyril Graham had been wrong in regarding the rival dramatist of the 80th Sonnet as Chapman. It was obviously Marlowe who was alluded to. At the time the Sonnets were written, such an expression as "the proud full sail of his great verse" could not have been used of Chapman's work, however applicable it might have been to the style of his later Jacobean plays. No: Marlowe was clearly the rival dramatist of whom Shakespeare spoke in such laudatory terms; and that

> Affable familiar ghost
> Which nightly gulls him with intelligence,

was the Mephistopheles of his *Doctor Faustus*. No doubt, Marlowe was fascinated by the beauty and grace of the boy-actor, and lured him away from the Blackfriars Theatre, that he might play the Gaveston of his *Edward II*. That Shakespeare had the legal right to retain Willie Hughes in his own company is evident from Sonnet 87, where he says:

> Farewell! thou art too dear for my possessing,
> And like enough thou know'st thy estimate:
> The *charter of thy worth* gives thee releasing;
> My *bonds* in thee are all determinate.
> For how do I hold thee but by thy granting?
> And for that riches where is my deserving?
> The cause of this fair gift in me is wanting,
> *And so my patent back again is swerving.*
> Thyself thou gavest, thy own worth then not knowing,
> Or me, to whom thou gavest it, else mistaking;
> So thy great gift, upon misprision growing,
> Comes home again, on better judgement making.
> Thus have I had thee, as a dream doth flatter,
> In sleep a king, but waking no such matter.

But him whom he could not hold by love, he would not hold by force. Willie Hughes became a member of Lord Pembroke's company, and, perhaps in the open yard of the Red Bull Tavern, played the part of King Edward's delicate minion. On Marlowe's death, he seems to have returned to Shakespeare, who, whatever his fellow-partners may have thought of the matter, was not slow to forgive the wilfulness and treachery of the young actor.

How well, too, had Shakespeare drawn the temperament of the stage-player! Willie Hughes was one of those

> That do not do the thing they most do show,
> Who, moving others, are themselves as stone.

He could act love, but could not feel it, could mimic passion without realizing it:

> In many's looks the false heart's history
> Is writ in moods and frowns and wrinkles strange,

but with Willie Hughes it was not so. "Heaven," says Shakespeare, in a sonnet of mad idolatry—

> Heaven in thy creation did decree
> That in thy face sweet love should ever dwell;
> Whate'er thy thoughts or thy heart's workings be,
> Thy looks should nothing thence but sweetness tell.

In his "inconstant mind" and his "false heart", it was easy to recognize the insincerity and treachery that somehow seem inseparable from the artistic nature, as in his love of praise that desire for immediate recognition that characterizes all actors. And yet, more fortunate in this than other actors, Willie Hughes was to know something of immortality. Inseparably connected with Shakespeare's plays, he was to live in them.

> Your name from hence immortal life shall have,
> Though I, once gone, to all the world must die
> The earth can yield me but a common grave,
> When you entombèd in men's eyes shall lie.
> Your monument shall be my gentle verse,
> Which eyes not yet created shall o'er-read,
> And tongues to be your being shall rehearse,
> When all the breathers of this world are dead.

There were endless allusions, also, to Willie Hughes's power over his audience—the "gazers", as Shakespeare calls them; but perhaps the most perfect description of his wonderful mastery over dramatic art was in *A Lover's Complaint*, where Shakespeare says of him:

> In him a plenitude of subtle matter,
> Applied to cautels, all strange forms receives,
> Of burning blushes, or of weeping water,
> Or swooning paleness; and he takes and leaves,
> In either's aptness, as it best deceives,
> To blush at speeches rank, to weep at woes,
> Or to turn white and swoon at tragic shows.
>
> So on the tip of his subduing tongue,
> All kind of arguments and questions deep,
> All replication prompt and reason strong,
> For his advantage still did wake and sleep,
> To make the weeper laugh, the laugher weep.
>   He had the dialect and different skill,
>   Catching all passions in his craft of will.

One evening I thought that I had really found Willie Hughes in Elizabethan literature. In a wonderfully graphic account of the last days of the great Earl of Essex, his chaplain, Thomas Knell, tells us that the night before the Earl died, "he called William Hewes, which was his musician, to play upon the virginals and to sing. 'Play,' said he, 'my song, Will Hewes, and I will sing it to myself.' So he did it most joyfully, not as the howling swan, which, still looking down, waileth her end, but as a sweet lark, lifting up his hands and casting up his eyes to his God, with this mounted the crystal skies, and reached with his unwearied tongue the top of highest heavens." Surely the boy who played on the virginals to the dying father of Sidney's Stella was none other but the Will Hews to whom Shakespeare dedicated the Sonnets, and who, he tells us, was himself sweet "music to hear". Yet Lord Essex died in 1576, when Shakespeare himself was but twelve years of age. It was impossible that his musician could have been the Mr. W. H. of the Sonnets. Perhaps Shakespeare's young friend was the son of the player upon the virginals? It was at least something to have discovered that

Will Hews was an Elizabethan name. Indeed the name Hews seemed to have been closely connected with music and the stage. The first English actress was the lovely Margaret Hews, whom Prince Rupert so madly loved. What more probable than that between her and Lord Essex's musician had come the boy-actor of Shakespeare's plays? But the proofs, the links—where were they? Alas, I could not find them. It seemed to me that I was always on the brink of absolute verification, but that I could never really attain to it.

III

It was not for some weeks after I had begun my study of the subject that I ventured to approach the curious group of Sonnets that deal with the dark woman who, like a shadow or thing of evil omen, came across Shakespeare's great romance, and for a season stood between him and Willie Hughes. Who was she, this black-browed, olive-skinned woman, with her amorous mouth "that Love's own hand did make", her "cruel eye", and her "foul pride", her strange skill on the virginals and her false, fascinating nature? An over-curious scholar of our day had seen in her a symbol of the Catholic Church, of that Bride of Christ who is "black but comely". Professor Minto, following in the footsteps of Henry Brown, had regarded the whole group of Sonnets as simply "exercises of skill undertaken in a spirit of wanton defiance and derision of the commonplace". Mr. Gerald Massey, without any historical proof or probability, had insisted that they were addressed to the celebrated Lady Rich, the Stella of Sir Philip Sidney's sonnets, the Philoclea of his "Arcadia", and that they contained no personal revelation of Shakespeare's life and love, having been written in Lord Pembroke's name and at his request. Mr. Tyler had suggested that they referred to one of Queen Elizabeth's maids-of-honour, by name Mary Fitton. But none of these explanations satisfied the conditions of the problem. The woman that came between Shakespeare and Willie Hughes was a real woman, black-haired, and married, and of evil repute. Lady Rich's fame was evil enough, it is true, but her hair was of—

"fine threads of finest gold,
In curlèd knots man's thoughts to hold,"

and her shoulders like "white doves perching". She was, as King James said to her lover, Lord Mountjoy, "a fair woman with a black soul". As for Mary Fitton, we know that she was unmarried in 1601, the time when her amour with Lord Pembroke was discovered, and besides, any theories that connected Lord Pembroke with the Sonnets were, as Cyril Graham had shewn, put entirely out of court by the fact that Lord Pembroke did not come to London till they had been actually written and read by Shakespeare to his friends.

It was not, however, her name that interested me. I was content to hold with Professor Dowden that "To the eyes of no diver among the wrecks of time will that curious talisman gleam". What I wanted to discover was the nature of her influence over Shakespeare, as well as the characteristics of her personality. Two things were certain: she was much older than the poet, and the fascination that she exercised over him was at first purely intellectual. He began by feeling no physical passion for her. "I do not love thee with mine eyes", he says:

> Nor are mine ears with thy tongue's tune delighted;
> Nor tender feeling to base touches prone,
> Nor taste, nor smell, desire to be invited
> To any sensual feast with thee alone.

He did not even think her beautiful:

> My mistress' eyes are nothing like the sun;
> Coral is far more red than her lips' red:
> If snow be white, why then her breasts are dun;
> If hairs be wires, black wires grow on her head.

He has his moments of loathing for her, for not content with enslaving the soul of Shakespeare, she seems to have sought to snare the senses of Willie Hughes. Then Shakespeare cries aloud:

> Two loves I have of comfort and despair,
> Which like two spirits do suggest me still:
> The better angel is a man right fair,
> The worser spirit a woman colour'd ill.

To win me soon to hell, my female evil
Tempteth my better angel from my side,
And would corrupt my saint to be a devil,
Wooing his purity with her foul pride.

Then he sees her as she really is, the "bay where all men ride," the "wide world's common place," the woman who is in the "very refuse" of her evil deeds, and who is "as black as hell, as dark as night". Then it is that he pens that great sonnet upon Lust ("The expense of spirit in a waste of shame"), of which Mr. Theodore Watts says rightly that it is the greatest sonnet ever written. And it is then, also, that he offers to mortgage his very life and genius to her if she will but restore to him that "sweetest friend" of whom she had robbed him.

To compass this end he abandons himself to her, feigns to be full of an absorbing and sensuous passion of possession, forges false words of love, lies to her, and tells her that he lies:

My thoughts and my discourse as madmen's are,
At random from the truth vainly expressed;
For I have sworn thee fair, and thought thee bright,
Who art as black as hell, as dark as night.

Rather than suffer his friend to be treacherous to him, he will himself be treacherous to his friend. To shield his purity, he will himself be vile. He knew the weakness of the boy-actor's nature, his susceptibility to praise, his inordinate love of admiration, and deliberately set himself to fascinate the woman who had come between them.

It is never with impunity that one's lips say Love's Litany. Words have their mystical power over the soul, and form can create the feeling from which it should have sprung. Sincerity itself, the ardent, momentary sincerity of the artist, is often the unconscious result of style, and in the case of those rare temperaments that are exquisitely susceptible to the influences of language, the use of certain phrases and modes of expression can stir the very pulse of passion, can send the red blood coursing through the veins, and can transform into a strange sensuous energy what in its origin had been mere aesthetic impulse, and desire of art. So, at least, it seems to have been with Shakespeare. He begins by pretending to love, wears a lover's apparel and has a lover's words upon his lips.

What does it matter? It is only acting, only a comedy in real life. Suddenly he finds that what his tongue had spoken his soul had listened to, and that the raiment he had put on for disguise is a plague-stricken and poisonous thing that eats into his flesh, and that he cannot throw away. Then comes Desire, with its many maladies, and Lust that makes one love all that one loathes, and Shame, with its ashen face and secret smile. He is enthralled by this dark woman, is for a season separated from his friend, and becomes the "vassal-wretch" of one whom he knows to be evil and perverse and unworthy of his love, as of the love of Willie Hughes. "O, from what power", he says,—

> hast thou this powerful might,
> With insufficiency my heart to sway?
> To make me give the lie to my true sight,
> And swear that brightness does not grace the day?
> Whence hast thou this becoming of things ill,
> That in the very refuse of thy deeds
> There is such strength and warrantise of skill
> That in my mind, thy worst all best exceeds?

He is keenly conscious of his own degradation, and finally, realising that his genius is nothing to her compared to the physical beauty of the young actor, he cuts with a quick knife the bond that binds him to her, and in this bitter sonnet bids her farewell:

> In loving thee thou know'st I am forsworn,
> But thou art twice forsworn, to me love swearing;
> In act thy bed-vow broke, and new faith torn,
> In vowing new hate after new love bearing.
> But why of two oaths' breach do I accuse thee,
> When I break twenty? I am perjur'd most;
> For all my vows are oaths but to misuse thee,
> And all my honest faith in thee is lost:
> For I have sworn deep oaths of thy deep kindness,
> Oaths of thy love, thy truth, thy constancy;
> And, to enlighten thee, gave eyes to blindness,
> Or made them swear against the thing they see;
> For I have sworn thee fair; more perjur'd I,
> To swear against the truth so foul a lie!

His attitude towards Willie Hughes in the whole matter shews at once the fervour and the self-abnegation of the great love he bore him. There is a poignant touch of pathos in the close of this sonnet:

> Those pretty wrongs that liberty commits,
> When I am sometime absent from thy heart,
> Thy beauty and thy years full well befits,
> For still temptation follows where thou art.
> Gentle thou art, and therefore to be won,
> Beauteous thou art, therefore to be assailed;
> And when a woman woos, what woman's son
> Will sourly leave her till she have prevailed?
> Ay me! but yet thou mightst my seat forbear,
> And chide thy beauty and thy straying youth,
> Who lead thee in their riot even there
> Where thou art forc'd to break a two-fold truth,—
> Hers, by thy beauty tempting her to thee,
> Thine, by thy beauty being false to me.

But here he makes it manifest that his forgiveness was full and complete:

> No more be grieved at that which thou hast done:
> Roses have thorns, and silver fountains mud;
> Clouds and eclipses stain both moon and sun,
> And loathsome canker lives in sweetest bud.
> All men make faults, and even I in this,
> Authorising thy trespass with compare,
> Myself corrupting, salving thy amiss,
> Excusing thy sins more than thy sins are;
> For to thy sensual fault I bring in sense,—
> Thy adverse party is thy advocate,—
> And 'gainst myself a lawful plea commence:
> Such civil war is in my love and hate,
> That I an accessary needs must be
> To that sweet thief which sourly robs from me.

Shortly afterwards Shakespeare left London for Stratford (Sonnets 43 to 52), and when he returned Willie Hughes seems to have grown tired of the woman who for a little time had fascinated him. Her name is never mentioned again in the Sonnets, nor is there any allusion made to her. She had passed out of their lives.

But who was she? And, even if her name has not come down to us, were there any allusions to her in contemporary literature? It seems to me that although better educated than most of the women of her time, she was not nobly born, but was probably the profligate wife of some old and wealthy citizen. We know that women of this class, which was then first rising into social prominence, were strangely fascinated by the new art of stage-playing. They were to be found almost every afternoon at the theatre, when dramatic performances were being given, and "The Actors' Remonstrance" is eloquent on the subject of their amours with the young actors.

This passion for the dark lady also enabled me to fix with still greater certainty the date of the Sonnets. From internal evidence, from the characteristics of language, style, and the like, it was evident that they belonged to Shakespeare's early period, the period of "Love's Labour's Lost" and "Venus and Adonis". With the play, indeed, they are intimately connected. They display the same delicate euphuism, the same delight in fanciful phrase and curious expression, the artistic wilfulness and studied graces of the same "fair tongue, conceit's exposition." Rosaline, the

> "whitely wanton with a velvet brow,
> With two pitch-balls stick in her face for eyes,"

who is born "to make black fair", and whose "favour turns the fashion of the days," is the dark lady of the Sonnets who makes black "beauty's successive heir". In the comedy as well as in the poems we have that half-sensuous philosophy that exalts the judgment of the senses "above all slower, more toilsome means of knowledge," and Berowne is perhaps, as Mr. Pater suggests, a reflex of Shakespeare himself "when he had just become able to stand aside from and estimate the first period of his poetry."

Now though *Love's Labour's Lost* was not published till 1598, when it was brought out "newlie corrected and augmented" by Cuthbert Burby, there is no doubt that it was written and produced on the stage at a much earlier date, probably, as Professor Dowden points out, in 1588-9. If this be so, it is clear that Shakespeare's first meeting with Willie Hughes must have been in 1585, and it is just possible that this young actor may, after all, have been in his boyhood the musician of Lord Essex.

It is clear, at any rate, that Shakespeare's love for the dark lady must have passed away before 1594. In this year there appeared, under the editorship of Hadrian Dorell, that fascinating poem, or series of poems, *Willobie his Avisa*, which is described by Mr. Swinburne as the one contemporary book which has been supposed to throw any direct or indirect light on the mystic matter of the Sonnets. In it we learn how a young gentleman of St. John's College, Oxford, by name Henry Willobie, fell in love with a woman so "fair and chaste" that he called her Avisa, either because such beauty as hers had never been seen, or because she fled like a bird from the snare of his passion, and spread her wings for flight when he ventured but to touch her hand. Anxious to win his mistress he consults his familiar friend W.S., "who not long before had tried the courtesy of the like passion, and was now newly recovered of the like infection". Shakespeare encourages him in the siege that he is laying to the Castle of Beauty, telling him that every woman is to be wooed, and every woman to be won; views this "loving comedy" from far off, in order to see "whether it would sort to a happier end for this new actor than it did for the old player," and "enlargeth the wound with the *sharpe* razor of a willing conceit," feeling the purely æsthetic interest of the artist in the moods and emotions of others. It is unnecessary, however, to enter into this curious passage in Shakespeare's life, as all that I wanted to point out was that in 1594 he had been cured of his infatuation for the dark lady, and had already been acquainted for at least three years with Willie Hughes.

My whole scheme of the Sonnets was now complete and, by placing those that refer to the dark lady in their proper order and position, I saw the perfect unity and completeness of the whole. The drama—for indeed they formed a drama and a soul's tragedy of fiery passion and of noble thought—is divided into four scenes or acts. In the first of these (Sonnets 1-33)—Shakespeare invites Willie Hughes to go upon the stage as an actor, and to put to the service of Art his wonderful physical beauty, and his exquisite grace of youth, before passion has robbed him of the one, and time taken from him the other. Willie Hughes, after a time, consents to be a player in Shakespeare's company, and soon becomes the very centre and keynote of his inspiration. Suddenly, in one red-rose July (Sonnets 33-52, 61, and 127-152) there comes to the Globe Theatre a dark woman with wonderful eyes, who falls passionately in love with Willie Hughes. Shakespeare, sick with the malady of jealousy, and made mad by many doubts and fears, tries to fascinate the woman who has come between him and his friend. The love, that is at first feigned, becomes real, and he finds himself enthralled and dominated by a woman whom he knows to be evil and unworthy. To her the genius of a man is as nothing to a boy's beauty. Willie Hughes becomes for a time her slave and the toy of her fancy, and the second act ends with Shakespeare's departure from London. In the third act her influence has passed away. Shakespeare returns to London, and renews his friendship with Willie Hughes, to whom he promises immortality in his plays. Marlowe, hearing of the wonder and grace of the young actor, lures him away from the Globe Theatre to play Gaveston in the tragedy of *Edward II*, and for the second time, Shakespeare is separated from his friend. The last act (Sonnets 100-126) tells us of the return of Willie Hughes to Shakespeare's company. Evil rumour had now stained the white purity of his name, but Shakespeare's love still endures and is perfect. Of the mystery of this love, and of the mystery of passion, we are told strange and marvellous things, and the Sonnets conclude with an envoi of twelve lines, whose motive is the triumph of Beauty over Time, and of Death over Beauty.

From Willie Hughes's life I soon passed to thoughts of his death. I used to wonder what had been his end.

Perhaps he had been one of those English actors who in 1611 went across sea to Germany and played before the great Duke Henry Julius of Brunswick, himself a dramatist of no mean order, and at the Court of that strange Elector of Brandenburg, who was so enamoured of beauty that he was said to have bought for his weight in amber the young son of a travelling Greek merchant, and to have given pageants in honour of his slave all through that dreadful famine year of 1606-7, when the people died of hunger in the very streets of the town, and for the space of seven months there was no rain. We know at any rate that *Romeo and Juliet* was brought out at Dresden in 1613, along with *Hamlet* and *King Lear*, and it was surely to none other than Willie Hughes that in 1617 the death-mask of Shakespeare was brought by the hand of one of the suite of the English ambassador, pale token of the passing away of the great poet who had so dearly loved him. Indeed there would have been something peculiarly fitting in the idea that the boy-actor, whose beauty had been so vital an element in the realism and romance of Shakespeare's art, should have been the first to have brought to Germany the seed of the new culture, and was in his way the precursor of that *Aufklärung* or Illumination of the eighteenth century, that splendid movement which, though begun by Lessing and Herder, and brought to its full and perfect issue by Goethe, was in no small part helped on by another actor—Friedrich Schroeder—who awoke the popular consciousness, and by means of the feigned passions and mimetic methods of the stage showed the intimate, the vital, connection between life and literature. If this was so—and there was certainly no evidence against it—it was not improbable that Willie Hughes was one of those English comedians (*mimæ quidam ex Britannia*, as the old chronicle calls them), who were slain at Nuremberg in a sudden uprising of the people, and were secretly buried in a little vineyard outside the city by some young men "who had found pleasure in their performances, and of whom some had sought to be instructed in the mysteries of the new art." Certainly no more fitting place could there be for him to whom Shakespeare said, "thou art all my art", than this little vineyard outside the city walls. For was it not from the sorrow of Dionysos that Tragedy sprang? Was not the light laughter of Comedy, with its careless merriment and quick replies, first heard on the lips of the Sicilian vine-dressers? Nay, did not the purple and red stain of the wine-froth on face and limbs give the first suggestion of the charm and fascination of disguise—the desire for self-concealment, the sense of the value of objectivity thus showing itself in the rude beginnings of the art? At any rate, wherever he lay—whether in the little vineyard at the gate of the Gothic town, or in some dim London churchyard amidst the roar and bustle of our great city—no gorgeous monument marked his resting-place. His true tomb, as Shakespeare saw, was the poet's verse, his true monument the permanence of the drama. So had it been with others whose beauty had given a new creative impulse to their age. The ivory body of the Bithynian slave rots in the green ooze of the Nile, and on the yellow hills of the Cerameicus is strewn the dust of the young Athenian; but Antinous lives in sculpture, and Charmides in philosophy.

IV

Week after week I pored over these poems, and each new form of knowledge seemed to me a mode of reminiscence. Finally, after two months had elapsed, I determined to make a strong appeal to Erskine to do justice to the memory of Cyril Graham, and to give to the world his marvellous interpretation of the Sonnets—the only interpretation that thoroughly explained the problem. I have not any copy of my letter, I regret to say, nor have I been able to lay my hand upon the original; but I remember that I went over the whole ground, and covered sheets of paper with passionate reiteration of the arguments and proofs that my study had suggested to me. It seemed to me that I was not merely restoring Cyril Graham to his proper place in literary history, but rescuing the honour of Shakespeare himself from the tedious memory of a commonplace intrigue. I put into the letter all my enthusiasm. I put into the letter all my faith.

No sooner, in fact, had I sent it off than a curious reaction came over me. It seemed to me that I had given away my capacity for belief in the Willie Hughes theory of the Sonnets, that something had gone out of me, as it were, and that I was perfectly indifferent to the whole subject. What was it that had happened? It is difficult to say. Perhaps, by finding perfect expression for a passion, I had exhausted the passion itself. Emotional forces, like the forces of physical life, have their positive limitations. Perhaps the mere effort to convert any one to a theory involves some form of renunciation of the power of credence. Perhaps I was simply tired of the whole thing and, my enthusiasm having burnt out, my reason was left to its own unimpassioned judgment. However it came about, and I cannot pretend to explain it, there was no doubt that Willie Hughes suddenly became to me a mere myth, an idle dream, the boyish fancy of a young man who, like most ardent spirits, was more anxious to convince others than to be himself convinced.

I must admit that this was a bitter disappointment to me. I had gone through every phase of this great romance. I had lived with it, and it had become part of my nature. How was it that it had left me? Had I touched upon some secret that my soul desired to conceal? Or was there no permanence in personality? Did things come and go through the brain, silently, swiftly, and without footprints, like shadows through a mirror? Were we at the mercy of such impressions as Art or Life chose to give us? It seemed to me to be so.

It was at night-time that this feeling first came to me. I had sent my servant out to post the letter to Erskine, and was seated at the window looking out at the blue and gold city. The moon had not yet risen, and there was only one star in the sky, but the streets were full of quickly moving and flashing lights, and the windows of Devonshire House were illuminated for a great dinner to be given to some of the foreign princes then visiting London. I saw the scarlet liveries of the royal carriages, and the crowd hustling about the sombre gates of the courtyard.

Suddenly I said to myself: 'I have been dreaming, and all my life for these two months has been unreal. There was no such person as Willie Hughes.' Something like a faint cry of pain came to my lips as I began to realise how I had deceived myself, and I buried my face in my hands, struck with a sorrow greater than any I had felt since boyhood. After a few moments I rose and going into the library took up the Sonnets, and began to read them. But it was all to no avail. They gave me back nothing of the feeling I had brought to them: they revealed to me nothing of what I had found hidden in their lines. Had I merely been influenced by the beauty of the forged portrait, charmed by that Shelley-like face into faith and credence? Or, as Erskine had suggested, was it the pathetic tragedy of Cyril Graham's death that had so deeply stirred me? I could not tell. To the present day I cannot understand the beginning or the end of this strange passage in my life.

As I had said some very unjust and bitter things to Erskine in my letter, I determined to go and see him at once, and to make my apologies to him for my behaviour. Accordingly the next morning I drove down to Birdcage Walk, and found Erskine sitting in his library, with the forged picture of Willie Hughes in front of him.

"My dear Erskine!" I cried, "I have come to apologize to you."

"To apologize to me?" he said. "What for?"

"For my letter," I answered.

"You have nothing to regret in your letter," he said. "On the contrary, you have done me the greatest service in your power. You have shown me that Cyril Graham's theory is perfectly sound."

"You don't mean to say that you believe in Willie Hughes?" I exclaimed.

"Why not?" he rejoined. "You have proved the thing to me. Do you think I cannot estimate the value of evidence?"

"But there is no evidence at all," I groaned, sinking into a chair. "When I wrote to you I was under the influence of a perfectly silly enthusiasm. I had been touched by the story of Cyril Graham's death, fascinated by his romantic theory, enthralled by the wonder and novelty of the whole idea. I see now that the theory is based on a delusion. The only evidence for the existence of Willie Hughes is that picture in front of you, and the picture is a forgery. Don't be carried away by mere sentiment in this matter. Whatever romance may have to say about the Willie Hughes theory, reason is dead against it."

"I don't understand you," said Erskine, looking at me in amazement. "Why, you yourself have convinced me by your letter that Willie Hughes is an absolute reality. Why have you changed your mind? Or is all that you have been saying to me merely a joke?"

"I cannot explain it to you," I rejoined, "but I see now that there is really nothing to be said in favour of Cyril Graham's interpretation. The Sonnets are addressed to Lord Pembroke. For heaven's sake don't waste your time in a foolish attempt to discover a young Elizabethan actor who never existed, and to make a phantom puppet the centre of the great cycle of Shakespeare's Sonnets."

"I see that you don't understand the theory," he replied.

"My dear Erskine," I cried, "not understand it! Why, I feel as if I had invented it. Surely my letter shows you that I not merely went into the whole matter, but that I contributed proofs of every kind. The one flaw in the theory is that it presupposes the existence of the person whose existence is the subject of dispute. If we grant that there was in Shakespeare's company a young actor of the name of Willie Hughes, it is not difficult to make him the object of the Sonnets. But as we know that there was no actor of this name in the company of the Globe Theatre, it is idle to pursue the investigation further."

"But that is exactly what we don't know," said Erskine. "It is quite true that his name does not occur in the list given in the first folio; but, as Cyril pointed out, that is rather a proof in favour of the existence of Willie Hughes than against it, if we remember his treacherous desertion of Shakespeare for a rival dramatist."

We argued the matter over for hours, but nothing that I could say could make Erskine surrender his faith in Cyril Graham's interpretation. He told me that he intended to devote his life to proving the theory, and that he was determined to do justice to Cyril Graham's memory. I entreated him, laughed at him, begged of him, but it was of no use. Finally we parted, not exactly in anger, but certainly with a shadow between us. He thought me shallow, I thought him foolish. When I called on him again his servant told me that he had gone to Germany. The letters that I wrote to him remained unanswered.

Two years afterwards, as I was going into my club, the hall-porter handed me a letter with a foreign postmark. It was from Erskine, and written at the Hôtel d'Angleterre, Cannes. When I had read it I was filled with horror, though I did not quite believe that he would be so mad as to carry his resolve into execution. The gist of the letter was that he had tried in every way to verify the Willie Hughes theory, and had failed, and that as Cyril Graham had given his life for this theory, he himself had determined to give his own life also to the same cause. The concluding words of the letter were these: "I still believe in Willie Hughes; and by the time you receive this, I shall have died by my own hand for Willie Hughes's sake: for his sake, and for the sake of Cyril Graham, whom I drove to his death by my shallow scepticism and ignorant lack of faith. The truth was once revealed to you, and you rejected it. It comes to you now stained with the blood of two lives, —do not turn away from it."

It was a horrible moment. I felt sick with misery, and yet I could not believe it. To die for one's theological beliefs is the worst use a man can make of his life, but to die for a literary theory! It seemed impossible.

I looked at the date. The letter was a week old. Some unfortunate chance had prevented my going to the club for several days, or I might have got it in time to save him. Perhaps it was not too late. I drove off to my rooms, packed up my things, and started by the night-mail from Charing Cross. The journey was intolerable. I thought I would never arrive. As soon as I did I drove to the Hôtel d'Angleterre. They told me that Erskine had been buried two days before in the English cemetery. There was something horribly grotesque about the whole tragedy. I said all kinds of wild things, and the people in the hall looked curiously at me.

Suddenly Lady Erskine, in deep mourning, passed across the vestibule. When she saw me she came up to me, murmured something about her poor son, and burst into tears. I led her into her sitting-room. An elderly gentleman was there waiting for her. It was the English doctor.

We talked a great deal about Erskine, but I said nothing about his motive for committing suicide. It was evident that he had not told his mother anything about the reason that had driven him to so fatal, so mad an act. Finally Lady Erskine rose and said, "George left you something as a memento. It was a thing he prized very much. I will get it for you."

As soon as she had left the room I turned to the doctor and said, "What a dreadful shock it must have been to Lady Erskine! I wonder that she bears it as well as she does."

"Oh, she knew for months past that it was coming," he answered.

"Knew it for months past!" I cried. "But why didn't she stop him? Why didn't she have him watched? He must have been mad."

The doctor stared at me. "I don't know what you mean," he said.

"Well," I cried, "if a mother knows that her son is going to commit suicide——"

"Suicide!" he answered. "Poor Erskine did not commit suicide. He died of consumption. He came here to die. The moment I saw him I knew that there was no hope. One lung was almost gone, and the other was very much affected. Three days before he died he asked me was there any hope. I told him frankly that there was none, and that he had only a few days to live. He wrote some letters, and was quite resigned, retaining his senses to the last."

At that moment Lady Erskine entered the room with the fatal picture of Willie Hughes in her hand. "When George was dying he begged me to give you this," she said. As I took it from her, her tears fell on my hand.

The picture hangs now in my library, where it is very much admired by my artistic friends. They have decided that it is not a Clouet, but an Ouvry. I have never cared to tell them its true history. But sometimes, when I look at it, I think that there is really a great deal to be said for the Willie Hughes theory of Shakespeare's Sonnets.

The Harlot's House

WE CAUGHT the tread of dancing feet,
We loitered down the moonlit street,
And stopped beneath the harlot's house.

Inside, above the din and fray,
We heard the loud musicians play
The "Treues Liebes Herz" of Strauss.

Like strange mechanical grotesques,
Making fantastic arabesques,
The shadows raced across the blind.

We watched the ghostly dancers spin
To sound of horn and violin,
Like black leaves wheeling in the wind.

Like wire-pulled automatons,
Slim silhouetted skeletons
Went sidling through the slow quadrille.

They took each other by the hand,
And danced a stately saraband;
Their laughter echoed thin and shrill.

Sometimes a clockwork puppet pressed
A phantom lover to her breast,
Sometimes they seemed to try to sing;

Sometimes a horrible marionette
Came out, and smoked its cigarette
Upon the steps like a live thing.

Then, turning to my love, I said,
"The dead are dancing with the dead,
The dust is whirling with the dust."

But she—she heard the violin,
And left my side, and entered in:
Love passed into the house of lust.

Then suddenly the tune went false,
The dancers wearied of the waltz,
The shadows ceased to wheel and whirl.

And down the long and silent street,
The dawn, with silver-sandalled feet,
Crept like a frightened girl.

The Decay of Lying

*A DIALOGUE. Persons: Cyril and Vivian. Scene: The library of a
country house in Nottinghamshire.*

CYRIL
(coming in through the open window from the terrace)
MY DEAR Vivian, don't coop yourself up all day in the library. It is a
perfectly lovely afternoon. The air is exquisite. There is a mist upon
the woods like the purple bloom upon a plum. Let us go and lie on the
grass, and smoke cigarettes, and enjoy Nature.

VIVIAN
Enjoy Nature! I am glad to say that I have entirely lost that faculty.
People tell us that Art makes us love Nature more than we loved her
before; that it reveals her secrets to us; and that after a careful study of
Corot and Constable we see things in her that had escaped our observation. My own experience is that the more we study Art, the less we
care for Nature. What Art really reveals to us is Nature's lack of design,
her curious crudities, her extraordinary monotony, her absolutely unfinished condition. Nature has good intentions, of course, but, as Aristotle once said, she cannot carry them out. When I look at a landscape
I cannot help seeing all its defects. It is fortunate for us, however, that
Nature is so imperfect, as otherwise we should have had no art at all.

Art is our spirited protest, our gallant attempt to teach Nature her proper place. As for the infinite variety of Nature, that is a pure myth. It is not to be found in Nature herself. It resides in the imagination, or fancy, or cultivated blindness of the man who looks at her.

CYRIL

Well, you need not look at the landscape. You can lie on the grass and smoke and talk.

VIVIAN

But Nature is so uncomfortable. Grass is hard and lumpy and damp, and full of dreadful black insects. Why, even Morris' poorest workman could make you a more comfortable seat than the whole of Nature can. Nature pales before the furniture of "the street which from Oxford has borrowed its name", as the poet you love so much once vilely phrased it. I don't complain. If Nature had been comfortable, mankind would never have invented architecture, and I prefer houses to the open air. In a house we all feel of the proper proportions. Everything is subordinated to us, fashioned for our use and our pleasure. Egotism itself, which is so necessary to a proper sense of human dignity, is entirely the result of indoor life. Out of doors one becomes abstract and impersonal. One's individuality absolutely leaves one. And then Nature is so indifferent, so unappreciative. Whenever I am walking in the park here, I always feel that I am no more to her than the cattle that browse on the slope, or the burdock that blooms in the ditch. Nothing is more evident than that Nature hates Mind. Thinking is the most unhealthy thing in the world, and people die of it just as they die of any other disease. Fortunately, in England at any rate, thought is not catching. Our splendid physique as a people is entirely due to our national stupidity. I only hope we shall be able to keep this great historic bulwark of our happiness for many years to come; but I am afraid that we are beginning to be over-educated; at least everybody who is incapable of learning has taken to teaching— that is really what our enthusiasm for education has come to. In the meantime, you had better go back to your wearisome uncomfortable Nature, and leave me to correct my proofs.

CYRIL

Writing an article! That is not very consistent after what you have just said.

VIVIAN

Who wants to be consistent? The dullard and the doctrinaire, the tedious people who carry out their principles to the bitter end of action, to the *reductio ad absurdum* of practice. Not I. Like Emerson, I write over the door of my library the word "Whim". Besides, my article is really a most salutary and valuable warning. If it is attended to, there may be a new Renaissance of Art.

CYRIL

What is the subject?

VIVIAN

I intend to call it "The Decay of Lying: A Protest".

CYRIL

Lying! I should have thought that our politicians kept up that habit.

VIVIAN

I assure you that they do not. They never rise beyond the level of misrepresentation, and actually condescend to prove, to discuss, to argue. How different from the temper of the true liar, with his frank, fearless statements, his superb irresponsibility, his healthy, natural disdain of proof of any kind! After all, what is a fine lie? Simply that which is its own evidence. If a man is sufficiently unimaginative to produce evidence in support of a lie, he might just as well speak the truth at once. No, the politicians won't do. Something may, perhaps be urged on behalf of the Bar. The mantle of the Sophist has fallen on its members. Their feigned ardours and unreal rhetoric are delightful. They can make the worse appear the better cause, as though they were fresh from Leontine schools, and have been known to wrest from reluctant juries triumphant verdicts of acquittal for their clients, even when those clients, as often happens, were clearly and unmistakably innocent. But they are briefed by the prosaic, and are not ashamed to appeal to precedent. In spite of their endeavours, the truth will out. Newspapers, even, have degenerated. They may now be absolutely relied upon. One feels it as one wades through their columns. It is always the unreadable that occurs. I am afraid that there is not much to be said in favour of either the lawyer or the journalist. Besides, what I am pleading for is Lying in art. Shall I read you what I have written? It might do you a great deal of good.

CYRIL

Certainly, if you give me a cigarette. Thanks. By the way, what magazine do you intend it for?

VIVIAN

For the *Retrospective Review.* I think I told you that the elect had revived it.

CYRIL

Whom do you mean by "the elect"?

VIVIAN

Oh, The Tired Hedonists of course. It is a club to which I belong. We are supposed to wear faded roses in our buttonholes when we meet, and to have a sort of cult for Domitian. I am afraid you are not eligible. You are too fond of simple pleasures.

CYRIL

I should be black-balled on the ground of animal spirits, I suppose?

VIVIAN

Probably. Besides, you are a little too old. We don't admit anybody who is of the usual age.

CYRIL

Well, I should fancy you are all a good deal bored with each other.

VIVIAN

We are. That is one of the objects of the club. Now, if you promise not to interrupt too often, I will read you my article.

CYRIL

You will find me all attention.

VIVIAN

(reading in a very clear, musical voice)

"THE DECAY OF LYING: A PROTEST.—One of the chief causes that can be assigned for the curiously commonplace character of most of the literature of our age is undoubtedly the decay of Lying as an art, a sciehce, and a social pleasure. The ancient historians gave us delightful fiction in the form of fact; the modern novelist presents us with dull facts under the guise of fiction. The Blue-Book is rapidly becoming his ideal both for method and manner. He has his tedious *document humain*, his miserable little *coin de la création*, into which he peers with his microscope. He is to be found at the Librairie Nationale, or at the British Museum, shamelessly reading up his subject. He has not even the courage of other people's ideas, but insists on going dirrectly to life for everything, and ultimately, between encylcopædias and personal experience, he comes to the ground, having drawn his types from the family circle or from the weekly washerwoman, and having acquired an amount of useful information from which never, even in his most meditative moments, can he thoroughly free himself.

"The loss that results to literature in general from this false idea of our time can hardly be overest'mated. People have a careless way of talking about a 'born liar', just as they talk about a 'born poet'. But in both cases they are wrong. Lying and poetry are arts—arts, as Plato saw, not unconnected with each other—and they require the most careful study, the most disinterested devotion. Indeed, they have their technique, just as the more material arts of painting and sculpture have, their subtle secrets of form and colour, their craft-mysteries, their deliberate artistic methods. As one knows the poet by his fine music, so one can recognize the liar by his rich rhythmic utterance, and in neither case will the casual inspiration of the moment suffice. Here, as elsewhere, practice must precede perfection. But in modern days while the fashion of writing poetry has become far too common, and should, if possible, be discouraged, the fashion of lying has almost fallen into disrepute. Many a young man starts in life with a natural gift for exaggeration which, if nurtured in congenial and sympathetic surroundings, or by the imitation of the best models, might grow into something really great and wonderful. But, as a rule, he comes to nothing. He either falls into careless habits of accuracy——"

CYRIL

My dear fellow!

VIVIAN

Please don't interrupt in the middle of a sentence. "He either falls into careless habits of accuracy, or takes to frequenting the society of

MM

the aged and the well-informed. Both things are equally fatal to his imagination, as indeed they would be fatal to the imagination of anybody, and in a short time he develops a morbid and unhealthy faculty of truth-telling, begins to verify all statements made in his presence, has no hesitation in contradicting people who are much younger than himself, and often ends by writing novels which are so like life that no one can possibly believe in their probability. This is no isolated instance that we are giving. It is simply one example out of many; and if something cannot be done to check, or at least to modify, our monstrous worship of facts, Art will become sterile, and Beauty will pass away from the land.

"Even Mr. Robert Louis Stevenson, that delightful master of delicate and fanciful prose, is tainted with this modern vice, for we know positively no other name for it. There is such a thing as robbing a story of its reality by trying to make it too true, and *The Black Arrow* is so inartistic as not to contain a single anachronism to boast of, while the transformation of Dr. Jekyll reads dangerously like an experiment out of the *Lancet*. As for Mr. Rider Haggard, who really has, or had once, the makings of a perfectly magnificent liar, he is now so afraid of being suspected of genius that when he does tell us anything marvellous, he feels bound to invent a personal reminiscence, and to put it into a footnote as a kind of cowardly corroboration. Nor are our other novelists much better. Mr. Henry James writes fiction as if it were a painful duty, and wastes upon mean motives and imperceptible 'points of view' his neat literary style, his felicitous phrases, his swift and caustic satire. Mr. Hall Caine, it is true, aims at the grandiose, but then he writes at the top of his voice. He is so loud that one cannot hear what he says. Mr. James Payn is an adept in the art of concealing what is not worth finding. He hunts down the obvious with the enthusiasm of a short-sighted detective. As one turns over the pages, the suspense of the author becomes almost unbearable. The horses of Mr. William Black's phaeton do not soar towards the sun. They merely frighten the sky at evening into violent chromo-lithographic effects. On seeing them approach, the peasants take refuge in dialect. Mrs. Oliphant prattles pleasantly about curates, lawn-tennis parties, domesticity, and other wearisome things. Mr. Marion Crawford has immolated himself upon the altar of local colour. He is like the lady in the French comedy who keeps talking about 'le beau ciel d'Italie'. Besides, he has fallen into a bad habit of uttering moral platitudes. He is always telling us that to be good is to be good, and that to be bad is to be wicked. At times he is almost edifying. *Robert Elsmere* is of course a masterpiece—a masterpiece of the 'genre ennuyeux,' the one form of literature that the English people seem thoroughly to enjoy A thoughtful young friend of ours once told us that it reminded him of the sort of conversation that goes on at a meat tea in the house of a serious Nonconformist family, and we can quite believe it. Indeed it is only in England that such a book could be produced. England is the home of lost ideas. As for that great and daily increasing school of novelists for whom the sun always rises in the East End, the only thing that can be said about them is that they find life crude, and leave it raw.

"In France, though nothing so deliberately tedious as *Robert Elsmere* has been produced, things are not much better. M. Guy de Maupassant, with his keen mordant irony and his hard vivid style, strips life of the few poor rags that still cover her, and shows us foul sore and festering wound. He writes lurid little tragedies in which everybody is ridiculous; bitter comedies at which one cannot laugh for very tears. M. Zola, true to the lofty principle that he lays down in one of his pronunciamentos on literature, 'L'homme de génie n'a jamais d'esprit,' is determined to show that, if he has not got genius, he can at least be dull. And how well he succeeds! He is not without power. Indeed at times, as in *Germinal* there is something almost epic in his work. But his work is entirely wrong from beginning to end, and wrong not on the ground of morals, but on the ground of art. From any ethical standpoint it is just what it should be. The author is perfectly truthful, and describes things exactly as they happen. What more can any moralist desire? We have no sympathy at all with the moral indignation of our time against M. Zola. It is simply the indignation of Tartuffe on being exposed. But from the standpoint of art, what can be said in favour of the author of *L'Assommoir*, *Nana*, and *Pot-Bouille*? Nothing. Mr. Ruskin once described the characters in George Eliot's novels as being like the sweepings of a Pentonville omnibus, but M. Zola's characters are much worse. They have their dreary vices, and their drearier virtues. The record of their lives is absolutely without interest. Who cares what happens to them? In literature we require distinction, charm, beauty, and imaginative power. We don't want to be harrowed and disgusted with an account of the doings of the lower orders. M. Daudet is better. He has wit, a light touch, and an amusing style. But he has lately committed literary suicide. Nobody can possibly care for Delobelle with his 'Il faut lutter pour l'art,' or for Valmajour with his eternal refrain about the nightingale, or for the poet in *Jack* with his 'mots cruels,' now that we have learned from *Vingt Ans de ma Vie littéraire* that these characters were taken directly from life. To us they seem to have suddenly lost all their vitality, all the few qualities they ever possessed. The only real people are the people who never existed, and if a novelist is base enough to go to life for his personages he should at least pretend that they are creations, and not boast of them as copies. The justification of a character in a novel is not that other persons are what they are, but that the author is what he is. Otherwise the novel is not a work of art. As for M. Paul Bourget, the master of the *roman psychologique*, he commits the error of imagining that the men and women of modern life are capable of being infinitely analysed for an innumerable series of chapters. In point of fact what is interesting about people in good society—and M. Bourget rarely moves out of the Faubourg St. Germain, except to come to London—is the mask that each one of them wears, not the reality that lies behind the mask. It is a humiliating confession, but we are all of us made out of the same stuff. In Falstaff there is something of Hamlet, in Hamlet there is not a little of Falstaff. The fat knight has his moods of melancholy, and the young prince his moments of coarse humour. Where we differ from each other is purely in accidentals: in dress, manner, tone of voice, religious opinions, personal appearance, tricks of habit, and the like. The more one analyses people, the more all reasons for analysis disappear. Sooner or later one comes to that dreadful universal thing called human nature. Indeed, as any one who has ever worked among the poor knows only too well, the brotherhood of man is no mere poet's dream, it is a most depressing and humiliating reality; and if a writer insists upon analysing the upper classes, he might just as well write of match-girls and costermongers at once." However, my dear Cyril, I will not detain you any further just here. I quite admit that modern novels have many good points. All I insist on is that, as a class, they are quite unreadable.

CYRIL

That is certainly a very grave qualification, but I must say that I think you are rather unfair in some of your strictures. I like *The Deemster*, and *The Daughter of Heth*, and *Le Disciple*, and *Mr. Isaacs*, and as for *Robert Elsmere* I am quite devoted to it. Not that I can look

upon it as a serious work. As a statement of the problems that confront
the earnest Christian it is ridiculous and antiquated. It is simply Arnold's
Literature and Dogma with the literature left out. It is as much behind
the age as Paley's *Evidences,* or Colenso's method of Biblical exegesis.
Nor could anything be less impressive than the unfortunate hero gravely
heralding a dawn that rose long ago, and so completely missing its true
significance that he proposes to carry on the business of the old firm
under the new name. On the other hand, it contains several clever cari-
catures, and a heap of delightful quotations, and Green's philosophy
very pleasantly sugars the somewhat bitter pill of the author's fiction. I
also cannot help expressing my surprise that you have said nothing about
the two novelists whom you are always reading, Balzac and George
Meredith. Surely they are realists, both of them?

VIVIAN

Ah! Meredith! Who can define him? His style is chaos illumined by
flashes of lightning. As a writer he has mastered everything except
language: as a novelist he can do everything, except tell a story: as an
artist he is everything, except articulate. Somebody in Shakespeare—
Touchstone, I think—talks about a man who is always breaking his
shins over his own wit, and it seems to me that this might serve as the
basis for a criticism of Meredith's method. But whatever he is, he is
not a realist. Or rather I would say that he is a child of realism who is
not on speaking terms with his father. By deliberate choice he has made
himself a romanticist. He has refused to bow the knee to Baal, and after
all, even if the man's fine spirit did not revolt against the noisy assertions
of realism, his style would be quite sufficient of itself to keep life at a
respectful distance. By its means he has planted round his garden a hedge
full of thorns, and red with wonderful roses. As for Balzac, he was a
most remarkable combination of the artistic temperament with the
scientific spirit. The latter he bequeathed to his disciples: the
former was entirely his own. The difference between such a book
as M. Zola's *L'Assommoir* and Balzac's *Illusions Perdues* is the
difference between unimaginative realism and imaginative reality.
"All Balzac's characters," said Baudelaire, "are gifted with the same
ardour of life that animated himself. All his fictions are as deeply coloured
as dreams. Each mind is a weapon loaded to the muzzle with will. The
very scullions have genius." A steady course of Balzac reduces our

living friends to shadows, and our acquaintances to the shadows of
shades. His characters have a kind of fervent fiery-coloured existence.
They dominate us, and defy scepticism. One of the greatest tragedies
of my life is the death of Lucien de Rubempré. It is a grief from
which I have never been able completely to rid myself. It haunts
me in my moments of pleasure. I remember it when I laugh. But
Balzac is no more a realist than Holbein was. He created life, he did not
copy it. I admit, however, that he set far too high a value on modernity
of form, and that, consequently, there is no book of his that, as an
artistic masterpiece, can rank with *Salammbô* or *Esmond*, or *The
Cloister and the Hearth*, or *The Vicomte de Bragelonne*.

CYRIL
Do you object to modernity of form, then?

VIVIAN
Yes. It is a huge price to pay for a very poor result. Pure modernity
of form is always somewhat vulgarizing. It cannot help being so. The
public imagine that, because they are interested in their immediate surroundings, Art should be interested in them also, and should take them
as her subject-matter. But the mere fact that they are interested in these
things makes them unsuitable subjects for Art. The only beautiful
things, as somebody once said, are the things that do not concern us. As
long as a thing is useful or necessary to us, or affects us in any way, either
for pain or for pleasure, or appeals strongly to our sympathies, or is a
vital part of the environment in which we live, it is outside the proper
sphere of art. To art's subject-matter we should be more or less indifferent. We should, at any rate, have no preferences, no prejudices,
no partisan feeling of any kind. It is exactly because Hecuba is nothing
to us that her sorrows are such an admirable motive for a tragedy. I do
not know anything in the whole history of literature sadder than the
artistic career of Charles Reade. He wrote one beautiful book, *The
Cloister and the Hearth*, a book as much above *Romola* as *Romola* is
above *Daniel Deronda*, and wasted the rest of his life in a foolish attempt
to be modern, to draw public attention to the state of our convict prisons,
and the management of our private lunatic asylums. Charles Dickens
was depressing enough in all conscience when he tried to arouse our
sympathy for the victims of the poor-law administration; but Charles

Reade, an artist, a scholar, a man with a true sense of beauty, raging and roaring over the abuses of contemporary life like a common pamphleteer or a sensational journalist, is really a sight for the angels to weep over. Believe me, my dear Cyril, modernity of form and modernity of subject-matter are entirely and absolutely wrong. We have mistaken the common livery of the age for the vesture of the Muses, and spend our days in the sordid streets and hideous suburbs of our vile cities when we should be out on the hillside with Apollo. Certainly we are a degraded race, and have sold our birthright for a mess of facts.

Cyril

There is something in what you say, and there is no doubt that whatever amusement we may find in reading a purely modern novel, we have rarely any artistic pleasure in re-reading it. And this is perhaps the best rough test of what is literature and what is not. If one cannot enjoy reading a book over and over again, there is no use reading it at all. But what do you say about the return to Life and Nature. This is the panacea that is always being recommended to us.

Vivian

I will read you what I say on that subject. The passage comes later on in the article, but I may as well give it to you now:

"The popular cry of our time is 'Let us return to Life and Nature; they will recreate Art for us, and send the red blood coursing through her veins; they will shoe her feet with swiftness and make her hand strong.' But, alas! we are mistaken in our amiable and well-meaning efforts. Nature is always behind the age. And as for Life, she is the solvent that breaks up Art, the enemy that lays waste her house."

Cyril

What do you mean by saying that Nature is always behind the age?

Vivian

Well, perhaps that is rather cryptic. What I mean is this. If we take Nature to mean natural simple instinct as opposed to self-conscious culture, the work produced under this influence is always old-fashioned, antiquated, and out of date. One touch of Nature may make the whole world kin, but two touches of Nature will destroy any work of Art. If, on the other hand, we regard Nature as the collection of phenomena external to man, people only discover in her what they bring to her. She has no suggestions of her own. Wordsworth went to the lakes, but he was never a lake poet. He found in stones the sermons he had already hidden there. He went moralizing about the district, but his good work was produced when he returned, not to Nature, but to poetry. Poetry gave him *Laodamia*, and the fine sonnets, and the great Ode, such as it is. Nature gave him *Martha Ray* and *Peter Bell*, and the address to Mr. Wilkinson's spade.

CYRIL

I think that view might be questioned. I am rather inclined to believe in the "impulse from a vernal wood," though of course the artistic value of such an impulse depends entirely on the kind of temperament that receives it, so that the return to Nature would come to mean simply the advance to a great personality. You would agree with that, I fancy. However, proceed with your article.

VIVIAN
(reading)

"Art begins with abstract decoration, with purely imaginative and pleasurable work dealing with what is unreal and non-existent. This is the first stage. Then Life becomes fascinated with this new wonder, and asks to be admitted into the charmed circle. Art takes life as part of her rough material, recreates it, and refashions it in fresh forms, is absolutely indifferent to fact, invents, imagines, dreams, and keeps between herself and reality the impenetrable barrier of beautiful style, of decorative or ideal treatment. The third stage is when Life gets the upper hand, and drives Art out into the wilderness. This is the true decadence, and it is from this that we are now suffering.

"Take the case of the English drama. At first in the hands of the monks Dramatic Art was abstract, decorative, and mythological. Then she enlisted Life in her service, and using some of life's external forms, she created an entirely new race of beings, whose sorrows were more terrible than any sorrow man has ever felt, whose joys were keener than lover's joys, who had the rage of the Titans and the calm of the gods, who had monstrous and marvellous sins, monstrous and marvellous virtues. To them she gave a language different from that of actual use, a language full of resonant music and sweet rhythm, made stately by solemn cadence, or made delicate by fanciful rhyme, jewelled with wonderful words, and enriched with lofty diction. She clothed her children in strange raiment and gave them masks, and at her bidding the antique world rose from its marble tomb. A new Cæsar stalked through the streets of risen Rome, and with purple sail and flute-led oars another Cleopatra passed up the river to Antioch. Old myth and legend and dream took shape and substance. History was entirely re-written, and there was hardly one of the dramatists who did not recognize that the object of Art is not simple truth but complex beauty. In this they were perfectly right. Art itself is really a form of exaggeration; and selection, which is the very spirit of Art, is nothing more than an intensified mode of over-emphasis.

' But Life soon shattered the perfection of the form. Even in Shakespeare we can see the beginning of the end. It shows itself by the gradual breaking up of the blank-verse in the later plays, by the predominance given to prose, and by the over-importance assigned to characterization. The passages in Shakespeare—and they are many—where the language is uncouth, vulgar, exaggerated, fantastic, obscene even, are entirely due to Life calling for an echo of her own voice, and rejecting the intervention of beautiful style, through which alone should Life be suffered to find expression. Shakespeare is not by any means a flawless artist. He is too fond of going directly to life, and borrowing life's natural utterance. He forgets that when Art surrenders her imaginative medium she surrenders everything. Goethe says, somewhere—

In der Beschrankung zeigt sich erst der Meister,

'It is in working within limits that the master reveals himself,' and the limitation, the very condition of any art is style. However, we need not linger any longer over Shakespeare's realism. *The Tempest* is the most perfect of palinodes. All that we desired to point out was, that the magnificent work of the Elizabethan and Jacobean artists contained within itself the seeds of its own dissolution, and that, if it drew some of its strength from using life as rough material, it drew all its weakness from using life as an artistic method. As the inevitable result of this substitution of an imitative for a creative medium, this surrender of an imaginative form, we have the modern English melodrama. The characters in these plays talk on the stage exactly as they would talk off it;

they have neither aspirations nor aspirates; they are taken directly from life and reproduce its vulgarity down to the smallest detail; they present the gait, manner, costume, and accent of the real people; they would pass unnoticed in a third-class railway carriage. And yet how wearisome the plays are! They do not succeed in producing even that impression of reality at which they aim, and which is their only reason for existing. As a method, realism is a complete failure.

"What is true about the drama and the novel is no less true about those arts that we call the decorative arts. The whole history of these arts in Europe is the record of the struggle between Orientalism, with its frank rejection of imitation, its love of artistic convention, its dislike to the actual representation of any object in Nature, and our own imitative spirit. Wherever the former has been paramount, as in Byzantium, Sicily, and Spain, by actual contact, or in the rest of Europe by the influence of the Crusades, we have had beautiful and imaginative work in which the visible things of life are transmuted into artistic conventions and the things that Life has not are invented and fashioned for her delight. But wherever we have returned to Life and Nature, our work has always become vulgar, common, and uninteresting. Modern tapestry, with its aerial effects, its elaborate perspective, its broad expanses of waste sky, its faithful and laborious realism, has no beauty whatsoever. The pictorial glass of Germany is absolutely detestable. We are beginning to weave possible carpets in England, but only because we have returned to the method and spirit of the East. Our rugs and carpets of twenty years ago, with their solemn depressing truths, their inane worship of Nature, their sordid reproductions of visible objects, have become even to the Philistine, a source of laughter. A cultured Mahomedan once remarked to us, 'You Christians are so occupied in misinterpreting the fourth commandment that you have never thought of making an artistic application of the second'. He was perfectly right, and the whole truth of the matter is this: The proper school to learn Art in is not Life but Art."

And now let me read you a passage which seems to me to settle the question very completely.

"It was not always thus. We need not say anything about the poets, for they, with the unfortunate exception of Mr. Wordsworth, have been really faithful to their high mission, and are universally recognized as being absolutely unreliable. But in the works of Herodotus, who, in spite of the shallow and ungenerous attempts of modern sciolists to verify his history, may justly be called the 'Father of Lies'; in the published speeches of Cicero and the biographies of Suetonius; in Tacitus at his best; in Pliny's *Natural History*; in Hanno's *Periplus*; in all the early chronicles; in the Lives of the Saints; in Froissart and Sir Thomas Mallory; in the travels of Marco Polo; in Olaus Magnus, and Aldrovandus, and Conrad Lycosthenes, with his magnificent *Prodigiorum et Ostentorum Chronicon*; in the autobiography of Benvenuto Cellini; in the memoirs of Casanova; in Defoe's *History of the Plague*; in Boswell's *Life of Johnson*; in Napoleon's dispatches, and in the works of our own Carlyle, whose *French Revolution* is one of the most fascinating historical novels ever written, facts are either kept in their proper subordinate position, or else entirely excluded on the general ground of dullness. Now, everything is changed. Facts are not merely finding a footing-place in history, but they are usurping the domain of Fancy, and have invaded the kingdom of Romance. Their chilling touch is over everything. They are vulgarizing mankind. The crude commercialism of America, its materializing spirit, its indifference to the poetical side of things, and its lack of imagination and of high unattainable ideals, are entirely due to that country having adopted for its national hero a man who according to his own confession, was incapable of telling a lie, and it is not too much to say that the story of George Washington and the cherry-tree has done more harm, and in a shorter space of time, than any other moral tale in the whole of literature."

CYRIL
My dear boy!

VIVIAN
I assure you it is the case, and the amusing part of the whole thing is that the story of the cherry-tree is an absolute myth. However you must not think that I am too despondent about the artistic future of America or of our own country. Listen to this:

"That some change will take place before this century has drawn to its close we have no doubt whatsoever. Bored by the tedious and improving conversation of those who have neither the wit to exaggerate nor the genius to romance, tired of the intelligent person whose reminiscences are always based upon memory, whose statements are invariably limited by probability, and who is at any time liable to be corroborated by the merest Philistine who happens to be present, Society sooner or later must return to its lost leader, the cultured and fascinating liar. Who he was who first, without ever having gone out to the rude chase, told the wondering cavemen at sunset how he had dragged the Megatherium from the purple darkness of its jasper cave, or slain the Mammoth in single combat and brought back its gilded tusks, we cannot tell, and not one of our modern anthropologists, for all their much-boasted science, has had the ordinary courage to tell us. Whatever his name or race, he certainly was the true founder of social intercourse. For the aim of the liar is simply to charm, to delight, to give pleasure. He is the very basis of civilized society, and without him a dinner party, even at the mansions of the great, is as dull as a lecture at the Royal Society, or a debate at the Incorporated Authors, or one of Mr. Burnand's farcical comedies.

"Nor will he be welcomed by society alone. Art, breaking from the prison-house of realism, will run to greet him, and will kiss his false, beautiful lips, knowing that he alone is in possession of the great secret of all her manifestations, the secret that Truth is entirely and absolutely a matter of style; while Life—poor, probable, uninteresting human life—tired of repeating herself for the benefit of Mr. Herbert Spencer, scientific historians, and the compilers of statistics in general, will follow meekly after him, and try to reproduce, in her own simple and untutored way, some of the marvels of which he talks.

"No doubt there will always be critics who, like a certain writer in the *Saturday Review*, will gravely censure the teller of fairy tales for his defective knowledge of natural history, who will measure imaginative work by their own lack of any imaginative faculty, and will hold up their inkstained hands in horror if some honest gentleman, who has never been farther than the yew-trees of his own garden, pens a fascinating book of travels like Sir John Mandeville, or, like great Raleigh, writes a whole history of the world, without knowing anything whatsoever about the past. To excuse themselves they will try and shelter under the shield of him who made Prospero the magician, and gave him Caliban and Ariel as his servants, who heard the Tritons blowing their horns round the coral reefs of the Enchanted Isle, and the fairies singing to each other in a wood near Athens, who led the phantom kings in dim procession across the misty Scottish heath, and hid Hecate in a cave with the weird sisters. They will call upon Shakespeare—they always do—and will quote that hackneyed passage about Art holding the mirror up to Nature, forgetting that this unfortunate aphorism is deliberately said by Hamlet in order to convince the bystanders of his absolute insanity in all art-matters."

CYRIL

Ahem! Another cigarette, please.

VIVIAN

My dear fellow, whatever you may say, it is merely a dramatic utterance, and no more represents Shakespeare's real views upon art than the speeches of Iago represent his real views upon morals. But let me get to the end of the passage:

"Art finds her own perfection within, and not outside of, herself. She is not to be judged by any external standard of resemblance. She is a veil, rather than a mirror. She has flowers that no forests know of, birds that no woodland possesses. She makes and unmakes many worlds, and can draw the moon from heaven with a scarlet thread. Hers are the 'forms more real than living man', and hers the great archetypes of which things that have existence are but unfinished copies. Nature has, in her eyes, no laws, no uniformity. She can work miracles at her will, and when she calls monsters from the deep they come. She can bid the almond tree blossom in winter, and send the snow upon the ripe cornfield. At her word the frost lays its silver finger on the burning mouth of June, and the winged lions creep out from the hollows of the Lydian hills. The dryads peer from the thicket as she passes by, and the brown fauns smile strangely at her when she comes near them. She has hawk-faced gods that worship her, and the centaurs gallop at her side."

CYRIL

I like that. I can see it. Is that the end?

VIVIAN

No. There is one more passage, but it is purely practical. It simply suggests some methods by which we could revive this lost art of Lying.

CYRIL

Well, before you read it to me, I should like to ask you a question. What do you mean by saying that Life, "poor, probable, uninteresting

human life", will try to reproduce the marvels of Art? I can quite understand your objection to Art being treated as a mirorr. You think it
would reduce genius to the position of a cracked looking-glass. But you
don't mean to say that you seriously believe that Life imitates Art, that
Life in fact is the mirror, and Art the reality?

VIVIAN

Certainly I do. Paradox though it may seem—and paradoxes are
always dangerous things—it is none the less true that Life imitates Art
far more than Art imitates Life. We have all seen in our own day in
England how a certain curious and fascinating type of beauty, invented
and emphasized by two imaginative painters, has so influenced Life that
whenever one goes to a private view or to an artistic salon one sees, here
the mystic eyes of Rossetti's dream, the long ivory throat, the strange
square-cut jaw, the loosened shadowy hair that he so ardently loved,
there the sweet maidenhood of "The Golden Stair", the blossom-like
mouth and weary loveliness of the "Laus Amoris", the passion-pale face
of Andromeda, the thin hands and lithe beauty of the Vivien in "Merlin's
Dream". And it has always been so. A great artist invents a type, and
Life tries to copy it, to reproduce it in a popular form, like an enterprising
publisher. Neither Holbein nor Vandyck found in England what they
have given us. They brought their types with them, and life with her
keen imitative faculty set herself to supply the master with models.
The Greeks, with their quick artistic instinct, understood this, and
set in the bride's chamber the statue of Hermes or of Apollo, that she
might bear children as lovely as the works of art that she looked at in
her rapture or her pain. They knew that Life gains from Art not
merely spirituality, depth of thought and feeling, soul-turmoil or soul-
peace, but that she can form herself on the very lines and colours of
Art, and can reproduce the dignity of Pheidias as well as the grace of
Praxiteles. Hence came their objection to realism. They disliked it on
purely social grounds. They felt that it inevitably makes people ugly,
and they were perfectly right. We try to improve the conditions of the
race by means of good air, free sunlight, wholesome waters and hideous
bare buildings for the better housing of the lower orders. But these things
merely produce health, they do not produce beauty. For this, Art is
required, and the true disciples of the great artist are not his studio-
imitators, but those who become like his works of art, be they plastic

as in Greek days, or pictorial as in modern times; in a word, Life is
Art's best, Art's only pupil.

As it is with the visible arts, so it is with literature. The most obvious
and the vulgarest form in which this is shown is in the case of the silly
boys who, after reading the adventures of Jack Sheppard or Dick Turpin,
pillage the stalls of unfortunate apple-women, break into sweet-shops
at night, and alarm old gentlemen who are returning home from the
city by leaping out on them in suburban lanes, with black masks and
unloaded revolvers. This interesting phenomenon, which always occurs
after the appearance of a new edition of either of the books I have
alluded to, is usually attributed to the influence of literature on the
imagination. But this is a mistake. The imagination is essentially
creative and always seeks for a new form. The boy-burglar is simply
the inevitable result of life's imitative instinct. He is Fact, occupied as
Fact usually is, with trying to reproduce Fiction, and what we see in him
is repeated on an extended scale throughout the whole of life. Schopenhauer has analysed the pessimism that characterizes modern thought,
but Hamlet invented it. The world has become sad because a puppet
was once melancholy. The Nihilist, that strange martyr who has no
faith, who goes to the stake without enthusiasm, and dies for what he
does not believe in, is a purely literary product. He was invented by
Turgénieff, and completed by Dostoievski. Robespierre came out of
the pages of Rousseau as surely as the People's Palace rose out of the
débris of a novel. Literature always anticipates life. It does not copy it,
but moulds it to its purpose. The nineteenth century, as we know it,
is largely an invention of Balzac. Our Luciens de Rubempré, our Rastig-
nacs, and De Marsays made their first appearance on the stage of the
Comédie Humaine. We are merely carrying out, with footnotes and
unnecessary additions, the whim or fancy or creative vision of a great
novelist. I once asked a lady, who knew Thackeray intimately, whether
he had had any model for Becky Sharp. She told me that Becky was
an invention, but that the idea of the character had been partly suggested
by a governess who lived in the neighbourhood of Kensington Square,
and was the companion of a very selfish and rich old woman. I inquired
what became of the governess, and she replied that, oddly enough, some
years after the appearance of *Vanity Fair*, she ran away with the nephew
of the lady with whom she was living, and for a short time made a great
splash in society, quite in Mrs. Rawdon Crawley's style, and entirely

by Mrs. Rawdon Crawley's methods. Ultimately she came to grief, disappeared to the Continent, and used to be occasionally seen at Monte Carlo and other gambling places. The noble gentleman from whom the same great sentimentalist drew Colonel Newcome died, a few months after *The Newcomes* had reached a fourth edition, with the word "Adsum" on his lips. Shortly after Mr. Stevenson published his curious psychological story of transformation, a friend of mine, called Mr. Hyde, was in the north of London, and being anxious to get to a railway station, took what he thought would be a short cut, lost his way, and found himself in a network of mean, evil-looking streets. Feeling rather nervous he began to walk extremely fast, when suddenly out of an archway ran a child right between his legs. It fell on the pavement, he tripped over it, and trampled upon it. Being of course very much frightened and a little hurt, it began to scream, and in a few seconds, the whole street was full of rough people who came pouring out of the houses like ants. They surrounded him, and asked him his name. He was just about to give it when he suddenly remembered the opening incident in Mr. Stevenson's story. He was so filled with horror at having realized in his own person that terrible and well-written scene, and at having done accidentally, though in fact, what the Mr. Hyde of fiction had done with deliberate intent, that he ran away as hard as he could go. He was, however, very closely followed, and finally he took refuge in a surgery, the door of which happened to be open, where he explained to a young assistant, who was serving there, exactly what had occurred. The humanitarian crowd were induced to go away on his giving them a small sum of money, and as soon as the coast was quite clear he left. As he passed out, the name on the brass door-plate of the surgery caught his eye. It was "Jekyll." At least it should have been.

Here the imitation, as far as it went, was of course accidental. In the following case the imitation was self-conscious. In the year 1879, just after I had left Oxford, I met at a reception at the house of one of the Foreign Ministers a woman of very curious exotic beauty. We became great friends, and were constantly together. And yet what interested me most in her was not her beauty, but her character, her entire vagueness of character. She seemed to have no personality at all, but simply the possibility of many types. Sometimes she would give herself up entirely to art, turn her drawing-room into a studio, and spend two or three days a week at picture-galleries or museums. Then she would take to attending race-meetings, wear the most horsey clothes, and talk about nothing but betting. She abandoned religion for mesmerism, mesmerism for politics, and politics for the melodramatic excitements of philanthropy. In fact, she was a kind of Proteus, and as much a failure in all her transformations as was that wondrous sea-god when Odysseus laid hold of him. One day a serial began in one of the French magazines. At that time I used to read serial stories, and I well remember the shock of surprise I felt when I came to the description of the heroine. She was so like my friend that I brought her the magazine, and she recognized herself in it immediately, and seemed fascinated by the resemblance. I should tell you, by the way, that the story was translated from some dead Russian writer, so that the author had not taken his type from my friend. Well, to put the matter briefly, some months afterwards I was in Venice, and finding the magazine in the reading-room of the hotel, I took it up casually to see what had become of the heroine. It was a most piteous tale, as the girl had ended by running away with a man absolutely inferior to her, not merely in social station, but in character and intellect also. I wrote to my friend that evening about my views on Giovanni Bellini, and the admirable ices at Florio's, and the artistic value of gondolas, but added a postscript to the effect that her double in the story had behaved in a very silly manner. I don't know why I added that, but I remember I had a sort of dread over me that she might do the same thing. Before my letter had reached her, she had run away with a man who deserted her in six months. I saw her in 1884 in Paris, where she was living with her mother, and I asked her whether the story had had anything to do with her action. She told me that she had felt an absolutely irresistible impulse to follow the heroine step by step in her strange and fatal progress, and that it was with a feeling of real terror that she had looked forward to the last few chapters of the story. When they appeared, it seemed to her that she was compelled to reproduce them in life, and she did so. It was a most clear example of this imitative instinct of which I was speaking, and an extremely tragic one.

However, I do not wish to dwell any further upon individual instances. Personal experience is a most vicious and limited circle. All that I desire to point out is the general principle that Life imitates Art far more than Art imitates Life, and I feel sure that if you think seriously about it you will find that it is true. Life holds the mirror up

NN

to Art, and either reproduces some strange type imagined by painter or sculptor, or realizes in fact what has been dreamed in fiction. Scientifically speaking, the basis of life—the energy of life, as Aristotle would call it—is simply the desire for expression, and Art is always presenting various forms through which this expression can be attained. Life seizes on them and uses them, even if they be to her own hurt. Young men have committed suicide because Rolla did so, have died by their own hand because by his own hand Werther died. Think of what we owe to the imitation of Christ, of what we owe to the imitation of Cæsar.

CYRIL

The theory is certainly a very curious one, but to make it complete you must show that Nature, no less than Life, is an imitation of Art. Are you prepared to prove that?

VIVIAN

My dear fellow, I am prepared to prove anything.

CYRIL

Nature follows the landscape painter then, and takes her effects from him?

VIVIAN

Certainly. Where, if not from the Impressionists, do we get those wonderful brown fogs that come creeping down our streets, blurring the gas-lamps and changing the houses into monstrous shadows? To whom, if not to them and their master, do we owe the lovely silver mists that brood over our river, and turn to faint forms of fading grace curved bridge and swaying barge? The extraordinary change that has taken place in the climate of London during the last ten years is entirely due to this particular school of Art. You smile. Consider the matter from a scientific or a metaphysical point of view, and you will find that I am right. For what is Nature? Nature is no great mother who has borne us. She is our creation. It is in our brain that she quickens to life. Things are because we see them, and what we see, and how we see it, depends on the Arts that have influenced us. To look at a thing is very different from seeing a thing. One does not see anything until one sees its beauty. Then, and then only, does it come into existence. At present, people see fogs, not because there are fogs, but because poets and painters have taught them the mysterious loveliness of such effects. There may have been fogs for centuries in London. I dare say there were. But no one saw them, and so we do not know anything about them. They did not exist till Art had invented them. Now, it must be admitted, fogs are carried to excess. They have become the mere mannerism of a clique, and the exaggerated realism of their method gives dull people bronchitis. Where the cultured catch an effect, the uncultured catch cold. And so, let us be humane, and invite Art to turn her wonderful eyes elsewhere. She has done so already, indeed. That white quivering sunlight that one sees now in France, with its strange blotches of mauve, and its restless violet shadows, is her latest fancy, and, on the whole, Nature reproduces it quite admirably. Where she used to give us Corots and Daubignys, she gives us now exquisite Monets and entrancing Pissaros. Indeed there are moments, rare, it is true, but still to be observed from time to time, when Nature becomes absolutely modern. Of course she is not always to be relied upon. The fact is that she is in this unfortunate position. Art creates an incomparable and unique effect, and having done so, passes on to other things. Nature, upon the other hand, forgetting that imitation can be made the sincerest form of insult, keeps on repeating this effect until we all become absolutely wearied of it. Nobody of any real culture, for instance, ever talks nowadays about the beauty of a sunset. Sunsets are quite old-fashioned. They belong to the time when Turner was the last note in art. To admire them is a distinct sign of provincialism of temperament. Upon the other hand they go on. Yesterday evening Mrs. Arundel insisted on my coming to the window, and looking at the glorious sky, as she called it. Of course I had to look at it. She is one of those absurdly pretty Philistines, to whom one can deny nothing. And what was it? It was simply a very second-rate Turner, a Turner of a bad period, with all the painter's worst faults exaggerated and over-emphasized. Of course, I am quite ready to admit that Life very often commits the same error. She produces her false Renés and her sham Vautrins, just as Nature gives us, on one day a doubtful Cuyp, and on another a more than questionable Rousseau. Still, Nature irritates one more when she does things of that kind. It seems so stupid, so obvious, so unnecessary. A false Vautrin might be delightful. A doubtful Cuyp is unbearable. However, I don't want to be too hard on Nature. I wish the Channel, especially at Hastings, did not look quite so often like a Henry Moore, grey pearl with yellow lights, but then, when Art is more varied, Nature will, no doubt, be more varied also. That she imitates Art, I don't think even her worst enemy would deny now. It is the one thing that keeps her in touch with civilized man. But have I proved my theory to your satisfaction?

CYRIL

You have proved it to my dissatisfaction, which is better. But even admitting this strange imitative instinct in Life and Nature, surely you would acknowledge that Art expresses the temper of its age, the spirit of its time, the moral and social conditions that surround it, and under whose influence it is produced.

VIVIAN

Certainly not! Art never expresses anything but itself. This is the principle of my new æsthetics; and it is this, more than that vital connection between form and substance on which Mr. Pater dwells, that makes music the type of all the arts. Of course, nations and individuals, with that healthy natural vanity which is the secret of existence, are always under the impression that it is of them that the Muses are talking, always trying to find in the calm dignity of imaginative art some mirror of their own turbid passions, always forgetting that the singer of life is not Apollo, but Marsyas. Remote from reality, and with her eyes turned away from the shadows of the cave, Art reveals her own perfection, and the wondering crowd that watches the opening of the marvellous, many-petalled rose fancies that it is its own history that is being told to it, its own spirit that is finding expression in a new form. But it is not so. The highest art rejects the burden of the human spirit, and gains more from a new medium or a fresh material than she does from any enthusiasm for Art, or from any lofty passion, or from any great awakening of the human consciousness. She develops purely on her own lines. She is not symbolic of any age. It is the ages that are her symbols.

Even those who hold that Art is representative of time and place and people, cannot help admitting that the more imitative an art is, the less it represents to us the spirit of its age. The evil faces of the Roman emperors look out at us from the foul porphyry and spotted jasper in which the realistic artists of the day delighted to work, and we fancy that in those cruel lips and heavy sensual jaws we can find the secret of the ruin of the Empire. But it was not so. The vices of Tiberius could not destroy that supreme civilization, any more than the virtues of the Antonines could save it. It fell for other, for less interesting reasons. The sibyls and prophets of the Sistine may indeed serve to interpret for some that new birth of the emancipated spirit that we call the Renaissance; but what do the drunken boors and brawling peasants of Dutch art tell us about the great soul of Holland? The more abstract, the more ideal an art is, the more it reveals to us the temper of its age. If we wish to understand a nation by means of its art, let us look at its architecture or its music.

Cyril

I quite agree with you there. The spirit of an age may be best expressed in the abstract ideal arts, for the spirit itself is abstract and ideal. Upon the other hand, for the visible aspect of an age, for its look, as the phrase goes; we must of course go to the arts of imitation.

Vivian

I don't think so. After all, what the imitative arts really give us are merely the various styles of particular artists, or of certain schools of artists. Surely you don't imagine that the people of the Middle Ages bore any resemblance at all to the figures on mediæval stained glass, or in mediæval stone and wood carving, or on mediæval metal-work, or tapestries, or illuminated MSS. They were probably very ordinary-looking people, with nothing grotesque, or remarkable, or fantastic in their appearance. The Middle Ages, as we know them in Art, are simply a definite form of style, and there is no reason at all why an artist with this style should not be produced in the nineteenth century. No great artist ever sees things as they really are. If he did, he would cease to be an artist. Take an example from our own day. I know that you are fond of Japanese things. Now, do you really imagine that the Japanese people, as they are presented to us in Art, have any existence? If you do, you have never understood Japanese art at all. The Japanese people are the deliberate self-conscious creation of certain individual artists. If you set a picture by Hokusai, or Hokkei, or any of the great native painters, beside a real Japanese gentleman or lady, you will see that there is not the slightest resemblance between them. The actual people who live in Japan are not unlike the general run of English people; that is to say, they are extremely commonplace, and have nothing curious or extraordinary about them. In fact, the whole of Japan is a pure invention. There is no such country, there are no such people. One of our most charming painters went recently to the Land of the Chrysanthemum in the foolish hope of seeing the Japanese. All he saw, all he had the chance of painting, were a few lanterns and some fans. He was quite unable to discover the inhabitants, as his delightful exhibition at Messrs. Dowdeswell's Gallery showed only too well. He did not know that the Japanese people are, as I have said, simply a mode of style, an exquisite fancy of Art. And so, if you desire to see a Japanese effect, you will not behave like a tourist and go to Tokio. On the contrary, you will stay at home, and steep yourself in the work of certain Japanese artists, and then, when you have absorbed the spirit of their style, and caught their imaginative manner of vision, you will go some afternoon and sit in the Park or stroll down Piccadilly, and if you cannot see an absolutely Japanese effect there, you will not see it anywhere. Or, to return again to the past, take as another instance the ancient Greeks. Do you think that Greek art ever tells us what the Greek people were like? Do you believe that the Athenian women were like the stately dignified figures of the Parthenon frieze, or like those marvellous goddesses who sat in the triangular pediments of the same building? If you judge from the art, they certainly were so. But read an authority, like Aristophanes, for instance. You will find that the Athenian ladies laced tightly, wore high-heeled shoes, dyed their hair yellow, painted and rouged their faces, and were exactly like any silly fashionable or fallen creature of our own day. The fact is that we look back on the ages entirely through the medium of Art, and Art, very fortunately, has never once told us the truth.

CYRIL

But modern portraits by English painters, what of them? Surely they are like the people they pretend to represent?

VIVIAN

Quite so. They are so like them that a hundred years from now no one will believe in them. The only portraits in which one believes are portraits where there is very little of the sitter, and a very great deal of the artist. Holbein's drawings of the men and women of his time impress us with a sense of their absolute reality. But this is simply because

Holbein compelled life to accept his conditions, to restrain itself within his limitations, to reproduce his type, and to appear as he wished it to appear. It is style that makes us believe in a thing—nothing but style. Most of our modern portrait painters are doomed to absolute oblivion. They never paint what they see. They paint what the public sees, and the public never sees anything.

CYRIL

Well, after that I think I should like to hear the end of your article.

VIVIAN

With pleasure. Whether it will do any good I really cannot say. Ours is certainly the dullest and most prosaic century possible. Why, even Sleep has played us false, and has closed up the gates of ivory, and opened the gates of horn. The dreams of the great middle classes of this country, as recorded in Mr. Myers's two bulky volumes on the subject and in the Transactions of the Psychical Society, are the most depressing things that I have ever read. There is not even a fine nightmare among them. They are commonplace, sordid, and tedious. As for the Church, I cannot conceive anything better for the culture of a country than the presence in it of a body of men whose duty it is to believe in the supernatural, to perform daily miracles, and to keep alive that mythopœic faculty which is so essential for the imagination. But in the English Church a man succeeds, not through his capacity for belief, but through his capacity for disbelief. Ours is the only Church where the sceptic stands at the altar, and where St. Thomas is regarded as the ideal apostle. Many a worthy clergyman, who passes his life in admirable works of kindly charity, lives and dies unnoticed and unknown; but it is sufficient for some shallow uneducated passman out of either University to get up in his pulpit and express his doubts about Noah's ark, or Balaam's ass, or Jonah and the whale, for half of London to flock to hear him, and to sit open-mouthed in rapt admiration at his superb intellect. The growth of common sense in the English Church is a thing very much to be regretted. It is really a degrading concession to a low form of realism. It is silly, too. It springs from an entire ignorance of psychology. Man can believe the impossible, but man can never believe the improbable. However, I must read the end of my article:

"What we have to do, what at any rate it is our duty to do, is to revive this old art of Lying. Much of course may be done, in the way of educating the public, by amateurs in the domestic circle, at literary lunches, and at afternoon teas. But this is merely the light and graceful side of lying, such as was probably heard at Cretan dinner parties. There are many other forms. Lying for the sake of gaining some immediate personal advantage, for instance—lying with a moral purpose, as it is usually called—though of late it has been rather looked down upon, was extremely popular with the antique world. Athena laughs when Odysseus tells her 'his words of sly devising,' as Mr. William Morris phrases it, and the glory of mendacity illumines the pale brow of the stainless hero of Euripidean tragedy, and sets among the noble women of the past the young bride of one of Horace's most exquisite odes. Later on, what at first had been merely a natural instinct was elevated into a self-conscious science. Elaborate rules were laid down for the guidance of mankind, and an important school of literature grew up round the subject. Indeed, when one remembers the excellent philosophical treatise of Sanchez on the whole question, one cannot help regretting that no one has ever thought of publishing a cheap and condensed edition of the works of that great casuist. A short primer, 'When to Lie and How,' if brought out in an attractive and not too expensive a form, would no doubt command a large sale, and would prove of real practical service to many earnest and deep-thinking people. Lying for the sake of the improvement of the young, which is the basis of home education, still lingers amongst us, and its advantages are so admirably set forth in the early books of Plato's *Republic* that it is unnecessary to dwell upon them here. It is a mode of lying for which all good mothers have peculiar capabilities, but it is capable of still further development, and has been sadly overlooked by the School Board. Lying for the sake of a monthly salary is of course well known in Fleet Street, and the profession of a political leader-writer is not without its advantages. But it is said to be a somewhat dull occupation, and it certainly does not lead to much beyond a kind of ostentatious obscurity. The only form of lying that is absolutely beyond reproach is Lying for its own sake, and the highest development of this is, as we have already pointed out, Lying in Art. Just as those who do not love Plato more than Truth cannot pass beyond the threshold of the Academe, so those who do not love Beauty more than Truth never know the inmost shrine of Art. The solid stolid British intellect lies in the desert sands like the Sphinx in Flaubert's marvellous tale and fantasy, *La Chimère*, dances round it, and calls to it with her false, flute-toned voice. It may not hear her now, but surely some day, when we are bored to death with the commonplace character of modern fiction, it will hearken to her and try to borrow her wings.

"And when that day dawns, or sunset reddens how joyous we shall all be! Facts will be regarded as discreditable, Truth will be found mourning over her fetters, and Romance, with her temper of wonder, will return to the land. The very aspect of the world will change to our startled eyes. Out of the sea will rise Behemoth and Leviathan, and sail round the high-pooped galleys, as they do on the delightful maps of those ages when books on geography were actually readable. Dragons will wander about the waste places, and the phœnix will soar from her nest of fire into the air. We shall lay our hands upon the basilisk, and see the jewel in the toad's head. Champing his gilded oats, the Hippo-griff will stand in our stalls, and over our heads will float the Blue Bird singing of beautiful and impossible things, of things that are lovely and that never happen, of things that are not and that should be. But before this comes to pass we must cultivate the lost art of Lying."

CYRIL

Then we must certainly cultivate it at once. But in order to avoid making any error I want you to tell me briefly the doctrines of the new æsthetic.

VIVIAN

Briefly, then, they are these. Art never expresses anything but itself. It has an independent life, just as Thought has, and develops purely on its own lines. It is not necessarily realistic in an age of realism nor spiritual in an age of faith. So far from being the creation of its time, it is usually in direct opposition to it, and the only history that it pre-serves for us is the history of its own progress. Sometimes it returns upon its footsteps, and revives some antique form, as happened in the archaistic movement of late Greek Art, and in the pre-Raphaelite movement of our own day. At other times it entirely anticipates its age and produces in one century work that it takes another century to understand, to appreciate, and to enjoy. In no case does it reproduce its age. To pass from the art of a time to the time itself is the great mistake that all historians commit.

The second doctrine is this. All bad art comes from returning to Life and Nature, and elevating them into ideals. Life and Nature may sometimes be used as part of Art's rough material, but before they are of any real service to Art they must be translated into artistic conventions. The moment Art surrenders its imaginative medium it surrenders everything. As a method Realism is a complete failure, and the two things that every artist should avoid are modernity of form and modernity of subject-matter. To us, who live in the nineteenth century, any century is a suitable subject for Art except our own. The only beautiful things are the things that do not concern us. It is, to have the pleasure of quoting myself, exactly because Hecuba is nothing to us that her sorrows are so suitable a motive for a tragedy. Besides, it is only the modern that ever becomes old-fashioned. M. Zola sits down to give us a picture of the Second Empire. Who cares for the Second Empire now? It is out of date. Life goes faster than Realism, but Romanticism is always in front of Life.

The third doctrine is that Life imitates Art far more than Art imitates Life. This results not merely from Life's imitative instinct, but from the fact that the self-conscious aim of Life is to find expression, and that Art offers it certain beautiful forms through which it may realize that energy. It is a theory that has never been put forward before, but it is extremely fruitful, and throws an entirely new light upon the history of Art.

It follows, as a corollary from this, that external Nature also imitates Art. The only effects that she can show us are effects that we have already seen through poetry, or in paintings. This is the secret of Nature's charm, as well as the explanation of Nature's weakness.

The final revelation is that Lying, the telling of beautiful untrue things, is the proper aim of Art. But of this I think I have spoken at sufficient length. And now let us go out on the terrace, where "droops the milk-white peacock like a ghost," while the evening star "washes the dusk with silver". At twilight nature becomes a wonderfully suggestive effect, and is not without loveliness, though perhaps its chief use is to illustrate quotations from the poets. Come! We have talked long enough.

THEODORE WRATISLAW

Song to Elizabeth

Ave Maris Stella

STAR OF the chaste inviolable sea,
I set my heart and lips to sing to thee.
Out of the cavern of my sin and pain
My soul turns toward thee, star, my star, again.
O sweet as comes the cool first wind of dawn
Across grey sea and shadowy cliffside lawn,
O sweet as breaks the faint first gleam of light
On eyelids watching with the weary night,
The memory of thy presence comes to bless
My soul bowed down with infinite weariness,
Chaste star, sweet star, star perfect and divine,
Too far from me not to be wholly mine,
Too near to me not to be very far,
My lamp, my love, my muse, my song, my star!

The Music-Hall

THE CURTAIN on the grouping dancers falls,
The heaven of colour has vanished from our eyes;
Stirred in our seats we wait with vague surmise
What haply comes that pleases or that palls.

Touched on the stand the thrice-struck baton calls,
Once more I watch the unfolding curtain rise,
I hear the exultant violins premise
The well-known tune that thrills me and enthralls.

Then trembling in my joy I see you flash
Before the footlights to the cymbals' clash,
With laughing lips, swift feet, and brilliant glance,

You, fair as heaven and as a rainbow bright,
You, queen of song and empress of the dance,
Flower of mine eyes, my love, my heart's delight!

Inscription

IF, PASSER-BY, who idly stand and read,
If thou bereft of love shouldst haply lead
Thy sorrow through these old forgotten graves,

And deem that I sleep well who lie beneath
These withered flowers and faded ivy wreath,
Without the soul that aches, the heart that craves,

Be glad, O traveller, of thy happy hours!
Thou hast the sunlight and renascent flowers,
And life is sweet and time may bring delight;

But I must yearn among the silent dead
For even the life of grasses on my head,
So sad it is, the shadow of the night.

W. B. YEATS

Aedh Tells of the Rose in his Heart

ALL THINGS uncomely and broken, all things worn out and old,
The cry of a child by the roadway, the creak of a lumbering cart,
The heavy steps of the ploughman, splashing the wintry mould,
Are wronging your image that blossoms a rose in the deeps of my heart.

The wrong of unshapely things is a wrong too great to be told;
I hunger to build them anew and sit on a green knoll apart,
With the earth and the sky and the water, remade like a casket of gold
For my dreams of your image that blossoms a rose in the deeps of my
    heart.

The Countess Cathleen

SHEMUS RUA, *a peasant.*
TEIG, *his son.*
ALEEL, *a young bard.*
MAURTEEN, *a gardener.*
THE COUNTESS CATHLEEN.
OONA, *her foster-mother.*
MAIRE, *wife of* SHEMUS RUA.

TWO DEMONS disguised as MERCHANTS, MUSICIANS, PEASANTS, SERVANTS, etc., ANGELICAL BEINGS, SPIRITS, and FAERIES.

The scene is laid in Ireland, and in old times.

ACT I

The cottage of SHEMUS RUA. *The door into the open air is at the right side of room. There is a window at one end of it, and a little Catholic shrine hangs at the other. At the back is a door opening into a bedroom, and at the left side of the room a pantry door. A wood of oak, pine, hazel, and quicken is seen through the window half hidden in vapour and twilight.* MAIRE *watches* TEIG, *who fills a pot with water. He stops as if to listen, and spills some of the water.*

MAIRE
You are all thumbs.

TEIG
                     Hear how the dog bays, mother,
And how the gray hen flutters in the coop.
Strange things are going up and down the land
These famine times: by Tubber-vanach cross-roads
A woman met a man with ears spread out,
And they moved up and down like wings of bats.

MAIRE
Shemus stays late.

TEIG

By Carrick-orus churchyard,
A herdsman met a man who had no mouth,
Nor ears, nor eyes: his face a wall of flesh;
He saw him plainly by the moon.

MAIRE [*going over to the little shrine*]
White Mary,
Bring Shemus safe home from the hateful forest;
Save Shemus from the wolves; Shemus is reckless;
And save him from the demons of the woods,
Who have crept out and pace upon the roads,
Deluding dim-eyed souls now newly dead,
And those alive who have gone crazed with famine.
Save him, White Mary Virgin.

TEIG

And but now
I thought I heard far-off tympans and harps.
[*Knocking at the door*]

MAIRE
Shemus has come.

TEIG

May he bring better food
Than the lean crow he brought us yesterday.
[MAIRE *opens the door, and* SHEMUS *comes in with a dead wolf on his
shoulder*]

MAIRE
Shemus, you are late home: you have been lounging
And chattering with some one: you know well
How the dreams trouble me, and how I pray,

Yet you lie sweating on the hill from morn,
Or linger at the crossways with all comers,
Gilding your tongue with the calamitous times.

SHEMUS
You would rail my head off. Here is a good dinner.
                              [*He throws the wolf on the table*]
A wolf is better than a carrion crow.
I searched all day: the mice and rats and hedgehogs
Seemed to be dead, and I could hardly hear
A wing moving in all the famished woods,
Though the dead leaves and clauber of four forests
Cling to my footsole. I turned home but now,
And saw, sniffing the floor in a bare cow-house,
This young wolf here: the crossbow brought him down.

MAIRE
Praise be the saints!   [*After a pause*]
         Why did the house-dog bay?

SHEMUS
He heard me coming and smelt food—what else?

TEIG
We will not starve awhile.

SHEMUS
                  What food is within?

TEIG
There is a bag half full of meal, a pan
Half full of milk.

SHEMUS
And we have Maive the hen.

TEIG
The pinewood were less hard.

MAIRE

                              Before you came
She made a great noise in the hen-coop, Shemus.
What fluttered in the window?

TEIG

                              Two horned owls
Have blinked and fluttered on the window-sill
From when the dog began to bay.

SHEMUS

                              Hush, hush.
[*He fits an arrow to the crossbow, and goes towards the door. A sudden
        burst of music without*]
They are off again: some lady or gentleman
Roves in the woods with tympan and with harp.
Teig, put the wolf upon the upper shelf
And shut the door.
        [TEIG *goes into the cupboard with the wolf: returns and fastens the door
        behind him*]
                              Sit on the creepy stool
And call up a whey face and a crying voice,
And let your head be bowed upon your knees.
                              [*He opens the door of the cabin*]
Come in, kind gentles: a full score of evenings
This threshold worn away by many a foot
Has been passed only by the snails and birds
And by our own poor hunger-shaken feet.
        [*The* COUNTESS CATHLEEN, ALEEL, *who carries a small square harp,*
        OONA, *and a little group of fantastically dressed musicians come
        in*]

CATHLEEN
Are you so hungry?

TEIG [*from beside the fire*]
                              Lady, I fell but now,
And lay upon the threshold like a log.

I have not tasted a crust for these four days.
  [*The* COUNTESS CATHLEEN *empties her purse on to the table*]

CATHLEEN
Had I more money I would give it you,
But we have passed by many cabins to-day
And if you come to-morrow to my house
You shall have twice the sum. I am the owner
Of a long empty castle in these woods.

MAIRE
Then you are Countess Cathleen: you and yours
Are ever welcome under my poor roof.
Will you sit down and warm you by the fire?

COUNTESS CATHLEEN
We must find out this castle in the wood
Before the chill o' the night.
  [*The musicians begin to tune their instruments*]
                            Do not blame me,
Good woman, for the tympan and the harp:
I was bid fly the terror of the times
And wrap me round with music and sweet song
Or else pine to my grave. I have lost my way;
Aleel, the poet, who should know these woods,
Because we met him on their border but now
Wandering and singing like the foam of the sea,
Is so wrapped up in dreams of terrors to come
That he can give no help.

MAIRE [*going to the door with her*]
                          Beyond the hazel
Is a green shadowed pathway, and it goes
To your great castle in malevolent woods.

ALEEL
When we are gone draw to the door and the bolt,
For, till we lost them half an hour ago,

OO

Two gray horned owls hooted above our heads
Of terrors to come. Tympan and harp awake!
For though the world drift from us like a sigh,
Music is master of all under the moon;
And play "The Wind that blows by Cummen Strand."

                                       [*Music*]

                [*Sings*]

Impetuous heart, be still, be still;
Your sorrowful love may never be told;
Cover it up with a lonely tune.
He who could bend all things to His will
Has covered the door of the infinite fold
With the pale stars and the wandering moon.
     [*While he is singing the* COUNTESS CATHLEEN, OONA, *and the musicians*
         go out]

ALEEL

Shut to the door and shut the woods away,
For, till they had vanished in the thick of the leaves,
Two gray horned owls hooted above our heads.
                                 [*He goes out*]

MAIRE [*bolting the door*]

When wealthy and wise folk wander from their peace
And fear wood things, poor folk may draw the bolt
And pray before the fire.
     [SHEMUS *counts out the money, and rings a piece upon the table*]

SHEMUS

                         The Mother of God,
Hushed by the waving of the immortal wings,
Has dropped in a doze and cannot hear the poor:
I passed by Margaret Nolan's; for nine days
Her mouth was green with dock and dandelion;
And now they wake her.

MAIRE

                I will go the next;
Our parents' cabins bordered the same field.

SHEMUS

God, and the Mother of God, have dropped asleep,
For they are weary of the prayers and candles;
But Satan pours the famine from his bag,
And I am mindful to go pray to him
To cover all this table with red gold.
Teig, will you dare me to it?

TEIG

                  Not I, father.

MAIRE

O Shemus, hush, maybe your mind might pray
In spite o' the mouth.

SHEMUS

            Two crowns and twenty pennies.

MAIRE

Is yonder quicken wood?

SHEMUS [*picking the bough from the table*]

                He swayed about,
And so I tied him to a quicken bough
And slung him from my shoulder.

MAIRE [*taking the bough from him*]

              Shemus! Shemus!
What, would you burn the blessed quicken wood?
A spell to ward off demons and ill faeries.
You know not what the owls were that peered in,
For evil wonders live in this old wood,
And they can show in what shape please them best.
And we have had no milk to leave of nights

To keep our own good people kind to us.
And Aleel, who has talked with the great Shee,
Is full of terrors to come.

[*She lays the bough on a chair*]

SHEMUS

                    I would eat my supper
With no less mirth if chaired beside the hearth
Were pooka, sowlth, or demon of the pit
Rubbing its hands before the flame of the pine.

[*He rings another piece of money. A sound of footsteps outside the door*]

MAIRE

Who knows what evil you have brought to us?
I fear the wood things, Shemus.

[*A knock at the door*]
Do not open.

SHEMUS

A crown and twenty pennies are not enough
To stop the hole that lets the famine in.

[*The little shrine falls*]

MAIRE

Look! look!

SHEMUS [*crushing it underfoot*]
                    The Mother of God has dropped asleep,
And all her household things have gone to wrack.

MAIRE

O Mary, Mother of God, be pitiful!

[SHEMUS *opens the door.* TWO MERCHANTS *stand without. They have
    bands of gold round their foreheads, and each carries a bag upon
    his shoulder*]

FIRST MERCHANT
Have you food here?

SHEMUS

For those who can pay well.

SECOND MERCHANT

We are rich merchants seeking merchandise.

SHEMUS

Gentles, come in.

MAIRE

Gentles, do not come in:
We have no food, not even for ourselves.

FIRST MERCHANT

There is a wolf on the third shelf in the cupboard.

[*They enter*]

SHEMUS

Forgive her: she is not used to quality,
And is half mad with being much alone.
How did you know I had taken a young wolf?
Fine wholesome food, though somewhat strong in the flavour.

[*The* SECOND MERCHANT *sits down by the fire and begins rubbing his
    hands. The* FIRST MERCHANT *stands looking at the quicken
    bough on the chair*]

FIRST MERCHANT

I would rest here: the night is somewhat chilly,
And my feet footsore going up and down
From land to land and nation unto nation:
The fire burns dimly; feed it with this bough.

[SHEMUS *throws the bough into the fire. The* FIRST MERCHANT *sits
    down on the chair. The* MERCHANTS' *chairs are on each side of
    the fire. The table is between them. Each lays his bag before him
    on the table. The night has closed in somewhat, and the main
    light comes from the fire*]

MAIRE

What have you in the bags?

SHEMUS

Gentles, forgive,
Women grow curious and feather-thoughted
Through being in each other's company
More than is good for them.

FIRST MERCHANT

Our bags are full
Of golden pieces to buy merchandise.
[*They pour gold pieces on to the table out of their bags. It is covered
with the gold pieces. They shine in the firelight.* MAIRE *goes to the
door of the pantry, and watches the* MERCHANTS, *muttering to
herself*]

TEIG

These be great gentles.

FIRST MERCHANT [*taking a stone bottle out of his bag*]
Come about the fire,
And here is wine more fragrant than all the roses.

SECOND MERCHANT

Wine that can hush asleep the petty war
Of good and evil, and awake instead
A scented flame flickering above that peace
The bird of prey knows well in his deep heart.

SHEMUS [*bringing drinking-cups*]
I do not understand you, but your wine
Sets me athirst: its praise made your eyes lighten.
May I, too, taste it?

FIRST MERCHANT

Ay, come drink and drink,
I bless all mortals who drink long and deep.
My curse upon the salt-strewn road of monks.
[TEIG *and* SHEMUS *sit down at the table and drink*]

TEIG
You must have seen rare sights and done rare things.

FIRST MERCHANT
What think you of the master whom we serve?

SHEMUS
I have grown weary of my days in the world
Because I do not serve him.

FIRST MERCHANT
                              More of this
When we have eaten, for we love right well
A merry meal, a warm and leaping fire
And easy hearts.

SHEMUS
                    Come, Maire, and cook the wolf.

MAIRE
I will not cook for you.

SHEMUS
                    Maire is mad.
[TEIG *and* SHEMUS *stand up and stagger about*]

SHEMUS
That wine is the suddenest wine man ever tasted.

MAIRE
I will not cook for you: you are not human:
Before you came two horned owls peered at us;
The dog bayed, and the tongue of Shemus maddened.
When you came in the Virgin's blessed shrine
Fell from its nail, and when you sat down here
You poured out wine as the wood sheogues do
When they entice a soul out of the world.
Why did you come to us? Was not death near?

FIRST MERCHANT
We are two merchants.

MAIRE

If you be not demons
Go and give alms among the starving poor.
You seem more rich than any under the moon.

FIRST MERCHANT
If we knew where to find deserving poor,
We would give alms.

MAIRE

Then ask of Father John.

FIRST MERCHANT
We know the evils of mere charity,
And would devise a more considered way.
Let each man bring one piece of merchandise.

MAIRE
And have the starving any merchandise?

FIRST MERCHANT
We do but ask what each man has.

MAIRE

Merchants,
Their swine and cattle, fields and implements,
Are sold and gone.

FIRST MERCHANT

They have not sold all yet.

MAIRE
What have they?

FIRST MERCHANT

They have still their souls.

[MAIRE *shrieks. He beckons to* TEIG *and* SHEMUS]
                    Come hither.
See you these little golden heaps? Each one
Is payment for a soul. From charity
We give so great a price for those poor flames.
Say to all men we buy men's souls—away.

                              [*They do not stir*]

This pile is for you and this one here for you,

MAIRE

Shemas and Teig, Teig—

TEIG

                    Out of the way.
                    [SHEMUS *and* TEIG *take the money*]

FIRST MERCHANT

Cry out at cross-roads and at chapel doors
And market-places that we buy men's souls,
Giving so great a price that men may live
In mirth and ease until the famine ends.

                    [TEIG *and* SHEMUS *go out*]

MAIRE [*kneeling*]

Destroyers of souls, may God destroy you quickly!

FIRST MERCHANT

No curse can overthrow the immortal demons.

MAIRE

You shall at last dry like dry leaves, and hang
Nailed like dead vermin to the doors of God.

FIRST MERCHANT

You shall be ours. This famine shall not cease.
You shall eat grass, and dock, and dandelion,
And fail till this stone threshold seem a wall,

And when your hands can scarcely drag your body
We shall be near you.

[To SECOND MERCHANT]

Bring the meal out.

[The SECOND MERCHANT brings the bag of meal from the pantry]

Burn it.   [MAIRE faints]

Now she has swooned, our faces go unscratched;
Bring me the gray hen too.

[The SECOND MERCHANT goes out through the door and returns with
the hen strangled. He flings it on the floor. While he is away the
FIRST MERCHANT makes up the fire. The FIRST MERCHANT
then fetches the pan of milk from the pantry, and spills it on the
ground. He returns, and brings out the wolf, and throws it
down by the hen]

These need much burning.

This stool and this chair here will make good fuel.

[He begins breaking the chair]

My master will break up the sun and moon
And quench the stars in the ancestral night
And overturn the thrones of God and the angels.

ACT II

A great hall in the castle of the COUNTESS CATHLEEN. There is a large
window at the farther end, through which the forest is visible. The
wall to the right juts out slightly, cutting off an angle of the room.
A flight of stone steps leads up to a small arched door in the jutting
wall. Through the door can be seen a little oratory. The hall is
hung with ancient tapestry, representing the loves and wars and
huntings of the Fenian and Red Branch heroes. There are doors
to the right and left. On the left side OONA sits, as if asleep, beside
a spinning-wheel. The COUNTESS CATHLEEN stands farther back
and more to the right, close to a group of the musicians still in their
fantastic dresses, who are playing a merry tune.

CATHLEEN

Be silent, I am tired of tympan and harp,
And tired of music that but cries sleep, sleep,
Till joy and sorrow and hope and terror are gone.

[The COUNTESS CATHLEEN *goes over to* OONA]

You were asleep?

OONA

No, child, I was but thinking
Why you have grown so sad.

CATHLEEN

The famine frets me.

OONA

I have lived now near ninety winters, child,
And I have known three things no doctors cure—
Love, loneliness, and famine; nor found refuge
Other than growing old and full of sleep.
See you where Oisin and young Niam ride
Wrapped in each other's arms, and where the Fenians
Follow their hounds along the fields of tapestry;
How merry they lived once, yet men died then.
Sit down by me, and I will chaunt the song
About the Danaan nations in their raths
That Aleel sang for you by the great door
Before we lost him in the shadow of leaves.

CATHLEEN

No, sing the song he sang in the dim light,
When we first found him in the shadow of leaves,
About King Fergus in his brazen car
Driving with troops of dancers through the woods.

[She crouches down on the floor, and lays her head on OONA'S *knees]*

OONA

Dear heart, make a soft cradle of old tales,
And songs, and music: wherefore should you sadden

For wrongs you cannot hinder? The great God
Smiling condemns the lost: be mirthful: He
Bids you be merry and old age be wise.

CATHLEEN

Tympan and harp awaken wandering dreams.

A VOICE [*without*]

You may not see the Countess.

ANOTHER VOICE

           I must see her.
    [*Sound of a slight struggle. A* SERVANT *enters from door to right*]

SERVANT

The gardener is resolved to speak with you.
I cannot stay him.

CATHLEEN

           You may come, Maurteen.
    [*The* GARDENER, *an old man, comes in from the right, and the* SERVANT
        goes out*]

GARDENER

Forgive my clay-soiled coat—my muddy shoes.
I bring ill words, your ladyship—too bad
To send with any other.

CATHLEEN

           These bad times,
Can any news be bad or any good?

GARDENER

A crowd of ugly lean-faced rogues last night—
And may God curse them! climbed the garden wall.
There is scarce an apple now on twenty trees,
And my asparagus and strawberry beds
Are trampled into clauber, and the boughs

Of beech and plum-trees broken and torn down
For some last fruit that hung there. My dog, too,
My old blind Simon, him who had no tail,
They murdered—God's red anger seize them.

CATHLEEN

I know how pears and all the tribe of apples
Are daily in your love—how this ill chance
Is sudden doomsday fallen on your year;
So do not say no matter. I but say
I blame the famished season, and not you.
Then be not troubled.

GARDENER

                    I thank your ladyship.

CATHLEEN

What rumours and what portents of the famine?

GARDENER

The yellow vapour, in whose folds it came,
That creeps along the hedges at nightfall,
Makes my new shrubs and saplings poor and sickly.
I pray against it.   [*He goes towards the door, then pauses*]
            If her ladyship
Would give me an old crossbow, I would watch
Behind a bush and guard the pears of nights
And make a hole in somebody I know of.

CATHLEEN

They will give you a long draught of ale below.
                            [*The* GARDENER *goes out*]

OONA

What did he say?—he stood on my deaf side.

CATHLEEN

His apples are all stolen. Pruning time,

And the slow ripening of his pears and apples,
For him is a long, heart-moving history.

OONA

Now lay your head once more upon my knees.
I will sing how Fergus drove his brazen cars.

[*She chaunts with the thin voice of age*]

Who will go drive with Fergus now,
And pierce the deep wood's woven shade,
And dance upon the level shore?
Young man, lift up your russet brow,
And lift your tender eyelids, maid,
And brood on hopes and fears no more.

You have dropped down again into your trouble,
You do not hear me.

CATHLEEN

                    Ah, sing on, old Oona,
I hear the horn of Fergus in my heart.

OONA

I do not know the meaning of the song.
I am too old.

CATHLEEN

                    The horn is calling, calling.

OONA

And no more turn aside and brood
Upon Love's bitter mystery;
For Fergus rules the brazen cars,
And rules the shadows of the wood,
And the white breast of the dim sea
And all dishevelled wandering stars.

THE SERVANT'S VOICE [*without*]

The Countess Cathleen must not be disturbed.

ANOTHER VOICE
Man, I must see her.

CATHLEEN

Who now wants me, Paudeen?

SERVANT [*from the door*]
A herdsman and his history.

CATHLEEN

He may come.
[*The* HERDSMAN *enters from the door to right*]

HERDSMAN
Forgive this dusty gear: I have come far.
My sheep were taken from the fold last night.
You will be angry: I am not to blame.
But blame these robbing times.

CATHLEEN

No blame's with you.
I blame the famine.

HERDSMAN

Kneeling, I give thanks.
When gazing on your face, the poorest, Lady,
Forget their poverty, the rich their care.

CATHLEEN
What rumours and what portents of the famine?

HERDSMAN
As I came down the lane by Tubber-vanach
A boy and man sat cross-legged on two stones,
With moving hands and faces famine-thin,
Gabbling to crowds of men and wives and boys
Of how two merchants at a house in the woods
Buy souls for hell, giving so great a price

That men may live through all the dearth in plenty.
The vales are famine crazy—I am right glad
My home is on the mountain near to God.

[*He turns to go*]

CATHLEEN

They will give you ale and meat before you go.
You must have risen at dawn to come so far.
Keep your bare mountain—let the world drift by,
The burden of its wrongs rests not on you.

HERDSMAN

I am content to serve your ladyship.

[*He goes*]

OONA

What did he say?—he stood on my deaf side.
He seemed to give you word of woeful things.

CATHLEEN

A story born out by the dreaming eyes
And crazy brain and credulous ears of famine.
O, I am sadder than an old air, Oona,
My heart is longing for a deeper peace
Than Fergus found amid his brazen cars:
Would that like Adene my first forbear's daughter
Who followed once a twilight's piercing tune,
I could go down and dwell among the Shee
In their old ever-busy honeyed land.

OONA

You should not say such things—they bring ill-luck.

CATHLEEN

The image of young Adene on the arras,
Walking along, one finger lifted up;
And that wild song of the unending dance

Of the dim Danaan nations in their raths,
Young Aleel sang for me by the great door,
Before we lost him in the shadow of leaves,
Have filled me full of all these wicked words.
  [*The* SERVANT *enters hastily, followed by three men. Two are peasants*]

SERVANT

The steward of the castle brings two men
To talk with you.

STEWARD

                              And tell the strangest story
The mouth of man has uttered.

CATHLEEN

                              More food taken;
Yet learned theologians have laid down
That he who has no food, offending no way,
May take his meat and bread from too-full larders.

FIRST PEASANT

We come to make amends for robbery.
I stole five hundred apples from your trees,
And laid them in a hole; and my friend here
Last night stole two large mountain sheep of yours
And hung them on a beam under his thatch.

SECOND PEASANT

His words are true.

FIRST PEASANT

                              Since then our luck has changed.
As I came down the lane by Tubber-vanach
I fell on Shemus Rua and his son,
And they led me where two great gentlemen
Buy souls for money, and they bought my soul.
I told my friend here—my friend also trafficked.

PP

SECOND PEASANT
His words are true.

FIRST PEASANT
                             Now people throng to sell,
Noisy as seagulls tearing a dead fish.
There soon will be no man or woman's soul
Unbargained for in fivescore baronies.

SECOND PEASANT
His words are true.

FIRST PEASANT
                        When we had sold we talked,
And having no more comfortable life
Than this that makes us warm—our souls being bartered
For all this money.

SECOND PEASANT
                          And this money here;
[*They bring handfuls of money from their pockets.* CATHLEEN *starts up*]
And fearing much to hang for robbery,
We come to pay you for the sheep and fruit.
How do you price them?

CATHLEEN
                           Gather up your money.
Think you that I would touch the demons' gold?
Begone, give twice, thrice, twenty times their money,
And buy your souls again. I will pay all.

FIRST PEASANT
We will not buy our souls again: a soul
But keeps the flesh out of its merriment.
We shall be merry and drunk from moon till moon.
Keep from our way. Let no one stop our way.

                                              [*They go*]

CATHLEEN [*to servant*]
Follow and bring them here again—beseech them.

[*The* SERVANT *goes*]

[*To steward*]
Steward, you know the secrets of this house.
How much have I in gold?

STEWARD

A hundred thousand.

CATHLEEN
How much have I in castles?

STEWARD

As much more.

CATHLEEN
How much have I in pastures?

STEWARD

As much more.

CATHLEEN
How much have I in forests?

STEWARD

As much more.

CATHLEEN
Keeping this house alone, sell all I have;
Go to some distant country and come again
With many herds of cows and ships of grain.

STEWARD
God's blessing light upon your ladyship;
You will have saved the land.

CATHLEEN

Make no delay.

[*He goes*]

[*re-enter servant*]
How did you thrive? Say quickly. You are pale.

SERVANT
Their eyes burn like the eyes of birds of prey
I did not dare go near.

CATHLEEN

God pity them!
Bring all the old and ailing to this house,
For I will have no sorrow of my own
From this day onward.

[*The* SERVANT *goes out. Some of the musicians follow him, some linger
in the doorway. The* COUNTESS CATHLEEN *kneels beside* OONA]
O, mother, tell me
How I may mend the times, how stanch this wound
That bleeds in the earth, how overturn the famine,
How drive these demons to their darkness again.

OONA
The demons hold our hearts between their hands,
For the apple is in our blood, and though heart break
There is no medicine but Michael's trump.
Till it has ended parting and old age
And hail and rain and famine and foolish laughter;
The dead are happy, the dust is in their ears.

ACT III

Hall of the COUNTESS CATHLEEN *as before.* SERVANT *enters and goes
towards the oratory door.*

SERVANT
Here is yet another would see your ladyship.

CATHLEEN [*without*]
Who calls me?

SERVANT
> There is a man would speak with you,
And by his face he has some pressing news,
Some moving tale.

CATHLEEN [*coming to chapel door*]
> > I cannot rest or pray,
For all day long the messengers run hither
On one another's heels, and every message
More evil than the one that had gone before.
Who is the messenger?

SERVANT
> > > Aleel, the poet.

CATHLEEN
There is no hour he is not welcome to me,
Because I know of nothing but a harp string
That can remember happiness.
> > > [SERVANT *goes out and* ALEEL *comes in*]
> > > And now
I grow forgetful of evil for awhile.

ALEEL
I have come to bid you leave this castle, and fly
Out of these woods.

CATHLEEN
> > > What evil is there here,
That is not everywhere from this to the sea?

ALEEL
They who have sent me walk invisible.

CATHLEEN
Men say that the wise people of the raths
Have given you wisdom.

ALEEL

                    I lay in the dusk
Upon the grassy margin of a lake
Among the hills, where none of mortal creatures
But the swan comes—my sleep became a fire.
One walked in the fire with birds about his head.

CATHLEEN

Ay, Aengus of the birds.

ALEEL

                    He may be Aengus,
But it may be he bears an angelical name.
Lady, he bid me call you from these woods;
He bids you bring Oona, your foster-mother,
And some few serving-men and live in the hills
Among the sounds of music and the light
Of waters till the evil days are gone.

                                        [*He kneels*]

For here some terrible death is waiting you;
Some unimaginable evil, some great darkness
That fable has not dreamt of, nor sun nor moon
Scattered.

CATHLEEN

                    And he had birds about his head?

ALEEL

Yes, yes, white birds. He bids you leave this house
With some old trusty serving-man, who will feed
All that are starving and shelter all that wander
While there is food and house-room.

CATHLEEN

                                    He bids me go
Where none of mortal creatures but the swan
Dabbles, and there you would pluck the harp, when the trees
Had made a heavy shadow about our door,

And talk among the rustling of the reeds
When night hunted the foolish sun away,
With stillness and pale tapers. No—no—no.
I cannot. Although I weep, I do not weep
Because that life would be most happy, and here
I find no way, no end. Nor do I weep
Because I had longed to look upon your face,
But that a night of prayer has made me weary.

ALEEL [*throwing his arms about her feet*]
Let Him that made mankind, the angels and devils
And death and plenty mend what He has made,
For when we labour in vain and eye still sees
Heart breaks in vain.

CATHLEEN
                        How would that quiet end?

ALEEL
How but in healing?

CATHLEEN
                        You have seen my tears.
And I can see your hand shake on the floor.

ALEEL [*faltering*]
I thought but of healing. He was angelical.

CATHLEEN [*turning away from him*]
No, not angelical, but of the old gods,
Who wander about the world to waken the heart—
The passionate, proud heart that all the angels
Leaving nine heavens empty would rock to sleep.
   [*She goes to the chapel door;* ALEEL *holds his clasped hands towards her
       for a moment hesitatingly, and then lets them fall beside him*]

Do not hold out to me beseeching hands.
This heart shall never waken on earth. I have sworn
By her whose heart the seven sorrows have pierced

To pray before this altar until my heart
Has grown to Heaven like a tree, and there
Rustled its leaves till Heaven has saved my people.

ALEEL [*who has risen*]
When one so great has spoken of love to one
So little as I, although to deny him love,
What can he but hold out beseeching hands
Then let them fall beside him, knowing how greatly
They have overdared?
    [*He goes towards the door of the hall. The* COUNTESS CATHLEEN *takes
      a few steps towards him*]

CATHLEEN
                  If the old tales are true
Queens have wed shepherds and kings beggar-maids;
God's procreant waters flowing about your mind
Have made you more than kings or queens; and not you
But I am the empty pitcher.

ALEEL
                  Being silent,
I have said all—farewell, farewell; and yet, no,
Give me your hand to kiss.

CATHLEEN
                  I kiss your brow,
But will not say farewell. I am often weary,
And I would hear the harp-string.

ALEEL
                  I cannot stay,
For I would hide my sorrow among the hills—
Listen, listen, the hills are calling me.
                  [*They listen for a moment*]

CATHLEEN
I hear the cry of curlew.

ALEEL
                    Then I will out
Where I can hear wind cry and water cry
And curlew cry: how does the saying go
That calls them the three oldest cries in the world?
Farewell, farewell, I will go wander among them,
Because there is no comfort under a roof-tree.

                                        [*He goes out*]

CATHLEEN [*looking through the door after him*]
I cannot see him. He has come to the great door.
I must go pray. Would that my heart and mind
Were as little shaken as this candle-light.
    [*She goes into the chapel. The* TWO MERCHANTS *enter*]

SECOND MERCHANT
Who was the man that came from the great door
While we were still in the shadow?

FIRST MERCHANT
                              Aleel, her lover.

SECOND MERCHANT
It may be that he has turned her thought from us
And we can gather our merchandise in peace.

FIRST MERCHANT
No, no, for she is kneeling.

SECOND MERCHANT
                              Shut the door.
Are all our drudges here?

FIRST MERCHANT [*closing the chapel door*]
                    I bid them follow.
Can you not hear them breathing upon the stairs?
I have sat this hour under the elder-tree.

SECOND MERCHANT

I had bid you rob her treasury, and yet
I found you sitting drowsed and motionless,
Your chin bowed to your knees, while on all sides,
Bat-like from bough and roof and window-ledge,
Clung evil souls of men, and in the woods,
Like streaming flames floated upon the winds,
The elemental creatures.

FIRST MERCHANT

                     I have fared ill,
She prayed so hard I could not cross the threshold
Till this young man had turned her prayer to dreams.
You have had a man to kill, how have you fared?

SECOND MERCHANT

I lay in the image of a nine-monthed bonyeen,
By Tubber-vanach cross-roads; Father John
Came, sad and moody, murmuring many prayers;
I seemed as though I came from his own stye;
He saw the one brown ear; the breviary dropped;
He ran; I ran, I ran into the quarry,
He fell a score of yards.

FIRST MERCHANT

                 Now that he is dead
We shall be too much thronged with souls to-morrow.
Did his soul escape you?

SECOND MERCHANT

               I thrust it in the bag.
But the hand that blessed the poor and raised the Host
Tore through the leather with sharp piety.

FIRST MERCHANT

Well, well, to labour—here is the treasury door.
  [*They go out by the left-hand door, and enter again in a little while
      carrying full bags upon their shoulders*]

FIRST MERCHANT

Brave thought, brave thought—a shining thought of mine!
She now no more may bribe the poor—no more
Cheat our great master of his merchandise,
While our heels dangle at the house in the woods,
And grass grows on the threshold, and snails crawl
Along the window-pane and the mud floor.
Brother, where wander all these dwarfish folk,
Hostile to men, the people of the tides?

SECOND MERCHANT [*going to the door*]

They are gone. They have already wandered away,
Unwilling labourers.

FIRST MERCHANT

             I will call them hither.
                          [*He opens the window*]
Come hither, hither, hither, water folk:
Come all you elemental populace;
Leave lonely the long-hoarding surges: leave
The cymbals of the waves to clash alone,
And, shaking the sea-tangles from your hair,
Gather about us.   [*After a pause*]
             I can hear a sound
As from waves beating upon distant strands;
And the sea creatures, like a surf of light,
Pour eddying through the pathways of the oaks;
And as they come, the sentient grass and leaves
Bow towards them, and the tall, drouth-jaded oaks
Fondle the murmur of their flying feet.

SECOND MERCHANT

The green things love unknotted hearts and minds;
And neither one with angels or with us,
Nor risen in arms with evil nor with good,
In laughter roves the litter of the waves.
     [*A crowd of faces fill up the darkness outside the window. A figure
         separates from the others and speaks*]

THE SPIRIT

We come unwillingly, for she whose gold
We must now carry to the house in the woods
Is dear to all our race. On the green plain,
Beside the sea, a hundred shepherds live
To mind her sheep; and when the nightfall comes
They leave a hundred pans of white ewes' milk
Outside their doors, to feed us when the dawn
Has driven us out of Finbar's ancient house,
And broken the long dance under the hill.

FIRST MERCHANT [*making a sign upon the air*]
Obey! I make a sign upon your heart.

THE SPIRIT

The sign of evil burns upon our hearts,
And we obey.
    [*They crowd through the window, and take out of the bags a small
        bag each. They are dressed in green robes and have ruddy hair.
        They are a little less than the size of men and women*]

FIRST MERCHANT
                    And now begone—begone!   [*They go*]

I bid them go, for, being garrulous
And flighty creatures, they had soon begun
To deafen us with their sea gossip. Now
We must go bring more money. Brother, brother,
I long to see my master's face again,
For I turn homesick.

SECOND MERCHANT
                    I too tire of toil.
[*They go out, and return as before, with their bags full*]

SECOND MERCHANT [*pointing to the oratory*]
How may we gain this woman for our lord?
This pearl, this turquoise fastened in his crown

Would make it shine like His we dare not name.
Now that the winds are heavy with our kind,
Might we not kill her, and bear off her spirit
Before the mob of angels were astir?
[*A diadem and a heap of jewels fall from the bag*]

FIRST MERCHANT
Who tore the bag?

SECOND MERCHANT
      The finger of priest John
When he fled through the leather. I had thought
Because his was an old and little spirit
The tear would hardly matter.

FIRST MERCHANT
      This comes, brother,
Of stealing souls that are not rightly ours.
If we would win this turquoise for our lord,
It must go dropping down of its freewill.
She will have heard the noise. She will stifle us
With holy names.
 [*He goes to the oratory door and opens it a little, and then closes it*]
     No, she has fallen asleep.

SECOND MERCHANT
The noise wakened the household. While you spoke
I heard chairs moved, and heard folk's shuffling feet.
And now they are coming hither.

A VOICE [*without*]
       It was here.

ANOTHER VOICE
No, further away.

ANOTHER VOICE
    It was in the western tower.

ANOTHER VOICE
Come quickly; we will search the western tower.

FIRST MERCHANT
We still have time—they search the distant rooms.
Call hither the fading and the unfading fires.

SECOND MERCHANT [*going to the window*]
There are none here. They tired and strayed from hence—
Unwilling labourers.

FIRST MERCHANT
                              I will draw them in.
                              [*He cries through the window*]
Come hither, you lost souls of men, who died
In drunken sleep, and by each other's hands
When they had bartered you—come hither all
Who mourn among the scenery of your sins,
Turning to animal and reptile forms,
The visages of passion; hither, hither—
Leave marshes and the reed-encumbered pools,
You shapeless fires, that were the souls of men,
And are a fading wretchedness.

SECOND MERCHANT
                              They come not.

FIRST MERCHANT [*making a sign upon the air*]
Come hither, hither, hither.

SECOND MERCHANT
                              I can hear
A crying as of storm-distempered reeds.
The fading and the unfading fires rise up
Like steam out of the earth; the grass and leaves
Shiver and shrink away and sway about,
Blown by unnatural gusts of ice-cold air.

FIRST MERCHANT

They are one with all the beings of decay,
Ill longings, madness, lightning, famine, drouth.
[*The whole stage is gradually filled with vague forms, some animal
shapes, some human, some mere lights*]
Come you—and you—and you, and lift these bags.

A SPIRIT

We are too violent; mere shapes of storm.

FIRST MERCHANT

Come you—and you—and you, and lift these bags.

A SPIRIT

We are too feeble, fading out of life.

FIRST MERCHANT

Come you, and you, who are the latest dead,
And still wear human shape: the shape of power.
[*The two robbing peasants of the last scene come forward. Their faces
have withered from much pain*]
Now, brawlers, lift the bags of gold.

FIRST PEASANT

              Yes, yes!
Unwillingly, unwillingly; for she,
Whose gold we bear upon our shoulders thus,
Has endless pity even for lost souls
In her good heart. At moments, now and then,
When plunged in horror, brooding each alone,
A memory of her face floats in on us.
It brings a crowned misery, half repose,
And we wail one to other; we obey,
For heaven's many-angled star reversed,
Now sign of evil, burns into our hearts.

FIRST MERCHANT

When these pale sapphires and these diadems

And these small bags of money are in our house,
The burning shall give over—now begone.

SECOND MERCHANT [*lifting the diadem to put it upon his head*]
                              No—no—no
I will carry the diadem.

FIRST MERCHANT
                        No, brother, not yet.
For none can carry her treasures wholly away
But spirits that are too light for good and evil,
Or, being evil, can remember good.
Begone. I bad them go, for they are lonely,
And when they see ought living love to sigh.
                                        [*Pointing to the oratory*]
Brother, I heard a sound in there—a sound
That troubles me.

SECOND MERCHANT [*going to the door of the oratory and peering through it*]
                        Upon the altar steps
The Countess tosses, murmuring in her sleep
A broken paternoster.

    [*The* FIRST MERCHANT *goes to the door and stands beside him*]
                              She is grown still,

FIRST MERCHANT
A great plan floats into my mind—no wonder,
For I come from the ninth and mightiest Hell,
Where all are kings. I will wake her from her sleep,
And mix with all her thoughts, a thought to serve.
                                        [*He calls through the door*]
May we be well remembered in your prayers!
    The COUNTESS CATHLEEN *wakes, and comes to the door of the oratory.*
        The MERCHANTS *descend into the room again. She stands at the*
        top of the stone steps]

CATHLEEN
What would you, sirs?

FIRST MERCHANT

We are two merchant men,
New come from foreign lands. We bring you news.
Forgive our sudden entry: the great door
Was open, we came in to seek a face.

CATHLEEN

The door stands always open to receive,
With kindly welcome, starved and sickly folk,
Or any who would fly the woeful times.
Merchants, you bring me news?

FIRST MERCHANT

We saw a man
Heavy with sickness in the bog of Allan,
Whom you had bid buy cattle. Near Fair Head
We saw your grain ships lying all becalmed
In the dark night, and not less still than they
Burned all their mirrored lanthorns in the sea.

CATHLEEN

My thanks to God, to Mary, and the angels,
I still have bags of money, and can buy
Meal from the merchants who have stored it up,
To prosper on the hunger of the poor.
You have been far, and know the signs of things:
When will this yellow vapour no more hang
And creep about the fields, and this great heat
Vanish away—and grass show its green shoots?

FIRST MERCHANT

There is no sign of change—day copies day,
Green things are dead—the cattle too are dead,
Or dying—and on all the vapour hangs
And fattens with disease and glows with heat.
In you is all the hope of all the land.

QQ

CATHLEEN

And heard you of the demons who buy souls?

FIRST MERCHANT

There are some men who hold they have wolves' heads,
And say their limbs, dried by the infinite flame,
Have all the speed of storms; others again
Say they are gross and little; while a few
Will have it they seem much as mortals are,
But tall and brown and travelled, like us, lady.
Yet all agree a power is in their looks
That makes men bow, and flings a casting net
About their souls, and that all men would go
And barter those poor flames—their spirits—only
You bribe them with the safety of your gold.

CATHLEEN

Praise be to God, to Mary, and the angels,
That I am wealthy. Wherefore do they sell?

FIRST MERCHANT

The demons give a hundred crowns and more
For a poor soul like his who lies asleep
By your great door under the porter's niche;
A little soul not worth a hundred pence.
But for a soul like yours, I heard them say,
They would give five hundred thousand crowns and more.

CATHLEEN

How can a heap of crowns pay for a soul?
Is the green grave so terrible a thing?

FIRST MERCHANT

Some sell because the money gleams, and some
Because they are in terror of the grave,
And some because their neighbours sold before,
And some because there is a kind of joy
In casting hope away, in losing joy,
In ceasing all resistance, in at last

Opening one's arms to the eternal flames,
In casting all sails out upon the wind:
To this—full of the gaiety of the lost—
Would all folk hurry if your gold were gone.

CATHLEEN

There is a something, merchant, in your voice
That makes me fear. When you were telling how
A man may lose his soul and lose his God,
Your eyes lighted, and the strange weariness
That hangs about you vanished. When you told
How my poor money serves the people—both—
Merchants, forgive me—seemed to smile.

FIRST MERCHANT
                                                Man's sins
Move us to laughter only, we have seen
So many lands and seen so many men.
How strange that all these people should be swung
As on a lady's shoe-string—under them
The glowing leagues of never-ending flame.

CATHLEEN

There is a something in you that I fear:
A something not of us. Were you not born
In some most distant corner of the world?
[*The* SECOND MERCHANT, *who has been listening at the door to the right, comes forward, and as he comes, a sound of voices and feet is heard through the door to his left*]

SECOND MERCHANT [*aside to* FIRST MERCHANT]
Away now—they are in the passage—hurry,
For they will know us, and freeze up our hearts
With Ave Marys, and burn all our skin
With holy water.

FIRST MERCHANT
                        Farewell: we must ride

Many a mile before the morning come;
Our horses beat the ground impatiently.

[They go out to right]
[A number of peasants enter at the same moment by the opposite door]

CATHLEEN

What would you?

A PEASANT

                   As we nodded by the fire,
Telling old shannachus, we heard a noise
Of falling money. We have searched in vain.

CATHLEEN

You are too timid. I heard naught at all.

THE OLD PEASANT

Ay, we are timid, for a rich man's word
Can shake our houses, and a moon of drouth
Shrivel our seedlings in the barren earth;
We are the slaves of wind, and hail, and flood;
Fear jogs our elbow in the market-place,
And nods beside us on the chimney-seat.
Ill-bodings are as native unto our hearts
As are their spots unto the woodpeckers.

CATHLEEN

You need not shake with bodings in this house.

[OONA enters from the door to left]

OONA

The treasure-room is broken in—mavrone—mavrone;
The door stands open, and the gold is gone.

[The peasants raise a lamenting cry]

CATHLEEN

Be silent.   *[The cry ceases]*
          Saw you any one?

OONA

Mavrone,
That my good mistress should lose all this money.

CATHLEEN

You three upon my right hand, ride and ride;
I will give a farm to him who finds the thieves.
    [*A man with keys at his girdle has entered while she was speaking*]

A PEASANT

The porter trembles.

THE PORTER

It is all no use;
Demons were here. I sat beside the door
In my stone niche, and two owls passed me by,
Whispering with human voices.

THE OLD PEASANT

God forsakes us.

CATHLEEN

Old man, old man, He never closed a door
Unless one opened. I am desolate,
For a most sad resolve wakes in my heart:
But always I have faith. Old men and women,
Be silent; He does not forsake the world,
But stands before it modelling in the clay
And moulding there His image. Age by age
The clay wars with His fingers and pleads hard
For its old, heavy, dull, and shapeless ease;
At times it crumbles and a nation falls,
Now moves awry and demon hordes are born.
                    [*The peasants cross themselves*]
But leave me now, for I am desolate,
I hear a whisper from beyond the thunder.
                    [*She steps down from the oratory door*]

Yet stay an instant. When we meet again
I may have grown forgetful. Oona, take
These two—the larder and the dairy keys.

[*To* THE OLD PEASANT]
But take you this. It opens the small room
Of herbs for medicine, of hellebore,
Of vervain, monkshood, plantain, and self-heal
And all the others; and the book of cures
Is on the upper shelf. You understand,
Because you doctored goats and cattle once.

THE OLD PEASANT
Why do you do this, lady—did you see
Your coffin in a dream?

CATHLEEN
                Ah, no, not that,
A sad resolve wakes in me. I have heard
A sound of wailing in unnumbered hovels,
And I must go down, down, I know not where.
Pray for the poor folk who are crazed with famine;
Pray, you good neighbours.
    [*The peasants all kneel. The* COUNTESS CATHLEEN *ascends the steps*
      to the door of the oratory, and, turning round, stands there motion-
      less for a little and then cries in a loud voice]
                  Mary, queen of angels,
And all you clouds on clouds of saints, farewell!

ACT IV

The cabin of SHEMUS RUA. *The* TWO MERCHANTS *are sitting one at each
    end of the table, with rolls of parchment and many little heaps of
    gold before them. Through an open door, at the back, one sees into
    an inner room, in which there is a bed. On the bed is the body of
    Maire with candles about it.*

FIRST MERCHANT

The woman may keep robbing us no more,
For there are only mice now in her coffers.

SECOND MERCHANT

Last night, closed in the image of an owl,
I hurried to the cliffs of Donegal,
And saw, creeping on the uneasy surge,
Those ships that bring the woman grain and meal;
They are five days from us.

FIRST MERCHANT

                            I hurried East,
A gray owl flitting, flitting in the dew,
And saw nine hundred oxen toil through Meath
Driven on by goads of iron; they, too, brother,
Are full five days from us.

SECOND MERCHANT

                            Five days for traffic.
[*While they have been speaking the peasants have come in, led by* TEIG
and SHEMUS, *who take their stations, one on each side of the door,
and keep them marshalled into rude order and encourage them
from time to time with gestures and whispered words.*]
Here throng they; since the drouth they go in the throngs,
Like autumn leaves blown by the dreary winds.
Come, deal—come, deal.

FIRST MERCHANT

                      Who will come deal with us?

SHEMUS

They are out of spirit, sir, with lack of food,
Save four or five. Here, sir, is one of these;
The others will gain courage in good time.

A MIDDLE-AGED MAN

I come to deal if you give honest price.

FIRST MERCHANT [*reading in a parchment*]
John Maher, a man of substance, with dull mind,
And quiet senses and unventurous heart.
The angels think him safe. Two hundred crowns,
All for a soul, a little breath of wind.

THE MAN

I ask three hundred crowns. You have read there,
That no mere lapse of days can make me yours.

FIRST MERCHANT

There is something more writ here—often at night
He is wakeful from a dread of growing poor.
There is this crack in you—two hundred crowns.

[THE MAN *takes them and goes*]

SECOND MERCHANT

Come, deal—one would half think you had no souls.
If only for the credit of your parishes,
Come, deal, deal, deal, or will you always starve?
Maire, the wife of Shemus, would not deal,
She starved—she lies in there with red wall-flowers,
And candles stuck in bottles, round her bed.

A WOMAN

What price, now, will you give for mine?

FIRST MERCHANT

                              Ay, ay,
Soft, handsome, and still young—not much, I think.

[*Reading in the parchment*]

She has love-letters in a little jar
On a high shelf between the pepper-pot
And wood-cased hour-glass.

THE WOMAN

                   O, the scandalous parchment!

FIRST MERCHANT [*reading*]
She hides them from her husband, who buys horses,
And is not much at home. You are almost safe.
I give you fifty crowns.   [*She turns to go*]
                              A hundred, then.
              [*She takes them, and goes into the crowd*]
Come—deal, deal deal; it is but for charity
We buy such souls at all; a thousand sins
Made them our master's long before we came.
Come, deal—come, deal. You seemed resolved to starve
Until your bones show through your skin. Come, deal,
Or live on nettles, grass, and dandelion.
Or do you dream the famine will go by?
The famine is hale and hearty; it is mine
And my great master's; it shall no wise cease
Until our purpose end: the yellow vapour
That brought it bears it over your dried fields
And fills with violent phantoms of the lost,
And grows more deadly as day copies day.
See how it dims the daylight. Is that peace
Known to the birds of prey so dread a thing?
They, and the souls obedient to our master,
And those who live with that great other spirit
Have gained an end, a peace, while you but toss
And swing upon a moving balance beam.
              [ALEEL *enters, the wires of his harp are broken*]

ALEEL
Here, take my soul, for I am tired of it;
I do not ask a price.

FIRST MERCHANT [*reading*]
                              A man of songs.
Alone in the hushed passion of romance,
His mind ran all on sheogues, and on tales
Of Fenian labours and the Red Branch kings,
And he cared nothing for the life of man:
But now all changes.

ALEEL

　　　　　　　　　　　　　　　　Ay, because her face,
The face of Countess Cathleen, dwells with me:
The sadness of the world upon her brow:
The crying of these strings grew burdensome,
Therefore I tore them; see; now take my soul.

FIRST MERCHANT
We cannot take your soul, for it is hers.

ALEEL
Ah, take it; take it. It nowise can help her
And, therefore, do I tire of it.

FIRST MERCHANT
　　　　　　　　　　　　　　No; no
We may not touch it.

ALEEL
　　　　　　　　　　　　Is your power so small,
Must I then bear it with me all my days?
May scorn close deep about you!

FIRST MERCHANT
　　　　　　　　　　　　　　Lead him hence;
He troubles me.
　　[TEIG and SHEMUS lead ALEEL into the crowd]

SECOND MERCHANT
　　　　　　　　　　　His gaze has filled me, brother,
With shaking and a dreadful fear.

FIRST MERCHANT
　　　　　　　　　　　　　　Lean forward
And kiss the circlet where my master's lips
Were pressed upon it when he sent us hither:
You will have peace once more.

[*The* SECOND MERCHANT *kisses the gold circlet that is about the head of
the* FIRST MERCHANT]

SHEMUS

                              He is called Aleel,
And has been crazy now these many days;
But has no harm in him: his fits soon pass,
And one can go and lead him like a child.

FIRST MERCHANT
Come, deal, deal, deal, deal, deal; are you all dumb?

SHEMUS
They say you beat the woman down too low.

FIRST MERCHANT
I offer this great price: a thousand crowns
For an old woman who was always ugly.
    [*An old peasant woman comes forward, and he takes up a parchment
        and reads*]
There is but little set down here against her;
She stole fowl sometimes when the harvest failed,
But always went to chapel twice a week,
And paid her dues when prosperous. Take your money.

THE OLD PEASANT WOMAN [*curtseying*]
God bless you, sir.   [*She screams*]
            O, sir, a pain went through me.

FIRST MERCHANT
That name is like a fire to all damned souls.
Begone [*she goes*]. See how the red gold pieces glitter.
Deal: do you fear because an old hag screamed?
Are you all cowards?

A PEASANT
                   Nay, I am no coward.
I will sell half my soul.

FIRST MERCHANT

How half your soul?

THE PEASANT

Half my chance of heaven.

FIRST MERCHANT

It is writ here
This man in all things takes the moderate course,
He sits on midmost of the balance beam,
And no man has had good of him or evil.
Begone, we will not buy you.

SECOND MERCHANT

Deal, come, deal.

FIRST MERCHANT

What, will you keep us from our ancient homes,
And from the eternal revelry? Come, deal,
And we will hence to our great master again.
Come, deal, deal, deal.

THE PEASANTS SHOUT

The Countess Cathleen comes!

CATHLEEN [entering]

And so you trade once more?

FIRST MERCHANT

In spite of you.
What brings you here, saint with the sapphire eyes?

CATHLEEN

I come to barter a soul for a great price.

FIRST MERCHANT

What matter, if the soul be worth the price?

CATHLEEN

The people starve, therefore the people go
Thronging to you. I hear a cry come from them,
And it is in my ears by night and day;
And I would have five hundred thousand crowns,
That I may feed them till the dearth go by;
And have the wretched spirits you have bought
For your gold crowns, released, and sent to God.
The soul that I would barter is my soul.

A PEASANT

Do not, do not; the souls of us poor folk
Are not precious to God as your soul is.
O! what would heaven do without you, lady?

ANOTHER PEASANT

Look how their claws clutch in their leathern gloves.

FIRST MERCHANT

Five hundred thousand crowns; we give the price,
The gold is here; the spirits, while you speak,
Begin to labour upward, for your face
Sheds a great light on them and fills their hearts
With whose unveilings of the fickle light,
Whereby our heavy labours have been marred
Since first His spirit moved upon the deeps
And stole them from us; even before this day
The souls were but half ours, for your bright eyes
Had pierced them through and robbed them of content.
But you must sign, for we omit no form
In buying a soul like yours; sign with this quill;
It was a feather growing on the cock
That crowed when Peter dared deny his Master,
And all who use it have great honour in Hell.

            [CATHLEEN *leans forward to sign*]

ALEEL [*rushing forward and snatching the parchment from her*]
Leave all things to the builder of the heavens.

CATHLEEN
I have no thoughts: I hear a cry—a cry.

ALEEL [*casting the parchment on the ground*]
I had a vision under a green hedge,
A hedge of hips and haws—men yet shall hear
The archangels rolling Satan's empty skull
Over the mountain-tops.

FIRST MERCHANT
                    Take him away.
[TEIG *and* SHEMUS *drag him roughly away so that he falls upon the
    floor among the peasants.* CATHLEEN *picks up the parchment and
    signs, and then turns towards the peasants*]

CATHLEEN
Take up the money; and now come with me.
When we are far from this polluted place
I will give everybody money enough.
[*She goes out, the peasants crowding round her and kissing her dress.
    ALEEL and the* TWO MERCHANTS *are left alone*]

SECOND MERCHANT
Now are our days of heavy labour done.

FIRST MERCHANT
We have a precious jewel for Satan's crown.

SECOND MERCHANT
We must away, and wait until she dies,
Sitting above her tower as two gray owls,
Watching as many years as may be, guarding
Our precious jewel; waiting to seize her soul.

FIRST MERCHANT
We need but hover over her head in the air,
For she has only minutes: when she came
I saw the dimness of the tomb in her,

And marked her walking as with leaden shoes
And looking on the ground as though the worms
Were calling her, and when she wrote her name
Her heart began to break. Hush! hush! I hear
The brazen door of Hell move on its hinges,
And the eternal revelry float hither
To hearten us.

SECOND MERCHANT
                      Leap, feathered, on the air
And meet them with her soul caught in your claws.
     [*They rush out.* ALEEL *crawls into the middle of the room. The twilight
     has fallen and gradually darkens as the scene goes on. There is a
     distant muttering of thunder and a sound of rising storm*]

ALEEL
The brazen door stands wide, and Balor comes
Borne in his heavy car, and demons have lifted
The age-weary eyelids from the eyes that of old
Turned gods to stone: Barach the traitor comes;
And the lascivious race, Cailitin,
That cast a Druid weakness and decay
Over Sualtam's and old Dectera's child;
And that great king Hell first took hold upon
When he killed Naisi and broke Deirdre's heart,
And all their heads are twisted to one side,
For when they lived they warred on beauty and peace
With obstinate, crafty, sidelong bitterness.
     [OONA *enters, but remains standing by the door.* ALEEL *half rises,
     leaning upon one arm and one knee*]

ALEEL
Crouch down, old heron, out of the blind storm.

OONA
Where is the Countess Cathleen? All this day
She has been pale and weakly: when her hand

Touched mine over the spindle her hand trembled,
And now I do not know where she has gone

ALEEL

Cathleen has chosen other friends than us,
And they are rising through the hollow world.

[He points downwards]

First, Orchil, her pale beautiful head alive,
Her body shadowy as vapour drifting
Under the dawn, for she who awoke desire
Has but a heart of blood when others die;
About her is a vapoury multitude
Of women alluring devils with soft laughter;
Behind her a host heat of the blood made sin,
But all the little pink-white nails have grown
To be great talons.
    [He seizes OONA *and drags her into the middle of the room and points
        downwards with vehement gestures. The wind roars.]*
                    They begin a song
And there is still some music on their tongues.

OONA *[casting herself face downwards on the floor]*
O maker of all, protect her from the demons,
And if a soul must need be lost, take mine.
    *[*ALEEL *kneels beside her, but does not seem to hear her words; he is
        gazing down as if through the earth. The peasants return. They
        carry the* COUNTESS CATHLEEN *and lay her upon the ground before*
        OONA *and* ALEEL.   *She lies there as if dead]*

OONA

O that so many pitchers of rough clay
Should prosper and the porcelain break in two.
    [She kisses the hands of the COUNTESS CATHLEEN*]*

A PEASANT

We were under the tree where the path turns
When she grew pale as death and fainted away,
And while we bore her hither, cloudy gusts

Blackened the world and shook us on our feet:
Draw the great bolt, for no man has beheld
So black, bitter, blinding, and sudden a storm.

[One who is near the door draws the bolt]

OONA

Hush, hush, she has awakened from her swoon.

CATHLEEN

O hold me, and hold me tightly, for the storm
Is dragging me away.

[OONA takes her in her arms. A woman begins to wail]

A PEASANT

Hush.

ANOTHER PEASANT

Hush.

A PEASANT WOMAN

Hush.

ANOTHER PEASANT WOMAN

Hush.

CATHLEEN *[half rising]*

Lay all the bags of money at my feet. *[They lay the bags at her feet]*
And send and bring old Neal when I am dead,
And bid him hear each man and judge and give:
He doctors you with herbs, and can best say
Who has the less and who the greater need.

A PEASANT WOMAN *[at the back of the crowd]*

And will he give enough out of the bags
To keep my children till the dearth go by?

ANOTHER PEASANT WOMAN

O Queen of Heaven and all you blessed saints,
Let us and ours be lost, so she be shriven.

RR

CATHLEEN

Bend down your faces, Oona and Aleel:
I gaze upon them as the swallow gazes
Upon the nest under the eave, before
He wander the loud waters: do not weep
Too great a while, for there is many a candle
On the high altar though one fall. Aleel,
Who sang about the people of the raths,
That know not the hard burden of the world,
Having but breath in their kind bodies, farewell!
And farewell, Oona, who spun flax with me
Soft as their sleep when every dance is done:
The storm is in my hair and I must go.

[She dies]

OONA

Bring me the looking-glass.
  [*A woman brings it to her out of the inner room.* OONA *holds the glass
    over the lips of the* COUNTESS CATHLEEN. *All is silent for a moment.
    And then she speaks in a half scream*]
        O, she is dead!

A PEASANT WOMAN

She was the great white lily of the world.

ANOTHER PEASANT WOMAN

She was more beautiful than the pale stars.

AN OLD PEASANT WOMAN

The little plant I loved is broken in two.
  [ALEEL *takes the looking-glass from* OONA *and flings it upon the floor
    so that it is broken in many pieces*]

ALEEL

I shatter you in fragments, for the face
That brimmed you up with beauty is no more:
And die, dull heart, for she whose mournful words

Made you a living spirit has passed away
And left you but a ball of passionate dust;
And you, proud earth and plumy sea, fade out,
For you may hear no more her faltering feet
But are left lonely amid the clamorous war
Of angels upon devils.

[*He stands up; almost every one is kneeling, but it has grown so dark that only confused forms can be seen*]
And I who weep
Call curses on you, Time and Fate and Change,
And have no excellent hope but the great hour
When you shall plunge headlong through bottomless space.

[*A flash of lightning followed immediately by thunder*]

A PEASANT WOMAN
Pull him upon his knees before his curses
Have plucked thunder and lightning on our heads.

ALEEL
Angels and devils clash in the middle air,
And brazen swords clang upon brazen helms:
[*A flash of lightning followed immediately by thunder*]
Yonder a bright spear, cast out of a sling,
Has torn through Balor's eye, and the dark clans
Fly screaming as they fled Moytura of old.

[*Everything is lost in darkness*]

AN OLD MAN
The Almighty wrath at our great weakness and sin
Has blotted out the world and we must die.
[*The darkness is broken by a visionary light. The peasants seem to be kneeling upon the rocky slope of a mountain, and vapour full of storm and ever-changing light is sweeping above them and behind them. Half in the light, half in the shadow, stand armed angels. Their armour is old and worn, and their drawn swords dim and dinted. They stand as if upon the air in formation of battle and look downward with stern faces. The peasants cast themselves on the ground*]

RR*

ALEEL

Look no more on the half-closed gates of Hell,
But speak to me, whose mind is smitten of God
That it may be no more with mortal things;
And tell of her who lies here.   *[He seizes one of the angels]*
                              Till you speak
You shall not drift into eternity.

THE ANGEL

The light beats down: the gates of pearl are wide,
And she is passing to the floor of peace,
And Mary of the seven times wounded heart
Has kissed her lips, and the long blessed hair
Has fallen on her face; the Light of Lights
Looks always on the motive, not the deed,
The Shadow of Shadows on the deed alone.
                    [ALEEL *releases the angel and kneels*]

OONA

Tell them who walk upon the floor of peace
That I would die and go to her I love;
The years like great black oxen tread the world,
And God the herdsman goads them on behind,
And I am broken by their passing feet.
    [*A sound of far-off horns seems to come from the heart of the light. The
        vision melts away, and the forms of the kneeling peasants appear
        faintly in the darkness.*]

End of the Play

Down by the Salley Gardens

DOWN BY the salley gardens my love and I did meet;
She passed the salley gardens with little snow-white feet.
She bid me take love easy, as the leaves grow on the tree;
But I, being young and foolish, with her would not agree.

In a field by the river my love and I did stand,
And on my leaning shoulder she laid her snow-white hand.
She bid me take life easy, as the grass grows on the weirs;
But I was young and foolish, and now am full of tears.

When You are Old

WHEN you are old and gray and full of sleep,
And nodding by the fire, take down this book,
And slowly read, and dream of the soft look
Your eyes had once, and of their shadows deep;

How many loved your moments of glad grace,
And loved your beauty with love false or true;
But one man loved the pilgrim soul in you,
And loved the sorrows of your changing face.

And bending down beside the glowing bars
Murmur, a little sadly, how love fled
And paced upon the mountains overhead
And hid his face amid a crowd of stars.

THE END

The End.

POSTSCRIPT

The publication of this anthology has been made possible by the helpful co-operation of many publishers, solicitors, literary executors, authors' agents, proprietors of copyright, the living representatives of dead authors, and of the one living author to whom I have taken the liberty of dedicating the collection. To all of these I tender my grateful thanks.

I wish in particular to thank Messrs. John Lane The Bodley Head Ltd. and Sir Max Beerbohm for permission to print two essays from the author's earliest publication, Works, *and the same publishers and the executors of Ernest Dowson for the use of two excerpts from their edition of the collected poems of that author; Mr. Vyvyan Holland for one poem and two prose pieces by Oscar Wilde; Mr. C. D. Medley, the owner of the copyright in George Moore's works for* The Lovers of Orelay, *taken from* Memoirs of my Dead Life, *published by Messrs. William Heinemann Ltd.; also the same publishers for two poems,* Stella Maris *and* Wanderer's Song, *by Arthur Symons.*

The executors of Kenneth Grahame grant permission for The Headswoman, *and the literary executor of the late A. J. A. Symons similarly for a story by Baron Corvo. Poems by Richard Le Gallienne and A. E. Housman appear by arrangement with the Society of Authors, and those of Lord Alfred Douglas by arrangement with Mr. E. A. Coleman, his literary executor. The story by M. P. Shiel is authorised by Mr. John Gawsworth, his literary executor and by Messrs. Victor Gollancz Ltd., who publish* The Best Short Stories of M. P. Shiel. *Mrs. W. B. Yeats gives permission for the three poems taken from* The Collected Poems of W. B. Yeats (*Messrs. Macmillan & Co. Ltd.*), *and for* The Countess Cathleen, *which is included in* The Collected Plays of W. B. Yeats, *issued by the same publishers. Applications for the right of performing this play, or of reading it in public, must be made to Messrs. Samuel French Ltd.*

Messrs. George G. Harrap & Co. Ltd. give permission for the inclusion of two poems from The Collected Poems of William Watson, *1878-1925. Mrs. T. Sturge Moore and Messrs. Macmillan & Co. Ltd. authorise four poems from* The Collected Poems of T. Sturge Moore, *these being printed on pp. 16, 138, and 178 of Volume I and on*

p. 186 *of Volume II, as I am asked to state. Messrs. Macmillan & Co. Ltd. and the author's representative give permission for the three poems by W. E. Henley, these appearing in their publication,* Poems, *by that author. I have to thank Mr. Wilfrid Meynell and Messrs. Burns Oates & Washbourne Ltd. for leave to print the poems by Alice Meynell and Francis Thompson, and Messrs. John Lane again for poems by Olive Custance and Victor Plarr, a story by Henry Harland and one by Ella D'Arcy. Messrs. George Allen & Unwin Ltd. give permission for three poems from* The Poetical Works of Lionel Johnson.

In a few cases my search to discover the present owners of certain publication rights, if they exist, has been unsuccessful, and I must therefore apologise for having printed some pieces without permission. If the appearance of this book should bring to light any such instances I should be glad if these owners would communicate with The Richards Press Ltd., when the matter will be rectified without delay in the proper manner, and the customary acknowledgement printed in any subsequent edition of the anthology. I have been unable to find out when Ella D'Arcy, Eugene Lee-Hamilton and Vincent O'Sullivan died.

I should like finally to thank my partner, Graeme Hutchison, for welcoming the idea of the anthology so cordially when it was first suggested over a year ago, for maintaining his constant belief in it, and for encouraging me from time to time when my spirits flagged by enquiries as to the progress of the work.

M.S.

Iver, May 1948.